NORTHERN HEMISPHERE.

W. Peck Delt.

THE OLD CONST

SOUTHERN HEMISPHERE.

LATION FIGURES.

OUTER SPACE:
Myths
Name Meanings
Calendars

*From the Emergence of History
to the Present Day*

by

Gertrude and James Jobes

The Scarecrow Press, Inc.
New York & London   1964

L. C. Card No. 64-11783

To the memory of

George and Josephine Jobes

FOREWORD

The authors must be congratulated for their prodigious effort to have brought such an encyclopedic work to fruition. Certainly the result of many years of exhaustive research, this book represents the most complete collection of facts concerning the myths and astrological backgrounds and, additionally, the meanings of the names of the stars and constellations that I have ever read.

It will serve as a reference work of inestimable value for libraries in every category of schools, planetaria, radio and television stations, and other institutions where the correct source of ancient origins of the myths, facts, and star and constellation names is of importance.

Phillip D. Stern, F.R.A.S.
Planetarium Director
Museum of Art, Science and
Industry

Bridgeport, Conn.

TABLE OF CONTENTS

Introduction

For some years I have been disturbed by the schism that exists in modern times between science, which has assumed an important role in man's physical accomplishments or flaunts as virtues the physical conveniences with which it has provided man, and what might be termed spiritual contemplation. Did such a separation exist when, say the wheel was invented? Hardly. To ancient man the wheel was not merely an implement which kept his back from breaking, it was a symbol of eternity, of the sun's or the moon's light, of the whirling heavens, which provided the changing seasons, and of other things he revered. Greeks in the classical age counted music as one of the sciences.

All through the years of research for my Dictionary of Mythology, Folklore and Symbols I was fascinated by the extent to which the beliefs in one culture relate to those in another and particularly delighted to see that in one field, astronomy, the material and the immaterial, the scientific and the poetic, continue to complement each other. Some scientists, such as Sir Isaac Newton, actually had tried to prove the dates of certain celestial discoveries or phenomena by passages in Homer. Richard H. Allen, John R. Kippax, and other moderns in their books on astronomy frequently exemplify a point with a few lines of poetry. Conversely, that which at a glance appears to be essentially a tender love lyric actually may be the medium for a flight of fancy into space. Who has done this more skillfully than the Persian astronomer-poet Omar Khayyam. In:

A Book of Verses underneath the Bough,
A Jug of Wine, A Loaf of Bread - and Thou

the Bough represents the sacred cosmic Tree of Life, the Haoma, which provides the Wine (rain) of fertility, which in turn provides the grain which becomes the Loaf. Another example of his poetry:

Come, fill the Cup, and in the fire of Spring
Your Winter-garment of Repentance fling;
The Bird of Time has but a little way
To flutter - and the Bird is on the Wing.

often is rendered as a drinking song. Pursuing the subject a bit

7

deeper, the Persian name for Crater, the celestial goblet, is Badiye, an earthen vessel for storing wine. The celestial bird, Corvus,
the Crater's neighboring constellation, is said to quench its thirst in
the cosmic cup. The stars of both constellations come to the meridian in the Spring, when the Garment of Repentance (austerity)
may be cast aside. In another version, the Tree had been brought
from heaven by a Bird and placed on a Sacred Mountain, where its
juice was mixed with the fat of Hadhayosh, the primordial ox, to assure resurrection (return of Spring). All this seems to have been
derived from an earlier myth in which a Bird supposedly brought
Fire (lightning) down from the skies for the benefit of mankind, and
the draught of immortality was known as Fire-water, which melted
snow and drove the cold away.

Throughout his life, Jim, my husband, who grew up on a farm
on the outskirts of Oxford, Ohio, has remained aware of the course
of nature. His interest ranges from the lizard that burrows its way
into the ground to the Lizard that wriggles in the sky. When I began this work, he became intrigued, worked out charts, and joined
me in tracing legends as well as the meanings of names given to
the celestial bodies. The unidentified poetry is mine. Thus, we
offer this as a joint effort. We have endeavored to follow this pattern: planets are listed in relation to their distance from the sun;
constellations, celestial phenomena, and stars are entered alphabetically; those legends associated with the celestial bodies which date
back to the Euphratean Valley are pursued first westward into Egypt,
Greece, the Teutonic countries, and the Celtic; then eastward into
Arabia, Persia, India, China, and across the Pacific onto the American continents, where the beliefs have many elements in common
with those of the East, and actually may have been carried by mi-
grators from Asia to the Americas. Additional titles of the celestial bodies are grouped within their various essays under their cultures, which are tabulated alphabetically. Calendars and tables are
included to provide anyone interested in the subject with basic information at a glance.

We offer thanks to the great library at Yale University, to libraries which sent books on loan to Milford, such as the University
of Bridgeport Library, the Burroughs Library of Bridgeport, Conn.,
and the New Haven Free Public Library, and, as always, we are
grateful to the New York Public Library for its wonderful facilities,
and in particular to Mr. Francis W. Paar and Mrs. Joan T. Choo

in the Oriental Division for translating and interpreting some of the Chinese and Arabic terms. Other translations and transliterations stand as they appear in the works of various writers. If some spellings seem obsolete or archaic, we came to the conclusion that changes might lead to confusion. Some terms are strange indeed, derived from catalogues organized during the middle ages, when Arabic was blended with Latin. Where modern configurations are identified with ancient forms, such identifications are mainly conjectural for the reason those who conceived Outer Space to be occupied by visible heroes, villains, maidens in distress, familiar animals, utensils, etc., did not leave explicit explanations for locating the exact stars involved, and, in their hypotheses, writers in the field argue with each other, the wiser agreeing that to be better than approximately correct would be miraculous. Thus we ask you to bear with us as Samuel Johnson asked his readers to bear with him in the preface of his Dictionary, where he said, ".... one enquiry gave occasion to another, book referred to book, to search was not always to find, and to find was not always to be informed." We are nevertheless deeply indebted to all who had the patience to probe and the courage to speculate, and in our bibliography we hope we have not overlooked any author who has helped to open avenues of contemplation that have enriched our lives.

Gertrude Jobes

Milford, Conn.

I

OUTER SPACE

Into Outer Space

Soar high, brave flyer, soar, soar, fly
your instruments, calculate
your time, and measure, as you lie
tied in space suit and mask, your rate
of speed into infinity.
Endless, timeless, the welkin vault
is without mind for all you see,
or hear, or feel. Your catapult,
nerve-fraught, plucky, fails to impress
the Mighties around whom shepherd
ancestors wove shimmery dress.
From jewel thrones, their unuttered
word is forever sealed to your
wisdom, though you eternify
a race or a lone signature.
Soar high, brave flyer, soar, soar, fly ...

Outer space. From his beginnings, man has been fascinated by reaches into everness. Now, that he has developed a machine which has projected him into a 'cosmonaut,' he nonchalantly designates his adventures as "trips into outer space." Although he has made himself a famililiar of the firmament (that which firmly supports the earth) and soon shall even pay a call, if not establish a permanent residence at one of its radiant mansions, its mysteries still elude him; neither has he been able to dispel the awe inspired by its beauties. In spite of modern man's clever computations, the legends propounded by ancient ancestors, who also sought to identify themselves with celestial powers, haunt him as a bewitching challenge.

Suppose one of our sons one day stands on Venus! Will he like an Odysseus on his wanderings, seek the goddess's throne? If, in his eagerness to get on and conquer a more distant star, he is too impatient for such an experience, will he at least pause to determine what his goal really is, or if he can leave to his world more than those who tried to comprehend and describe the nature of the mysterious wisdom of creation, and who thus provided the understructure of all religions known to man as well as various means of calculating time.

Different peoples told the Creation Story in different ways. All tales had one element in common: darkness existed before light. In the Euphratean Valley, where the first stories were invented, Tiamat the Dragon

11

who lived in Chaos, the dark
primordial sea, was worshipped
as Great Creatress and Destroyer, Death Bringer as well as
Great Mother of the Vast Com-
plex.   Throughout the ages her
legend has reappeared in all
parts of the world in a variety of
forms, a few of which relate how
a dragon (darkness) is overpowered by a hero (light), how
a dragon (stormy sea) devastates
the land, how a dragon (winter)
devours crops, or as in China,
how a dragon provides fertile
rains, and in modern tv dramas
how the villain is captured by
the valiant and righteous.

Primitive tillers of the soil
on the plains and hunters as well
as sheep and goat tenders herd-
ing flocks on lonely mountain
crests in time realized that
Tiamat alone did not control the
world, that objects seen from
time to time in the sky played an
important part in destiny.   Eventually the regular intervals at
which they reappeared and disappeared were noted and utilized
as a perpetual almanac which
indicated when seeds were to be
sown or harvests reaped, when
flocks were to be taken up onto
the slopes or brought down into
the valleys.   The discovery
made poets of them, and they
composed poetry never surpassed
or equaled.   They sang to stars
that controlled the dry season,
and they offered hymns to stars
that reigned during the floods, or
those that seemed to control
health or illness and victory or
defeat; they gave the stars
physical characteristics more
handsome, more regal, sometimes more terrifying than that
of any mortal creature.   Some
stars they conceived to be earthly
beings rewarded with a place in
the skies where they aided friends

and kin to reach the otherworld
or of beings that had been transformed because of grief (Hyades)
or punishment (Cassiopeia) or to
be saved (the Ursa constellations); others they perceived as
forms adopted by sky or celestial
sea deities for purposes of observation or as supernatural
messengers (angels or devils),
who assumed bird shape for
flight, human or animal shape
for traversing solid ground, fish
shape for submergence into
water.   They named stars after
animals which were the objects
of their affection or fear, according to whether the season was
auspicious or inauspicious during
a star's reign.   They described
stars as useful utensils or instruments, which deities with
human forms might require, or
as thrones of gold protected by
blazing fires in mansions studded
with diamonds, rubies, sapphires,
emeralds, and other gems, or as
barges with glittering canopies
in which deities sailed across
the Celestial Sea, or as chariots
drawn by winged horses.   And
with each new conception the
stories expanded.   Some peoples
in the East and Near East have
a philosophy that goes further
than "Turn the other cheek,"
they say, "No one has harmed
me."   The source of this profound wisdom can be traced to
stories told early in man's history.   The adventures of Ishtar,
derived from the Tiamat legend,
are not merely tender, passionate,
and dramatic; they exemplify this
philosophy.   When in search of
her lover-son, without complaint
or hesitation, she submits to the
request to shed at each of the
seven gates of the underworld
part of her queenly apparel of
lapis lazuli until at last she is
denuded.

When man acquired a skill with the chisel, histories of the Eternal Beings were carved in stone. Symbolic forms were used instead of names because the name supposedly was the seat of the soul or the source of power and strength; an evil magician might bring disaster by a potent use of a super-natural's name. Frequently the true names of deities were known only to a high priest. Since about the 7th century A.D. a fashion has existed among mystics, astrologers, and astronomers to aver that the symbols which appear instead of names on carvings found in tombs and other places represent particular stars, star groups, and constellations, configurations with which we of the present day are familiar. Some astronomers have assigned a date of 15,000 B.C. to certain astral designs, arguing that the adventures depicted relate to those of the sun or moon deity and that by calculating the precession of the equinoxes they have determined when the sun or moon appeared in certain signs (stars or constellations). One example of this sort of reasoning is the noted Triad of Stars found on a Babylonian Boundary Stone with a probable date of 1,200 B.C. The design is that of a crescent lying on its back and two stars:

Certain astronomers say that the meaning of the design is now clear, that 6,000 years ago, 4,000 years before the Christian era, two bright stars and the crescent were what men saw year after year in the early evening sky. The two bright stars were called Twins, which we know as Alpha and Beta Gemimorum

(Caster and Pollux). The notion supposedly was transferred from generation to generation for 2,800 years until it was carved on the stone.

Several, Sir Isaac Newton among them, support the theory that the chart of the skies as we know it was fixed about the time of the Argonaut expedition. Others hold that Eudoxus, who discovered that part of geometry now included in Euclid's Fifth book, who perceived that the solar year is longer than 365 days by six hours, and who invented scientific explanations of the paths of the planets, was the first to have charted the cosmic sphere as we are acquainted with it. Eudoxus flourished at Cnidus, Greece in the middle of the 4th century B.C., and his findings have come down to us in the Phaenomena, a poetical work by Aratus, which is an account of the Eudoxus astronomical observations. The custom in which knowledge was restricted to priests who made mysteries of most rites, has shrouded celestial as well as other symbols in obscurity, and George D'Oyly contends quite convincingly in his book, remarks on Sir William Drummond's Oedipus Judaicus, that all assignments, "........ can only be a matter of vague conjecture."

The likelihood is that early observers of the heavens at first were aware only of the moon, then of remarkable stars, and in time formed certain groupings to function as a sort of map through which might be charted the track followed by the bold, fickle, and bewitching satellite. Later, when the paths of planets and the sun, which showed itself briefly each morning and evening, were perceived and the appearance of certain stars at certain seasons was noted, additional groupings or constellations were formed. Quite naturally, the objects used to symbolize the realm (light, water, health, war, etc.) of the deity who governed or owned a star or group, or the season or conditions which pertained when a star or group rose, were those familiar to peoples of rustic or pastoral habits. One carving, perhaps the most ancient yet unearthed, with a probable date of 3,000 B.C. is a black stone (a matsebah) of ancient Sumer or Accad. It contains ten signs:

which are still in use; again whether they apply to the same stars or groups to which they originally were assigned is a matter of conjecture. Anciently, the cone was revered as a fire symbol, one of the mysterious forms of the universe and essential for life, here and hereafter; hence the pyramids. The cone is related to phallic or fertility charms, such as a column or tree-stem. The disc at the base of the cone symbolizes the female principle; the triangular side symbolizes father-mother-child; thus the monuments themselves are symbolic of the cycle of creation. A list of signs carved

Sign	Probable Deity Identification	Conjectured Correspondence
Crescent	Sin	Moon
Star)) Star)	Etalak Latarak	Pollux or Morning Star Castor or Evening Star (The Twins of Gemini)
Form erased by time	?	?
Lamp	?	Libra (1)
Fish	Kulilu or Kusariqqu	Aquarius or Capricornus
Fish coming out of a stream	Oannes (or Dagon or Ea-Oannes) rising from Eurphrates or Tigris	Pisces Austrinus or Aquarius coming out of Eridanus
Dog	Gula or Ninkarraka	Sirius or Canis Major
Scorpion	Girtablili	Scorpio or Sagittarius
Bird	Zu or Zamama	Aquila

(1) A. B. Grimaldi in his 17th century Catalogue of Zodiacs and Plainispheres assigns Libra as the correspondence. This probably is an error. Libra seems not to have existed at a remote period as a fixed sign. Stars in Scorpio, where the equinox once took place, may be more accurate.

On conical stones or pillars, with probably dates up to 1,500 or 1,000 B.C., signs appear

on these stones follows. Where the ancient deity has been identified, the name appears in parenthesis after the symbol or sign:

Sign	Conjectured Correspondence	Sign	Conjectured Correspondence
Altar cone	Ara	Man kneeling	Hercules
Altar with lance head	?	Man pouring two streams from a vase	Aquarius or the star Fomalhaut
Antelope (Iku)	Capricornus		
Archer shooting three arrows	Sagittarius	Man with crook and sickle	Bootes
Arrow	Sagittarius	Man with four-pointed star (Shamash)	Sun
Bear	Ursa Major		
Bifork	?	Man with weapon	Sagittarius
Bull (Sin)	Moon		
Bull, humped (Enlil or Gudanna)	Taurus	Oval animal (crab ?)	Cancer
Centaur (usually double-headed)	?	Palm	?
Crab	Cancer	Ram (Ea)	Aries
Eighteen star arrows	Corona Borealis	Ramhead (Ea)	Aries
		Satyr (Anshar)	Polaris
Figure holding globe (Shamash)	Sun	Serpent (snake or dragon)	Draco or Hydra
Figure, broken	Cancer	Three flaming altars	?
Fishgoat (Ea or Ea-Oannes)	Aquarius or Capricornus or both	Tower in receding stages (Babel)	?
Globe	?		
Goat (Ea or Anshar or Iku)	Capricornus or Polaris or Capella	Two streams (Tigris and Euphrates)	Aquarius & Eridanus or Aquarius & Pisces Austrinus
Horns (of bull or ox)	Taurus		
Horse	Pegasus	Two streams coming down mountain	Twins descending from Bull (Taurus)
Lamp on stand	Libra (?)		
Legs	Cepheus		
Lion (Nergal or Ugallu or Uridimmu)	Mars or Leo or Lupus	U-shaped staff holding bird	Gemini (Twins) holding Aquila
Man with sword in one hand, a head in the other	Mars or Perseus	Vase pouring water	Aquarius
		Wavy lines	Aquarius
		Winged lion treading on dragon	Leo treading on Hydra

Men went into caves or built huts with small openings on elevations or promitories that they might better observe the skies. Their starlore, developed in the cradle of civilization, spread in all directions, and eventually temples were oriented to stars that were worshiped.

A calendar composed of twelve columns, which was found buried with an Egyptian mummy, was made up of signs which, as those of the Euphratean Valley, reflect the beliefs and habits of the designers:

Sign	Conjectured Correspondence
Tank	Aquarius
Crowned woman with rod	Cassiopeia
Hog	Ursa Minor
Jackal-headed man	Aquila
Sow with shear	Ursa Major
Lituus	Bootes
Three women and a serpent	Ophiuchus
Dog	Sirius or Canis Austrinus
Hawk-headed man	Lyra
Cat-headed man	Leo
Ape with darts	Sagittarius
Bird with darts	?

On a circular plague, on a sandstone planisphere, on a ceiling and in other places in Egypt, several of the signs found are similar to those found in the Euphratean Valley, such as a bird-headed man, boat, branch (palm), bull, centaur, cow, crab, dove, eye, figure on a throne, fish, fish-goat, goat, hawk, human figure with two heads and two feathers, lily, lion, monkey, ram, scarabaeus, serpent, two vases.

A small Phoenician zodiacal bronze, probably of the type that influenced the Greeks, was found in Palmyra. It no doubt was revered as a charm that controlled the soul's fate:

Sign	Conjectured Correspondence
Cidaris	Corona
Star	Capella
Disc	Sun
Crescent	Moon
Seven stars	Pleiades
Seven planets and holy water kettle on tripod	Ara
Fish-headed man	Pisces Austrinus
Figure holding corn	Spica
Priest in fish robes	Aquarius
Lion-headed man	Leo
Man with eagle feet	Aquila
Man holding two serpents	Ophiuchus
Horse	Pegasus
Boat	Argo
Leg	Cepheus

Sign	Conjectured Correspondence
Arrows	Sagittarius
River	Eridanus
Fishes	Pisces
Two uprights	Gemini

The treatise which remained the fundamental astronomical text throughout the middle ages was written by Claudius Ptolemy at Alexandria sometime in the 2nd century A.D. Nothing is known of Ptolemy's life except that he is the source of all of our knowledge of Greek astronomy and perhaps of more ancient writings. The title of his original work is the Greek word Megiste (Greatest or Great Composition). Arabs called the Ptolemy system Al Magisti from which its present title Almagest is derived. No important discoveries were made in Arabia, but the accumulation of observations there are considerable; also they developed simplified mathematical methods and invented our present system of counting. Many terms, such as almanac, nadir, zenith, have been borrowed from the Arabs. Strangely enough, as in the case of Al Magisti, Arabic names for stars and other celestial phenomena were transliterations from the Greek, which found their way back into Europe in a corrupt Lato-Arabic form.

The Chinese, although keen observers, seem to have been influenced by Chaldean and Arabic astronomy through Hindu and Persian travelers. Little is known about the actual age of their configurations, which appear to have been named in two separate periods. Those of the first period pay tribute to animals or useful articles familiar to common people, which would indicate their first astronomers had been among the peasantry; those of the second period are known by titles, military rank, or names of feudal states, which would indicate these astronomers had been attached to the court. A carving on an ancient Chinese steel mirror pictures the following: the sun in the center of four dragons (perhaps planets or the four directions). In a circle around the center design, suggesting a zodiac, is a horse, goat, monkey, stork, dog, hog (Ursa Major), rat, bull, tiger, rabbit, dragon, serpent.

The Deluge story is touched upon in almost all ancient zodiacs. The section of the sky containing the constellations Aquarius, Capricornus, Cetus, Delphinus, Eridanus, Pisces, and Pisces Austrinus, has been almost universally recognized as the Celestial Sea, an ocean of pure, crystal-clear water, upon which celestial ships sail or celestial beings swim. When it overflows it causes a flood. A double-capped pot, which appears in an ancient Persian zodiac, probably symbolizes the two-peaked Ararat, haven of the Ark. A second Celestial Sea has been recognized in the vicinity of Crater, Hydra, and Vela (formerly of the ship Argo). Mythologically, both seas are extensions of the Primordial Sea in which Tiamat lived and which encircled earth like a vise.

Those who escape a serious situation often say they are protected by a lucky star or their lucky stars. Many persons make secret trips to occult establishments, where they presumably receive the advice, warnings, and guidance of the stars. During the middle ages secrecy was unnecessary; one was not ridiculed for such a visit; the practice was considered scientifically as well as spiritually valid. In the 15th century, Paolo dal Pozzo Toscanelli, who had provided Columbus with maps for a westward voyage to the Far East, was considered by the Florentine seigniory a celebrated and trustworthy astrologer, one consulted on state affairs. Important decisions were enacted on the advice of his so-called "judicial astrology." Tycho Brahe, in the 16th century, had a laboratory where he practiced alchemy and astrology next to his astronomical observatory. He announced a prince would be born in the north of Finland who would overrun Germany and then vanish in 1632. Gustavus Adolphus, who died in 1632, fulfilled the prophecy. His student, Johannes Kepler, wrote horoscopes and prophesied a hard winter, which came to pass. All these men, because of various fabrications they were required to make, believed the judicial art to be uncertain, if not completely false. Toscanelli, before he died in 1482 at the age of 85, offered several proofs, among them his age. According

to the celestial combinations prevailing at his birth, he was to lose his life in his youth.

In spite of the misgivings of the astrologers themselves, Napoleon believed in his star. Chaucer wrote an astrolabe. Richelieu used astrology as a guide in government. Prognostications was a word which commonly appeared in the titles of early almanacs. In England one read: "Pronostycacyon of Mayster John Thybault, medycyner and astronomer of the Emperyall Majestie, of the year of our Lorde God MCCCCCXXXIJ., comprehending the iiij. partes of this yere, and of the influence of the mone, of peas and warre, and of the sykenesses of this yere, with the constellacions of them that be under the vij. planettes, and the revolucions of kynges and princes, and of the eclipses and comets." An almanac with prognostications was issued yearly by John Partridge, beginning with the year 1680. Under the pseudonym Isaac Bickerstaff, Johnathan Swift cleverly parodied issues of this almanac and predicted Partridge's death. Partridge tried in vain to convince the public he was still alive. Alexander Pope further immortalized the Partridge name by including it in his Rape of the Lock.

II

THE PATH OF THE MOON

Captivator

Before you, although clothed,
I become naked, transparent;
but you, who are naked,
arc veiled from my view
by the luminous glow
with which you entice me.
You lure me into dark forests,
up precipitous cliffs,
along wave-thrashed sands,
and then tease me
with your departure.
Tantalizing beauty,
are you Lady or
Lord of the Night?

Centuries undoubtedly passed before primitive herdsmen, who tended flocks on unfrequented mountain ridges above the Euphratean Valley and were awed by radiant shapes that appeared in the sky, realized that the shapes were various aspects of one body, a fickle Moon. Who but a deity was qualified to possess a capricious beauty that excelled anything else to be seen at night! The deity was Nannar, the strong bull, son of Enlil, grandson of Tiamat, better known as Sin, lord of wisdom, controller of the seasons, giver of dreams and oracles; one to be feared as well as honored, and whose name survives in Sinai, Sinbad, sinister, etc. When in a generous mood, Sin appeared in all his rotund glory and cast a brilliant orange or silver glow that lighted up the countryside; when in an evil mood, he reduced himself to a mere curved hair-like white line, barely perceptible in the blackness of night. Such darkness was an indication he had withdrawn his protection, and, fearful that the day over which he ruled in this humor would be filled with danger, no one dared engage in usual occupations. Instead a festival, the Sabattu, source of the Hebrew Sabbath, was held to implore him to return to his full splendor. To entice the god, human or animal sacrifices were offered to the accompaniment of kettledrums, played with frenzied rhythms to drown out the screams of the slaughtered. These perilous moods appeared with such regularity, our ancient ancestors were able to count or mark days by them and carved lunar calendars to help note auspicious or inauspicious periods. Listed below is an archaic lunar zodiac with solar overtones. The conflict of light and darkness, relating to the seasons as well as to each day, is apparent here. The modern star, or constellation, names given are conjectural; authorities are not in complete agreement. When a solar calendar was formed, some months had 29, some 30, days. Nevertheless 31 star clusters appeared on these tablets. The extra asterism, or resting place of the Moon, may have been to accommodate intercalary days, which in most early cultures remained godless. Intricacies of the astronomico-astrological system are still obscure, as the carvings which record observations do not contain explanations.

SUMERO-ACCADIAN LUNAR ZODIAC*

Asterism (1)	Moon's Resting Place	English Meaning	Patron Deity (2)	English Form	Realm or Function	Region Now Occupied By:
1	Apin (3)	Foundation	Sar (4)	Anshar	All-father (Night-sky)	Sadalmelik (Aquarius)
2	Lik-bar-ra	Hyena, Jackal, or Leopard(5)	A-nu	Anu (6)	All-father (Day sky)	Markab (Pegasus)
3	Gam	Scimitar or Sickle	Kakku sa qati Maruduki	Weapon in Marduk's hand	Weapon of sun-deity	Sheratan (Aries)
4	Mas-tab-ba-gal-gal-la	Great Twins	Lugal-ner-ra u Gal-lam-ta-ud-du-a	King of ecliptic (yoke) and Bull-of rising-sun	Sun in conflict with storm or dark-ness	Pleiades and Hyades, or Pleiades and Alde-baran (Taurus)
4	(7)		Sin u Nergal	Sin and Nergal	Moon and Sun, the Great Hero	
5	Mas-tab-ba-tur-tur	Little Twins	Amarud u Nin-sar	Ox-of-Day (Marduk) and Lady of Rising (Nin-harsag)	Sun as conquer-or of dark-ness and Lady of Dawn	Meissa and phi (a double) Orionis
6	Lugal	Mighty Man	Maru-duku	Marduk	Sun	Betelgeuze (Orion)

Sumero-Accadian Lunar Zodiac, continued

Asterism (1)	Moon's Resting Place	English Meaning	Patron Deity (2)	English Form	Realm or Function	Region Now Occupied By:
7	Khigalla (7)	Canal of Water (8)	Gibil	Gibil	Fire and Lustration	Alhena (Gemini)
8	Pal-ura	Crossing of the Water-dog (9)	Na-na-a	Nana	Earth Mother	Procyon (Canis Minor)
9	Su-pa Beli sa pan matati i-sim-mu. Rubu beli Maruduku	Lustrous One of Bel, which before the region rules, and Prince of Lords Maru-duku	Su-pa Beli; Maru-duku	Namru, the Lustrous One, and Marduk	Evening and Morning Sun	Castor and Pollux (Gemini)
10	Gu-sir-kes-da-ili-Anim	Yoke of the en-closure of Anu	Rabu-sa-sam-e-rabi	Prince of the Great Heaven (Anu)	Creator, who spawned darkness	Cancer
11	Tur-us mal makh	Son of Supreme Temple	Danu	Anu	Divine Judge	Alphard (Hydra)
12	Gis-bar, namru, sa pan Mul-mo sarra	Wood-of-Light, Brilliance before the Lord-of-the-voice-of-heaven (10)	Nuzku	Gibil	Fire (Light-ning)	Algeiba (Leo)
13	Gub-ba (ra) mes-su-tu-E-kur	Fire-flame, Ruler (?) of Temple of Hosts-of-Earth	Sin u Nergal	Sin and Nergal	Moon and Sun, the Great Hero	Regulus (Leo) (11)
14	Ili Kua mes-su-tu E-kur	Oracle god; Ruler of Temple of Hosts-of-Earth	A-nu u Bel	Anu and Bel	Day Sky and Light	Zosma (Leo)

Sumero-Accadian Lunar Zodiac, continued

Aster-ism(1)	Moon's Resting Place	English Meaning	Patron Deity(2)	English Form	Realm or Function	Region Now Occupied By:
15	Lamas-su mikid-isati ili Ba-u	Flaming One, Burning Fire of Baau	Ur-ma-akh u Gu-la (12)	Great Lion; and Goddess Great One	Sun God and Goddess of Medicine	Denebola (Leo)
16	Nin-sar u ilu Ur-ra-gal	Lady of Heaven and Ruler of the Great City	Nergal u Akh-bi-tum (13)	Nergal and Ninhar-sag	Great Hero of Ur and Cosmic Mother	Porrima (Virgo)
17	Sakh, ilu Da-nu	Pros-perity of the sky god	A-nu	Anu	Day Sky	Spica (Virgo)
18	Ansu Kur-ra	Animal from the east	Im-dugud-khu	Great Storm Bird	Rain	Gienah (Corvus)
19	Lu-lim	He-Goat	Mul-mo-sar-ra	Lord-of-the-Voice-of Heaven	Thunder	iota and kappa Virginis
20	Mulu-izi-u La-ta-rak	Wander-ing Fire and Desert King	Sin u Nergal	Sin and Nergal	Moon and Sun	delta Librae
21	Belit	The Lady	Tin-tir-ki	Might-of-the-Grove-of Life	Fertility	Zubenelgen-ubi and Zuben-eschamali (Libra)
22	En-te-na-mas luv	Founda-tion of Brick-work	Ip	Creator	Creator	Hydra
23	Gis-gan-gusur-kakku sa ili Ea (7)	Tree of Garden of Light, Weapon of God Ea	sa ina libbi-su absi iskun	which in the midst of the Abyss he placed	Fresh Waters	beta, delta, pi Scorpionis
23	Mul-mul-la(7)	The Spear	kakku sa qati Maruduki	Weapon in Mar-duk's hand	Weapon of sun-deity	

Sumero-Accadian Lunar Zodiac, continued

Aster-ism(1)	Moon's Resting Place	English Meaning	Patron Deity(2)	English Form	Realm or Function	Region Now Occupied By:
24	Dar-lugal	Great-one, the King	Bilu sa ziri; Arakh Tisritu, ilu Lu-gal-tud-da (14)	Lord of Seed; month Tisri, God the Lusty King (15)	Waning Sun	Antares (Scorpio)
25	Mulu-bat	Man of Death	Pa-gar, a-sig	The Corpse, The Fever	Period of Dark-ness	Yed Posterior (Ophiuchus)
26	Tsir (7)	Snake	Nin-ki-gal	Queen of the Great Region	Dark-ness (After-world)	eta, xi, theta Ophiuchi and Serpens
26	Nabiu u Sar (7)	Prophet and King	Samas u Ramanu	Sun-god and Exalted god	Sun-god in the Ghost World	
27	Gir-tab	Scorpion	Is-kha-ra-tam-tim (16)	Ishtar of the sea	Mermaid	theta, iota, kappa, lambda, nu Scorpionis
27	(7)		Sar-ur u Sar-gaz	Director of Fire, Director of Sacrifice	Sacri-fice	
28	Ligbat, ilu Ku-su	Beast of Death; god of Sunset	Kur-gal	God of the Great Region	Dark-ness that con-sumes	alpha, beta, gamma, delta Lupi (17)
29	A-nu-ni-tum u Si-nu-nu-tum (18)	Great Goddess and the Swallow	Nahru mas-gu-gar u mahru Ud-kip-nun-na	River of Currents and River Light-of-the-Great Plain	Twin Rivers (19)	Kaus Borealis, Gau; and Al Nasl, Kaus Meri-dionalis, Kaus Australis (Sagittarius)
	(7)					(20)

Sumero-Accadian Lunar Zodiac, continued

Aster- ism (1)	Moon's Resting Place	English Meaning	Patron Deity (2)	English Form	Realm or Function	Region Now Occupied By:
30	Gu-sir-a-ab-ba (7)	Yoke of the Sea	Nun-ki	Lordly City	Patron of Ur, Sacred City	zeta, pi Sagittarii (21)
31	Ma-gur, Muna-kha	Ship-of-the-Bond i.e. of the He-Goat	Nabiu u Ur-me-tum	Prophet and Hero-Voice-of Fear	Prophecy	Capricorn

NOTES: *Later in this book certain constellations or stars may be identified as Euphratean lunar mansions, and they may not agree with those listed here. Dissimilarities appeared on tablets carved at different ages and in separated localities; furthermore scholars are not in agreement as to the date the moon visited a mansion; also various characteristics or deities have been assigned to identical celestial bodies. (1) Several resting places involve two tablets. (2) Ruling deities or hosts to the Moon on his journey through the days of the month sometimes appear at more than one astral inn. (3) The tablet actually reads, "Kakkab Apin." Kakkab simply means star or stars and has been omitted before all names in this column. (4) The tablet reads, "Ilu-Sar." Ilu means deity and has been omitted from names listed in this column. (5) Literally, Striped-Dog. (6) Son and successor of Anshar. (7) Two tablets composed this asterism. The second tablet of the 7th, 29th, and 30th days are either lost or unintelligible. (8) The Milky Way, where the star is located, and which Egyptians termed the Inaccessible Stream. (9) Alludes to a myth about a little dog, Canis Minor, that crossed the Canal, or Stream, of the Milky Way and was separated from his brother, a big dog, Canis Major. Thus is Procyon identified as wet, weeping, and watery-eyed. (10) Fire was produced in the ancient world by rubbing 2 sticks, one against the other. Firesticks whose points ignited were regarded with special veneration, and the 'Wood-of-Light' was exalted into a god, sometimes identified with Gibil, sometimes adored separately under the name of Saval (Savullu, Shaool, the Hebrew Saul). The 'Brilliance before the Lord-of-the voice' was the sun, which was the original disk hurled at darkness by the Heaven-power, who had a voice of thunder. A partly circular weapon of the Heaven-power, and sometimes used by the Sun-god in his contests with chaos and darkness, was the bow or lunar crescent. A third weapon was lightning. The 3rd day is sacred to the bow or curved weapon, and several have been described in the sky, such as the section of Leo known as the Sickle. The ideograph represents 2 sticks laid across each other as a kind of disc or weapon, such as was used by men to toss at enemies. (11) In late Babylonian astronomy

called Sharru, King, and located in the section of the cluster known
as the Sickle of the Lion, or the Curved Weapon.   (12) Gula is an
aspect of Baau, the cosmic-mother.   (13) Probably Ninharsag.
(14) Lugal-tud-da is identical with the Zu bird, thief, lightning-
god, storm-deity, and enemy of the sun.   (15) Tisri is the 7th
month, or period, in which the golden seed of heaven, the sun, is
swallowed by the dragon of darkness.   The primary meaning of
autumn, represented by Tisri, is that the sun begins to succumb
to his foes.   A secondary reference to agricultural operations may
be involved, but these do not form the basis of archaic symbolism,
inasmuch as man's observations of nature long preceded any
regular agricultural course.   (16)   A piscine and androgynous form
of Ishtar.   (17) These assignments have been taken from the works
of Robert Brown.   If this one is correct, the moon retraces his
steps during parts of the month; or this section may have something
to do with the extra (31st) day.   (18) The swallow is a bird of
destiny.   (19) The twin rivers are the Tigris, river of currents,
and the Euphrates, river of the plain, both of which supposedly had
celestial sources.   (20) The two clusters within this constellation
are side by side, like the Tigris and Euphrates, to which they are
respectively dedicated.   The annual migration connects them with
the autumn season, which Sagittarius represents.   (21)   These
stars form a yoke,   supposedly thrown across the ecliptic near the
great celestial sea.   Eridu was once at the mouth of the Euphrates
on the edge of the Persian Gulf, and thus was the Yoke of the
Sea.   Each earthly aspect supposedly had a celestial counterpart.
Time has dried up much of the area, and the ruins of the ancient
city are now about 120 miles from the head of the Gulf.

As measurer (of time) Sin, the
moon, was given the title Aku.
Shrines were decorated with his
images, that of a giant man with
a blue beard, blue to represent
light; or that of a bull, the
impregnator of all things, provider of the generative and reproductive force; or that of a
boatman who, with the title Udsar,
rowed the crescent-shaped boat
across the Celestial Sea.   However no one male could be that
full of whims, so he was conceived to be androgymous, and
when in female form was addressed
as Nin Aa (A, Ai), Lady Who Is
Brightest (or First), or as Nana,
Virgin Protectress of Cities.

Nomads carried this knowledge
in all directions, and Ah, later
called Khensu, the Sailor or
Wanderer, was worshiped in
Egypt.   Like his Euphratean
counterpart he measured the
days of the months, and as a
time deity he made crops to ripen
and he slaughtered souls (which
explains why stars vanish in his
path).   Isis, on her search for
the dismembered parts of the
body of Osiris, her murdered
brother-husband, replaced
Khensu.   Each morning before
she disappeared from the sky
her tears (dew) covered the
earth.

Early Semites fell under the
spell of the glamorous Astarte,
an adored harlot, who encouraged
sexual love.   This goddess was
as shameless and cruel as she
was wayward.   She consorted
with her son, the youthful spring

deity, and demanded of her faithful that they sacrifice first born children, first fruits, new-born animals and the virginity of maidens, as well as engage in orgiastic rites. Public prostitutes of both sexes, who negotiated their engagements at the temple were consecrated to her. Hot cross buns, probably to imply her authority was borne by the four winds, were eaten in her honor.

Phoenician maritime traders introduced Astarte at various Mediterranean ports. In Greece she was transformed into Artemis, whom Romans called Diana. Here she lost some of her carnality and became protectress of maidens; nevertheless she retained much of her cruelty.

Artemis prided herself on her virginity, her boyish figure, and her light-footedness. Her favorite pastime was hunting, and she ran across fields or lingered in forests unaccompanied save for her hounds, gifts from the wind god Pan. Although she boasted she could not be moved by love, she succumbed to the giant hunter Orion. In a jealous rage, when he violated Eos, the dawn, Artemis slew him, but the gods transformed him into a constellation, the most magnificent in the sky, that his beauty might have immortality. Just before sundown one day, the hunter Actaeon, the late afternoon sun, came upon a pool in which Artemis was bathing. The outraged goddess transformed him into a stag, whereupon he immediately was torn to pieces and devoured by his own dogs. His blood, which had spattered across the sky, was all that was left of him. Although Orion had been unable to violate her chastity,

inasmuch as it was renewed at each New Moon, after her experience with him she ran from any man who pursued her. Possessing the ability to change her shape she fled from the river deity Alpheus by plunging into the sea, where she assumed a mermaid form and lighted the way for seafarers at night. King Agamemnon, to obtain a safe voyage to Troy to rescue his brother's wife Helen, placed his daughter Iphigenia upon an altar in preparation for a sacrifice to Artemis. As he was about to strike the death blow the goddess, in the form of a giant bird, seized the maiden, placed a deer on the altar in her stead and carried her to Taurica, where she installed Iphigenia as priestess of the Temple. In the form of a fig tree with innumerable breasts Artemis played the role of nourisher. The Greeks loved her dearly, and her temple at Ephesus was ranked among the seven wonders of the ancient world. Its interiors contained 127 columns, each 60 feet high and each placed by a different king. In the innermost chamber was her statue, which was made of ebony and portrayed her with many breasts. Lions leaned against her arms and on her head she wore a turret crown to indicate that she protected cities and civilization. She finally was Christianized as Saint Artemidos.

As a tripartite goddess Artemis was portrayed in triple form, all three bodies back to back or with one torso and three heads, that of a horse, a dog, and a boar. In trivia form she was identified as the waxing, full, and waning moon, or as the united beings of Selene (Luna), goddess of moonlight on fields, guardian of birth, and mistress of Endymion to whom she appeared in dreams; Artemis (Diana), virgin who reigned in the open vault of heaven and was patroness of growth; Hecate, queen of the unseen afterworld and administratrix of death.

The robust tribes of northern Europe had a jovial and mischievous god, Mani, whose chariot was the moon. Two children, Hyuki and Bil, who became the Jack and Jill of nursery rhyme fame, were sent by their father to a mountain stream to fetch some magic song mead. Upon leaving the spring, the children slung across their shoulders the bar that held their pails and started down the slope. For a while Mani drove above them and made the treacherous path along the rocky ridge visible; then suddenly he reached down and seized the pair, pails and all. Their father pursued them. Although unsuccessful in an attempt to assault Mani, he succeeded in stealing some of the mead, and for this was condemned to dwell on the moon in a state of eternal drunkenness, in which state he was called Svigdur (Champion Drinker). Hyuki and Bil have become Mani's constant companions and can be seen at night as spots on the moon. Bil sometimes sprinkles her song-mead on the wind that mortals may be inspired by it. Hyuki favors skiers and illuminates the snow-covered peaks for those who have failed to find their way down before nightfall. The antics of their father cause the moon to sway and humans therefore see it from different angles. The Anglo-Saxons worshipped Mani under the name of Monan.

In southern Sweden the marks on the moon were imagined to be that of a brewing kettle from which those on the moon received nourishment. Neighboring Danes rejected the idea of the moon having anything to do with a deity, either in form or as an article of use to a god. In Danish folklore our satellite was a cheese churned from curds that had dropped out of the Milky Way. This notion is the source of Rabelais' statement that the moon is made of green cheese.

In Friesland the marks were conceived to be those of a man who had stolen cabbages. When the theft was discovered his aggrieved neighbors wished him in the moon. According to another fable the thief stole sheep. Accompanied by his dog he lured the animals with cabbages. In a third tale the thief was caught with a bundle of osier willows that did not belong to him, and he was transported to the moon with his plunder. Christian lore relates the story in this way: An old wood-cutter was traveling on Sunday with a bundle of sticks on his back. He met a fairy who upraided him for toiling on the Sabbath. "Sunday on earth or Monday in heaven; it's all one to me!" the wood-cutter answered. "Inasmuch as you disregard Sunday on earth, you shall carry your bundle for ever on the moon," the fairy cried. As she vanished, the woodcutter was caught up with his bundle and carried to the moon where he shall be seen eternally." Near Conway in Wales, in Gyffyn Church, a pictorial representation depicts the moon as a big round disk in which the Sabbath-breaker is portrayed with his bundle of sticks. Other early Christian writers interpreted the moon markings to be: Cain driven from the face of the earth to the face of the moon; Isaac with wood for the fire on which he was to be sacrificed; the patriarch Jacob; Judas Iscariot; the Magdalen in tears; a Hebrew sinner gathering sticks on the Sabbath. Chaucer described the figure on the moon as:

> Bearing a bush of thorns on
>   his back,
> Whiche for his theft might
>   clime so ner the heaven.

Scotchwomen in the 16th and 17th centuries made a curtsey to the new moon. In England it was customary for rustic belles, as soon as they saw the first new moon after midsummer to turn their back to a gate or turnstile, or sit astride it, and say:

> All hail, new moon, all hail
>   to thee!
> I prithee, good moon, reveal
>   to me
> This night who shall my true
>   love be;
> Who is he, and what he wears,
> And what he does all months
>   and years.

A dream was expected to follow which gave the information so urgently desired. Superstitions are attached to the moon even into the present day. Good luck is expected if the new moon first be seen over the right shoulder. It is common knowledge that when a line joining the horns of the moon's crescent lies nearly perpendicular to the horizon, the moon cannot hold water, and is called a 'wet moon,' and is a sign of wet weather; when it is almost horizontal, so that the crescent can gather and hold water, it is called a 'dry moon, because, retaining the water

above, fair weather blesses the earth. Sailors dread seeing a large star or planet near the moon, to use their expression, "a big star dogging the moon," for they consider it a sign of boisterous weather.

In European folklore, treasures wasted on earth, such as broken vows, fruitless tears, misspent time and wealth, unanswered prayers, find their way to the moon, thus we have the expression limbus of the moon.

Diarmaid, the Celtic Pagan moon deity, is a romantic figure. He had a love spot on his forehead that made him irresistible to women, and Princess Grainne, lady of the gloaming, betrothed to his uncle the sun god Fionn MacCoul, prevailed upon him to elope with her. Oegnus, deity of love, gave each a cloak of invisibility, but the brave Diarmaid refused to wear his. At night the lovers rested in a tree or near a dolmen. Often the brilliant beauty of Diarmaid could not be hidden; at other times he had some success and only a thin line of his manly figure was visible. Each morning, at the approach of Fionn, Oengus helped the lovers escape. For a year and a day Fionn pursued them; and then he announced he had forgiven his nephew. Diarmaid was overjoyed, and when his uncle asked him to capture the green boar Gulban, a storm demon, the youth was enchanted with the prospect of presenting the older man with a desired trophy. Diarmaid killed the boar and returned with the skin, whereupon Fionn suggested an error may have been made in figuring the size, and asked his unsuspecting nephew to verify the measurements by treading upon it in the opposite direction, which was against the lie of the bristles. One of the bristles pierced Diarmaid's heel and inflicted a poisoned and fatal wound.

Diarmaid's refuge in a tree is symbolic of grasping the sacred- or cosmic-tree for sanctuary. The practice of seeking sanctuary by grasping an altar is derived from this fable, which is told in miscellaneous ways in many parts of the world. It also is the source of the game tig-touch-wood. The Tristan and Iseult story is a later form of this legend.

The ancient Hebrews had three great festivals regulated by new moons: The Passover Feast, a spring festival corresponding to Easter or the Pascal Moon Feast; Pentecost (Shabuoth), the celebration of the gift of the Law to Moses on Mt. Siani and corresponding to Whitsuntide; and the Feast of Tabernacles, an autumn festival held under the harvest moon.

The Persian moon deity in female form was Metra, whose love penetrated everywhere. During daylight hours, like the Hecate form of Artemis, she penetrated into the realm of shades. In male form the deity was Ilmuqah, whom the Arabs called Il, a name which corresponds to El and Allah. Little is known about Ilmuquah.

The transit of Il was described in a 28-day calendar which the Arabs may have inherited from the Chaldeans. Il's mansions were called Al Ribatat, The Roadside Inns; Al Nujum al Alidh, The Stars of Entering; or Al Manazil al Kamr, which signifies the noonday halt or resting place of camel and rider in the desert. Manzil is the singular form of Manazil.

RESTING PLACES OF THE MOON-   Arabic, Persian

Day	Arabic Manzil	Name Meaning	Corresponding Persian Inn	Name Meaning	Bright Stars in Asterism
1	Sheratan or Al Ashrat	The Sign	Padevar	Protecting Pair	$a, \beta,$ Arietis
2	Butain or Nair al Butain (1)	Belly or Bright One of the Little Belly	Pish Parvis	Belly or Scabbard	Chief components of Musca Borealis
3	Al Thurayya (2) (Also Al Najm or Mesha) (3)	The Many Little Ones	Peren or Perv	The Begetters	The Pleiades
4	Aldebaran	Bright One or Follower	Taschter	Creator Spirit	$a,$ Tauri
5	Al Hakah	White Spot	Al Taj	The Crown	a, y, λ Orionis

Resting Places of the Moon - Arabic, Persian, Continued

Day	Arabic Manzil	Name Meaning	Corresponding Persian Inn	Name Meaning	Bright Stars in Asterism
6	Al Hena (Al Hunah)	Brand or Mark	Besn	The Arm	γ, η, ν, μ, ξ, Geminorum
7	Al Dhira or Al Zirr (Ziraa)	The Arm or The Button	Rakhvad or Taraha	The Canal or Two Stars	α, β, Geminorum
8	Al Nathrah or Al Himarain (4)	The Gap or Two Asses	Avra-k	The Cloud	γ, δ, ε Cancri
9	Al Tarf (Al Terf)	The Glance	Nahn	The Nose	ξ, Cancri and λ Leonis
10	Al Jabhah (Al Jebhah)	The Fore-head	Miyan	The Center	α, γ, ζ, η, Leonis
11	Al Zubrah	The Mane (of the Lion)	Zosma (Zozma)	The Girdle	δ, θ, Leonis
12	Al Sarfah (Serfah)	The Changer or the Turn (5)	Avdem	The One in the Tail	β, Leonis
13	Al Awwa	The Barker	Mashaha	Meaning Uncertain	β, γ, δ, ε, η Virginis
14	Al Simak al A'zal	The De-fenseless or Unarmed Simak (6)	Chushe	Ear of Wheat	α, Virginis
15	Al Ghafr	The Covering	Huçru	Good Goer	ι, κ, φ Virginis
16	Al Zubanah (Zaban)	To Push	Çrob	The Horned	α, β Librae
17	Iklil al Jabhah (Iclilu-jebbah)	Crown of the Forehead	Nur	Bright	β, δ, γ, π, ρ Scorpionis

Resting Places of the Moon - Arabic, Persian, Continued

Day	Arabic Manzil	Name Meaning	Corresponding Persian Inn	Name Meaning	Bright Stars in Asterism
18	Kalb al Akrab	Heart of The Scorpion	Gel (7)	The Red	a, Scorpionis
19	Shaula or Mushalah	Sting or Raised (8)	Ghezhdum or Kazhdum	Stinger	λ, Υ, Scorpionis
20	Al Naam (Al Naaim)	The Ostrich	Gau	Bull	$\varsigma, \sigma, \tau, \phi$ Sagit-Tarii
21	Al Baldah or Al Kiladah	The City or the Necklace	Kaman or Nimasp	Bow and Arrow	η, Sagittarii
22	Al Jady (Zabih) or Al Sa'd al Dhabih	The Goat or The Lucky One of the Slaughterers	Bushgali, Bahi, or Vahik	The Goat	a, β Capricorni
23	Al Bali or Al Sa'd al Bula (al Bulaan)	Brightest One or Good Fortune of the Swallower	Dol (Dul)	Water Bucket	ε, μ, Υ, Aquarii
24	Sadalsuud (Saud or Sund)	Luckiest of the Lucky	Bunda	Foundation	β, ς, Aquarii and e Capricorni
25	Ah'biyah	Lucky Star of Hidden Places	Khatsar	Uncertain	λ, Aquarii
26	Al Fargh al Mukdim	The Fore Spout (9)	Vaht	Uncertain but pertains to water	a, β, Pegasi
27	Al Fargh al Mu'hir	The Rear Spout (10)	Miyan	Wellmouth or	γ, Pegasi

Resting Places of the Moon - Arabic, Persian, Continued

Day	Arabic Manzil	Name Meaning	Corresponding Persian Inn	Name Meaning	Bright Stars in Asterism
				Spout	and δ, Andromedae
28	Batn al Hut or Al Risha	Fish's Belly or The Cord	Kaht	Cord	16 stars from ψ, Piscium to Υ, Andromedae, including β, ζ, Andromedae

NOTES: (1) Name does not correspond to present location of stars; probably a change from earlier drawings of Aries. (2) Al Thurayya is a diminutive of Tharwan, meaning abundance. (3) Al Najm signifies Constellation Par Excellence. (4) Other Arabic Names: Al Fum al Asad, The Mouth of the Lion; Al Anf al Asad, the Muzzle of the Lion; Al Liha, The Soft Palate. (5) That is, The Changer of the weather. (6) That is, unattended by any other star. (7) Sometimes identified as Satevis, one of the four Royal Stars. (8) That is, Raised, ready to sting. (9) That is, Fore Spout of the water bucket. (10) That is, Rear Spout of the water bucket.

Central Asians believed the moon to be a mirror that reflected everything in the world.

In India and other parts of the Orient, the moon deity was not a personification of the moon; rather, as in Teutonic lore, the moon was the car or cart of the deity, who guided it on a path among the stars, and the characteristics of the Hindu moon lord, Soma, were so much like those of the Norse Mani, he may have been Mani's prototype. Not only was Soma lord of the moon but of the Soma Tree, the cosmic plant from whose fruit came the wine of immortality and poetic inspiration (fertile rains). An Archer who desired the ambrosia shot at the eagle-mount of Soma. The eagle jerked, the god dropped some of his wine, and verdure sprang up on earth. Soma developed a thousand eyes (stars) that he might more efficiently herd his flocks of prolific cows (rain-giving clouds). Because he possessed the power to churn the ocean and cause dangerous waves and tides, seafarers were careful not to offend him. He married the twenty-seven daughters of Daksha, a sun deity. Each of his wives resided on a nakshatra (constellation) located on the path along the celestial equator.

As he traveled the sky, Soma rested for one night at each mansion, but he loved only Rohini, the most radiant and alluring, and neglected all the others, who complained to Daksha. The irate father excluded his son-in-law from the sacrifice and cursed him to die of consumption. As Soma weakened a blight fell upon earth, and all creatures faded until Daksha mitigated his curse and said that instead Soma should have periods of strength and weakness, thus the moon, which he ruled, waxed and waned with him, but in certain seasons, such as during a frost, he was unable to regain virility. From Soma came the lunar race of kings who ruled India.

Chandra replaced Soma, who was reduced to the position of lord of the moon mead. Chandra, as lunar regent, saw that Soma delivered dew to the crops, which ripened under the harvest moon. The new ruler, who swayed human life from birth until death, rode about on an antelope to exemplify his speed and grace.

In a third legend, the god Indra was walking in a forest disguised as a Brahman when he met a monkey, a fox, and a hare, who were traveling together. He pretended to be starving and asked the trio for food. They had none with them, but set off immediately to see what they might find. The monkey brought back a bunch of mangoes; the fox came with a pot of milk; but the hare had nothing. Reluctant to appear inhospitable, the hare informed the Brahman, "If you are very, very hungry, you may roast me on a fire and then eat me." The Brahman kindled a fire at the base of a rock. No sonner had he done so than the hare leaped in, but the god snatched the heroic animal from the flames and to reward him for his readiness to sacrifice himself carried him up to the moon, where he may be seen to this day.

Each of the twenty-seven (later twenty-eight) nakshatras or resting places, where the moon chariot was tied up at night, was governed by one who determined the destiny of those born while he entertained the moon lord. To establish communication with these divinities, the Hindus devised calendars, which probably were adopted from the Arabic. Thus each of the twenty-eight days of a Sanscrit month was dedicated to the nakshatra regent who was host to that day's phase of the moon. Intercalary days were introduced to adjust to the year's cycle. Children born on intercalary days were regarded as unfortunate; their stars were uncertain and therefore not to be trusted.

To simplify the presentation of the nakshatras and their regents a chart is presented here. The stars that compose the asterisms are in the neighborhood of the stars that compose the Arabian Manazil.

RESTING PLACES OF THE MOON - Hindu

Day	Nakshatra (1)	Name Meaning	Presiding Regent	Astral Configuration	Number of Stars & Bright Stars in Asterism (2)
1	Asvini	Horse-men	Asvins (Dawn and Gloaming)	Horse's Head	3- a, β, Arietis
2	Barani	Bearer	Yama (Death)	The Yama	3 in Musca Borealis
3	Krittika	General of Celestial Armies	Agni (Fire)	A Flame, a Razor, or a knife	7- The Pleiades and η, Tauri
4	Rohini	Red Antelope	Prajapati (Light)	Wheeled Carriage or a Temple	5- a, Tauri
5	Mrigasiras (Mrga)	Stag Head	Soma (Moon)	Antelope's Head	14- λ, Orionis
6	Ardra	Moist	Rudra (Storm)	A Gem	1- a, Orionis
7	Punarvasu	Two Good Again	Aditi (Mother)	A House	4- β, Ceminorum
8	Pushya or Tishiya	Flower or Auspicious	Brihaspati (Mediator)	An Arrow or Crescent	3- δ, Cancri
9	Aslesha (Açlesha)	Embracer	Sarpas, the Serpents	Potter's Wheel	5- a, Cancri
10	Magha	Mighty	The Pitri (Progenitor)	A House	5- a, Leonis
11	Purva Phalguni	(3)	Aryaman (Solar)	A Couch	2- δ, Leonis
12	Uttara Phalguni		Bhaga (Sun in storms)	A Bed	2- β, Leonis

Resting Places of the Moon - Hindu, continued

Day	Nakshatra(1)	Name Meaning	Presiding Regent	Astral Configuration	Number of Stars & Bright Stars in Asterism(2)
13	Hasta	The Hand	Savitri (Solar)	A Hand	5- γ, Corvi
14	Sitra (Chitra)	The Bright	Tvastr (Artisan)	A Lamp or Pearl	1- α, Virginis
15	Svati or Nishtya	Good Goer or Outcast	Vayu (Breeze)	Coral Bead, Pearl, or Other Gem	1- α, Bootis
16	Visakha	Branched	Indrani (Fertility)	A Festoon or Decorated Gateway	4- α, Librae
17	Anuradha	Propitious	Mitra (Solar)	A Row of Oblations or a Ridge	4- δ, Scorpionis
18	Jyestha	Oldest	Indra (Rain)	Earing	3- α, Scorpionis
19	Visritau or Mula	Two Releasers or Root	Nirrti (Death)	Lion's Tail or Couch	11 stars of Scorpio
20	Purvashadha	Former Unconquered	Apas (Mist)	A Couch or Elephant's Tooth	4- δ, Sagittarii
21	Uttarashadha	Latter Unconquered	Viswedevas (Demons)	An Elephant's Tooth or Bed	4- τ, Sagittarii
22	Abhijit(4)	Victorious	Brahma (Supreme)	Triangle or Tri-cornered Nut	3- α, Lyrae
23	Sravana, Srona, or Asvattha	The Ear, or Lame, Fig Tree	Vishnu (Solar)	A Trident (5)	3- α, Aquilae
24	Sravishtha or Dhanishtha	Most Favorable, Richest	The Vasus (Elements)	Drum or Tabor	5- α, Delphini

Resting Places of the Moon - Hindu, continued

Day	Nakshatra (1)	Name Meaning	Presiding Regent	Astral Configuration	Number of Stars & Bright Stars in Asterism (2)
25	Satabhisha (Catabhishaj)	The Hundred Physician	Varuna (Sky)	A Circle	1-λ, Aquarii
26	Purva (6) Bhadrapada	Beautiful, Auspicious, or Happy Feet	Aja Ekapada (Lightning)	A Double-faced Figure or Couch	2-α, Pegasi
27	Uttara (7) Bhadrapada		Ahi Budhya (Water Snake)	A Double-faced Figure or Couch	2-α, Andromedae
28	Revati	Abundant	Pusan (Solar)	Drum or Tabor	21-ζ, Piscium (8)

NOTES, (1) Some works give Krittika as the first Nakshatra, thus suggesting the lunar month ends with Barani. (2) Astronomers do not all agree as to which stars make up the asterisms; those listed here seem to be the stars most generally agreed upon. (3) Meaning of Phalguni uncertain, perhaps the Bad One. Purva means former, Uttar means latter. Sometimes the positions of the Phalguni asterisms are reversed. (4) When only 27 nakshatra are given, this one is omitted. (5) To symbolize the three steps of Vishnu. (6) Former. (7) Latter. (8) Some give the number of stars as 32.

As in Hindu and Teutonic lore, the Chinese associated the moon with a delicious intoxicating wine desired by everyone. For drinking some of the sacred elixir of life, which had been stolen, the beautiful maiden Ch'ang-O was transformed into a three-legged toad and forced to reside on the moon, midway between earth and heaven. Wu Kang, a woodsman who had cut down a sacred tree, was not only banished to the moon, but condemned to cut down a cassia tree. As fast as he hewed out a chip another grew in its place; hence he remains eternally working at his endless task. In another folktale the man in the moon is Yuelao, who favors lovers. The young men and women he desires to make husband and wife are tied together with an invisible silken cord, which cannot be severed until death. The greatest of all Chinese festivals is that of the Moon celebrated on the 15th day of the 8th month, when the Moon is brightest. This date corresponds to the harvest, the season of release, when offerings are made to departed spirits.

The first Chinese calendar was lunar and called Hsiu, Siuh, or Sieu, signifying Houses. The Houses were those of twenty-eight heroic warriors who upon death had been transported to the skies to keep in order the dwellings where the Moon rested each night; to act as deity messengers, i.e. transmit to mortals via signs in the sky information on events to come; or in other ways serve celestial beings. In the Hsiu presented here, the Moon's resting place of the first day corresponds to the Inn of the 14th day in the Arabic and Hindu calendars. Roughly it then follows the course given in the Arabic and Hindu tables. The small differences that do exist may have been brought about by the latitude from which observations had been made. The asterisms generally are located along the equator; occasional derivations include a bright star slightly off the path.

THE HSIU or CHINESE LUNAR ZODIACAL CONSTELLATIONS (1)							
Day	Constellation	Name Meaning	Corresponding Element	Animal Representation	Quadrant, Season, & Regent	Period's Fortune (2)	Constituent Stars
1	Chio (Chiao, Kio)	Horn, Corner, or Angle	Wood	Sea Serpent	Eastern Spring, Azure Dragon	Unlucky for land buying lucky for marraige of daughter	The star Spica & ξ, θ, ι, Virginis
2	K'ang	Neck or Overbearing	Metal	Dragon	"	Unfortunate	κ, λ, ρ, Virginis
3	Ti	Fundamental, Bottom	Earth	Badger	"	Lucky	α, β, γ, ι, Librae
4	Fang	A Room or Apartment	Sun	Rabbit or Hare	"	Very Unlucky	β, δ, π, ρ, Scorpionis.
5	Hsin	Heart	Moon	Fox	"	Lucky for weddings and construction	The star Antares and σ, τ Scorpionis.

The Hsiu, continued

Day	Constel-lation	Name Meaning	Corres-ponding Element	Animal Repre-sentation	Quadrant Season,& Regent	Period's Fortune (2)	Constit-uent Stars
6	Wei	A Tail	Fire	Tiger	Eastern, Spring, Azure Dragon	Un-fortun-ate	$\varepsilon, \varsigma, \xi, \eta, \theta,$ $\iota, \kappa, \lambda, \varsigma,$ Scorpi-onis.
7	Chi (Ki, Kit)	Winnower (Corn-fan) or Sieve	Water	Leopard	"	Lucky	$\gamma, \delta, \varepsilon, \beta,$ Sagit-tarii
8	Tow (Dew, Nan Tow, Tew, Tou)	A Peck, Ladle, or Measur-er (3)	Wood	Griffin	Northern Winter, Tor-toise	Bring-er of hap-piness	$\varsigma, \lambda, \varphi,$ $\sigma, \tau, \zeta,$ Sagit-tarii
9	Niu	Ox or Bull	Metal	Ox or Bull	"	Bad Omen	$\omega, \alpha, \beta,$ Sagit-tarii and α, β, π Capri-corni
10	Nü	The Girl	Earth	Bat	"	For-tunate	$\varepsilon, \varsigma, \gamma, \vartheta,$ Aquarii
11	Hsü (Heu, Hiu)	Empti-ness, Vacant	Sun	Rat or Mouse	"	Lucky	$\beta,$ Aquarii and $\alpha,$ Equ-ulei
12	Wei (Goei, Gui)	Danger, Peril, Steep	Moon	Sparrow	"	Dis-sen-sions	$\alpha,$ Aquarii and ε, θ Pegasi
13	Shih (4)	House	Fire	Bear	"	Pro-pitious	$\alpha, \beta,$ Pegasi
14	Pi	Wall or Fortress	Water	Porcu-pine	"	Evil for Wed-dings	$\gamma,$ Pegasi, and $\alpha,$ Andro-medae

The Hsiu, continued

Day	Constellation	Name Meaning	Corresponding Element	Animal Representation	Quadrant Season, & Regent	Period's Fortune (2)	Constituent Stars
15	K'uei	Astride	Wood	Wolf	Western, Autumn, White Tiger	Evil for Weddings	16 stars in Andromedae & Pisces
16	Lou (Leu, Lŭ)	Mound or Train of a Garment	Metal	Dog	"	Lucky for Building	α, β γ, Arietis
17	W'ei (Oei)	Stomach	Earth	Pheasant	"	Unlucky for Women	Musca Borealis
18	Mao (Maou, Mau, Mol)	Unknown	Sun	Cock or Hen	"	Lucky for Business	The Pleiades
19	Pi	Complete, The End	Moon	Crow	"	Lucky for Funerals, Unlucky for Business	The Hyades and β γ, Tauri
20	Tzu (Tsui)	To Bristle Up	Fire	Monkey	"	Unlucky for Land Sale	λ, φ, Orionis
21	Ts'an (Shen)	Confused, Mixed	Water	Ape	"	Discord, Calamity	α, β γ,δ ε, ζ,η,κ, Orionis
22	Ching (Tsing, Tiam)	Well, Pit, or Mine Shaft	Wood	Tapir	Southern Summer, Vermilion Bird	Fortunate for Land Buying & Weddings	4 Stars in the Knees and 4 in the Feet of Gemini

The Hsiu, continued

Day	Constel- lation	Name Meaning	Corres- ponding Element	Animal Repre- sentation	Quadrant Season, & Regent	Period's Fortune (2)	Constit- uent Stars
23	Kwei (Kuei, Kut)	Ghost or Imp or Cloud- like	Metal	Goat or Sheep	Southern, Summer, Vermi- lion Bird	Un- lucky for Build- ing, Lucky for Funer- als	γ, δ, η, θ, Cancri
24	Liu	The Willow	Earth	Muntjac	"	Lucky for Herds	δ, ε, ξ, η, θ, ρ, σ, ω, Hydrae
25	Hsing	The Star	Sun	Horse	"	Un- lucky	α, ι, τ, κ, ν, Hydrae
26	Chang	Draw A Bow	Moon	Deer	"	Un- lucky	τ, ς, ν, φ Hydrae
27	I (Yi)	Wing or To Assist	Fire	Snake	"	Long Life and Happi- ness	22 Stars in Hydra & Crater
28	Chen (Tchin)	Cross Bar of a Cart	Water	Earth Worm	"	Pros- perity	ε, γ, δ, ε, Corvi

NOTES: (1) The season in which the sun appears in a constellation is diametrically opposite the constellation in which the moon is
seen at night.   (2) For those born under the constellation.   (3)
Anciently it had names meaning Dew or a Temple.   (4) Anciently
called Sal or Shat.

Asiatic lore, in which the
beverage of life and the sacred
tree are associated with the
moon, drifted eastward onto islands in the Pacific Ocean. Rona,
a small girl, went to fetch water and was carried off by the
moon.   The tree onto which she
held fast was torn up by its
roots, and Rona, her water gourd,
and the tree are all in the moon.
In another version, Rona, a man,
went in pursuit of his wife.   His
search led him to the moon.   By
eating it, he causes it to wane.
In turn he is devoured by the
moon and both are restored to
life from time to time.   This

second version is derived from a Sanscrit eclipse myth related about Ketu and Rahu in the chapter The Seven Powers.

In the South Pacific, natives see a woman on the moon who toils away. Among Hervey Islanders she carries a pile of taro leaves and tongs of a split cocoanut branch. For the Samoans she pounds out the native paper cloth with a mallet. A child is with her. Among New Zealanders she pulls a gnatuh.

The Peruvian moon goddess was Mama Quilla, whose husband was Intu, the sun. By him she had a son, Manco Capac, and a daughter, Mama Ogllo, who married and founded a colony on the spot where they could sink into the ground a wedge given to them by their parents. The colony they founded was Cuzco, and they became the progenitors of the Inca royal line. Peruvians also knew the moon marking as a beautiful earth maiden who fell in love with the man in the moon and joined herself to him forever.

The Eskimos of North America think that Moon is a girl who flees her brother, Sun, after he has scarred her face with ashes. In Greenland their sexes are interchanged, and Moon, a male, pursues his sister, Sun, who rubs her sooty hands over his face (makes him sunburned). Both these versions trace back to the Khasis of the Himalayas, who say that every month Moon falls in love with his mother-in-law, who quite properly repulses his affections by throwing ashes at him.

To the Iroquois Indians the marks on the moon are those of an old woman. Longfellow tells the story in Hiawatha:

> Once a warrior, very angry,
> Seized his grandmother and threw her
> Up into the sky at midnight;
> Right against the sky he threw her;
> 'Tis her body that you see there.

Various American Indian tribes played a ball game in which the ball was used in sympathetic magic to assure the eternal motive power of the sun (or moon). In one tale, the waters of life are located on the lunar orb. A little girl cried out one night for water, but the sleeping mother, who was very exhausted when she retired, did not awaken. Moon felt sorry for the child and came down from heaven with a pot of water. "Here, little one, is water to drink," he said. Eagerly the child drank the water and did not resist when Moon carried her off to heaven. Before she left her room, the youngster picked up a little basket, and she can still be seen carrying it.

In Indian mythology, the toad frequently appears as a guardian of the cosmic tree located by a pool on the moon. The Salish Indians of the northwest tell of a toad that was dearly loved by a wolf. To find the toad, who had repulsed him, the wolf prayed to Moon to light up the way. Moon responded and just as the wolf was about to embrace the little toad, she jumped right onto Moon's face, and there to this day she looks down and laughs at the wolf.

Animals often figure in moon lore. In a Bushmen legend a hare is Moon's messenger. He falsifies a message in which

Moon promises that people will rise again after death as Moon does, and, because of this falsification, humans do not rise again and are mortal. The frustrated Moon hit the hare across the mouth and gave him a split, or what is now called a hare, lip. In Chinese and Japanese fables a hare inhabits the moon, where it pounds out with mortar and pestle the elixir of life. Gluskap, the hare of Algonquin Indian mythology, formed the moon from parts of his mother's dead body.

The Aztec and Toltec snake-woman Ciuateotl, grandmother of adversity, poverty, and toil, was mother of the stars. Her roaring voice announced her presence. At her festivals her priests, who invoked her as obsidian butterfly, old goddess of the sweat bath, wore phallic emblems by which they hoped to induce her, when she appeared in her great green skirt as the harvest moon, to provide good crops.

To interpret, that is without a powerful telescope, what is etched on the moon still remains a challenge to the fanciful. To Greeks of antiquity the moon was an abode where the good enjoyed perfect tranquility and furnished oracles for mortals on earth. The face Greeks knew as the terrifying Gorgon's Head, which scared away the evil who tried to force an entry onto the moon, some now call the slow Old Man. However, moderns who are more romantic assert that after the moon's 9th day of illumination the face of a beautiful young woman, which is slightly upturned toward the east, may be seen on the western surface. Garrett Putnam Serviss claims that through an opera-glass of low power this face is distinct.

Partially hidden
by the mountain, the moon
does not seem far away.

III

THE SOLAR WALK

Under the burning
desert sun, the sheik counts
the water bags.

In its earliest phases, sun worship appears to have been seasonal. During the summer, the sun deity poisoned or scorched Earth with his fire, and was a slayer of herds and men. He was greatly feared as a relentless warrior and was the predecessor of devils and demons. Those periods in which he was not causing damage with his spears (rays), he withheld much of his warmth and went underground where he churned fires and, without mercy, judged the souls of the dead. The wisest and bravest of each tribe, the priests or chiefs, were expected to anticipate and checkmate the moods of this capricious deity who never paused or rested. His temple was painted red and, except for the blood-stained garments and sacrifices that were offered to appease him, he was shunned at the great festivals, and the moon was worshiped as the supreme lord of life. As time moved on beneficial aspects of this one so greatly feared were recognized. Each day he brought light into the world, each spring he carried verdure up from beneath the soil. The regularity with which his various tempers came forward established the pattern for sowing or reaping, for leading flocks up or down the mountain slopes, and people depended on both lunar and solar injunctions. Gradually sun worwhip took precedence over that of the moon, and the characteristics and adventures attached to the first sun god were duplicated in all parts of the world. He was all-seeing; his lances (rays) never missed their marks; he was a trail blazer who, in a horse-drawn (breeze-drawn) chariot, constantly roamed, and because he never remained in one place he was an unfaithful lover, especially to the dawn; he was lonely, inventive; he was the animator of men's souls, the giver and taker of life. After his birth at the winter solstice (day on which the sun begins to increase) in a cave (underworld of the year, period of cold or darkness), his royal parents abandoned him by setting him adrift on the sea of the skies; by hiding him among reeds along the edge of a stream, where the brilliance of his body attracted a rescuer; or by placing him exposed on a mountain (cloud). Often he was suckled by an animal (air currents) until cared for by a peasant or shepherd (sky), from whom he learned the secrets of husbandry, which he later bestowed on man. His growth was miraculous (brief is the period needed to fill the air with light); his arms (rays) were long; his legs were so

short he was as imposing when
he sat down as when he stood.
He was portrayed as fiery red
or as a handsome youth with
blond hair (his yellow color) and
blue eyes (light), according to
the season he represented or the
mood he depicted. Sometimes
he was shown as a serpent biting
its own tail to represent the
circle of eternity or the year
consuming itself. He was accompanied by animals and
companions (atmosphere, winds,
clouds), and he served those
meaner than himself or engaged
in menial tasks (served mankind).
Powerful as he was, he was not
always able to control his steeds
(winds). He had a vulnerable
heel (succumbed when his base
or heel touched the horizon);
the loss of his hair (rays)
weakened him; his groin might
be pierced and cause him to bleed
(red skies at storms or gloaming). His wife (gloaming) betrayed him by revealing the secret
of his vulnerability to her lover
(darkness or winter). He constantly battled enemies which
appeared in the guise of dragons,
serpents, a form he sometimes
assumed, or demons, but in spite
of his bravery and strength,
they overcame him at the summer solstice (when the sun begins
to decrease), and placed a curse
on his treasures (vegetation). A
wound in the groin usually
coincided with the harvest when
grain is cut down by a scythe.
No beauty ever surpassed his,
which changed constantly.

Once the sun deity superseded
the moon, a solar zodiac was
introduced. Theories regarding
this zodiac are numerous, but
most writers agree that the first
configuration formed to act as a
sun mansion was that of Taurus,
the Bull, when it marked the

vernal equinox from 4,000 to
1,700 B.C. In time six signs
appeared: Taurus, Cancer,
Virgo, Scorpio, Capricornus,
and Pisces. Eventually these
enormous configurations were
divided to form ten. The pro-
cess of change was slow. Many
of the early zodiacal mansions
were irregular and reached
their bulk either above or below
the exact path, or walk, of the
sun. At first errors probably
were due to an ignorance of the
true progress of the seasons,
then from disinclination to alter
that which was considered
sacred. Finally, men awoke
to the fact that the sun by day
strolled over the same course
as the moon by night, and that
it took approximately 12 months
or moons to make a complete
circuit of the heavens, and the
stars were arranged into 12
constellations, three allotted to
each of the 4 seasons, whose
gates were called: Spring
Equinox (Aries), Summer
Solstice (Cancer), Autumn
Equinox (Libra), Winter Solstice
(Capricorn). Because of the
precession of the equinoxes over
the centuries, the sun's path in
one zodiacal sign is removed
from that of the constellation
bearing the same name, thus
when the sun is in the zodiacal
sign Aries, it is among the
stars of the constellation Taurus.
Some names given to the Zodiac,
or Solar Walk, and their meanings are listed here:

Accadian: Innum; Pidnu-sha-
shame, the Furrow of Heaven
ploughed by the heavenly Bull.

Anglo-Saxon: Mielan circul
zodiacum, Great zodiacal circle;
Twelf Tacna, Twelve Signs.

Arabian: Al Falak, Expanse of

of Sky; Al Mintakah al Buruj,
The Girdle of Signs, which in
Europe of the middle ages
degenerated into Almantica seu
Nitac.

Babylonian: Mizrata, Course of
the Sun, supposedly the word
from which the biblical
Mazzaroth was derived, and
probably a form of the Assyrian
word used for the Galaxy.
Mizrata may be from a root
signifying to watch, or from ezor,
girdle, or from zuhrah, glittering star.

Chaldean: Hadronitho Demalusche,
Circle of the Signs.

Chinese: Kung, Signs; also
known as the Yellow Road and as
Tsieki, which marked the course
of weather changes.

Christian: Corona seu Circulus
sanctorum Apostolorum, a sixth
century designation which attached eleven of the apostles to
eleven early signs and then placed
John the Baptist at Aquarius to
complete the circle.

English: Bestiary; Cercle of
Bestes; Eyrish Bestes, Journey
of the Beasts; Girdle of the Sky;
Houses of the Sun; Monthly
Abodes of Apollo; Our Ladye's
Waye; Solar Walk.

German: Thierkreis, Circle of
Little Animals.

Greek: Zodiac, of Animals, or

it may mean Path.

Hebrew: Galgal Hammazaloth,
Circle of Signs; Opus Phyr-
gionarum, Work of the Phrygians,
that is embroiderers in gold.

Hindu: Rsai chakra.

Italian: Rubecchio, Mill-wheel.

Latin: Balteus stellatus, Starry
Belt; Circulus signifer, Sign-
bearing Circle; Media Via Solis;
Orbis, Orb; Orbis signiferus;
Orbita Solis, Orbit of the Sun;
Signiportant; varii Mutator Circu-
lus anni.

Low Latin: Fascia, Band;
Limbus textilis, Woven Girdle;
Sigillarius, Little Images.

Persian: Akhtars, the twelve
generals who led the army of
Ormuzd. The enemies of the
Akhtars were the Awakhtars, the
Seven Powers who fought for
Ahriman.

Festivals were originated to
mark each season for some
purpose important to agriculture
or other human labor. The
ritual itself sought to induce
conditions favorable to the end
towards which the labor was
directed. The characters
portrayed in the myths enacted
in the sacred dance or drama
personified the natural forces
to which appeal was being made.
Calendars were a natural step
in the development. A Sumero-
Accadian planisphere represents
the idea of their Creation
scheme:

Accadian Month	Name Meaning	Semitic Name	Modern Parallel
1-Bara-ziggar	The Upright Altar	Nisannu	March-April
2-Gut-sidi	The Directing Bull	Iyyar	April-May
3-Mun-ga	The Making of Bricks	Sivanu	May-June
4-Su-kulna	Siezer of Seed	Duzu (Tammuz)	June-July
5-Ne-ne-gar	Fire-Making-Fire	Abu	July-August
6-Ki-gingir-ma	The Errand of Ishtar	Ululu (Elul)	August-Sept.
7-Tul-ku	The Holy Altar	Tisritu (Tisri)	Sept.-Oct.
8-Apin-dua	Opposite to the Fountain	Arakh-samna (Marchesvan)	Oct.-Nov.
9-Gan-ganna	The Very Cloudy	Kislimu (Kisleu)	November-Dec.
10-Abba-e	The Cave of the Rising	Dhabitu (Tebet)	December-Jan.
11-As-a-an	The Curse of Rain	Sabadhu (Sebat)	Jan.-Feb.
12-Se-kisil	The Sowing of Seed	Addaru (Adar)	February-March

(Ve-adar, an additional Adar or Addaru was added as
an intercalary month when necessary to properly adjust
the year.)

A Babylonian cuneiform inscription which dates sometime before
500 B.C. and undoubtedly is a copy of earlier tablets is here
shown with the months, probable number of days and the signs in
the sky to which they had been attached:

Month	Days	Ruling Sign	Sign's Name Meaning	Modern Name (1)
1-Nisannu	30	Agaru (Aggaru)	The Messenger, i.e. of the New Year	Aries
2-Airu (Iyyar)	29	Temennu and Alap-same	The Fountain and The Bull of Heaven	The Pleiades and Taurus
3-Sivanu	30	Ri-u-but-same and Tuame rabuti	The Shepherd Spirit of Heaven and The Great Twins	Orion and Gemini

Month	Days	Ruling Sign	Sign's Name Meaning	Modern Name (1)
4-Duzu	29	Namgaru or Nagar-asurra	The Crab or Workman of the River Bed	Cancer
5-Abu	30	Aru rabu	The Great Lion	Leo
6-Ululu	29	Siru	The Ear of Corn	Spica
7-Tisritu	30	Ziba (lacuna)	The Claws	Zubenelgenubi and Zuben-eschamali (2)
8-Arakh-samna (3)	29 (4)	Aqrabu	The Scorpion	Scorpius
9-Kislimu	30 (5)	Papilsak (6)	Winged Fire-head	Sagittarius
10-Dhabitu	29	Enzu	The Goat	Capricornus
11-Sabadhu	30	Ka (7)	The Urn	Aquarius
12-Addaru (8)	29	Riksu (9)	The Cord	Pisces

NOTES: (1) The constellations did not necessarily have their modern shapes, but each undoubtedly included the lucida. (2) alpha and beta Librae. (3) Name means Eighth-month. (4) One day more if required. (5) One day fewer if required. (6) This name may be Accadian; the Assyro-Babylonian name probably was Qastu, The Bow, while the Phoenician and Hebrew was Qesheth and the Arabic Qaus, whence Al Kaus for The Archer. (7) From Ka are formed the Phoenician and Hebrew Ka-d, whence the Greek Kados, a terra-cotta jar with a wide mouth. (8) Ve-adarru, an additional Adarru or intercalary month of 29 days was included when necessary to properly adjust the year. (9) A defacement on the inscription seems to read Dur-ki, Accadian for Cord Place, in allusion to the cord which fashions the two fishes.

The Chinese Kung or Tsieki (Solar Zodical Signs) were twelve and related to twelve double seasons, which indicated the weather associated with the sun's visit to the mansion:

THE CHINESE KUNG

Approx. Dates	Solar Season (1)	Solar Branch Chinese Term	Sign	Term After Jesuits	Sign	Western Term
Mar. 20	Vernal Equinox	Heang Lou or Kiang Leu	Dog	Pih Yang	White Sheep	Aries
Apr. 5	Clear & Bright					

THE CHINESE KUNG continued

Approx. Dates	Solar Season(1)	Solar Branch Chinese Term	Sign	Term After Jesuits	Sign	Western Term
Apr. 20 May 5	Grain Rains Summer Begins	Ta Leang	Great Bridge or Cock(2)	Kin Neu	Golden Ox	Taurus
May 21 June 6	Grain Fills Grain in Ears	Shih Chin or Shih Ch'en	Ape	Yang- Yin or Jidim	Male- Female or Icon	Gemini
June 21 July 7	Summer Solstice Slight Heat	Shun Show	Quail's Head or Ram	Keu Hea	Crab	Cancer (3)
July 23 Aug. 7	Great Heat Autumn Begins	Shun Ho	Quail's Fire or Horse	Sze Tsze	Lion	Leo (4)
Aug. 23 Sept. 8	Heat's Limit White Dew	Shun Wei	Quail's Tail or Ser- pent	She Sang Neu	Frigid Maid- en	Virgo
Sept. 23 Oct. 8	Autumnal Equinox Cold Dew	Show Sing (5)	Star of Lon- gevity	Tien Ching	Celes- tial Balance (6)	Libra
Oct. 23 Nov. 7	Hoar Frost Descends Winter Begins	Ta Huo	Hare (7)	Tien He	Scor- pion	Scorpio
Nov. 22 Dec. 7	Little Snow Heavy Snow	Sheih Muh	Cleft Tree (fire- wood) or Tiger	Jin Ma	Man- Horse	Sagit- tarius
Dec. 21 Jan. 6	Winter Solstice Little Cold	Hsin Chi	Bull or Ox	Mo Ki	Goat- Fish	Capri- corn (8)
Jan. 21 Feb. 5	Severe Cold Spring Begins	Hiuen Wu, Hiuen Heaou, or Hiven Mao(9)	Deluge (10) or Rat	Paou Ping	Pre- cious Vase	Aquarius

THE CHINESE KUNG continued

Approx. Dates	Solar Season(1)	Solar Branch Chinese Term	Sign	Term After Jesuits	Sign	Western Term
Feb.19 Mar.5	Rain Water Excited Insects	Tseu Tsze	Pig	Shwung Yu	Two Fishes	Pisces

NOTES: (1) The season in which the sun appears in a constellation is diametrically opposite the one in which the moon is seen at night.   (2) The Great Bridge in still earlier times was a designation of the Hyades and Pleiades, which are in Taurus.   (3) Also included in the Chinese configuration is a cluster in Gemini called Tsing.   (4) The space between Leo and Virgo was designated Tae Wei or Shaou Wei; the western part of Leo with Leo Minor was regarded as a Yellow Dragon. Leo also was one of the Heavenly Chariots of Imperial China.   (5) In early zodiacs represented by a dragon or crocodile, the national emblem.   (6) The Chinese had a law for the annual regulation of weights which supposedly was enacted in this season.   (7) In the time of Confucius called Shing Kung, Divine Temple, and Ta-Who, The Great Fire, which also is a name for its star Antares. (8) With stars in Sagittarius anciently known as Sing Ki, Starry Record, and with a part of Aquarius as Hiuen Hiau, the significance of which is unknown.   Still earlier with Aquarius and Sagittarius it composed Heung Woo, Dark Warrior.   (9) Very anciently in China called Tien Yuen, Serpent or Turtle, or Hiuen Ying, Dark Warrior, Hero, or Darkly Flourishing One, and included Capricorn, Pisces, and a part of Sagittarius as well as Aquarius.   (10) Symbolizes the great deluge which took place during the reign of Tchoun Hin of the Han Dynasty.

Everywhere the New Year has been and continues to be celebrated to commemorate the completion of one cycle of life and the birth of a new cycle. It may be observed with regret or rejoicing, according to ethnic factors. The Babylonian feast Zagmuk was held in the month of Nisannu, which corresponds to March-April in modern calendars, to praise gods who assembled to decree the fates for the coming year. Marduk rose from his tomb, and a ram was sacrificed to him in expiation of the sins of the nation. In Egypt the ceremony corresponded with the Nile flood, and the people became drunk with Hathor, the great cosmic mother who had a throne in the underworld and frequently, with a promise of eternal nourishment to the ba (soul of the departed), enticed those to whom she had given life to rejoin her in the realm of the dead. When Ra decided to stop the slaughter she was causing, he flooded the Nile and made her drunk with the waters so that she would forget mankind. Christians, who deplored the license with which Romans celebrated the holiday,

made it a period of prayer. In
Northern Europe a boar was
sacrificed. The head with an
apple in its mouth was carried
into the banqueting hall, decked
with bays and rosemary on a
gold and silver dish to the sound
of trumpets and the song of
minstrels. Boar-shaped cakes
also were served. This animal
was the favorite of Frey, the
sun god, and it was shared with
him, not only in an endeavor to
get him to provide courage and
plenty during the year, but to
prevail upon him to dispel the
headless spirits (winter storms)
that wandered about. Some
Occidental countries mark with
elaborate balls and orgiastic
behavior; bells are rung, horns
are blown, toasts are made;
thus sorrow for the passing year
is merged into a joyous greeting
for the new one.

In Islam, it is the day on
which God returns Solomon's
ring; even the Devil brings him
gifts, and swallows sprinkle water
on him; so great is the rejoicing
for the sun's return. Only new
foods, such as grain, are eaten
by the Hindus. The festival
marks the turning of the sun at
the winter solstice, and a great
pilgrimage is made to the Ganges
for purification in the sacred river. The Bengalis don wet clothes
on this day in the belief that will
keep them from want in the coming year. An ancient Chinese
custom is still observed by these
people. Doors and windows are
decorated with paper scrolls containing mottoes and religious
quotations which are expected to
act as wealth charms. It is
the most important festival of
the year and lasts for fifteen
days, beginning with the presentation of rice to heaven and
earth. The procession of the

cow (passing year) is held, and
the festival ends with the parade
of the dragon, fertility to come.
The Japanese Shintos offered
a male cake to the sun goddess
Amaterasu, and a female cake
to the moon god Tsuki-yomi.
Pilgrims were made to shrines
to ask Amaterasu for a bright
and happy year.

Perhaps no homage to the New
Year was as weird and awe
inspiring as that of the Indians
of Mexico at the end of every
fifty-two year cycle. The eve
was feared as one that might
be the last for the whole nation.
The soothsayers knew that the
world was doomed to disappear
in a terrible cataclysm of
storms and earthquakes, but
they could not say at which
cycle's end the destruction
would come. Everyone dressed
in resplendent burial garments.
Friends visited each other to
pass a few words of cheer or
ask forgiveness. Whole families
were united. Little house gods
and amulets in whose protective
power they had lost faith were attacked with stone hammers until
they were shattered into small
pieces. Holy fires at the temples and all lights throughout
the land were blown out. Hearths
in homes remained cold and
gloomy. Everything which had
served to give joy and comfort in
the old year was destroyed.
Palaces as well as modest dwellings seemed to be abodes of the
dead. Should a new year arrive
nothing that had existed in the
old year was worthy of it, and
if a new year did not come,
no one would remain to make
use of the treasures or to light
a pyre. The soundlessness of
death existed everywhere.

Close to midnight the priests,

their long unkempt hair falling over their rich robes and partially hiding their sad gloomy faces, left the temple, and the people came out of their homes to follow them. One priest carried the mamahuaztli, the two pieces of wood by whose friction fires were kindled. The other priests surrounded the sacrificial victim. If the gods were pleased with the offering, the lights of dawn would come before the smell of burning flesh had passed away and the last embers of the sacrificial fire had turned gray, and the world would be safe for another fifty-two years. When morning came ecstatic cries and drums pierced the stillness; the day was greeted with frenzy.

The Mexican year had eighteen months of twenty days, or seventy-two five-day weeks. A seventy-third five-day intercalary week completed the year. Every fifty-two years thirteen days were intercalated to adjust the calendar. Thus each of these thirteen days or half a lunation was a bisextile year. Intercalary days, like those of other nations, were dangerous to anyone born during the period, because they were godless. The eighteen months of the year were:

Month	Name Meaning	Georgian Beginning Date
1-Pop	Mat of Reeds	July 16
2-Uo	Frog	August 5
3-Zip	Tree	August 25
4-Tzoz (Zotz)	Bat	September 14

Month	Name Meaning	Georgian Beginning Date
5-Tzec	Death's Head	October 4
6-Xul	The End	October 24
7-Yaxkin	Summer	November 13
8-Mol	To Unite	December 3
9-Chen	A Well	December 23
10-Yax	First	January 12
11-Zac	White	February 1
12-Ceh	Deer	February 21
13-Mac	Lid, Cover	March 13
14-Kankin	Yellow Sun	April 2
15-Muan	Strong	April 22
16-Pax	Musical Instrument	May 12
17-Kayab	Song	June 1
18-Cumhu	Noise, Thunder	June 21

The five intercalary days were from July 11 to 15 and were called Uayeyab or Uayeb.

The twenty days that made up each Mexican month were:

Day	Name Meaning	Ruling Deity	Deity's Form	Deity's Realm
1-Kan	Yellow, Sun	Cipactli	Sea Animal	Abyss
2-Chiccan	Little	Eheactli (Ce-Acatl)	Wind	Air
3-Cimi (Quimij)	To Die	Calli	House	Hearth
4-Manik	Feast(?)	Cuetzpalin	Small Lizard	Earth
5-Lamat	(?)	Cohuatl (Kukulcan)	Serpent	Vegetation
6-Muluc	To Unite	Miquiztli	Skeleton	Death
7-Oc	Leg	Mazatl (Xochipilli)	Deer	Flowers
8-Chuen	Tree	Tochtli (Totchtin)	Rabbit	Drunkenness
9-Ebs (Eb)	Ladder	Alt (Altcanals)	Water	Sea Storms
10-Ben (Been)	To Go	Itzcuintli (Itzcuinan)	Dog	Sexual Pleasure
11-Ix (Gix, Hix)	Rust, Mildew	Ozomatli (Azomatli)	Ape	Earth
12-Men	To Build	Malmalli	Twisted Grass	Immortality
13-Cib (Quib)	Wax, Copal	Acatli (Ceacatl)	Reed	Drought
14-Caban	When(?)	Occolotl (Ocetotl)	Tiger	Nocturnal Heavens
15-Eznab	Sorcery(?)	Quauhil (Ciuateteo)	Eagle	Lust, Infant Maladies
16-Cauac	(?)	Cozcoquauhtli (Coxcox)	Bird	Supreme Creator
17-Ahau (Ajau)	King	Ollin (Yoel)	Motion of Sun	Four Directions
18-Imix (Ymix)	(?)	Tecpatl	Flint Stone	Sacrifice

Day	Name Meaning	Ruling Deity	Deity's Form	Deity's Realm
19-Ik (Yk)	Courage, Air	Quiahuitl	Rain	Clouds
20-Akbul (Akbal)	A Plant	Xochitl	Flower	Paradise

Each so-called month was composed of four five-day periods. The Uayeyab, or intercalary days, that made up the year's three hundred sixty-five, being useless (nemontemi), were not given names; they simply were called by those of the first five days of each month, viz.: Kan, Chiccan, Cimi, Manik, and Lamat. The one quarter of a day lost each year was made up, as explained above, by thirteen intercalary days every fifty-two years.

The last five days of every twenty day period were market days (Tianquiztli). Despite the different time division, the method of marking or counting cycles by animals, plants, or other natural things answers to those of Asiatics and confirms the strong probability that intercommunication with the Orient existed at some time and place before American Indians became acquainted with Europeans. Eventually, a more accurate solar computation of time was employed in Mexico:

MEXICAN CALENDAR PANELS

Panel Number	Approximate European Asterism	Mexican Sign (1)	Name Meaning	Accompanied By
1	Aries (Perhaps Pleiades)	Obliterated from Panel		Obliterated from Panel
2	Taurus (Perhaps Hyades)	Tzab-ek	Rattle of a Snake	Tzontemoc (Rattlesnake)
3	Gemini	Xolotl (2) & Quetzalcoatl	Servant, Culture Hero	Cuculcan (Bird-Serpent)
4	Cancer	Imix (3)	Water-monster	Kinich Ahau (4) (Red Macaw)
5	Leo	Balam or Tzakmul	Jaguar	A Pelican (5)
6	Virgo	Cuetzpalin	Lizard	Can (6) (Maize)

MEXICAN CALENDAR PANELS, continued

Panel Number	Approximate European Asterism	Mexican Sign (1)	Name Meaning	Accompanied By
7	Libra	Chichen Izta (Chicchan) (7)	Serpent	Mictlante- cutli (Owl)
8	Scorpio	Chilan or Tlahtoani	Oracular Priest	Camazotz (Bat) (8)
9	Sagittarius	Ocelotl	Puma	Obliterated, but antlers of a stag are apparent (9)
10	Capricorn	Bare trace of a flame-like object remains (10)		An unknown Bird
11	Aquarius	Itzcuintli	Rodent, perhaps Squirrel	Unclear, per- haps a Vul- ture (11)
12	Pisces	Uo	Frog	Obliterated

NOTES: (1) Mexican sign usually bears the name of the deity
whose festival is celebrated when the sun is in the asterism.
(2) Xolotl, a lord of twins or other monstrous beings, was
a dwarf deity, who appeared as a jester and merry-maker.
When he accompanied the sun into the under world he transformed into a dog.   (3) Name probably originally was Mex,
the cuttlefish. It may have been corrupted to mean sea-monster
or crocodile.   (4) Represents the sun's eye or fire which
descends from the sky to consume things.   The celestial drum
(thunder) also appears in the drawing, as this is the season
of storms.   (5) This bird not used elsewhere as a Leo symbol,
but appropriate inasmuch as a festival of fishermen was held
at this time.   (6) Dancers also appear in the panel and may
suggest harvest rites.   (7) This name appears to be related to
the roots chuch and tzec (scorpion).   Perhaps the position of
this and the bat following have been incorrectly placed and
should be interchanged.   (8) Symbols of sound issue from the
bat's mouth, confirming the oracular interpretation.   The bat
is a devourer of light, ruler of subterranean caverns into
which the sun sinks at evening.   Undoubtedly a sign of autumn,
when darkness prevails.   The Evening Star appears twice, at
each wing.   (9) Antlers symbolize arrows, attributes of the
war god.   (10) Probably indicates December solstice.   (11)
The bird may be intended for Ciuateteo, which was composed
of the souls of women who died in childbirth and who, in the

NOTES: continued

form of this large bird, struck children with epilepsy and inspired men with lust.

Peruvians worked out a system in which the year was divided into four seasons, which then was subdivided into three months, the first two arbitrarily given 30 days, the third month the remaining days of the quarter year. An early system of measuring time was observed by the rising and setting of conspicuous star groups. Probably long before any zodiac had been devised by them, seasonal changes had been attributed to Mama Allpa, the many-breasted goddess who provided the harvest. Each stellar form seen at night in conjunction with the moon was due to the presence of a Great Mother, a prototype of one of the Mamas, or a seasonal aspect of Mama Allpa (Earth). When it became known that the solar orb by day passed through asterisms six signs distant from one that rose at sunset, a solar cult sprang up and modified the purely lunar system of the Mamas. During the Mama cult, individual asterisms were identified by counterparts on earth that were forms of the Great Mother; thus an asterism that appeared in June when the beautiful cantua bloomed was the celestial prototype of the flower. With a recognition of the nature of the passage of the solar orb, a new series of asterisms came into being, the Mamas of which were believed to exert their strongest influence on earth in conjunction with the sun rather than when in opposition to it. This change had something of the nature of changes that had taken place in Sumer and elsewhere when a solar took precedence over a lunar zodiac. The Peruvian year probably began at the winter solstice, when the sun was at the height of its power. The course of the Inca year was portrayed on the star chart of Salcamayhua. A calendar worked up from the twelve scenes of the chart is given here and following the calendar is a detailed explanation of the panels.

PERUVIAN CALENDAR

Panel Number	Approx. Month	Approx. European Asterism	Peruvian Names	Name Meaning
1	December-January	Capricorn	Nucca or Cayau Cachi	The Beard The Footprint
2	January-February	Aquarius	Mama Cocha or Chaquill Chaca	Mother of Waters, Eagle Bridge, or Foot Bridge
3	February-March	Pisces(1)	Curicancha or Collcam Pata and Pichu	Golden Place, Granaries Terrace, Knot or Tie

PERUVIAN CALENDAR, continued

Panel Number	Approx. Month	Approx. European Asterism	Peruvian Names	Name Meaning
4	March-April	Aries	Katu Quilla or Quilli Pata	Market Moon, Kneeling Terrace
5	April-May	Taurus (1)	Pirua or Collca (2) and Tupa Taruca (3)	The Granaries Pasturing Stag
6	May-June	Gemini (1)	Camach Pacha and Huaca Punca (4) or Husque	Creation Time Sacred Gate Sandals
7	June-July	Hydra in Cancer (1)	Nayraccunapa (Nauin) or Umaa Umina and Cantua Pata	Grindstone Eyes Head Gem Cantua Terrace
8	July-August	Leo	Chuqui Chinchay or Puma Cuncu	Western Lance or Puma Bean
9	August-September	Spica and surrounding Virgo stars	Sara Mama or Pacha Mama or Toco Cachi	Maize Mother, Earth Mother Female Symbol (Salt Hole)
10	September-October	Serpens; and parts of Libra & Ophiuchus	Munay Ssenca	Male Symbol (Loving Nose)
11	October-November	Scorpius (1)	Mallqui & Rimac Pampa	Tree & Immortal Speaking Place

PERUVIAN CALENDAR, continued

Panel Number	Approx. Month	Approx. European Asterism	Peruvian Names	Name Meaning
12	November- December	Sagittarius	Pumpa Chupa or Pumap Chupam	Drunken Puma Puma's Tail

NOTES: (1) Represented by two Peruvian asterisms. (2) Possibly the Pleiades. (3) Possibly the Hyades. (4) Possibly the stars Pollux and Procyon.

The foregoing calendar was developed from Stansbury Hagar's interpretation of the scenes depicted on the Salcamayhua Star Chart. Herbert J. Spinden disagrees with Hagar and states that the year was divided into 13 parts, as shown by Herman Beyer. The manner in which Hagar detailed his explanation appealed to us, and we give a digest of it here:

Panel 1. The Bearded One, a man in his prime, marks the zenith of his strength by leaving his foot print on a rock. For a few days at the solstice he seemed scarcely to move either north or south, so he was said to be resting. Out of respect for him, his faithful worshipers likewise refrained from work during this period and devoted themselves to ritual dances in which the participants wore long beards (rays). This festival, the most important of the year, was called Capuchay (Festival of the Beard) or Capac Raymi (Principal Festival).

Panel 2. Mama Cocha,

mother of waters, was believed to be a cosmic lake located in the neighborhood of Aquarius, probably between Pisces Austrinus and Grus. From the lake flowed the river of death, one of the black bands in the Milky Way, and the bridge by which souls crossed the river was lofty and narrow, almost identical to the swaying suspension bridges which span Andean currents, and which are dangerous and terrifying. The period was one that marked the season in which rivers were flooded, and the festival celebrated was the Capac Cocha (Offering to the Mother of Waters), in which a llama was sacrificed.

Panel 3. Curicancha, Golden Place, suggests the celestial counterpart of a Cuzco district in which the principal temple stood. In this third month maize was first sown on the terraces of Collcam Pata, and the king ritually worked a furrow with a golden plow, a rite connected with the renewal of vegetation after the subsidence of heavy rains. Pichu, the name of the second asterism of this period, refers to the ribbon which tied the two fish of Pisces together. This time of the year was excellent for fishing, and a fish in a net or basket appears in the scene. In several parts of the world the origin of the fish species supposedly took place when the sun was in this sign.

Panel 4. This period was one in which early crops were harvested and placed on the backs of llamas, which carried them to storage places. The festival of the month was That of the Axe and referred to reaping. A llama was sacrificed, and a petition for a good harvest was attached to an offering of its wool.

Panel 5. The Pleiades governed the crops at harvest. Crops previously reaped were placed in granaries. The stag, which frequently invaded the grain fields, became the symbol of the harvest eater. The name of the festival of this period meant Sack Full of Crops. Ceremonies concluded with dancing in deer costumes. Drunkenness prevailed.

Panel 6. Camach Pacha (Time of Creation) was depicted as a man and a woman, undoubtedly Manco Capac (Mighty Man or Sun), the first man, and his sister-wife Mama Ogllo (Mother Egg or Moon). Together they founded the city of Cuzco (Navel, meaning world navel) and became progenitors of the Inca royal line. Huaca (Sacred), the name of the second asterism, derives from Huauque (Double or Brother of a Brother), the festival name. Thus rites connected with the second asterism seem to have been in honor of Manco Capac and his twin

brother rather than his wife. The sacred gate may have been the stars between which the sun passed or a gate or cave-like opening in the Milky Way beneath the sun's path between Orion and Gemini. The first Inca couple was said to have come out of Paccari Tampu (Cave of Dawn). The festival was devoted to the raising of children. The women's festival of the 9th period was devoted to marriage, and was probably an effort to locate births at this time of the year. Another name for the sign is Husque (Sandals) to suggest the journey made at this time of the year to the sacred city, Cuzco, to commemorate the sun's birth.

Panel 7. The stars that composed this group were evidently those in the head of Hydra, directly under Cancer. The first name refers to the deep red and viridescent eyes of the cuttle fish, which were substituted for human eyes in mummies. The head gem, being emerald, was believed to have marvelous healing properties. The Cantua (Cantut), the figure of the second asterism, was a sacred Inca flower. Fields around Cuzco in late June and early July were generally red with them. In connection with Intip Raymi (Festival of the Sun), the Anta Asitua (Copper Great Dance) was performed. This was a solstice period, hence one in which the sun appeared to take a brief rest, and the second most important festival season of the year. The Anta Asitua was named for the dark red objects used by dancers. Sacred cakes, the Cancu, made of crushed maize reddened with animal blood, were eaten. The dancers wore suits of similar color. The theme was dark red, the color of the hidden fire of the distant dying, but ever returning, sun.

Panel 8. This depicts the puma springing upon his prey. The Puma, which takes the place of the Lion in European zodiacs, symbolizes the warrior, whose lance was the Chuqui Chinchay. Ritual consisted of military dances, in which troops exercised to the accompaniment of wild music. Songs of triumph were sung.

Panel 9. The festival of the month, Coya Raymi (Women's Festival), was dedicated to the maize or earth mother and women in general. This was the only month of the year in which women predominated in all dances and rites, which included ceremonial spinning and weaving. Marriages were celebrated at this time; any performed in other months were not legal. Prayers were offered to the Great Earth Mother to ensure fruitfulness for both mankind and crops.

Panel 10. Symbols of the Rainbow, Lightning, Celestial River, and Earth were portrayed. The myth explains the genesis of life on earth, and shows the union of Pacha Mama, Earth Mother, with the Male Principle, spirit of light, lightning, and thunderstorms, whose symbol is the Munay Ssenca. The Situa, rites of the autumn equinox, opened the ceremonies of the Uma Raymi, in which the wet season, the rain which would fertilize earth for the coming harvest, was ushered in with fireworks that included rainbows. A ceremonial bathing was performed at the junction of two streams. As the previous month was dedicated to women, this

was dedicated to men. A census of the male heads of families was taken, and the total number determined the annual division and assignments of lands, especially to the newly married.

Panel 11. Two asterisms were recognized in this period. One, Mallqui, was composed of stars in Scorpius near Libra, in the form of a tree, and the name means tree as well as immortal. The other, Rimac Pampa (Speaking Place), seems to refer to a cosmic mountain, the celestial counterpart of a sacred district in Cuzco where all laws were announced, probably during this month. The Ayamarca (Carrying of the Corpse) was the festival of the month. Mummies of the dead were brought from their sepulchres and carried in procession around the city in honor of the spirits which were believed to revisit earth in this month.

Panel 12. In one period this asterism was called Pumap Chupa and in another period, Pumap Chupam. Which is the earlier name is unknown, but, as in the Puma of the Leo stars, the ritual is of the warrior type. Trials at the initiation rites of young men suggest steps up the celestial stairway, and Stairway in another designation of some of these stars. Novices were required to climb a hill and to enter as contestants in a footrace, in which they ran in imitation of a certain idol, which appeared as a puma running. The valor of novices was tested in a sling contest and they were exorted to live in the future as brave men. Their arms were presented to them and they danced in puma skins. Prayers were offered that the new

warriors might be fortunate in
war. In contrast with the Leo
warrior festival, this was con-
fined to those of high rank and
to those about to be initiated.
The Leo ceremony honored all
warriors.

IV

THE TWELVE MANSIONS

Circle of the Year

Within your rimless wheel,
trapped in time, a hero roams.
His horse is shadowless,
his chariot reinless;
illusory mansions
provide no couch. On, on,
he goes, with no haven,
without a place to pause
or rest. Seen or unseen,
his destiny: to move
eternally without
discontent. His motion
determines all motion;
his light diffuses all
light; his warmth gifts all warmth.
He carries the seasons,
sowers of life and death.

At Nineveh, when men
realized that twelve full moons
occurred in the course of a year,
that the year thus consistently
divided itself into twelve almost
equal divisions, each division
was associated with a phase of
the sun. Because the sun was
vulnerable, or mortal, subject
to intervals of waste or decline,
and the destiny of the human
race as well as all life in the
universe was subject to the
sun's existence, its dark periods
(winter or winter's daily counterpart, night), which supposedly
were spent in the underworld,
became the source of beliefs
related to the fall of man. To
avoid nihility, the catastrophe of
no return, and to protect the
cycle of birth-death-rebirth,
celestial guardians watched over
each of the sun's so-called
houses. A chart of such
guardians throughout various
ages is given here.

61

ZODIACAL GUARDIANS OR RULERS AND THEIR SYMBOLS

Mansion(1)	Assyrian(2)	Christian(3)	Egyptian(4)	Greek	Hebrew(5)	Norse	Roman	Occultist Angel
Aries	San A Lamb	Peter Two Keys	Sebek Crocodile	Athena Owl	Gad Tent	Odin Ravens	Minerva Aegis	Malchediel Ruby
Taurus	Marduk Subduer	Simon-Zelotes A Saw	Maau Cat	Aphrodite Dove	Isaacher Ass	Thor Hammer	Venus Cestus	Ashmodiel Topaz
Gemini	Yav Shall Come	James-the-Less Fuller's Club	Atum Double-Crown	Apollo Lyre, or Plutus Dog	Simeon-Levi Sword & Pitcher	Tyr Sword	Apollo Lyre	Amriel Carbuncle
Cancer	Bar Producer (as of cattle)	Andrew Crux Decusata	Mut Lioness or Papyrus	Hermes Caduceus or Tortoise	Benjamin Wolf	Balder Mistletoe	Mercury Harpe	Muriel Emerald
Leo	Nabu Sent Forth	John Eagle	Tefnut(6) Lioness	Zeus Eagle or Thunderbolt	Ephraim Bull, Ox, or Grapes	Bragi Harp	Jupiter Lightning	Verchiel Sapphire
Virgo	Mylitta or Allita To Bring Forth	Philip Serpent	Nut Cow	Demeter Cist	Asher Olive Branch or Cup	Vidar Forest	Ceres Corn	Hamatiel Diamond

ZODIACAL GUARDIANS OR RULERS AND THEIR SYMBOLS - continued

Mansion(1)	Assyrian(2)	Christian(3)	Egyptian(4)	Greek	Hebrew(5)	Norse	Roman	Occultist Angel
Libra	Uncertain	Bartholomew-Nathaniel Knife	Maa Scales of Justice	Hephaestus Helmet	Manasseh Palm Tree or Vine	Hoder Arrow Dart	Vulcan Anvil	Tsuriel Jacinth
Scorpio	Bel The Lord	Thomas Builder's Square	Khensu Ankh	Ares She-wolf	Dan Serpent or Apple	Hermod Draupner Ring	Mars Ancile	Bariel Agate
Sagittarius	Shamash Ministering	James-the-Greater Shells	Mentu Hawk	Artemis Hounds	Judah Lion	Hoener Runes on Wood	Diana Hounds	Adnachiel Amethyst
Capricorn	Ishtar Wounding	Matthew Angel	Thoth Ibis	Hestia Lamp	Naphtali African Deer	Svipdag Severed Hand	Vesta Hearth	Humiel Beryl
Aquarius	Anu Deluge	Judas-Thaddeus Oar	Qeb Goose	Hera Peacock	Reuben Man or a Sunburst Above Water	Loki Lightning	Juno Tiara	Gabriel Onyx

ZODIACAL GUARDIANS OR RULERS AND THEIR SYMBOLS- continued

Mansion(1)	Assyrian(2)	Christian(3)	Egyptian(4)	Greek	Hebrew(5)	Norse	Roman	Occultist Angel
Pisces	Uncertain; Perhaps Dagon, the Fish	Judas-Iscariot Coins	Hathor Stream	Poseidon Dolphins, or Dionysus Scepter	Zebulun Ship	Vali Vegetation	Neptune Trident	Barchiel Jasper

NOTES: (1) Configurations in various cultures differ; asterisms are only approximately the same. (2) The first Assyrian sign may have been Taurus. Asshur, a sun deity, was king of the circle and presided over the twelve who were guardians of his mansions. Instead of symbols, the meaning of the deity's name or his office is given. (3) Christian apostles were assigned by various writers in the middle ages, few of whom agreed on the order. (4) The first order of Egyptian deities was an octad assigned to the planets; when the eight were increased to twelve, the second order, the deities were assigned to the zodiac. This was a fairly late development, perhaps influenced by the Greeks. (5) Various biblical writers disagree on the assignment. The order listed here seems to be the one most often given. (6) Sometimes with her twin Shu, a bull deity, identified as the Twins (Gemini), in which case Atum appeared at Cancer, Mut at Leo.

In some legends carriers assisted the supernatural guardians of the sun's houses by transporting the sun ball from mansion to mansion.

CONDUCTORS OF THE SUN THROUGH THE ZODIAC

Sign	Babylonian	Celtic	Egyptian	European	Greek	Hindu	Japanese	Tibetan
Aries	Sacrificer	Alder	Cat	Ram	Cat	Ram	Peach Blossom	Ruined House
Taurus	Bull	Willow	Jackal	Bull	Dog	Bull	Cherry Blossom	Traveler
Gemini	Shepherd or Twins	Hawthorn	Serpent	Lovers or Twins	Snake	The Pair	Wisteria	Two Seated
Cancer	Crab	Oak	Scarab	Crab	Crab	Crab	Iris	Monkey
Leo	Lion or Dragon	Holly or Gorse	Ass	Lion	Ass	Lion	Morning Glory	Man Dying
Virgo	Corn Ear	Hazel	Lion	Maiden	Lion	Maiden	Lotus	Woman & Child
Libra	Scales or Lamp	Vine	Goat	Scales	Goat	Scales	Seven Grasses (Herbs)	Woman Picking Fruit
Scorpio	Scorpion	Reed	Cow	Scorpion	Ox	Scorpion	Maple	Madman
Sagittarius	Archer or Centaur	Elder	Falcon	Archer or Centaur	Hawk	A Bow	Chrysanthemum	Arrow

CONDUCTORS OF THE SUN THROUGH THE ZODIAC - continued

Sign	Babylonian	Celtic	Egyptian	European	Greek	Hindu	Japanese	Tibetan
Capricorn	Goat-Fish	Birch	Baboon	Goat	Monkey	Sea Monster	Camellia	Woman & Man
Aquarius	Waterman or Vase	Rowan	Ibis	Waterman	Ibis	Water-pot	Pine	Potter
Pisces	Fishtails	Ash	Crocodile	Fish or Ship	Crocodile	The Fishes	Plum Blossom	Man & Beast

The Chinese conveyers were excluded from the foregoing table because their positions have been so confused they require a chart of their own. Before Jesuit missionaries went into the East, the first Chinese sign was Aquarius with the rat, and the animals progressed counterclockwise or opposed to the sun's annual course in the heavens. Translators in error either reversed the progression of the early order, dispatching the animals from left to right instead of in the old Chinese fashion from right to left, or they made Aries with the rat the first sign. Under the influence of the Jesuits in the 16th century, the Chinese adopted our zodiac.

CHINESE CONDUCTORS OF THE SUN*

Mansion	Sun Enters	Pre-Jesuit, Aquarius First	Hours Ruled	Popular Name	Order Reversed	Order Reversed, Aries First	Hours Ruled	Post-Jesuit Influence	Plant
Aries	Mar. 21	Dog (Hsii)	7 PM-9 PM	Twilight	Tiger	Rat	11 PM-1 AM	White Sheep	Tree Peony
Taurus	Apr. 20	Cock (Yu)	5 PM-7 PM	Sunset	Hare	Ox	1 AM-3 AM	Golden Ox	Cherry Blossom
Gemini	May 21	Ape (Shen)	3 PM-5 PM	Late Afternoon	Dragon	Tiger	3 AM-5 AM	Lovers or Icon	Magnolia
Cancer	Jun. 22	Ram (Wei)	1 PM-3 PM	Early Afternoon	Serpent	Hare	5 AM-7 AM	Crab	Pomegranate
Leo	Jul. 21	Horse (Wu)	11 AM-1 PM	Midday	Horse	Dragon	7 AM-9 AM	Lion	Lotus
Virgo	Aug. 22	Serpent (Szu)	9 AM-11 AM	Forenoon	Goat or Ram	Serpent	9 AM-11 AM	Frigid Maiden	Pear Blossom

CHINESE CONDUCTORS OF THE SUN* - continued

Mansion	Sun Enters	Pre-Jesuit, Aquarius First	Hours Ruled	Popular Name	Order Reversed	Order Reversed, Aries First	Hours Ruled	Post-Jesuit Influence	Plant
Libra	Sep. 23	Dragon (Ch'en)	7 AM- 9 AM	Break-fast time	Monkey or Ape	Horse	11 AM- 1 PM	Celestial Balance	Mallow
Scorpio	Oct. 21	Hare (Mao)	5 AM- 7 AM	Sunrise	Cock	Sheep or Goat	1 PM- 3 PM	Scorpion	Chrysanthemum
Sagit-tarius	Nov. 21	Tiger (Yin)	3 AM- 5 AM	Dawn	Dog	Monkey	3 PM- 5 PM	Man-horse	Gardenia
Capri-corn	Dec. 22	Ox (Cho'u)	1 AM- 3 AM	Crowing Rooster	Boar	Cock	5 PM- 7 PM	Goat-fish	Poppy
Aquarius	Jan. 21	Rat (Tzu)	11 PM- 1 AM	Mid-night	Rat	Dog	7 PM- 9 PM	Precious Vase	Prunus
Pisces	Feb. 21	Boar (Hai)	9 PM- 11 PM	Hour of Rest	Ox	Boar	9 PM- 11 PM	Two Fishes	Peach Blossom

*The stars which compose the asterisms are not necessarily identical with those of our Western zodiac. They are only approximately the same.

Tales of the life and exploits of the continually dying and reborn spirit of the year were astronomical allegories. In spite of being carried around the ecliptic in a luxurious barge or golden chariot (sun-lit cloud) drawn by swift steeds (air currents), the sun hero suffered many hardships. A weary pilgrim, he was forced to pass through his mansions without stopping to rest or refresh himself. In dangerous adventures he sought immortality for himself and mankind; pandered to the whims of those, who, though less noble than he, had by a streak of fate acquired him in bondage as a boon; or he sacrificed himself to purge the human race of sin and therefore the despair of death without rebirth. Men, who comprehended that their lives depended on his, carved on stone his progression through the seasons. This art was perhaps as much an act of sympathetic magic as of homage. A chart of the twelve scenes depicted on several monuments follows:

ZODIACAL LEGENDS OR YEARLY TRANSIT OF THE SUN -
(Spring and Summer)

Hero	Aries	Taurus	Gemini	Cancer	Leo	Virgo
Buddha (1)	Markings	Education	Marriage	Life of Pleasure	Revelation	Retirement
Christ	Entry into Jerusalem	Washing Disciples' Feet	Last Supper	Betrayal	Before Caiaphas	Peter's Denial
Christ's Passion	Death Sentence Resurrection	Receiving Cross	First Fall	Meeting Mary	Helped by Simon	Veronica
Gilgamesh (2)	With Enkidu in the Underworld	Releasing Vegetation	Slaying Bull (heat)	Enkidu Slain	Bemoaning Enkidu Death	Visiting Utnapishtim
Hebraic-Christian	Israelites in Egypt Resurrection	Moses as Leader	Crossing the Jordan	Promised Land	David Prepares Temple	Solomon Builds It
Heracles' Labors	Nemean Lion	Lernean Hydra	Arcadian Stag	Erymanthian Boar	Augeas' Stables	Stymphalus Birds

ZODIACAL LEGENDS OR YEARLY TRANSIT OF THE SUN
(Autumn and Winter)

Hero	Libra	Scorpio	Sagittarius	Capricorn	Aquarius	Pisces
Buddha (1)	Temptations and Death	< In Tushita Before Birth	Maya Receiving White Elephant	Deities Attending Birth	Buddha Walking	Maya's Death
Christ	Before Pilate	Mockery	Calvary Road	Crucifixion	Descent	Resurrection
Christ's Passion	Second Fall	Speaking to Women	Third Fall	Stripped of Garments	Nailed to Cross	Death
Gilgamesh (2)	Seeking Immortality Plant	Losing Plant	Death	< Birth	Enkidu (wind) Opposes Him	Friendship With Enkidu
Hebraic-Christian	Temple Completed	Flight of Jesus	Sermon on the Mount	Choosing Disciples	New Church Established	Crucifixion
Heracles' Labors	Cretan Bull	Diomedes' Mares	Hippolyta's Girdle	Geryon's Oxen	Hesperidian Apples	The Dog Cerberus

< Indicates mansion in which legend starts. For additional legends see below.

NOTES: (1) Buddha legend begins in the house of Scorpio. After Pisces on the Autumn and Winter chart it continues through the houses of Spring and Summer and finally concludes at Libra. (2) After Pisces on the Autumn and Winter chart, the Gilgamesh legend, which starts at Capricorn, continues through the houses of Spring and Summer, then passes into Libra and Scorpio and concludes at Sagittarius.

ZODIACAL LEGENDS OR YEARLY TRANSIT OF THE SUN
(Spring and Summer) - continued

Hero	Aries	Taurus	Gemini	Cancer	Leo	Virgo
Izdubar (1)	Stele Missing	Stele Missing	Rejecting Ishtar	Stele Missing	Stele Missing	Stele Missing
Jason (2)	Golden Fleece Procured	< Light	Marries	Chaos	They Cohabit	Nature Emerges

ZODIACAL LEGENDS OR YEARLY TRANSIT OF THE SUN
(Spring and Summer) - continued

Hero	Aries	Taurus	Gemini	Cancer	Leo	Virgo
Moses (1)	Egyptian Plagues	Red Sea Crossing	Pharaoh's Destruction	Manna Gathering	At Horeb Rock	Ten Commandments
Odysseus Journey (2)	At Home	＜Lotus Eaters	Cyclops	Aeolus Island	Laestrygonians	Circe

ZODIACAL LEGENDS OR YEARLY TRANSIT OF THE SUN
(Autumn and Winter) - continued

Hero	Libra	Scorpio	Sagittarius	Capricorn	Aquarius	Pisces
Izdubar (1)	Stele defaced	Deluge	Obtains promise of Immortality	＜Makes Sacrifice	Eabani (wind) Opposes Him	Friendship with Eabani
Jason (2)	Happy and Balanced	Until Evil (Ino)	Chases Game (Children who Flee on ram)	Into the Underworld (Colchis)	Jason	Traverses the Sea
Moses (1)	Golden Calf	Brazen Serpent	Death	＜Bulrushes	With Midianites	Burning Bush
Odysseus Journey (2)	In Hades	Sirens	Scylla and Charybdis	Thrinacia	Calypso	Scheria Island

＜ Indicates mansion in which legend starts. For additional legends, see page 69.

NOTES: (1) After Pisces on the Autumn and Winter chart, the Izdubar and Moses legends, which start at Capricorn, continue through the houses of Spring and Summer, then pass into Libra and Scorpio, and conclude at Sagittarius. (2) The Jason and Odysseus legends, after Virgo, continue through the houses of Autumn and Winter, then return to the Spring chart and conclude at Aries.

In early and later middle ages, the months were symbolized in calendar art by occupations. Invariably the signs of the zodiac as well as the months were mentioned. But whether the signs were mentioned or not, zodiac influence always was understood. Such zodiacs frequently appeared as part of church decorations on fonts, porches, doors, archways, tympanums, or on objects, such as branched candlesticks and medallions. Palaces and public buildings were decorated with illustrated zodiacs. One reason they were placed at church doorways is associated with the idea that Christ as Sun of Righteousness is the Door to His Church. In early Christian tradition, each apostle presided over the sign of the zodiac and the labor of the month during which his festival fell. With the destruction of monastaries, many of the early works were lost; also errors and alterations made by manuscript copyists have obliterated a knowledge of the initial order. The arrangement now generally accepted is listed in the chart headed Zodiacal Guardians and Rulers, shown previously. Occupations pictured on various illustrated calendars or zodiacs are given here:

LABORS OF THE MONTH RELATED TO ZODIACAL MANSIONS

Month and Zodiacal House	Anglo-Saxon 8th Century	English	French	German	Italian	Spanish
Aries March	Vine Pruning and Seed Sowing	Blowing Horn; Digging; Pruning	Pruning	Digging; Pruning	Warrior Blowing Horn	Pruning
Taurus April	Stag Hunting	Carrying Flowers; Knight Taking Vows	Bearing Flowers	Bearing Flowers; Cultivating Vines	Carrying Foliage; Sheep Shearing	Bearing Flowers; Knight Taking Vows
Gemini May	Rogation Procession	Hunting With Falcon	Riding Toward Right with Sickle	Hunting Birds; Playing Music	Crowning With Flowers	Gathering Fruit; Riding Horse
Cancer June	Sheep Shearing; Felling Trees	Weeding	Mowing;	Mowing; Plowing	Reaping	Mowing; Reaping
Leo July	Hay Making	Mowing; Hay Making	Reaping	Mowing; Reaping	Hay Making; Man with 2 Horses	Threshing & Storing Grain

LABORS OF THE MONTH RELATED TO ZODIACAL MANSIONS, cont'd.

Month and Zodiacal House	Anglo-Saxon 8th Century	English	French	German	Italian	Spanish
Virgo August	Reaping Corn	Reaping	Threshing	Reaping	Asleep in Chair	Repose
Libra September	Gathering Apples & Driving Swine into Woods	Grape Gathering; Threshing	Treading Grapes	Treading Grapes	Carrying Grapes	Treading Grapes
Scorpio October	Wine Making; Autumnal Fishing; Wood Carving	Feeding Hogs, Filling Casks; Hawking	Fattening Hogs with Acorns	Sowing	Digging; Wood Hewing	Feeding Hogs; Filling Casks
Sagittarius November	Oak Beating; Preparing Goose of Martinmas	Warming at Fire; Killing Hogs	Feeding Oxen	Killing Oxen; Threshing	Catching Birds; Man with Gourds	Killing Hogs
Capricorn December	Yule Pig Cheer; Killing Swine; Feasting; Spinning	Cutting Wood; Yule Feasting	Feasting, Sitting Frontally	Killing Hogs	Killing Pigs	Yule Feasting
Aquarius January	Feasting at Fire; perhaps New Year Feast	Feasting at New Year	Feasting, Seated Facing Right	Feasting Hunting Hares	Carrying Wood; Tilling	New Year Feasting
Pisces February	Felling Trees	Warming at Fire	Warming at Fire	Wood Hewing	Warming at Fire	Warming at Fire

*Anglo-Saxon month names are - March: Hlyd-monath, stormy month; April: Eosturmonath, after the Anglo-Saxon goddess Eostre, whose festival celebrated in April later signified Easter; May: Unne-monath, flower month (Old German Bloumonat, also flower month), and sometimes illustrated with flowers and singing birds; June: Weyd-monath, month of abundance; July: Hey-monat, hay month (Old German Hooy-monath); August: Arn-monath, harvest

month (Old German Oostmonath); September: Gerst-monat, barley
month or month beer was brewed from barley; October: Wyn-
monat, wine month; November: Blod-monath, blood or slaughter
month (Old German Slagt-monat); December Erra-geola, before
Yule; January: Giuli, after Yule, and later called Heligh-monat,
holy month (Old German Launmonat for cold or frosty month);
February: Sprokkel-monat, sprouting month.   Monat and monath
both mean month.

The sky being peopled with
genii, they exerted a controlling
influence on terrestrial life. Not
only did they send heat, rain, or
frost, they decided the fates of
those born under their influence,
and took sides in battles, directed
the success or failures of coloni-
zation, resolved trades between
nations, etc. The Chaldeans
established schools in which
priests or masters of divination
were taught how to read the
astral signs.   Greek philosophers
elevated astrology to a pseudo-
science.   Early in the Christian
era tables were in common use
which marked lucky and unlucky
days and hours, and showed how
man's destiny for good or evil
was subjected to these heavenly
bodies.

portant people.   They held
positions of honor at the courts
of kings, princes, and dukes. No
enterprise was undertaken before
they were consulted. They succeeded the Roman harupices,
and at the Universities of Bologna
and Padua, chairs of astrology
were established as part of the
program of polite learning, and
astrology was closely associated
with magic, alchemy, and
medicine.   For hundreds of
years the rising and the setting
of stars, eclipses, comets,
conjunctions and oppositions of
the planets were believed to be
related to the outbreak, as well
as the relief, of diseases. The
moon supposedly caused mental
illnesses, and blood-letting was
perilous when the light of the
moon and the tides were waxing.

As the centuries rolled on
belief in astrology increased. By
the 13th century astronomy was
rarely studied for its own sake,
the comings and goings of the
sun, moon and planets were
probed with a view to designating
holy days; the stars were observed mainly for the purpose of
casting horoscopes.

Medieval astrologers were im-

The physical universe, supposedly endowed with a soul,
was analogous to man, an
intimate correlation between the
universe and man was held to
exist, and the terms macrocosm,
the great world (universe), and
microcosm, the little world
(man), became popular terms.
A comparison of the two was
made:

Macrocosm contains	Microcosm contains
Rivers, springs, seas	Internal organs, intestines, veins, canals
Aerial animals	Gnats and winged insects
Snakes	Intestinal worms
Volatile spirits of winds, thunder, lightning	Internal gases and pordas of diseases
Two luminaries, sun and moon	Two luminaries, right eye represents sun, left eye, the moon.
Mountains and hills	Head and ears
Twelve signs of the zodiac	Twelve divisions from head to feet

Astrology has been kept alive mainly through the distribution of almanacs, useful aids of every-day life. The term almanac was taken from Arabian astronomers, whose almanacs were calendars. Astrology, connected with medicine, naturally led makers of cure-alls to advertise in these almanacs, especially after the printing press was invented. A feature in all these patent-medicine almanacs was the figure of a nude man surrounded by signs of the zodiac. The man's face was melancholy, for he was worried about the state of his health; his limbs were outstretched, his bowels were exposed and sundry parts of his body were pierced by lines suggesting the martrydom of a saint, but in reality led to the zodiacal signs, a leaping ram, playful lovers, a crouching lion, a weary bull, a balance, a haughty and self-imposing virgin, a resolute archer, a careless water-pourer, a lusty goat, two fishes, a crab, and a mean-looking scorpion, to indicate which parts of the body and which signs were related.

ANATOMICAL ZODIAC

Constellation with its Element, Character, Color	Ruling Planet & Significance	Anatomical Part Influenced	Personal Aptitude	Personal Type	Temperament of Native of Sign	Signs Fortunate For Mating
Aries Fire Bestial Red	Mars Energy	Head & Face	Pioneer	Agent of Social Change	Impulsive, Idealistic, Courageous, Quicktempered, Jealous	Sagittarius, Aries, Leo

ANATOMICAL ZODIAC - continued

Constellation with its Element, Character, Color	Ruling Planet & Significance	Anatomical Part Influenced	Personal Aptitude	Personal Type	Temperament of Native of Sign	Signs Fortunate For Mating
Taurus Earth Bestial Red-Orange	Venus Beauty Love	Neck	Builder	Actional	Conservative, Industrious, Persistent, Loyal, Fault-finding, Influenced by flattery	Virgo, Capricorn, Scorpio
Gemini Air Human Orange	Mercury Intellect	Shoulders & Arms	Thinker	Mental	Dual-natured, Restless, Versatile, Imaginative, Artistic, Impatient	Libra, Gemini Aquarius
Cancer Water Mute Orange-Yellow	Moon Soul, Imagination	Breast	Parenthood	Emotional	Reserved, Domestic, Sentimental, Hoarding	Pisces, Cancer, Taurus
Leo Fire Bestial Dark Yellow	Sun Spirit Life	Heart	Ruler	Agent of Social Change	Magnetic, Generous, High Spirited, Opinionated, Pleasure Loving	Aries, Sagittarius, Aquarius
Virgo Earth Human Light Yellow	Mercury Intellect	Bowels	Critic	Actional	Reserved, Candid, Analytical, Skeptical, Sincere, Fault Finding	Taurus, Libra, Capricorn
Libra Air Mute Yellowish Green	Venus Beauty, Love	Reins	Artist	Mental	Just, Originator, I conscious, Amorous, Intellectual	Gemini, Virgo, Aquarius

ANATOMICAL ZODIAC - continued

Constellation with its Element, Character, Color	Ruling Planet & Significance	Anatomical Part Influenced	Personal Aptitude	Personal Type	Temperament of Native of Sign	Signs Fortunate For Mating
Scorpio Water Mute Greenish Blue	Mars Energy	Phallus or Vulva	Investigator	Emotional	Managerial, Dramatic, Persevering, Self-absorbed Jealous	Scorpio, Cancer, Virgo
Sagittarious Fire Bestial or Human Blue	Jupiter Abundance	Thighs	Philosopher	Agent of Social Change	Candid, Prophetic, Impatient, Just, Shrewd, Ambitious, Argumentative	Aries, Aquarius, Sagittarius
Capricorn Earth Bestial Bluish Violet	Saturn Limitation, Crystalization	Knees	Realist	Actional	Serious, Exacting, Uncompromising, Cautious, Undemonstrative, Discontent	Libra, Virgo, Taurus
Aquarius Air Human Violet	Uranus Altruism	Legs	Humanitarian	Mental	Sympathetic, Scientific, Tolerant, Unconventional, Generous, Meditative	Aquarius, Leo, Gemini
Pisces Water Mute Violet-Red	Neptune Intuition	Feet	Mystic	Emotional	Sensitive, Impressionable, Psychic, Gentle, Unaggressive	Taurus, Cancer, Pisces

Each sign had its flower and gem. The flower, which aided lovers, usually was one that bloomed while the sun was pass- ing through the mansion; the gem was worn as an amulet by one born in that season of the year.

Mansion	Sun Enters About	Flower	Astrological Gem	Birthstone 1912 Jewelers' Convention*
Aries	Mar. 21	Violet	Diamond	Aquarmarine or Bloodstone
Taurus	Apr. 20	Hyacinth	Sapphire	Diamond
Gemini	May 21	Iris	Agate	Emerald
Cancer	June 21	Orchid	Emerald	Pearl or Moon- stone
Leo	July 23	Dandalion	Sardonyx	Ruby or Carnelian
Virgo	Aug. 23	Goldenrod	Carnelian	Sardonyx or Peridot
Libra	Sep. 23	Corn Flower	Opal	Sapphire
Scorpio	Oct. 22	Blue Gentian	Beryl	Opal or Tourmaline
Sagit- tarius	Nov. 21	Chrysan- themum	Topaz	Topaz
Capricorn	Dec. 21	Snow Drop	Ruby	Lapis Lazuli or Turquoise
Aquarius	Jan. 21	Primrose	Garnet	Garnet
Pisces	Feb. 21	Water Lily	Amethyst	Amethyst

NOTE: * The Jewelers assigned the gem to the month rather than to the zodiacal house, thus the stone for March was the aquamarine or bloodstone, the one for April was the diamond. Ancients assigned gems to signs of the zodiac; for such charts see the Dictionary of Mythology, Folklore & Symbols by Gertrude Jobes, Vol. 1, page 218.

Esoteric priests of the middle ages, who believed they had achieved communication with God and therefore comprehended truths beyond normal human understanding, established the doctrine that certain biblical books as well as cards of the tarot deck were attuned to zodiacal signs and, in certain rituals during the period of concordance, had the power to bring good fortune in various wordly undertakings. Each book and card also was related to an episode of Christ's Passion (which may be seen in the chart Zodiacal Legends) and was accredited as an agent in the steps which brought about crucifixion, which in turn assured rebirth. All pictures of the tarot deck were double to suggest the dual law in nature and all portraits had calm unsmiling expressions to indicate peace, contentment. Later occultists had a formula for creative action in all fields of human endeavor, which applied to those who were synchronized to the seasons of the year.

ESOTERIC CHART (Occult Zodiac)

Mansion	Biblical Book	Tarot Deck Card	Occultist Formula Receiving, Opposing, Diffusing Function For Creative Action
Aries	Genesis Revelation	Magician	Ego brings creative energy to will
Taurus	Exodus	High Priestess	Will opposes energy
Gemini	Leviticus, Numbers, Deuteronomy	Empress	Reason diffuses the rational into the emotional
Cancer	Joshua, Judges, Samuel, Chronicles	Emperor	Emotion brings memory into being
Leo	Prophets	Hierophant	Ego opposes creative energy
Virgo	Psalms	Lovers	Will diffuses creative energy into rationality
Libra	Proverbs	Chariot	Reason brings calculation into being
Scorpio	Song of Solomon	Justice	Emotion opposes memory
Sagittarius	Ecclesiasticus	Hermit	Ego diffuses rational energy into will's sphere
Capricorn	Gospels	Wheel	Will brings its force into being

ESOTERIC CHART (Occult Zodiac) - continued

Mansion	Biblical Book	Tarot Deck Card	Occultist Formula Receiving, Opposing, Diffusing Function For Creative Action
Aquarius	Acts	Strength	Reason opposes rational or calculating energy
Pisces	Letters	Hanged Man	Emotion diffuses into ego's sphere

Strangely enough, twelve, number of houses of the zodiac, and therefore symbol of divine guidance, is the most divisible of numbers. It can be halved, quartered, parted in thirds and sixths. Wherever it appears in mythology, it suggests that many aspects of the sun, "the reason that holds together and regulates the universe;" thus the gates of New Jerusalem, gems of Aaron's breastplate, generals of Ahura Mazda's army, noblest knights of Arthur and Charlemagne, oxen driven by Elisha, pieces of Ahijah's garment, salii or priests of Mars, and stones of Gorsedd or Stonehenge were all twelve.

V

THE SEVEN POWERS

The Seven Fortunes

Timeless, you have provided Time,
seven days: Sunday, day of light,
ruler of the heart, most sublime
period for a leader to sight,
in contemplation, of course, which
road to travel, high or low, on
Monday with its nervous itch
that leads to Tuesday, champion
of wrath, bringer of victory.
In Wednesday's mopping up, although
science and trade ability
are protected, a steady, slow
decay begins to attach lung
and limb. By Thursday, best for works
of politics, no silver tongue
can persuade decarnated clerks
to erase entries which decree
that liver swell and veins contract.
One gift is Friday's, Eau de Vie,
and then, on Saturday, the act
is ended; the final curtain
falls on bones inert and arid.
Mourning tears are futile; again
the Timeless taunt; He who is rid
of Time reproduces his play.
On, on, cycle after cycle;
no actor is granted delay;
some say the wheel's spin is psychal.

The joke digs deeper. Timeless Czar
set six men and a wench to
sentinel the days; each a star
with authority to undo
any Day that fails to maintain
the cycle. Mortals may resist,
complain, fawn, weep, pray, show disdain;
the Seven Fortunes must persist.

Seven. Mystic number since
man first speculated on the
creation of the visible universe.
Seven Ancient Elders assisted
the Babylonian Marduk; they
furnished all the magic arts and
secrets of divination. Ishtar
passed through seven gates on

81

her way to the realm of darkness.
From the eye of the Egyptian Ra
came Seven Wise Ones, Hawks,
that flew upward and presided
over learning. Ptah had seven
sons; Hathor had seven aspects.
The Cabiri, originally seven
deities worshiped by the
Phrygians, were adopted by the
Greeks. Also appearing in
Greek mythology are the Seven
Against Thebes.

In Christian tradition, the
number of angels before God's
throne is seven. The Ophites
worshipped seven archons:
Ialdabaoth, the leader, with a
man's head, Erathaoth with a
dog's head, Gabriel with an eagle's
head, Michael with a lion's head,
Onoel with an ass's head, Suriel
with a bull's head, Tautabaoth
with a bear's head. In gnostic
lore, Sophia is attended by
Seven Maidens. Chnuphis, gnostic
lion-headed and maned serpent,
wore a seven-rayed crown. The
Cabala describes Seven Heavens.
Moslem lore likewise has seven,
composed of two mansions and
five gardens. The Chief
Armenian Pagan deities were
seven: Aramazd (supreme),
Anahit (fecundity), Baal Shamin

(sky), Arusyak (love), Mihr
(fire), Nane (war), Tiur (scribe).
Later a local sun god, Vahagn,
replaced Mihr.

The Siberian Over-god has a
suite of seven assistants, his
sons, the Kudai or Torem-
Karevels (Heaven-watchers),
who dwell in a tent next to a
golden tethering pole, the heaven-
post (North Star). Fate deities,
they control human life and the
heavenly laws of nature. The
Yakut sky-lord likewise has
seven helpers, the Satta-kuro-
Dzusagai-ai. The Shinto
Japanese worship seven deities
of happiness, the Shichi Fukujin,
as well as Seven Divine Genera-
tions, that is deities born without forebears. In a Mexican
carving, the sun is portrayed
with seven extending arms.

The Seven in these and other
legends are identified as aspects
of the Seven Powers (Sun, Moon,
and Five Planets), sometimes
called the Wandering Deities
or Sentinels of Law and Order,
watchman of the heavens who
wandered among the stars and
prepared occurences on earth. In
the list that follows the five are
given in relation to their distance
from the sun, Mercury being the
closest.

THE SEVEN POWERS

	Sun (Sol)	Moon (Diana, Luna)	Mercury	Venus	Mars	Jupiter	Saturn
Modern (Roman) Ruler	Sun (Sol)	Moon (Diana, Luna)	Mercury	Venus	Mars	Jupiter	Saturn
Anglo-Saxon	Sonnan	Monan	Woden (Vodenes)	Frigg (Frige)	Tiw (Tives)	Thumores	Soeternes
Arabic	Shams	Qamar	'Utarid	az-Zuhara	Mirrikh	Mushtart	Zuhal
Babylonian Bali (1)	Guski Aditye	Babbar Haoma	Zakur Budha	Nabi (Nebu) Hookooroo	Kha-urud Angare	Urud Brahaspaty	Dusia Hoone-kerroo
Cabalistic Intelligence (2)	Nagiel	Elimiel	Tiriel	Hagiel	Graphael	Sophiel	Agiel
Cabalis tic Spirit (2)	Smeliel	Lamaneal	Cochabiel	Noguel	Modiniel	Zadkiel	Sabathiel
Ceylanese Buddhist (3)	Irru	Kandu	Buduha	Sikura	Angare	Braspaty	Henhaura
Egyptian	Ra, Amen, or Osiris	Khensu or Isis	Aroeris (4)	Mut or Nephthys	Knemu or Hor-tas(5)	Set	Her-ka (6)
Esoteric Astrology (7)	Anabata	Ajna	Manipura	Vishuddhi	Sahasrara	Svadist- thana	Muladhara
Euphratean	Shamash	Sin	Nabu (Nebo)	Ishtar or Bellil	Nergal	Marduk or Baal	Ninib or Ninurta

THE SEVEN POWERS - continued

	Sunna (Sonn)	Monan	Wotan	Freia	Ziu	Donor	Saeter
German	Sunna (Sonn)	Monan	Wotan	Freia	Ziu	Donor	Saeter
Gnostic Angelology	Raphael	Gabriel	Michael	Haniel or Jophiel	Chamuel	Zadkiel	Uriel
Greek	Apollo or Helios	Artemis or Selene	Hermes	Aphrodite	Ares	Zeus	Cronus
Hebrew Medieval Angelology	Michael	Gabriel	Raphael	Haniel	Madimial	Zadkiel	Cassiel
Hindu (8)	Surya, Aditya, or Adi-Daivata	Soma or Chandra	Buddha	Sukra	Skanda	Brihaspati or Guru	Sani
Mandaean (9)	Il or Il ll, Kadush, Adunay	Sin	Enba or Yishu M'shiha	Estera or Ruha d'Qudsha	Nirig	Bil	Kewan
Norse	Sol (Sunna)	Mani	Odin	Freya or Frigg	Tyr	Thor	Saeter
Persian	Khurshed, the Cook	Mahi, the Beautiful	Tir, the Secretary	Esther, the Star or Nahid, the Dancer	Bahram, the Killer	Hurmuz, the Judge	Kaiwan, the Guardian

THE SEVEN POWERS - continued

Sabaean(10)	Samas	Sin	Nebo	Beltis	Nergal	Bel	Cronus
Sumero-Accadian(11)	Samash	Sin	Sul-pa-ud-du (Messenger)	Dilbat (Proclaimer)	Zal-bat-anu (Death)	Lubat-gudibir (Old Sheep)	Sak-us- (Eldest)

NOTES (Seven Powers): (1) Hinduism, which once was their religion, blended with Buddhism and Moslemism. Deity names seem to be a blend of the Sanscrit and local terms. (2) The names parody the Hebrew. The Cabala also refers to Seven Mirrors. (3) The Ceylonese originally had a religion that related to Hinduism; about the 3rd century B.C. they converted to Buddhism. The deity names seem to be a blend of Sanscrit and local terms. (4) Aroeris is Horus as lord of the setting sun. (5) Hor-tas is the Red Horus or Planet Bruiser, a god of war. (6) Her-ka is Horus, the Bull. (7) Names parody Hindu names. (8) The Hindus recognized two additional powers, nodes of the moon: Rahu, the head of the dragon, and Ketu, the tail. Together they inerrupted the regular order of the universe by causing eclipses. They ride an owl, bird of death, and are a bad omen because they finally will cause the destruction of all things. To drive them away, women beat brass pans. The tailless Rahu represents the north or ascending node; the headless Ketu is the south or descending node. Rahu is called Ras in Arabia and Rawhoe in Ceylon; Ketu is called Zanab in Arabia and Kehatoe or Kehettu in Ceylon. The Persian name for the pair is Gavzihr or Gochihar. (9) The Mandaean Powers are the seven children of Ruha (mother of falsehood, lies and fornication) and Ur (son of Ruha and personified fire of Hell). The names play on those in Babylonian, Persian, Hebrew, and Arabian mythologies. All are feared as demons. (10) Sabaean names derived from the Eurphratean and Greek. (11) The Seven were the Sibu kakkabani Lubati or Seven Old Sheep Stars. Each of the seven had several names, each actually an adjective, descriptive of a function.

Whence the Seven sprang into being or how they were created is related in a variety of ingenious ways, each commemorating the versatility of man's imagination, all revealing that their invention was brought about by a desire for light in a world of chaos or darkness. In Hinduism, the gods stood at one end of the Great Serpent, which was used as a rope; the demons stood at the other end, and in the Sea of Milk (Galaxy) churned until the moon and other useful or poisonous things were formed. The Japanese Amaterasu, Lady Sun, hid in a cave after she had been defiled by her brother Susa-no-wo, the male principle in nature. Hearty laughter at the cave's entrance cut through her shame and aroused her curiosity. Once she was lured outside, she remained to enjoy a baudy comic dance being performed by a maiden in her suite, a myth which exemplifies the setting and rising of the sun.

In a Polynesian myth, Vatea (sky lord) and Tangaroa (the cosmic or world soul) both claimed to be the father or the first born of Papa (mother earth). To settle the argument, Papa tore the child in half and gave each his portion. Vatea cast his half into the sky, where it became the sun; Tangaroa kept his until it began to decompose; then he threw it into the sky, where it became the pale and marked moon. Australian primitives tossed an Emu's egg into the sky, and it became the sun.

Apache Indians made a huge disk, painted it yellow, and attached it to the ceiling above. Delighted with it, they made a companion piece, the moon. Coyote, chief of the Mariposan Indians, ordered Wolf to bring back a fire that burned in a lake on a mountain. Wolf was able to seize only a part of the blaze, out of which Coyote shaped the moon. Perceiving the light to be insufficient for man's needs, Coyote molded the sun. The Cherokees set a sun on a track above the ground and sent it traveling from east to west each day. The sun's heat scorched the shell of the crawfish, and made it red. Having been touched by the sun, it became sacred and therefore taboo as food. Conjurers kept raising the sun until it was seven handbreadths high and just under the sky's arch. At the end of each day the sun disappeared in the west under the arch; it reappeared at the starting place in the east each morning.

Solar temples of the Egyptians were oriented to the sun at either the summer or winter solstice. The famous Colossus of Rhodes was a gigantic statue of Apollo set up in 280 B. C. It stood astride the entrance of the harbor for fifty-six years, and then was overthrown by an underworld deity, who broke it to pieces with an earthquake. At Stonehenge, the imposing ruins of a sanctuary built by pre-Druids about three thousand years ago on the Salisbury Plains may be seen. Among the few rocks still standing is one so placed that, as the sun rises on Midsummer Day, the day on which the oak (sun) king was sacrifically burned, its shadow falls on the central stone or so-called altar. Many cathedrals of the middle ages were so built that the sun penetrated into the structure on the festal day of the patron saint through a door that opened toward the east. The Peruvian capital city Cuzco was the pride of the Sun. In it stood a magnificent temple with the Sun's image emblazoned upon its western wall. The figure was etched on an enormous and massive gold plate, which was lavishly decorated with emeralds and other precious stones. It was so situated that, when the huge doors of the eastern portal were opened, rays of the rising sun fell upon it.

In ancient Sumer, Sun was an Old Sheep, bellwether of a flock composed of the planets, stars, and other celestial phenomena. In many legends, the Five Planets, along with other stars, are children, assistants, or guardians of Sun and Moon, which die (fade away or set) when their heels touch Earth. Although buskins or sandals are provided to protect the sacred heels of the mortal pair, they constantly succumb and must be resurrected. Sometimes the Five Planets are said to be aspects or disguises of chief deities, as Jupiter or Saturn, or they are described as thrones or mansions of divine beings, as their fires, or assistants. In some theologies they are said to be celestial realms where the souls of kings, heroes, ancestors, maidens, who died as virgins, or mothers, who died in childbirth, determine earthy affairs and keep opposite forces in balance. In others, as in Mandaean belief, they are provided with moods, happy, or angry, mild or severe, generous or demanding, forgiving or vengeful.

Modern scientists have discovered planets and star clusters that were unknown to our ancient ancestors. Following the classical tradition they have assigned Greek or Latin names to them; thus they are known as the Asteroids, Ceres, Eros, Juno, Neptune, Pluto, Uranus, Vesta, etc. By the twentieth century over six hundred planets, so-called twinkling wanderers, were known to exist; at the present time the number is much greater. Some are so small they might be termed cometoids, but large or small, only the original seven are recognized as agents of supernatural power. Many believe that the existence of the universe depends on the harmony of the Seven, that they are related to the seven days of creation and control the cycle of the week, are the link between the Will of Heaven and events on earth, effect changes, determine the course or length of life, and they are consulted in human destiny. The dots on a die, often used as a means of contact with the Powers, are so arranged that opposite faces add to seven. Dice, the oldest known implement in games of chance, were used for purposes of divination back into antiquity. Some of the supposedly inherent abilities of the Seven are charted here:

POTENCY OF THE SEVEN POWERS

	Sun	Moon	Mercury	Venus	Mars	Jupiter	Saturn
Day Assigned	Sunday	Monday	Wednesday	Friday	Tuesday	Thursday	Saturday*
Action Influenced	Contemplation	Divination or Travel	Science	Love	Wrath	Politics	Mourning

POTENCY OF THE SEVEN POWERS - continued

	Sun	Moon	Mercury	Venus	Mars	Jupiter	Saturn
Color	Gold	Silver	Blue	Pale Yellow	Red	Orange	Black
Gift Influenced	Leadership	Imagination	Business Ability	Beauty	Strength	Wisdom	Sorcery
Organ Influenced	Heart	Nerves & Brain	Lungs & Limbs	Genitals & Stomach	Face	Liver & Veins	Bones
Part of Head Influenced	Right Eye	Left Eye	Mouth	Nose	Forehead	Right Ear	Left Ear
Realm Influenced	Light	Darkness	Scribe	Love	War	Sky	Harvest
Sin Influenced	Pride	Laziness	Envy	Passion & Luxury	Temper	Greed	Hypocrisy
Virtue Influenced	Knowledge	Intelligence	Ingenuousness	Love	Courage	Integrity	Prudence
Virtuous Metal +	Gold	Silver	Quicksilver	Copper	Iron	Brass	Lead

NOTE *The Norse called this Laugar (Washing or Laundry) Day as well as Sater Dei or Dagr. +Medals of these metals supposedly brought good luck to the wearer when the planet was at culmination or in conjunction.

To the Chinese, the Powers were known as The Seven Goers, the authority of the Sun and Moon being greater than that of the other five. Sun, Jih Tou (the yang or male principle), was associated with gold, controlled the eyes, and was represented by the cock; Moon, Yueh (the yin or female principle) was associated with silver, controlled the ears and was represented by the hare. The five planets, premonitory stars par excellence, which had been created by the five elements, developed affinities for other things created by the elements, such as the five colors, metals, and tastes. In addition to the things they cause to come into being, the five elements influence the ten celestial stems and produce and conquer each other according to a definite and eternal law, large quanities prevailing over smaller ones; thus water produces wood but destroys metal (non-substance over substance), metal produces water but destroys wood (hardness over softness), wood produces fire but destroys earth (density conquering incoherence), earth produces metal but destroys water (solidity over insolidity). All misfortune comes from disturbances of the five elements, and for this reason Taoists oppose interference with nature. Earth, ruler of the middle kingdom, is represented by a square; water, ruler of the north, by a ball or circle; fire, ruler of the south, by a triangle; air, ruler of the east, by a crescent; ether, ruler of the west, by a mani or jewel of the lotus. The pattern is used as a memorial pole and as a talisman. Adopted by medieval European alchemists, who considered the two upper symbols of the disgram as one, it was shown in this form:

THE TEN STEMS

Stem	Chinese Number	Astrological Name	Planet	Chinese Name	Viscera Controlled	Virtue
1	Chia	O-Feng	Jupiter	Mu Hsing	Liver	Humaneness
2	I (Yi)	Chan-Meng		(Wood Star)		
3	Ping	Jou Chao	Mars	Huo Hsing	Heart	Propriety
4	Ting	Ch'iang Yu		(Fire Star)		
5	Wu	Chu Yung	Saturn	T'u Hsing	Stomach	Fidelity
6	Chi	T'u Wei		(Earth Star)		
7	Keng	Shang-chang	Venus	Chin Hsing	Lungs	Uprightness
8	Hsin	Chung-kuang		(Metal Star)		
9	Jen	Hsuan-I	Mercury	Shui Hsing	Spleen; Kidneys	Insight
10	Kuei	Chao-yang		(Water Star)		

Stem	Planet	Affinity	Affinity	Color Affinity	Metal Affinity	Taste Affinity
1	Jupiter	Fir	Trees	Green	Pewter	Sour
2		Bamboo	Timber		(Tin)	
3	Mars	Wood fire	Lightning	Red	Iron	Bitter
4		Lamp flame	Incense			
5	Saturn	Hill	Hills	Yellow	Lead	Sweet
6		Plain	Earthernware			

THE TEN STEMS - continued

Stem	Planet	Affinity	Affinity	Color Affinity	Metal Affinity	Taste Affinity
7	Venus	Weapons	Ore	White	Copper	Pungent
8		Kettle	Kettles			
9	Mercury	Waves	Salt Seas	Black	Quick-	Salt
10		Brooks	Streams		silver	

The 10 stems were used in a system for the numbering of hours, days, months, and years, by joining the first of the 12 celestial branches (12 zodiacal signs) to the first of the 10 celestial stems until the tenth of the latter was reached, when a fresh commencement was made, the eleventh of the 12 branches being attached to the first stem.

The Cabalists read the will of the Seven Powers in seven mirrors, which they consulted on the proper days: The Sun mirror, made of gold, was consulted on Sundays as to great persons on earth. Moon mirror of silver was consulted on Mondays as to dreams and plans. Mars mirror of iron was consulted on Tuesdays as to enmities and lawsuits. Mercury mirror of crystal filled with quicksilver was consulted on Wednesdays as to questions of money. Jupiter mirror of tin was consulted on Thursdays as to probable success. Venus mirror of copper was consulted on Fridays as to questions of love. Saturn mirror of lead was consulted on Saturday as to lost articles and secrets.

A Marduk epic has been preserved in seven tablets. They correspond to, and may be the prototype of, the biblical account of six days of creation and one day of rest. 1-In the vast slimy waste of the abyss the primordial deities appear, headed by Tiamat (Bitter Sea), queen of chaos, her husband Apsu, who despised order, and her son and evil counselor Mummu. Apsu and Mummu are destroyed by Ea, a descendant. 2-Tiamat creates eleven monsters that spit out poison (darkness, drought, storms, frost) to attack her offspring the gods of light Anu, Bel, and Ea. Marduk, son of Ea, is asked to undertake the task of slaying Tiamat. He agrees to do so if granted immortality. (Marduk, the sun, dies daily). 3-Anu, Bel, and Ea hold a feast, agree to Marduk's terms, and select him to lead the forces against Tiamat. 4-Marduk is made immortal. He seizes the tablets of fate from Kingu, one of Tiamat's warriors, slays Tiamat, and from her body creates heaven, earth, and the sea. 5-Marduk places the eleven monsters of chaos in heaven along with his own star Sirius (or the planet Jupiter), chief light of the night sky, to make the twelve mansions of the zodiac. 6-The gods pay homage to Marduk with a hymn of praise and ask for someone to pay them honor, so Marduk brings Kingu before Ea, who slays Kingu and makes a man from his blood. 7-Marduk absorbs fifty-one names and assumes the form of each of the deities. Marduk, the immortal, the lord of many existences, invented the calendar and sometimes retreated into the underworld, on which occasions darkness fell upon the world.

VI

CELESTIAL PHENOMENA

Evening stillness;
One by one the stars appeared
in the winter sky.

In the ever-changing expanse, which at night casts an enormous shadow that completely blankets earth, and at noon lifts all shade until earth stands naked and exposed, man gradually located mansions, pavilions, workshops, playgrounds, streams, fields, and roads of the deities. There gods came into being and disappeared, there they frolicked or made war, determined the fate of mortals, or deferred to fates mightier than themselves. Some rose to a cool crystal-clear realm high in the zone; those who had fallen into evil or slothful ways sank into a blazing fire below the horizon. Eventually various levels were defined. A notion of nine or seven heavens rising one above the other like the stories of a building was quite common. The Egyptian heavenly spheres numbered ten, the first seven being those of the planets; the eighth contained all fixed stars; the ninth, crystalline, held the precession of the equinoxes; the tenth was the primum mobile, which revolved diurnally and gave motion to the inner spheres of the planets, and in this way became the great symbol of any mainspring of action. In Greek and Roman antiquity heaven was a region reserved to gods, deified heroes, and demi-gods. The Scandinavian Niflheim con-tained nine worlds constructed from the skull of Ymir and ruled over by Odin.

Early in Old Testament lore, the Firmament was a lower heaven, a solid vault, a sort of storehouse that held the upper waters from which was distributed rain, sleet, snow, and winds. Above it was a heaven of gauzy material with a curtain-like motion. The sun, moon, and stars were attached to the gauze or veil-like embroidery. This high realm, called Heaven of Heavens, completely encircled the earth and firmament, and remained free of death, sin, and all other evils. In this kingdom, an inheritance of holy bliss, where glorious lights, rapturous songs, rivers of pleasure, trees of life, feasting, mirth, beautiful robes, treasures and triumphs were to be found, the degrees of glory varied, and the most righteous dwelled in the presence of Jehovah, whose seat was above all others, and who sometimes gave the order to "Stretch out the Heaven of Heavens," an expression that could not apply to the solid vault. Jewish mystics speak of Seven Heavens, the first the space between the clouds and earth; second, the region of the clouds; third, fourth, fifth, and sixth, the

home of various grades of
angels; seventh, the abode of
God and the seraphim.

Moslems similarly have
seven: Darel-Jelal, Glory;
Dares-Selam, Peace; Jennet el
Mawa, Rest; Jennet en Khuld,
Eternity; Jennet en Na'im,
Delight; Jennet el Firdos,
Paradise; Jennet 'Adu, Perpetual
Abode. The first two are
mansions, the last five are
gardens.

The Iranians, like early
Hebrews, were of the opinion
that two heavens existed: one,
the Twasha, Exterior, in which
the stars appeared, was con-
stinually in motion; the second,
the Asman, Interior, was composed of a transparent blue stuff
that corresponded to the Firmament of the Bible.

Although deities rarely left
their spheres and never revealed themselves in full glory
to a living mortal, man, by
dint of his intelligence and
imagination, conceived the color,
size, features, temperament,
habits, and other characteristics
of certain infinite beings, and
by observing various sounds and
signs out in space, often has
been able to read their wills.

Thunder warned of floods or
conflagration by lightning to follow. An eclipse, in a far-
reaching belief, was the swallow-
ing of the sun or moon by a
monster. In Babylonia, darkness was caused by seven devils
who invaded the vault of heaven.
The Chinese believed a dragon
did the damage when an emperor
lacked virtue. By and large an
eclipse was regarded as a
catastrophe or a pronouncement
of divine chastisement; only a

miracle or a forgiving heart
above saved the world from
coming to an end.

Nebulae, which hang like cloudy
mazes of light in the blackness
that surrounds them, have since
very ancient times been used
to foretell weather. When they
become invisible in a haze, wind
and rain might be expected.
These nebulae are among the
beauties of the Southern Sky,
which lacks constellations as
striking as those of the Bears.
Most appear within dark areas
of the Milky Way and are called
Black Holes or Ink Spots. In a
Coal Sack or Soot Bag located
near Crux, Peruvians imagined
they saw a heavenly Doe suckling
her fawn. According to a
native Australian legend, which
seems to carry overtones of a
Christian parable, probably
related by missionaries, the
dark spot near Crux is the
embodiment of evil in the shape
of an Emu, who lies in wait at
the foot of a sacred tree, represented by the Southern Cross,
where an opossum driven by his
persecutions takes refuge among
the holy branches.

Early navigators called the
Great Magellanic clouds (Nubeculae
Magellani) Cape Clouds since
they were prominent heavenly
objects seen as they neared the
Cape of Good Hope. Later they
were named for the 16th century
Portuguese navigator Ferdinand
Magellan, who had described
them. The Latin part of the
title is a diminutive of nubes,
literally, Little Clouds. They
have been called Magellan
Patches, Coal Sacks, and by
the Polynesians, Mahu (Mist).
This last also is written Nga
Mau.

Nebecula Major, Greater Cloud, lies in the constellations Dorado and Mons. The Arabic name is Al Bakr, The White Ox.

Nubecula Minor, Lesser Cloud, lies within Hydrus and Tucana. Christian lore has fashioned this into the archangel Raphael.

Other interesting and important nebulae are: Beehive in Canes Venatici, Dumb-bell in Vulpecula, Great Looped in Dorado, Horseshoe or Swan in Scutum, Keyhole in Carina, Lace-work in Cygnus, Pin-wheel in Coma Berenices, Sword-hand of Persus, Whirlpool or Spiral in Canes Venatici.

Comets and meteors still strike terror in the hearts of many who see them, fearful they will bring about the immediate destruction of the world. Even up to Elizabethan times, popular belief supposed they were signs by which heaven foretold great events on earth, especially were royal deaths heraled by these mysterious visitants. In Julius Caesar, Shakespeare has Calpurnia plead with her husband Caesar not to venture forth on the Ides of March. She says:

When beggars die, there are no comets seen,
The Heavens themselves blaze forth the death of Princes.

Astrologically they forebode evil, bring war and pestilence. In the Bible, the stones the Lord cast from heaven on the day the sun's course stopped to drive the enemy from Israel were probably meteorites, although some say the barrage from heaven may have been with hail-stones. The Pairikas, Zoroastrian female spirits of seduction, fly between earth and sky in Staro-Keremao (Worm Star) shape. These shooting-star fairies or sorcerers cast evil spells on the fixed stars and keep them from providing proper seasonal changes. Cherokee Indians called a comet or meteor atsil thuntutsi, fire panther, probably because they move so rapidly and their tails resemble the frosty breath of a panther. In Hebraic-Christian tradition, when Lucifer sinned, the speed with which he was hurled from his lofty home generated him into a dreaded shooting star.

Tears of Fire

In the fearful infinity of space,
the dethroned Lucifer, infuriate,
indignant, lashed his flame-
    flashing tail
and fiery tongue. Although he
    barely scorched
the wings of his cold white kin,
    he ignited
a realm where an eternal blaze
    conceals
his refurbished royal seat. Yet
    with rage
he weeps. Rebelliously he
    sweeps his red
scimitar form across the
    swarthiness
of night to spray tears of fire.
    Briefly seen,
he disappears, but he spares
    neither prince
nor beggar. Paralyzed with
    fright are those
who momentarily escape; they
    know
the portent of these ash-set tears
    is death.

Rain and wind were ministers of either goodness or wrath from above. The waters that fell did not return on high but changed into seed or fruit or caused destruction, disease, gloom. American

Indians believed that rain was a form in which departed ancestors appeared to bless or smite those who were still alive, and the ghost might have no greater cause for mischief than a disgruntled mood. For this reason the Indians never neglected to honor their dead with proper sacrifices. Winds were sources of inspiration, inducers of prophetic trances, revealers of oracles. As messengers of the gods, they delivered their advice by humming among the leaves, noisily whirling about in a cave, or forcing waves to sound against a rocky shore. Wind deities not only properly distributed seeds, but were eloquent speakers, players of music on the harp, lyre, or reed pipes. They whistled so magnificently no human has ever been able to match their tones. Quite naturally they had the capriciousness of charmers and bruised grain, crushed cities, stole. In stories told about them they grow miraculously and sometimes have more than one head and two arms, their feet are turned backwards that they might move with greater speed, and they ride air currents on brooms made of fagots (such brooms are currently used in Europe by street and highways sweepers). Properly understood they are forewarners of atmospheric conditions, thus we might say these prognosticators over the air waves were originally, or rather were the original, weather witches. No power ever has restrained them from that which they set out to do; no eye has ever traced their paths; nothing has been able to withstand their furies; at work they are fierce, but they conclude their labors with gentle soothing sounds and light caresses. In popular belief, those born when

wind is from the east are laden with gold and never know want; those born when wind is from the south will experience interesting companionships; when from the west will receive only life's barest necessities; when from the north will experience war; and those born when no wind blows will be fools.

Ancient Jews, who noted only four directions and thus four winds, alluded so often to the "Four Winds of Heaven," the old Testament expression has become common usage.

At Memphis the diurnal motion of the sun was symbolized by the triad Osiris-Isis-Horus, the annual course by Amen-Mut-Khensu. These father-mother-son trinities established the seasons, which once were three, summer-winter-spring. When the celestial hemisphere was divided into four quarters, or seasons, it was overseen by a four-faced deity or by four creatures. A few with four faces or heads are: the Assyrian Asshur, Buddhist Avalokistesvara; Greek Axieros; Hindu Siva; Mayan Bacabab; Roman Janus. Audhumla, the Norse primeval cow, had four breasts; Buddha had four crucial moments; Krishna, the Hindu, had four arms. The Cherubim, which Ezekiel likened to four living creatures, man who controlled water; lion who controlled fire; ox or calf who controlled earth; eagle who controlled air, directed the winds from the four corners of the Garden of Eden, where they kept trespassers from the Tree. From the whirling Cherubim developed the whirling Celtic Caer Sidi. The four faces of Asshur were identical to the four forms of the Cherubim, and later the four animals were

assigned to the Christian evange-
lists, Matthew, Mark, Luke,
and John. The Chinese and
Japanese also had four sacred
animals: Azure Dragon, who
presided over the east, spring,
and water; Vermilion Bird, who
presided over the south, summer,
and fire; White Tiger, who
presided over the west, autumn,
and earth; Black Tortoise or
Somber Warrior, who presided
over the north, winter, and air.

In Hinduism and Buddhism
four stars nourish and guard the
world as well as see that the
seasons appear in their proper
order. These four great kings,
or Lokapalas, dwell on the four
pillars of Mount Meru, which is
of gold and round as a ball.
Mount Meru is the navel of the
universe, and its pillars separate heaven and earth. The
Lokapalas compare with the Four
Royal Stars mentioned in the
Zend-Avesta, namely Tishtrya
(Tascheter), Vanad (Venant),
Sataves (Satevis), Hapto-iringas
(Hastorang). The four supposedly form a cross, each point
marking one cardinal direction.
Much disagreement exists as to
exactly which stars are involved.

An old peasant sat
on a slope counting stars
while his goat nibbled grass.

Within the four quarters
flowed the primordial ocean,
which had been the habitation of
Tiamat, whose name seems
originally to have meant Eastern
Sea. This dragon, mother of
all life, occupied these waters
until she had been dispossessed
by her son Ea, who also so-
journed on the constellation
Capricorn. In the center of the
sea, also known as Lake of Immortality because its waters

constantly renewed themselves,
was an island on which grew
the cosmic tree, widely
described as with roots deep
in the sacred pool or sea and
turning with the winds or
seasons. The top branches
supported luminous space bodies,
and the tree sustained all things,
was the judgment seat of the
gods and supplied the deities on
high and chosen dead with
nourishment. Its fruit or
leaves (stars) held the records
of the past and future. Not
only was it a seat of fate and a
ladder on which souls climbed
from earth to heaven, but it
was the gallows on which the
fertility hero was hung after
emasculation and with whose
leaves in spring he was resurrected. Frequently a bird sat
on a top branch, while a dragon
or other amphibious animal, a
follower or descendant of Tiamat,
loitered at the roots in the dark
depths. When the bird gained
the advantage he forced the
dragon to release fertile rains
and was able to spread milder
weather over the earth; when the
advantage was on the side of the
dragon, frost covered earth and
verdure withered. The tree was
symbolized by a cross, and in
some cultures a cross replaced
the tree.

The Pool
A tadpole wagged its tail,
and the quiet pool
at the roots of the pomegranate
    tree,
formed a languid stream.
Birds sang to its rhythm,
a snake turned in earth,
and grass sprang up.
A fragrance of blossoms
pervaded the air.
Excited insects gathered seeds.
Lights flashed,
like those of fireflies.

Somewhere in the distance
a flintstone pierced a toad,
and the stream became a
frozen pool.

Many members of Tiamat's
family rose from this bathyal
zone, strange creatures, half
man and half fish or half beast.
These monstrous beings, some
of whom let their rear ends loll
in the water while the fore
parts of their bodies glistened in
the crystalline air above, became admired as constellations.
Across this vast sea, the Ship
Argo sailed in search of the
Golden Fleece, and from it
streamed many branches, the
Eridanus, which formed the Po,
where it touched earth, and
emptied into the Adriatic; the
Euphrates; the Tigris and the
Nile.

To bridge the celestial waters, which had no beginning and
no end, and which flowed from
horizon to horizon, was the
Rainbow. In Japan it was called
Ama-no-uki-hashi, Floating-
bridge-of-heaven, or Ame-no-iha-
fune, Heavenly-rock-boat. On it
stood Izanagi and Izanami, the
male and female principles,
who churned the stream below
with their jeweled spear (phallus),
and created the island of Onogoro,
where they settled, copulated, the
first divine pair to do so, and
begat forests, winds, etc., as
well as mortal progeny. In
Norse mythology it was called
Bifrost, Tremble-path, and
was the narrow road that connected Asgard, Garden of Light,
and Midgard, Earth, midway up
the Tree. Asgard, a realm with
silver and gold palaces, was
surrounded by an invincible wall
from which all the gods looked
down upon the rest of the universe. Rainbow's various colors

were reflections of the precious
gems of which it was composed.
It was guarded by Heimdal,
Heaven's defender, who had been
born on the horizon where land
meets the cosmic sea, to prevent it from falling into the
hands of frost and mountain
giants. The gods rode over
it daily to their tribunal held
under the Yggdrasil Tree, and
the Valkyrie crossed it to
choose the heroes from among
those slain in battle for Valhalla.
The heroes marched back over it
in triumph to the great wassail
held to welcome them. Sky
deities also used it as a bow
from which they shot their
arrows (rays, or lightning) at
storm deities. Because it came
and vanished without warning the
Greek gods found it a useful
messenger and personified it as
the beautiful maiden Iris. Among
Hebrews it symbolizes blessings,
God's covenant, a sign of the
presence of God as manifested
in Joseph's coat of many colors.
It was the Dahomey great serpent
Aido Hwedo which transported
Mawu, creator goddess. Excrement left by Aido Hwedo created
mountains. By Iroquois Indians
it was revered as the mate of
Hino, the Thunder Bird. Cherokees believed it to be the tongue
of the Celestial Serpent drinking in water. The Mayans worshiped the rainbow as Ix-chel, a
goddess giver of fecundity,
guardian of women in childbirth,
patroness of the art of medicine,
sender of fertilizing showers.

In parts of the world the
Galaxy or Milky Way was said
to have been one of the rivers
formed by waters of the Celestial
Sea or by vapors that gathered
under the stars. Like the sea
itself, the Milky Way, which
seems to wind sometimes as a

placid stream, sometimes as rapids overflowing its banks, was believed to be the source, at or beyond the horizon, of several of the great rivers of earth. This strip of diffused light that encircles the heavens and which may be seen on any clear moonless night, varies in breadth and brightness in different sections of the sky. To a great extent it is pale and filmy, but, in the northern hemisphere, in Perseus and Cygnus, and in the southern hemisphere at Sagittarius, it becomes ravishingly radiant. Speculation concerning its nature has been almost as diversified as the people who have observed it. It was thought to be the sunbeams left behind in the tracks of the sun's chariot or the reflected light of the sun. Early philosophers said it was the gases from earth set on fire in the sky, the shadow of the earth as the sun passed beneath it, the sperma of gods, the bones of souls, or the dust or ashes of old stars. Like the Rainbow it also served as a bridge of heaven.

The Galaxy was the Snake-river Nana, Sumerian virgin mother, who conceived by the magic use of an almond or pomegranate. This goddess, a protectress of flocks and cities, formed a complete circle, biting her tail to girdle the universe and letting surge from her the prodigious waters that held in all the lands known to man. This effervescent Snake-river was also the golden rope of Nabu, her mate, the sun-god of the autumn equinox, that connected the hill of the god with the abyss on high in which she reclined, suggesting an umbilical cord. Ghosts of those who had left their bodies below

passed over the river on their way to homes in the world beyond. The serpent biting its own tail symbolizes eternity or power feeding on itself; a serpent encircling a mountain is phallic in character. Snake dances have been performed to charm the release of fertility inherent in earth and rain and to delight and win the good will of dead ancestors who frequently had a voice in how fertility should be distributed.

In Babylonian hypothesis the Galaxy was the seam where two star-studded hemispheres were fastened together to make a perfect orb. The vague light was the glow of fires seen through the seam. Manilius, a Roman poet wrote:

Whether here the Heavens two
    halves are joined,
But oddly closed, still leave a
    seam behind.

One theory attributed its formation to the tragic Egyptian goddess Isis. Fearful of Set, who pursued her, she dropped particles of the stalks of wheat she carried as she fled across the sky. These grain scraps spread into the uneven shadowy path.

Hera, the Greek goddess, too was credited with creating it. The wife of Zeus, personification of the regions of upper air, she was under him and personified the lower atmosphere. A scolding wife, she frequently countermanded the orders he gave, and variations in the air were thought to result from frequent domestic quarrels of the couple. Jealous, unforgiving, vain, vindictive, she caused the fall of Troy because

Paris, son of its king, had proclaimed Aphrodite to be more beautiful. She had the power to cause insanity and struck Dionysus crazy. The ugliness of her son Hephaestus displeased her, and she cast him from Olympus into the lower regions. In a rare mood she agreed to suckle an abandoned infant, not realizing the child was Heracles whom she hated because he was the son of her husband by Alcmene. When he bit hard at her breasts (the sun stung the sky), she threw him from her, and drops of her milk spattered to form the Milky Way. In spite of her many faults, she was set up as the model wife and revered as the noblest of goddesses. The wet-nurse troubles of Hera are almost identical to those told of the Hindu Sarama, mother of Saramaya, air in motion. Drippings from this milky froth nourished the vegetable world.

Greeks characterized the Galaxy as the main thoroughfare of heaven, lined by the palaces of the great gods, whereas lesser supernaturals lived in dark recesses a distance from this road of soft lights. Pythagoreans said that when the hapless Phaethon lost control of the sun chariot he burnt the stars, and ashes that dropped from them formed this track.

By the Norse it was known as Midhgardhsormr, the Weltunspanner, or the Midyard (Earth) Serpent that stretched around the universe. Its legends interthreaded with those of the Rainbow, and so it also was a Path of Ghosts, a road over which heroes, chosen by the Valkyries from those who had fallen in battle, marched to their palace Valhalla (Valholl) in the gleaming Glasir grove, whose trees bore red-gold leaves (sunset). Odin likewise trumpeted forth along this road on his eight-legged gray steed Sleipner (directions) to hunt or to greet the heroes, whom he entertained with mead (dew). Each night Odin commissioned the heroes to go out as stars and sentinel Gladsheim, the castle where he held court. A company of dawn lights harassed the stars each morning until they were drawn into a fight. The wounds they suffered in this daily combat were healed by the Valkyries, and a banquet was prepared for them in the caldron Eldhrimnir (Earth) from the boar Saehrimnir (Darkness), which magically came back to life after each killing. Ivalde, great giant watchman of the Hvergelmir, ancient kettle at the base of the Yggdrasil Tree from which poured the river of souls, and father of the clan Waetla or Wate (Vate), source of the Anglo-Saxon title Waetlinga Straet. Of this clan, the twins Hyuki and Bil were abducted by the moon, where they aided minstrels and skiers who wandered about at night; Orvandel showed himself as the constellation Orion, and Thjasse as the star Sirius. The whole race of giants was related to the stars, and quite possibly in pre-Odin times they were worshiped in their own right as astral bodies. To the Anglo-Saxons, it also was the Way of Irmin or Iringe, deity of wisdom, who drove over the softly glowing track in a great bronze chariot, which he tied when it was not in use to the heaven pole (Polaris), and it was seen as the Little Wain.

In Brythonic legend it was

the castle of Gwydion or track made by Gwydion when he sought his son Llew Llaw. Llew Llaw, a sun deity, had as a mate the frivolous Blodeuwedd, whose soul was as fickle as the blossoms from which she had been created. She wormed out of her husband the secret of his vulnerability, and then betrayed him to her lover Gronw Pebyr, lord of darkness. Gronw Pebyr hurled his spear into Llew Llaw's groin, but only succeeded in wounding him. The injured hero transformed into an eagle and hid in a tree. Gwydion, king of fairies, eventually located his son, treated the poisoned laceration and magically restored him to his own shape. Whereupon Llew returned home and killed Gronw. This myth relates to the course of the year as well as the day. The eagle, bird that rises to the greatest height in flight is a natural insignia of the sun.

According to the Celts, the Galaxy was the chain by which Lug, the sky deity, pulled men up to heaven.

Medieval Christians adopted the idea of a bridge or pathway on which angels descended from and returned to the world above, or on which they stood as lights to show mortals the way to paradise. One name for it was Walsyngham Way, the path of Virgin Mary in heaven. Its counterpart on earth was to her shrine in Norfolk, where she was the Lady of Walsyngham. This association may have come from the impression that a road swarming with pilgrims resembled the highway dense with stars. In time it was commonly known as the duplicate of many roads, all of which led to especially

sacred shrines, and among the names attached to it were El Camino de Santiago, Road of Saint Jacques of Compostella, Saint Hilda's Street. One legend, derived either from that of Isis or from a similar tale told in the Near East, related that the chopped straw with which this heavenly thoroughfare for pilgrims was marked had been dropped by Saint Venere (Venus Christianized) after she had stolen it from Saint Peter, and as a result of this her Armenian title was Hartacol or Hartacogh, Straw-thief. In a Russian version the bridge to heaven is located at the end, wherever that may be, of the Milky Way and is guarded by four monks who flash swords and are ready to cut into pieces any mortal who attempts to cross it.

The lovers Zulamith and Salami, in Finnish folklore, built the bridge that they might be united in heaven as they were on earth. They were at their task a thousand years, but as soon as they had completed it, they flew into each other's arms and melted together into the single star Sirius. The Finns, as well as the Lithuanians, also knew it as the Birds' Lane, believing that spirits became winged and flew along it to the happy land.

Bushmen of Africa prized it as a band of ashes in which the flame was still alive, that travelers overtaken by night might see their way home.

Ganga, Hindu personification of abundance, had her bed close by the feet of Brahma in this milky stream. It overflowed and she was caught in the torrent. The force of her fall was so powerful, she was afraid the impact of her body would split earth into two. Seeing Siva near her, she reached for him and was caught up in the tangled masses of his hair. This broke the intensity of her plunge, and she was able to roll gently over the land. Since that time the holy water of the Ganges has been used for sacrifices, and ashes of the dead are cast into it for the journey to the otherworld. In early medieval times the Ganges stood for the far east as it was believed to flow on the eastern confines of the inhabited world.

In another account it was the channel over which Aryaman passed at night on the way to his throne in the east, where he appeared in his full glory each morning. The gods knew that in its inaccessible depths the elixir of life lay hidden and without it even they must die, so they tied two serpents, Sesa, who had a thousand heads (stars) and his companion, Vasuki, around Mount Mandara, which was the navel of the universe. The two snakes were wound together and used as a churning rope. While the gods held onto their heads, demons far below grasped the tails, and as the waters were agitated, poisons as well as the nectar of immortality and other beneficent things came to the surface.

Khotun, a Yakut goddess of birth, lived in a lake of milk under the Tree of Life. Her breasts were as large as leather sacks, and the plentousness of her milk was the origin of the Milky Way.

Everywhere its fascination was apparent. Those who related folktales in Mongolia and Tibet said it was a seam sewn by the eternal spirits to hold their terrain together. A different version was written in the sacred books, which said that an elephant stood in the ocean that encircles the world. Although its feet were firmly implanted in the mud at the bottom, his head rose above the water, and he breathed heavily. The steam of his breath rose into the air and, carried high by the wind into the cold currents, frosted and became the Milky Way. Sometimes the elephant grew restless and moved so that first he faced one way, then another. This caused his breath to rise irregularly, and the width of the heavenly zone varied from month to month. The Siamese also worshiped an elephant and called the ring the Road of the White Elephant. They saw it as the royal road the elephant followed across the sky.

To the Chinese it was the Silver River and, they said, when the New Moon appeared, because it was shaped like a hook, the fish became frightened and hid at the bottom. It was the source of the Yellow River, which was inconstant and uncontrollable, and frequently flooded entire provinces, carrying thousands of people to death. In Chinese belief, the regions above corresponded in every detail to those here on earth, except that they were without suffering, violence, and poverty. The River, which here made the lot of mankind difficult and unpredictable, had been contaminated by the soil of the Middle Kingdom, but beyond the horizon it was still pure and so remained clear and silvery. Its varying width and brilliance were signs of its frequent rise and fall.

A poor fisherman, who lived on the banks of the Yellow River, sailed its waters daily. One morning he was caught in a severe storm. His rudder became water-soaked and ceased to function, and for an interminable time he lay on the floor of his flat-bottomed boat, where he was continuously tossed from side to side, wondering how soon it would be before it capsized. He was only able to guess that he was being carried westward, upstream. When, at last, the wind and rain subsided he sat up and saw that the river was bordered by steep cliffs. Never before has he been in this part of the country, and he was about to turn around when the cliffs tapered off into pleasant meadows that were white with peach blossoms. In midstream there was a small island dotted with houses. He steered his boat toward it, and the inhabitants extended a cordial welcome. He was taken into a hut where his clothes were dried and he was given a bowl of rice and a cup of tea. When he asked the name of the place the villagers said they were strangers who had recently fled from their province to escape the persecutions of the emperor, and the fisherman was somewhat confounded when they mentioned a tyrant dead more than 500 years.

Once he was refreshed he started for home. At first the river was bordered by meadows covered with peach groves, then the bleak cliffs hid out the sunlight. All through the night he sailed downstream never passing another boat or hearing a mortal's voice. After several hours the palisades disappeared, and he was relieved to see a bright quarter moon. At dawn he saw before him the low mud huts of his native village. None of his neighbors was able to tell him anything about the province he had visited so he consulted the priest, who told him, "You have sailed on the Silver River and visited the land of immortals. Peach trees are abundant there. Had they been ripe, and had you tasted a single one, you would have remained on that island forever and you, as those you visited, would have no sense of the passing of time." One who sojourns in a divine world and tastes the food of the gods may not return to earth with impunity is a theme found universally in mythology. Those who eat such food are blessed with immortality.

The Japanese Shinto name for the Galaxy is Ama-no-kawa, Heaven's River. Tahitians regarded it a shark-infested creek. Polynesian islanders knew it as the Long Blue Cloud-eating Shark. Ottawa Indians saw in it muddy waters churned up by a turtle as he swims. Pawnee Indians said it was a cloud of dust kicked up by a buffalo and a horse in a race. Algonquins believed it was the Path of Souls leading to villages of the sun. The journey was difficult and tiresome, and the campfires of weary spirits appeared as bright stars. The Blackfeet tribe called it Makoye-osokay, Wolf Way. Cherokees tell a story of two hunters, one who lived in the north and hunted big game, and one who lived in the south and hunted

small game. The former became jealous of the latter because he never came back from
the hunt empty handed. One
day the man in the north perceived the other's wife grinding
corn into meal, and he carried
her away to his home. Her dog
ate the meal she had left behind
and then followed her, the
particles of food falling from
his mouth as he ran and forming a trail. The spell of the
southern captive caused weather
in the north to turn warmer and
warmer until all ice and snow
in the region melted and big
game disappeared. Neither could
the hunter endure the heat. Compelled to release his prisoner,
he permitted her to return home
with her dog. Once she was
gone weather in the north resumed its natural aspects. The woman and her pet found their way
back over the Galaxy, which the
dog had marked, and which was
called Giliustun stanunyi, Where
the dog ran. This is a seasonal
myth, the hunters personify
stars near the northern and
southern points of the Milky Way,
the dog and the woman, who is an
Indian version of Persephone,
represent other stars.

Tonacatecutli, Aztec all-
father, the male expression of
the infinite and self-created
deity, whose emblem was the
maize, had his abode on the
Milky Way. The Borros of
Brazil fancied it to be the scar
left by a great conflagration,
which had almost completely
destroyed the world, whereas
the Incas said it was a path over
which llamas roamed. In
Patagonia the natives say it is
the trail followed throughout the
night by their dead friends who
hunt for ostriches. At dawn
they hurry to warm themselves
at fires of the sun, to which they
stay so close they remain hidden until they set out again on
the hunt after sunset.

Galaxy, perhaps its most
fitting title, is from the Greek
Gala, Milk. Additional designa-
tions are: Ashen Path; Band;
Circle of the Galaxy; Crooked
Serpent; Galactic Circle;
Galaxure; The Lovely One,
perhaps a personification of the
Galaxy; Milky Way; Mylke Way;
Mylke Whyte Way; River of
Heaven; River-of-the Shepherd's
Hut; Dust-cloud High (from a
Euphratean title).

Accadian: Hiddagal, Great
River (in Genesis, Hiddekel);
Hid-In-ni-na, River-of-the-
Divine-Lady; Hid tsirra, Great
Serpent or Snake River; Hid
turra An gal, River-of-the-cord-
of-the-God Great; Hid-zuab gal,
River-of-the-Abyss Great.

Anglo-Saxon: Iringe's, or
Irmin's, Ueg (Wec, Weg),
Iringe's, or Irmin's,Way.
Waetlinga Straet (Vaelinga,
Vaetlinga, Watlingastrete), var-
iously known as Vatlant Street,
Wadlyn Street, Watling Street,
and Werlan Street.

Arabian: Al Majarrah, The
Milky Track, which appeared in
Italy as Almegiret. Al Nahr,
The River; Darb al Tabanin,
Path of the Chopped Straw Car-
riers; Tarik al Laban, Road of
Milk; Tarik al Tibn, Road of
Straw; Umm al Sama, Mother of
the Sky, whose legend of dropping
milk from her breast resembles
that of Hera.

Assyrian: Masarati (Masrati
or Maiarati), Course of the
Sun God, which may be the
source of the Phaethon story.

Nahru Apshi rabi, River-of-
the-Abyss Great; Nahru markasi
Ili rabi, River-of-the-cord-of-
the-God Great; Nahru tsiri,
River of the Snake.

Basque: Ceruco Esnibidia.

Celtic: Arianrhod (Arianrod),
Silver Circle or Road; Caer
Gwydion, Castle, or Seat, of
Gwydion.

Chinese: Tien Ho, Celestial
River. With the zodiac it
shared the name Hwang-Ho, Yellow River, probably from the
color of the scattered straw,
so often associated with it in
mythology.

Christian: Jakobs Strasse or
Weg, Jacob's Road; also
Jacob's Ladder. Jacob's Staff
is composed of the Belt of Orion
and lies alongside the road.
Walsyngham Way, Heavenly
Road of Virgin Mary. Way of
(or to) Saint James.

Coptic: Pimoit ende pitch,
Straw Road.

Dutch: Hilde or Hulde
Strasse, Saint Hilda or Hulda
Street; Vronelden Straet, the
Women's Street.

Ethiopian: Chasara tsaman-
gadu or Pasare Zamanegade, both
presumably attempts by Europeans
to transliterate a phrase meaning
Straw Stalks lying in the Road.

Finnish: Linnunrata, Bird's
Way, from the belief that
winged spirits fly over it to a
free and happy land or because
all bird-songs once joined and
turned into a cloud of snow-white
dovelets still seen overhead.

French: Voie lactee, Milky

Way.

French peasantry: Road of
Saint Jacques of Compostella.

Friesland: Harmswith, Harm's
Way; Melkpath.

German: Milch Strasse, Milk
Street.

Greek: Eridanus, the stream
of Ocean, also applied to a
constellation in the Southern Sky.
Galatea, the Milk White, offspring of Oceanus.

Hebrew: Aroch, Long Bandage;
Nehar di Nur, River of Light;
Nethibbath, and less correctly,
Nedhibath Tebhen, Straw Road.

Hindu: Akash Ganga, Bed of
the Ganges; Bhagwan ki Kachahri,
Court of God; Kshira, meaning
unknown; Nagavithi, Path of the
Snake; Path of Aryaman; Swarga
Duari, Dove of Paradise.

Hungarian: Hada Kuttya, Road
of War, since in journeys of
war and migration from Asia
their ancestors followed this
glistening path.

Italian: Strada di Roma, Way
of Rome, i.e. only through the
church's capital might access to
heaven be assured. Via Lattea,
Milky Way.

Jutland: Veierveien, or Brunel,
Straet.

Latin: Circulus Junonius,
Circle of Juno; Circulus lacteus,
Circle of Milk; Coeli Cingulum,
Heavenly Girdle; Fascia, Band;
Heroum Sedes, Hero's Heavenly
Sanctuary; Orbis lacteus, Orb
of Milk; Semita lactea, Milky
Footpath; Vestigium Solis,
Vestiges or Footsteps of the

Sun; Via coeli regia, Heavenly
Region Way; Via lactea, or
Lactis, Milky Way; Via perusta,
Burned Way; Zona perusta,
Girdle Burned.

Lithuanian: Paukszcziu Kielis.

Norse: Asgard Bridge,
Heaven's Bridge, indiscriminately
applied to the Milky Way and the
Rainbow. Bil-Idun's Wec (Way),
seems to have applied solely to
the Galaxy, Bil being a moon
goddess, Idun being her sister
and guardian of the fruit of immortality. Vetrarbraut, Winter
Street; Wuotanes Weg or Straza,
Woden's (Odin's) Way or Street.

Persian: Rah Kakeshan,
Straw Road.

Slovakian: Zesta v'Rim,
Way of Rome.

Spanish: El Camino de
Santiago, the patron saint of
Spaniards in battle.

Sumerian: River of Nana, a
moon and earth goddess, virgin
wife of Nabu, sun-god of the
autumn equinox, when days are
shortest. This may be the
source of the Hera myth in Greek
mythology.

Swedish: Winter Gatan,
Winter Street.

Swiss: Weg uf Rom, Way of
Rome.

Syrian: Arocea, Long
Bandage; Shebhil Tebhna, Straw
Road.

Turkish: Hagjiler Yuli,
Pilgrim's Road, corresponding
to the one traversed on their
annual trek to Mecca. Saman
Ughrisi, Straw Road.

Westphalian: Mulen Weg,
Milky Way; Wiar Strate, Weather
Street.

On and on we might go with
the title list, which seems to be
as endless as the alluring circle
itself, a circle mainly conceived
to be a promenade for ghosts,
a gallery or esplanade along
which were located the castles
of star-spirits where one might
find immortality and everlasting
contentment. In mythology death
invariably is coupled with life,
the deceased are reborn, light
deities alternately win in their
conflicts with deities of darkness, verdure and frost concede
to each in proper time. So
too, this misty magic ring of
the dead, like that of underworld
dwarfs, supplied a nourishing
drink. The Danes have a folk
saying that solves the mystery
of the moon's green cheese,
for they relate that the moon
was churned from the milk of
this mighty stream.

Within the tropics the Milky
Way has a rival, the Zodiacal
Light, a pillar or pyramid of
a dreamy, quiet beauty that can
be seen right after twilight on
clear evenings or just before
dawn on clear mornings. In
the northern hemisphere, the
months of February and March
are best for evening observations; the most favorable morning conditions prevail from
September to November. Little
is known about personifications
of the Light, and the few inscriptions that have been found
are confounded with those of the
Morning and Evening Stars. The
worship seems to trace back to
the Euphratean Valley. In
Phoenicia the twin sons of
Shamash, the sun, stood for
the two phases of this delicately

tinted glow. They were Sydyk (Sudus, Zedek), the early riser who left his bed in the darkness to greet his father in the east, and Misharu (Misor), who lingered for a while on the horizon before he followed his father into the west. The names originally meant straight, upright, erect, undoubtedly in a phallic sense, and were derived from the light's pyramid or pillar-like form. From these meanings the Hebrew's connoted the abstract conception of justice and equity now associated with the names. Sydyk, the mighty of dawn, was a victorious god of war, the prototype of the Syrian Azizos, who in turn was the forerunner of the Greek Ares. Misharu was the precursor of the Syrian Monimos and the Greek Hermes.

In Assyria and Babylonia the offices of Sydyk and Misharu were held by the double-sexed Ishtar, who was the daughter of Sin, the moon, and Shamash (or Ea), the sun, also androgynous deities, and with them she formed a trinity composed of parents and child. Mornings she was a war deity, evenings she persided over love and harlotry.

The twin pillars, Boaz, the waxer, and Jachin, the waner, in the porch of King Solomon's Temple, were phallic emblems of strength and beauty that operated as the gateway to eternity They probably typified these columns of Zodiacal Light. At Canaan, Shahru was a pillar of dawn, Shalmu a pillar of sunset.

Azizos (Azizu) and Arsu were the Palmyrene names, and these reappeared in the feminine forms Al Ussa (Al-Uzza) and

Ruda among Arabic angels. Azizos may be a literal translation of the Aramaic Attar or old Arabic Athtar, which is from the root Atara, meaning hard and strong as of a lance, instrument of war, given as the light's morning aspect, and hard, erect, as of a phallus or lover, given as the light's evening aspect. The root word also means power, stem, or stock, as of a tree, and the same root appears in the Hebrew asherah (grove), which answers symbolically to the tree of life or sacred pole of Asherah, a love goddess worshiped in orgiastic rites.

The Arabic Athtar was a male love and war deity, and obviously a later aspect of Ishtar (Ashtoreth) and Asherah. Strangely enough, Athtar appears in a triad with a sun goddess, Sham (from Shamash), and a Sabaean moon deity, Sin. Athtar, however is the father of Sin, whereas in Babylonian tradition the child is Ishtar, the love deity. In older inscriptions Athtar, the warrior, and Almaqa (Almakah), the harlot (the planet Venus), are always mentioned together. To assume that they are lovers is quite natural for they appear in in the sky close together in space and time, and mythologically the love goddess usually is the mistress of the war god. It follows the dual pattern, the contrast of love and hate. In Eastern Arabia, Athtar and Athtar Dhu Kabd, or Wadd and Nikrah, are the love and hate personalities. Another name for the harlot goddess is al-Zuhara, and she is linked with Bilqis, who is none other than Dhu-l-qarnain, the name of Athar in South Arabia.

Dhu-l-qarnain (Dhu'l Karnein) traversed the sky before sunrise and after sunset, moving from east to west to inspect heaven and earth. At the request of Allah, in one adventure in which he was said to be Alexander the Great who had taken up the Moslem cause, he built an impenetrable rampart of iron and brass between two mountains to hold predatory tribes imprisoned until resurrection day. He was described as a man who owned two horns, the meaning of which is vague. Horns on deities are said to indicate radiance (rays of the crescent moon or sun), wisdom (received from the light of god), protection, the warding off of evil, trophy of the hunt. The power and wealth, thus the dignity of primitive peoples, consisted principally of flocks and herds, and horns hung on a sacred altar designated social standing. Horns were sacred to Ashtoreth and appeared on carvings of Alexander, who as we have seen, was none other than Dhu-1-qarnain. Arabs were so devoted to this old heathen deity of confused sex, Mahomet dared not desert him, and smuggled him into Islam under the guise of a prophet and miracle doer or as an angel and viceregent of Allah.

If the Zodiacal Light rivaled the Milky Way in the torrid zone, it was rivaled by the Aurora Borealis in the frigid north and the Aurora Australis in the frigid south. In some sections of the world a great conflagration rather than a deluge by water destroyed life on earth. The conflagration was sometimes called water by fire, and a raft or ship was the rescue vessel. This idea may have been inspired by the fanlike waves of auroral displays, the primrose yellow and other tints in a translucent white.

Under the primrose yellow glow, lovers forget they are lovers.

The Norse revered the Aurora Borealis as movements of the Valkyrie. Among Esthonians it was a heavenly war, where those who died in battle on earth continued fighting each other. Finns said it was the fire of the Arctic Ocean which had become Rutja's (Turja's) Rapids, a river of the dead which swallows up all rivers, with the nature of a flaming vortex or maelstrom. To Russian-Lapps it was the spirits of the murdered, who were afraid of the sun but came out at night to stab one another until blood spilled. Northern Siberians declared it was the track of the White Horse on which the Earth-watching Man rode. Eskimos described it as a dance of the dead, the spirit of ancestors who disported in white raiment while the sun was away. Other Indians of both American continents believed the auroral lights were merry dancers, supernaturals who capered across the star-lit skies until they were frightened away by the dawn. Among Australian aborigines the Aurora Australis was the light of the camp fire of Cuchi, a demon who went forth at night as a bird or snake and caused sickness. Thunder was the growl of his anger, his breath was composed of whirlwinds.

VII

THE CONSTELLATIONS

Pax Dei

Chase and conquest
in the skies, so
the poets say,
are constant; but
to most mortals,
far from such fray,
the skies seem quite
a placid place.
A cloud may stray
into the blue,
a star may streak,
the moon delay
its glow, lightning
flash, thunder
roll; yet Pax Dei
comes down to those
who muse upon
the stellar way.

One theory has persisted, and that is: ever since the constellations first were conceived, even though original forms dating back to Sumer may have differed from the shapes now assigned to the names, one cluster of stars is continuously pursued by a neighbor, is overtaken and succumbs, but in time, because it is under divine protection, is resurrected to reengage in the chase. This concept is a duplication of the notion of death and rebirth attached to the sun, and in several instances constellations have been given the names of sun heroes, and actually imagined to be phases of the sun, or of one hostile to the sun. Most, if not all myths, have Euphratean prototypes, which in turn are allegories personifying the warfare of the seasons: summer vs. winter, light vs. darkness, dryness vs. rain. Quite naturally, the progression of the sun through the months of the year provided the chapters of a serial story, and the sky became the field or sea on which events took place that were told in six episodes or signs, Taurus, Cancer, Virgo, Scorpio, Capricorn, and Pisces, eventually divided because of the annual occurence of 12 moons in successive parts of the zodiac. In the course of time, the precession of the equinoxes, the breaking down of one constellation into two or more, additional discoveries, etc. distorted or disrupted initial episodes and an early continuity of certain incidents has been lost, but the supernaturals with their implements, vehicles, and animals continue to inhabit outer space. Nevertheless, some epics can be reconstructed by titles now used or those known once to have been attached to a group of stars. Thus we have a clue to the Argonaut adventures in stars that composed the ship Argo. Even where the plan of an epic may be lost, the element of strife predominates: Ophiuchus struggles with the serpent that tries to strangle him while he tramples on Scorprion, which in turn stings him; Bootes urges on his hunting dogs when in pursuit of the Great Bear; Hercules swings his club at the same time he crushes the Dragon's head with his foot; Lepus, the hapless hare, is stepped on by Orion, who also threatens the Bull. So we see, whether told in the form of epics or isolated incidents involving only two or three clusters, the appearance and disappearance of the constellations reaffirm the course of nature.

Anciently the Arabs called stars adjacent to a constellation Al H'arij min al Surah (Outside the Image), and Greeks referred to such stars as Unformed or Scattered. While each of the presently identified millions of stars is placed within some design, no unanimous agreement exists on precisely where the limits or boundaries of a cluster are to be placed and few look anything like the figures they supposedly portray. Modern astronomers do not concur on the exact number of arrangements to be acknowledged as constellations for a variety of reasons. To illustrate: in the 18th and 19th centuries some

scientists attempted to flatter their monarchs by attaching the ruler's names to groups of stars; other scientists ignored such designations and omitted them from their maps; or a cluster might have been called after a pet or favorite instrument, which seemed too sentimental to chart markers.

Arabs knew the constellations as Al Suwar (Figures); Greeks termed them Animals, Bodies, Figures, Semblances, Signs, Things in Heaven; Latin names included Astra (Stars), Constellatio (Star-studded), Decan (Ruler of Ten), Sidera (Starry), Signa (Sign), Stellatio (Set with Stars). Decan refers to a period in antiquity when the circle of the year was partitioned into thirty-six periods of approximately ten days each. To provide regents for each of these ten days the stars were alligned into thirty-six constellations, each extending about 10° and responsible for universal order during that period. This left about five day of the year which were intercalary, days that were godless and therefore unlucky.

By the 2nd century A.D., the skies had been recharted to show forty-eight constellations; today eighty-eight generally are recognized, and astrologers, too knowing to be discommoded by any scientific discovery, read in the conjunction of several of these divine ones in a given calendar period the course of human destiny.

What is known of the myths or fables, configurations, names in various parts of the world, astrological significance, location, culmination, and bright stars of constellations follows.

When the source of the present title is other than Latin, it is indicated.

ANDROMEDA (CHAINED LADY). Perhaps the earliest story ever told is that of Tiamat, a name which literally is bitter ocean. She was the Babylonian or Sumerian Great Mother, the chaos dragon who characterized the primordial waters from which all things sprang. Her first husband, Apsu, personified the nether sea of fresh waters. They became parents of deities, who provided the fertile aspects of nature, and demons, who spit out frost and drought. The parents, who thrived in the static dark, annoyed with the deity progeny who with consistent and constant movements caused light and seasonal changes, resolved to destroy them. In the conflict Apsu was castrated and overpowered by his son Ea, who then imprisoned him in a house (buried him in earth). Ea, afraid of his mother, retreated from her presence. She was not one given to mourning, and upon the loss of her husband, she became the spouse of her son Kingu, who shepherded her flocks (earthquakes, storms, volcanoes, etc.). Again she plotted against the deities, and in this provocation, her grandson, the sun-hero Marduk, son of Ea who had taken over the realm of fresh waters, agreed to slay her. The old woman was invulnerable as long as her mouth remained closed. Marduk solicited the aid of the winds, who held her mouth open while he sent an arrow (ray) through it to pierce her heart. Her blood formed the salt sea, half her body was used to make the firmament,

half to provide verdure on earth. In all likelihood it is not only the first story ever narrated, but the one most often repeated. In effect, throughout the ages, it has appeared in all parts of the world; its most popular version is that of the Greek myth Perseus and Andromeda.

Andromeda was the daughter of Cepheus and Cassiopeia, king and queen of Ethiopia. Cassiopeia boasted that her own and her daughter's beauty were greater than any ever seen, including that of Hera, celestial queen, and that of Atergatis, mermaid form of Artemis when one of the Nereids. The Nereids, favorites of Poseidon, lord of the waters, resented this, and to pacify the nymphs and punish Cassiopeia for her sacrilege, Poseidon sent the sea monster Cetus to ravage the land and devour the people. The alarmed Cepheus and Cassiopeia appealed to an oracle and were promised deliverance if the princess were offered to Cetus as a sacrifice, whereupon Andromeda was chained to a rock. Meanwhile, Perseus was sent by his stepfather on the hopeless task of obtaining the Medusa head. Aided by Athena and other deities, Perseus succeeded in slaying Medusa, queen of stormy darkness. When he cut off her head some of her blood fell and mingled with the foam of the sea. From the mixture a marvelous winged horse, Pegasus, sprang up. Perseus bridled the animal and set out for home. On his way he came upon the chained maiden. Her innocent fragile beauty touched him, and he went to her aid. Although blood spattered all about when he attached Cetus with his sword, the monster instead of becoming weaker seemed to grow stronger

and indeed was about to devour
Perseus as well as Andromeda.
Desperate, the hero displayed
the hideous snake-crowned Medusa head and Cetus paralyzed
and turned into stone. Perseus
married the lovely princess and
set the fairy-tale fashion for
the hero who marries the
maiden in distress. Proud
Persian kings are said to have
claimed descent from Perses, the
first born son of Perseus and
Andromeda. In this version of
the myth, Cetus plays the role
of Tiamat, Perseus that of
Marduk. The combat, in which
the fertility-giving sun-hero
vanquishes darkness and decay
or drought, is endless, and
must be fought each day as well
as each season. The maiden
usually is dawn, snatched from
the clutches of darkness, or
spring growth, rescued from a
cold underworld prison.

In a Japanese version,
Kushi-nada-hime, the rice
goddess, is rescued by Susa-no-
wo, sea-lord, as she is about
to be snatched by the eight-
headed dragon Koshi (tides),
to whom seven of her sisters
already had been sacrificed.
The dragon demanded one each
year. Susa-no-wo transformed
her into a comb which he wore
in his hair until he killed the
dragon by putting all its heads
to sleep with an intoxicating
brew. Her name signifies
Princess-Comb-Ricefield. In
the dragon's tail, Susa-no-wo
found the magic sword Kusanagi
(rays-upon-water). Similar legendary battles were fought by
the Algonquin Michabo and Kabun,
the Christian Saint George and
the Dragon, Egyptian Horus and
Set, Hindu Krishna and Kamsa.

The fable's antiquity is borne

out by a Chaldean designation for
this configuration, Chained Maiden.
Its origin may have been a
ritualistic statement inspired by
spring floods which swept across
the plains and finally were dis-
persed by sun and winds which
left calm seas, clear skies, and
a flowering land. It may also
have reflected primitive life in
which brutal sea-faring men were
prevented from abducting maidens
on the land by stronger rivals
on the shore.

Some interesting sidelights
may help to verify that land-sea
elements played leading parts in
the drama. To ancient Hebrews
and Phoenicians a city or country
was the daughter of the rocks,
deserts, rivers, or mountains
that surrounded her or that were
enclosed within her walls.
Jerusalem, as an example, was
known as the daughter of Zion
(Sion), thus she was the daughter
of arid, barren hills. Cepha
signifies stone; Andromeda is
related to a Phoenician word meaning long chain or ridge; hence
the long sometimes flat and sandy,
sometimes rocky, coast of Palestine is veritably the daughter of
Cepheus. Also, the Phoenicians
were great maritime people and
on the stern of their barks
frequently painted as a talisman
the figure of a winged horse to
lift them over the waves. In
this way their ships appeared as
horses magically rising from the
sea. On some they showed a
horseman who carried something
that looked like a Medusa head,
and which may have been the
arms of the city of Sais on the
Nile. In the vulgar Phoenician
tongue a bark was called
Perseus, which meant runner or
horseman, in which case Andromeda (a coastal town of Palestine
or Syria) was saved, not by men

on shore, but by the riders of
a winged horse who came from
the sea (Phoenician bark), to
whom the goddess of Sais had
given the hideous Medusa head,
that they might turn their
enemies into stone with terror.
In this manner we see how
myth and history blended.

Configurations: On Classical sky atlases illustrated as a
beautiful maiden with her arms
extended and chained at wrists
and ankles to rocks, with
Cetus, the whale or sea
monster, about to destroy her.
A Phoenician sphere displayed
a Threshing Floor, with some
stars of the nearby Cassiopeia
as the Gleaners in a large
Wheat Field. Thus is borne
out the idea that this was a
section of land contiguous to a
celestial sea in which a sea-
monster (Pisces) swam.

Andromeda is a Greek name.
Additional designations are;
Boast of Cassiopeia, Chaining,
Daughter of Cepheus and Cass-
iopeia, Woman with the girdle.

Arabian: Alarmalah (the
Widow); Al Mar'ah al Musalsalah. Pictured as a sea-calf
or seal with a chain around its
neck that unites it to one of the
fish in Pisces. A drawing of
the human figure is prohibited
by the Koran.

Euphratean: Ama (The
Pregnant).

Hindu: Antamarda, a variation of the classical name.

Medieval: Andromada or
Anroneda, erroneous forms of
the classical name. Asnade or
Ansnade, from the Latin translation of an Arabic text.

Cepheis, from her father. Mulier
Catenata (Woman Chained).
Persea, as bride of Perseus.
Some medieval biblical scholars
called some of its stars: Abigail,
of the Book of Samuel; Holy
Sepulchre; Schachar (Morning
Red), bride of Bar-Sav (Solar
Hero); Sepulchrum Christi (the
new sepulchre in which no man
has yet been laid).

Astrologically it portends
honors and riches. It is located
in the northern skies south-east
of Cassiopeia, between Perseus
and Pegasus, and north of
Pisces. It rises early in
autumn in the eastern sky and
culminates about November 23rd.
Bright stars are: Alpheratz,
alpha; Merach, beta; Almach,
gamma.

ANTLIA PNEUMATICA (THE
PUMP). An unimportant constellation in the southern sky between
Hydra and Vela, discovered in
the mid 18th century. Its name,
which means air pump, reflects
one of the idiosyncrasies of its
founder. No fable has been attached to it, and it is without a
star bright enough to be identified
on any chart. Its culmination
is about April 10th. Antila, or
Antila Pneumatica, comes from
the Latin, and additional designations are: Air Pump, the German Luft Pumpe, and the low
Latin Machina Pneumatica or
Machine Pneumatique.

APUS (BIRD OF PARADISE). An
inconspicuous cluster, probably first
seen in the 16th century by sea-faring men in the southern sky. It lies
below the Triangulum Australe,
about 13⁰ from the Pole. In ancient
Greek the meaning of Apus was without feet and applied to the swallow.
In modern Latin the title means
Bird of Paradise. Originally it was
called Avis Indica referring to a

species obtained in the East Indies which lacked feet. Other designations are: House Swallow; Chinese E Cho (Curious Sparrow), French: Oiseau de Paradis; German: Indianischer Vogel, Paradies Vogel; Italian: Uccello Paradiso; Latin and Low Latin: Apous, Apus Indica, Avis (Bird), Paradisaeus Ales. It culminates about July 5th.

AQUARIUS (WATER BEARER) Located in the heart of one of the great celestial seas, it has been from earliest times a natural sign of the rainy season and identified with Ea, who had castrated his father Apsu and took from him his abode, the fresh waters. A capricious deity, Ea was at once the source of death-dealing floods and fertilizing rains. When his more powerful brother, Bel, lord of light, decreed a deluge was to destroy all people because they had failed in virtue, that is failed to make proper sacrifices to the gods, Ea, who helped create the human race, warned Pir-na-pishtim, who saved his family, his field laborers, his servants, and a seed of every kind of life. For the role of protective angel he was given the title karubu, borrowed by the Hebrews as kerub (cherub). A fertility god in snake form, he became the serpent in the Adam legend. Ea was the special god of Eridu, the main seat of his worship. The town was a flourishing seaport on the Persian Gulf until silt carried by the Tigris and Euphrates left it stranded inland. Some chief or leader from the coast drifted north in prehistoric times, leaving whereever he stopped a knowledge of law, science, construction, and other arts of civilization. His

history became blended with that of the god's, and in this way Ea became credited with being a culture hero with a human head and sturdy legs and feet, or as a merman, one who came out of the sea to utter words of wisdom. His forms were interchangeable and his habit was to spend the daylight hours on land and to retire at dusk into the water. This belief, like that mentioned under Andromeda, may have related to men who traveled the seas in small craft and startled shore dwellers, who saw them as half fish.

Babylonians had no favorable opinion of these stars, which they called the Curse of Rain, and identified with Kulilu, a destructive fish-man created by Tiamat. During this month, a torrent aided by hurricanes left the world desolate. Gilgamesh, the sun, was vanquished by Enkidu, the wind. Weeks later, Enkidu calmed down and he and Gilgamesh became friends, wandering over the universe together. When Enkidu was slain, Gilgamesh became disconsolate. He visited Utnapishtim (Pir-na-pishtim) in the world of immortality to discover how to rescue his friend, but his heroism simply brought about his own death. If Gilgamesh had not been resurrected, the world would have remained in darkness. Soon after the rebirth of Gilgamesh, Enkidu was revived, and, once again among the dim stars of Aquarius, the drama of the year was reenacted. This season was the most dismal in the Euphratean Valley. Days had a penetrating dampness, the sun had barely enough strength to lift itself from the sea. Monsters of Tiamat's realm controlled the world. Oannes sometimes is identified with these stars, sometimes with Capricorn.

In Egypt the Nile overran the land, but this was welcomed as a blessing. The soil, arid and cracked, sucked in the waters sent by Khnemu, the divine potter, who caused the river to overflow when, to fill his huge bucket, he dipped it into the stream.

Among the Greeks, in the era that this constellation marked the winter solstice, it was a symbol of Zeus, creator who poured out the waters that fertilized seeds deep in earth. When the solstice passed into Capricorn, the figure seemed less important and was identified as Ganymede, cup-bearer to the god. In another account these stars outline the figure of Deucalion, king of Thessaly, who with his wife Pyrrha (fire) composed the only human pair to survive a terrible nine-day flood sent by Zeus. The couple lived in an ark which grounded on Mount Parnassus. After the rains they found themselves a-lone on a depopulated and barren earth. All that remained with them on the mountain crest was a temple. There they consulted an oracle, who instructed them to cast the bones of their mother behind them. Perplexed, they pondered on how to obey this order, until Deucalion inter-preted "mother" to mean mother Earth, and bones to mean stones. The stones he cast turned into men; those Pyrrha cast turned into women. His name means sweet wine, and he is said to have planted the vine and to have become its deity. He was placed in the realm above surrounded by flood waters as he had been on earth.

Varuna, bestower of rains, was the Hindu patron of these stars. A ruler of the west, he owned refreshment-yielding kine (clouds). His consorts were the river goddesses Ganges and Jumna. Astride the sea-monster Makara (Capricorn) he rode across the heavens holding a vessel of gems (fertility) in one hand and in the other a noose with which to ensnare non-believers.

In China, with Pisces and Capricorn, and some stars of Sagittarius, it constituted an early serpent or tortoise, T'ien Yuen. Later, as the tortoise Kuei Shen, the Somber Warrior or darkly flourishing one who was third in rank of the four benevolent creatures, he guarded the north, presided over the destiny of the Chinese empire, and was consulted in divination. He was a symbolic representa-tion of Emperor Tchoun Hin, in whose reign a great deluge occurred. These stars contained three Hsiu, and in pre-Jesuit days headed the solar zodiac as the Rat, a far Eastern ideograph for water.

Configurations: Generally shown as a man pouring water from an urn, as a water-pot, or as a jug from which water runs into the mouth of the Southern Fish or unites with the river Eridanus. Other presentations are those of a measuring rod in the hand of a figure known as Norma Nilotica, to suggest the ancient Nilometer, or of doves over water, which relates to the deluge myth. In rare in-stances it has been figured as an oven. Arabs adopted a water jug or a mule saddled with two bags of water. In their faith, human images are tabu; at Judgment Day anyone so brought into being might rise up and claim the soul of such a creator. In Egypt the giant water-carrier Khnemu dipped his huge jug into a stream, probably the Nile, adored as the life-giving waters of earth. A Roman zodiac's illustration is a peacock, emblem of Juno in whose month, January-February, the sun was in the sign. At times, the goose, also sacred to the queen of heaven, was used instead of the peacock. S symbol for water, 〰〰, is the pictorial emblem of the zodiacal Aquarius.

Additional designations: Aquary, Aquarye, Butler of the Gods, Skinker (a tapster or one who pours out liquor), Stream, Water, Waterman, Water Pourer.

Accadian: Imma, a pourer of water from a jug; Ku-ur-ku (Seat of Flowing Waters); Ramman or Rammanu, storm god. Another name had the significance of Lord of Canals.

Anglo-Saxon: Waeter-gyt (Water Pourer).

Arabic: Al Dalw (Well-bucket), which degenerated in the middle ages into Edeleu; Al Sa'd al Ahbiyah (Felicity of the Tents); Al Sakib al Ma' (Water Pourer), which in Europe contracted into Eldelis.

Babylonian: Gu (an over-flowing water jar).

Chinese: Hiuen Heaou, Hiuen Wu, Hiuen Ying, Hiuen Mao, all renderings of Kuei Shen. Paou Ping (Precious Vase), a name given after Jesuit influence.

Ceos: Aristaeus, who brought forth rain.

Christian: John the Baptist; Judas Thaddaeus; Moses taken out of the Nile; Naaman healed in the waters of the Jordan.

Egyptian: Hapi, Khnemu (Khnum), both water gods. Monius from muau or mw (water).

Euphratean: Khumba or Kumbaba (Coumbun), which is similar to the Elamite Humbaba, a merciless storm demon who roamed in the cedar forests of Lebanon.

French: le Verseau.

German: der Wassermann.

Greek: Deucalion, Ganymede, Zeus.

Hebrew: Deli or Delle (jar).

Hindu: Hridroga and Udruvaga were names given to it under Greek influence.

Italian: il Aquario.

Latin and Low Latin: Aequoreus Juvenis; Amphora; Aqua; Aquitenens; Diota or Dolium (jar with a neck and two handles); Effusio Aquae; Effusor; Fluvius Aquarii, Frigidus; Fundens latices; Fusor aquae; Ganymede Juvenis; Ganymedes, the Phrygian; Hauritor aquae; Hermidone, a name for the stream flowing toward Pisces; Hydridurus; Hydrochous; Idrudurus; Iliacus; Juonis astrum (Juno's star); Juvenis gerens aquam (frequent allusions make Jove the water pourer); Puer Idaeus; Situla (Well-bucket); Tyrannus aquae.

Persian: Dol or Dul (jar);

Vahik.

Syrian: Daulo (jar).

Tamilian: Kumbha (Watering
Pot); Tai.

Turkish: Kugha (jar).

Astrologically a masculine
sign, therefore fortunate. Astrologers included it with Gemini
and Libra to compose their configuration called Airy Trigon,
which possessed the virtue and
efficacy to alter the air and
seasons. An almanac of 1386
said it governered a period in
which "it is gode to byg caltel-
lis and to wed, and lat blode."
When Saturn is here he has
man completely in his clutches
because he controls man's
head and neck, whereas when
Jupiter is here he only controls
man's shoulders, breast, and
legs. Uranus, its natural
guardian, provides altruism.

A major portion lies south
of the ecliptic, west of Pisces
and east of Capricorn. The sun
enters it about February 14 and
stays until the middle of March.
It culminates about October 9.
Meteors are visible in its
boundaries from April 29 to
May 2. Bright stars are:
alpha, Sadalmelik; beta, Sadalsuud; delta, Skat.

AQUILA (EAGLE) The Soar-
ing or Flying Eagle as opposed
to Vega, a star in Lyra, which
Arabians knew as Falling or
Swooping Eagle. This bird was
the pet of Zeus, stood near his
throne, and bore his thunderbolt, a feat which aided the sky
lord in his struggle with the Titans to establish his supremacy.
Manilius, a Roman poet, in his
admiration for this feathered

giant, wrote:

The towering Eagle next doth
    boldly soar,
As if the thunder in his claws
    he bore:
He's worthy Jove, since he,
    a bird, supplies
The heavens with sacred bolts,
    and arms the skies.

Zeus, struck by the wondrous
beauty of Ganymede, son of Tros,
king of Troy, gave Tros six fine
horses in exchange for the youth
he wished to make his cup-
bearer, and sent the Eagle to
carry Ganymede up to his place
in heaven, whereafter as the
constellation now known as
Aquarius he served the god. The
ambrosia Ganymede poured was
the morning dew. Earlier, the
Eagle had brought nectar for the
nourishment of Zeus when his
mother Rhea (Earth) hid him in
a cave on Mount Ida to protect
him from his father Cronus (Time)
who had devoured his other
children.

The Greek Eagle resembles
one in the Rig-Veda, in which the
eagle Gayatri rushed to the Vase
or Urn (Aquarius) for Soma
(fertilizing waters) and was shot
at by the archer Krsanu. The
arrow knocked off a feather
(lightning), which broke through
the clouds and water poured over
the earth. The three bright stars
that compose the Shaft of Altair,
or shaft of its lucida, symbolize
the three gigantic footsteps which
the god Vishnu takes as he strides
across heaven. The first takes
him to the far bounds of the
eastern horizon from which he
(sun) rises; with the second he
reaches the zenith of high noon;
the third brings him down again
to the horizon in the west.

Roman poets sang of Merops (Bee-Eater), king of the island of Cos, whom Juno favored and transformed into this eagle to be placed among the stars. In another version the King is Cepheus of Ethiopia, who also is identified with a constellation close by the North Pole and bearing his name. A more piquant story is told of Antinous, beloved of Emperor Hadrian. In an act of self sacrifice that his master's life might be prolonged after an oracle at Bezza had asserted that only by the death of the one most loved by the emperor might greater danger to the ruler be averted, Antinous drowned himself in the Nile. Hadrian's grief was so great he had a temple erected in Arcadia to his favorite's memory, and on the eastern banks of the Nile founded the city Antinoopolis. The gods sent the Eagle to lift up to heaven this youth so greatly honored. At one time the southern stars, those directly below the Shaft of Altair composed a separate constellation, Antinous, but on modern globes all this group represents either both figures or the bird alone, in which case Antinous is associated with Aquarius.

Among Australians, a hero named Totyarguil, while bathing, was killed by an evil water sprite and translated to the stars.

Throughout the ages these stars have been recognized as a bird of the winds, thus a bird of prey, most often as an eagle, sometimes as a falcon or vulture flying up from the south along the banks of the river Milky Way with one wing shadowing the stream. This is the only bird in the sky that had wings strong enough to carry him the long distance to the realm of the stars. Other birds or fowls had to be raised or lifted into place by the gods.

The section of the sky in which this constellation appears is just above the region known as the Celestial Sea. It holds three birds, Aquila, Vega (Falling Eagle), and Cygnus (Swan). The idea has been presented that the birds represent the Stymphalian Birds which Heracles (Hercules) slays as his fifth labor Its adjoining constellation is Serpens, an enemy, and this exemplifies the age-old theme related to the Cosmic Tree, which has a bird in the upper branches in conflict with a snake or dragon at the roots for mastery of the seasons.

Configurations: A solitary bird flying eastward across the Milky Way. This, presumably, is the same bird that appears on a uranographic stone dated 1,200 B.C. and said to be Idxu Zamama or Zu. An eagle with a bow and arrow, with an arrow, or with a youth in its talons. Arabs portrayed with outspread wings.

Additional designations: Altair, from the name of its lucida; The Bird; Brandenburg Eagle, in which Dolphin was included (a 17th century title); The Eagle; Flying Eagle or Vulture; Military Eagle of Rome; Soaring Eagle.

Arabic: Al Ghurab (The Crow or Raven); Al 'Okab (The Black Eagle); Al Thalimain (The Two Ostriches) for those stars which once composed the constellation Antinous; Al Mizan (The

Scale Beam) for others of the stars; Al Nasr al Tair (The Flying Eagle) for those stars which compose the Shaft of Altair.

Assyro-Babylonian: Alallu, bird of the sun-hero Gilgamesh, which daily is pursued by the moon-goddess Ishtar; Alula, worshiped as a form of the noon sun; Idzu Zamama (Eagle or Living Eye), a form of the solar deity Ninurta who slays a chaos dragon; Zu, a storm eagle slain by Ninurta, who then took the bird's rapacious claws to be his emblem. Because of these claws, variously identified in ancient zodiacs with the crab (chaos principle) or with Scorpio (evil principle). Zu is specifically described as a personification of summer sand storms, the sun as a deadly searing agent.

Chinese: Draught Oxen. The three bright stars are the Cowherd for whom the Magpie's Bridge gave access to the Spinning Maid (Lyra) across the River of the Sky (Milky Way). See Altair.

Christian: Eagle of Saint John; Saint Catherine the Martyr; Standard of Rome; Wounded Prince (Christ).

English, Old: Flying Grype, to whom astrologers acribed mighty virtues.

French: Aigle

German: Adler; Adler mit dem Antinous.

Greek: Bird of Zeus; King of Birds; Torturer, a reference to the eagle which gnawed the liver of Prometheus.

Hebrew: Neshr (Eagle, Falcon, or Vulture); Son of the Shunammite.

Italian: Aquila.

Latin: Aquila Antinous; Aquila cum Antinoo; Aquila Promethei (Bird which preyed on the liver of Prometheus); Aquila vel Antinous; Ganymedes Raptrix (attender of Jove); Jovis Ales (Jove's Bird); Jovis Armiger Ales (Jove's Armor-bearing Bird); Jovis Nutrix (Jove's Nurse); Merops; Pincerna, Polcellator (Cup Bearer); Servans Antinoun (Servant Antinous); Tortor Prometheir; Vultur volans.

Persian Shahin tara zed (Plundering Falcon).

Turkish: Taushaugjil (Hunting Eagle) for the three bright stars.

Location: It is situated on the opposite side of the sky from the Belt of Orion, which is seen in winter. This constellation is prominent in summer and early autumn, and its distinguishing feature, the line composed of three of its bright stars which is called Shaft of Altair, inexperienced star gazers sometimes confuse with those of Orion's Belt. The Orion trio is first seen in the east in mid-October while the Shaft or last of Aquila sets. The Greek fable of the eagle attacking the swan but defeated by it is exemplified by Aquila, which rises in the east immediately after Cygnus, but when setting in the west goes down before the more northerly constellation. A similar conflict takes place with Delphinus, as Aquila is southwest of the dolphin. Another neighbor and enemy is Serpens.

Culmination is about August 30, and among its bright stars are: alpha, Altair; beta, Alshain; gamma, Tarazed.

ARA. (THE ALTAR) In classical times some conceived this to be Tartarus, the abyss into which Zeus had hurled the Titans he had vanquished, and where they caused disturbances, earthquakes, volcanoes, or other upheavels. Their overthrow by Zeus symbolizes one season supplanting another. Others thought it was the celestial counterpart of the altar on which the votive plant was burned, or the one placed in the sky after the war with the Titans when it was needed by the deities for their mutual vows.

In biblical lore it was said to be the altar built by Noah after the Deluge; one erected by Moses; or the permanent golden altar in the Temple at Jerusalem.

Illustrated as an altar; a tripod censer with burning incense; an altar from which flames ascended with demons on either side; an altar which sent off flames and smoke that drifted northwards through the Milky Way; or the Milky Way was conceived to be the flames and smoke that rose from the altar. It also was shown to be an enormous pit from which devils thrust humans into the abyss. This last is probably a Christianized version of the story in which Zeus imprisoned the giants he had defeated. In medieval times the altar had been turned so that it now appears in an inverted position on sky maps, which is appropriate for a southern constellation.

Additional designations: Altar; Censer; Perfuming Pot; Pharus, which refers to the fact that altars once were placed on summits or temple towers to serve as lighthouses, of which the one of marble at Pharos near Alexander was the most famous example.

Accadian: Tul-ku (Holy Altar or Illustrious Mound). This may have been formed by other stars.

Arabian: Al Mijmarah (A Censer), from which came the medieval European terms Almegramith and Almugamra.

Chinese: Choo (Club or Staff) for the alpha star; Low (Trailing) for alpha, beta, gamma, and iota; Tseen O (Sky's Ridge) for iota; Tseen Yin (Dark Sky) for delta and zeta; Tso Kang (Light Watch) for epsilon.

Egyptian: Cynocephalus (Baboon).

French: Autel (Altar), Encensoir (Incense Burner).

German: Altar.

Greek: Thymele (Sacrifice, referring to the offering placed on the altar of Bacchus or Dionysus).

Italian: Altare.

Latin and Low Latin: Acerra (small altar on which perfumes were burned before the dead). Altarium; Apta Altaria; Ara Centauri (Altar of Centaurus); Ara Thymiamatis (altar on which the sacrifice of incense was burned); Arula; Batillus (an incense burner); Focus, Ignitabulum, Lar (all meaning hearth); Mundi Templum (Temple of the World) Prunarum Conceptaculum (a brazier); Puteus (Pit or Well); Sacrarium (Sacred Place); Sacris; Templum (Temple); Thuribulum (Censer) or Turibulum; Vesta (goddess of the hearth).

Early star gazers used it to predict wind and weather changes. Located in the Southern Sky below Scorpius, east of Norma, Lupus and Centaurus, west of Corona Australis. Before Norma was formed it may have been with Lupus a part of Centaurus. July 25 is its culmination date. Its bright stars are unnamed.

ARGO (JASON'S SHIP) Built by Glaucus or Tiphys (dawn or spring), the ship's helmsman, or by a shipbuilder Argus (the bright one) for Jason's expedition to obtain the Golden Fleece, the acquisition of which was to be the culminating episode in the vicissitudes of a branch of the Aeolos family. Athamas, son of Aeolos, was the father of Phryxus and Helle, whose jealous stepmother Ino plotted their death. As Athamas was about to sacrifice Phryxus to Zeus, the children's mother Nephele and the divorced wife of Athamas, let loose a ram with golden fleece (sun-lit cloud), which lifted Phryxus and Helle, who had jumped onto its back, into the air. Helle fell into the sea and was drowned, by Phryxus was borne to Colchis, where the ram was sacrificed to Zeus (sky) and its fleece hung on an oak (sacred tree), where it was guarded by dragons until seized by Jason. Jason was a solar hero; his fifty companions were rays, winds, and other attendants of the sun, each of which worked one of the ship's oars. The journey, usually portrayed in two series of twelve

adventures, one covering the outbound voyage, the other the return voyage, relates to the transit of the sun through the year or zodiacal houses. The ship was a magic one, endowed by Pallas Athena with the power of speech and a gift of prophecy as well as an understanding of the thoughts of all aborad. It needed no man to steer it and refused to descend into the water at the time of the expedition until charmed by the lyre of Orpheus (voice of the wind). Like the Ark, the vessel that had been supplied to Odysseus by Alcinous, and other sacred craft, it was symbolic of the nourishing forces of nature and contained the germ of all living things; thus the Argonauts returned from their adventure with renewed vigor, i.e. went through the year to return reenergized in spring. In another version it was built for Heracles or for Danaus who, long before Jason's time, was king of Argos. Danaus had fifty daughters, with whom he fled from his brother Aegyptus, conqueror of Egypt, to Rhodes. The full-rigged boat moved along the horizon from east to west, blown by the wind until it reached its destination safely. After its passengers disembarked, it drifted out to sea and passed out of sight.

A boat appears on a small Phoenician zodiacal bronze, which leads to the conclusion that the constellation was a very ancient one. Prototypes and correspondents of the Argo were the bark that bore the Egyptian Osiris and Isis over a Deluge; the Ark in which Noah, his family, and all kinds of things sailed; the ship constructed by Manu in accordance with instructions from Vishnu, who in fish form, when the flood

came, towed it until it rested
safcly on Mount Himalaya. In
another Hindu tradition, Isi and
Iswara (Isvara) were saved on
the ship Argha (Yoni) steered
by Agastya (drought), the star
Canopus. The source of the
name may have been the Sanscrit Argha or the Hebrew Arek
(Ark), used by Phoenicians to
mean long. The consecrated
ship in almost all accounts is famous as the first that ever took
a long journey or ventured out
to sea. Modern phantom or
spectral vessels, such as
Carmilhan and Flying Dutchman
owe their introduction to these
ancient craft.

In art generally depicted
without a prow, which is said
to have been lost when it passed
through the Bosphorous between
floating rocks.

Additional designations are:
Argo Navis; Jason's Ship;
The Ship.

Arabian: Al Safinah (A
Ship), translated by Europeans
as Alsephina; Markab, a vehicle
of some sort, which Europeans
transcribed into Markeb.

Chinese: Tien Meaou,
probably for some components
of the greater constellation.

French: Navire Argo.

German: Schiff.

Hindu: Sata Vaesa (One
Hundred Creators).

Italian: Nave Argo.

Latin: Argoa Puppis;
Argolica Navis; Argolica Puppis;
Argo Ratis; Carina Argoa;
Celox Jasonis; Currus Maris

(Sea Chariot); Currus Volitans;
Equus Neptunius (Neptune's
Horse); Iasonia Carina; Navigium
Praedatorium (Pirate Ship);
Navis; Navis Jasonis; Osiridis;
Pagasaea Carina; Pagasaea
Puppis (from the Thessalian sea-
port where it supposedly was
built); Ratis Heroum (Hero's
Raft); Vehiculum Lunae (Luna
Vessel).

Medieval biblical scholars
called it Arca Noachi; Archa
Noae; Noah's Ark.

For convenience, modern
astronomers have divided it into
four parts: Carina, the Keel;
Puppis, the Stern; Pyxis, the
Compass; Vela (the German
Segel), the Sail. An earlier
subdivision consisted of: Lochium
Funis (Logleine), Log and Line;
Malus, the Mast; Pyxis Nautica
(Sea Compass), Nautical Box or
Mariner's Compass, which the
French called Boussole or
Compas de Mer and the Italians
called Bussola. Before it was
abandoned, Argo spread over a
great portion of the expanse of
the Southern Sky, largely in the
Milky Way, west of Centaurus,
east of Columba and Canis Major.
It sailed along the horizon, its
full rigs blown before the wind.
The stars rose no great distance
from where the sky met land or
sea and kept fairly level until
they disappeared like a ship on
an even keel. Every night that
they were visible they followed
the same course, moving at great
speed from east to west, following
a channel that brought them back
through the invisible realms below the horizon so that they might
begin their journey at the proper
place the next evening.

The center of this greater
cluster culminates about March

1, the section furthese east,
Vela, culminates about March
30. Its brightest star is Canopus, located in the section known
as Carina.

ARIES (THE RAM). Con-
stellation often said to symbolize
the Lamb of the World. The
sign is believed to have originated
in Chaldea, where the ram may
simply have donated an animal
cared for the shepherds; or it
may have been a deity emblem.
Robert Brown, Jr. contends that
the alpha star was adored as
The Ram and the constellation
later formed around it. Located
in a section of the heavens which
has remained inconspicuous
and contains only three notable
stars, the constellation has
enjoyed a reputation out of all
proportion to its brilliance.
This may be due to the fact
that about eight or nine thousand
years ago it coincided with the
position of the sun at the winter
solstice. Mortals, who then
worshiped the stars as vital
to their existence, believed
those located along the ecliptic,
or organized into zodiacal constellations, kept the sun, which
was compared to a ram, bull,
or ox, on its course. Prayers
and sacrifices were offered that
the sun might be released from
this section of the sky which
held him in mid-winter that
frost might be destroyed and
warmth brought back into the
world. One Babylonian priest
related the world had been
created when the sun was in
Aries, in other words, at the
winter solstice, a period which
marks the festival of rebirth in
countless parts of the world.
Due to the precession of the
equinoxes the dominant status
of the Ram was affected and
for centuries the constellation

was hardly noticed. About 2,450
B.C. it became the home of the
spring equinox, where the sun
marks the opening of the year.
Once again Aries was honored.
Lubat, the Old Sheep, within its
gates marked a period for
rejoicing, and the stars themselves became the "Leader of
the Host of the Zodiac," the
bell-wether of the starry-flock,
although the shape of the constellation has not the remotest
resemblance to a four-footed
animal, a fact which confirms
the suspicion that the names
anciently given to stars were
purely symbolic. At the New
Year's feast, Babylonians
sacrificed a ram in expiation of
the sins of the nation. Some
astronomers hold that Aries had
been mapped out when the spring
equinox fell in the middle of
the constellation Taurus, in which
case we might parody words on
March and apply them to the
behavior of the sun during the
course of the year, namely: "In
like a bull, out like a lamb."

Early Egyptian calendars made
no reference to Aries, but a ram
appeared in the Theban triad and
Amen-Ra, the supreme deity,
was portrayed with a ram's head
when represented as a god of
reproduction, and the avenue
which leads to his great temple
is through two lines of huge ram-
headed sphinxes. Statues of the
ram-headed Amen were carried
in a procession when Aries
dominated the ecliptic. About
1,250 B.C., when Rameses II
dedicated a temple on the left
bank of the Nile, and the sun,
which penetrated into the temple's
shrine, was in conjunction with
the first stars of Aries, a ram was
crowned with flowers, and Egyptians called the constellation Lord
of the Head. Another form of the

ram god was Amen-Khnum,
personification of the vast unknown darkness transcending all
intellectual perception, from
whose mouth emerged the
perfect serpent, Ptah, lord of
truth. This might seem to
connect Aries with the winter
solstice. A later myth, which
brings the constellation back
into conjunction with the vernal
equinox, is that related about
the Bennu, sacred bird with
red and gold wings that appeared
once in every five hundred years
on the day the sun entered
Aries, deposited the body of
Osiris embalmed in an egg-
shaped ball of myrrh at the
temple of the sun at Heliopolis,
and then destroyed itself in a
fire. This bird, a solar
emblem, may have been intended
to symbolize regeneration, the
way the sun rises daily out of
darkness or returns with renewed strength in spring.

In Greek mythology, when
the Titans, the elder divinities,
mighty giants of frost and darkness, drove the deities of light
and air from their abode on
Mount Olympus, the younger
gods disguised themselves as
animals and fled to Egypt, where
they waited for an auspicious
time (the proper season) to
depose the invaders from the
Olympus stronghold. The form
taken by Zeus was that of a
ram. In this manner has Zeus
been identified with the Egyptian
ram Amen-Khnum. These stars
are also said to represent the
Ram with Golden Fleece, which
had been supplied to the children
of Athamas. As mentioned in
the essay on Argo, Athamas, a
sun hero and king of Thessaly,
divorced his first wife, Nephele,
the mist, by whom he had two
children, Phryxus and Helle.

Ino, the dawn, became the wife
of Athamas and sought the death
of her stepchildren. To save
them Nephele sent Chrysomallus,
the ram with golden fleece (sun-
drenched cloud) to carry them
to safety. Helle, the light
warm air, fell into the sea, which
was named Hellespont to honor
her. Phryxus, the cold upper
air, which cannot be destroyed,
reached Colchis safely. There,
he sacrificed the Ram to Zeus
and presented the fleece to King
Aeetes, a power of darkness,
who hung it on a sacred oak as
a votive offering. An oracle
predicted the king's life depended
on the safe-keeping of the fleece,
which eventually was stolen by
the Argonauts, forces of light.
Myths, such as this, of hidden
or stolen treasures, typify awareness of the invaluable fertilizing
heat and light of the sun which
is carried away from the realm
of darkness to the realm of
dawn or spring. The Fleece is
a magic vehicle, a counterpart
of the magic carpet. This
legend of the acquisition of the
Golden Fleece helps to bear
out the contention of mythologists
that the twelve zodiacal signs
represent twelve stellar symbols
of the passage of time through
the circle of the year. The
Greeks offered a ram or lamb to
Athena and Poseidon as well as
to Zeus. It was the Minoan god
of the waxing year; opposed to
the goat, god of the waning year.

As a Hebrew symbol of sacrifice, it alluded to the animal
that miraculously appeared to
take the place of Isaac when
Abraham drew his knife to prove
his love for God was greater
than his love for his son. Biblical
scholars of the middle ages asserted it was the ram Abraham
had caught in the thicket; the

lamb sacrificed on Calvary for all sinful humanity; Saint Peter, bishop (leader) of the early church, with the Triangulum as his mitre; or the deliverer Christ; and that Gad (others claim Simeon) was assigned to be its guardian. Josephus said that when the sun was in Aries (the Jewish Nisan or March-April), his people were released from bondage in Egypt. In Nisanu, the same Assyrian month, Aries represented the Altar on which a ram usually was the victim. The Hebrew word ramah (ram) means lofty place.

The first manzil or lunar station of the Arabs was formed by its stars alpha and beta, and they were known as Two Tokens, that is to say the opening year. Persians, to whom these stars were the lunar station Protecting Pair and the constellation a symbol of virility as well as an emblem of the empire, anciently celebrated a festival similar to the procession held in Egypt. All great nations of the East had rituals to commemorate the entrance of the sun and moon into Aries each year. The two stars alpha and beta (others dispute this and say beta and gamma) mark the lunar station named Asvini in the Rig-Veda. Joyous hymns were addressed to these twin heroes, whose appearance before sunrise heralded the approach of the great festive day of the Hindu New Year. The Hindu asterism acted as the steed of Agni.

This cluster or some of its stars were known to Peruvians as the Market Moon or Kneeling Terrace. At this season early crops were harvested and transported on the backs of llamas.

The festival of the month was That of the Axe or that in which crops were cut down, a conception at variance with ideas of the East, where the season is generally one of sowing.

Among its figure representations in art are: a ram reclining, its head reverted to admire its own golden fleece; a ram looking with astonishment at the Bull rising backwards; a ram running in a westerly direction with a zodiac belt around his body. The horns of a ram ♈ is its pictorial symbol. In heraldry its configuration is used to signify a duke or leader.

Additional designations: Leader of the Zodiacal Host; Prince of Celestial Signs; Prince of the Zodiac.

Accadian: Gam (a scimetar or weapon with a curved blade, which protected the kingdom against Seven Evil Spirits or Tempest Powers). Probably stars in Pisces were included in this figure. I-ku, Iku-u, Ku, all equivalents of the Assyrian Rubu (Prince), appropriate name when it became the leader of the stellar groups.

Anglo-Norman: Multuns.

Anglo-Saxon: Ramm.

Arabic: Al Hamal (The Sheep or full grown lamb); also the name of its alpha star; Al Kabash al 'Alif (Tame Ram).

China: First known as a Dog, then as a Tiger, finally as a White Sheep.

Egyptian: Amen-Khnum; Arnum (Lord of the Head, that is stars which held sway over the head and face). Part of

the constellation was known as
The Fleece, part as The Goose.

Euphratean: Dum-uzi or
Tammuz (Only Son of Life), whom
Aries one time represented in
the heavens as Orion did at a
previous period. Lubat (Old
Sheep).

French: Belier (Ram).

German: Widder (Ram).

Hebrew: Teli.

Hindu: Aja, Mesha.

Italian: Ariete, Montone
(Ram).

Latin and Low Latin: Acquin-
octialis, in allusion to its posi-
tion; Ammon Libycus; Arcanus,
in reference to secret rites per-
formed at this season; Athamas,
Caput arietinum; Chrysomallus
or Chrysovellus; Corniger;
Cornus (Horn); Deus Libycus;
Ductor exercitus zodiaci; Dux
opulenti gregis; Jovis Sidus;
Jupiter Ammon (Amen); Jupiter
Libycus; Minervae Sidus (daughter
of Jove or Jupiter); Ovis aurea;
Phrixea Ovis, Phrixeum Pecus,
Phrixi Vector, Phrixus, Portitor
Phrixi, all of which relate to the
Golden Fleece; Princeps signor-
um coelestium; Princeps Zodiaci;
Regum Ammonis (Regent Ammon
or Amen); Vernus Portitor (Spring
Bringer); Vervex (Weather).

Parsi: Varak (Ram).

Persian: Bara, Bere or
Berre (Ram).

Sanscrit: Rama (Husband,
Man).

Syrian: Amru or Emru (Ram).

Tamil: Kriya (Ram),

Mesham.

Turkish: Kuzi (Ram).

Astrologically a masculine,
fortunate sign, included with Leo
and Sagittarius to compose the
Fiery Trigon, ruler of all forms
of fire. It symbolizes the birth
of new thought, the dawn of a
new era. Ninth century A.D.
mystics, expanding upon the
Babylonian pronouncement, al-
leged that creation took place
when the Seven Powers were in
conjunction here and foretold
that the world's destruction would
come when they should be in the
same position in the last degree
of Pisces. An appearance of a
comet within its borders portends
great wars and widespread
mortality, abasement of the great,
and elevation of the small. Those
who contend that its influence is
not fortunate aver that it is
ruled by Mars and therefore is
to be dreaded, that those born
under this influence are impul-
sive, have a hasty, passionate
temper, will suffer bodily hurt,
and that when the sun is in the
sign many shall die of the rope.
They concede however that herbs
will be abundant. Mars here
governs all diseases relating to
man's head and face. Others
place guardianship under Pallas
Minerva, exponent of reason.
The southwest wind is in its
charge.

It lies in the northern sky east
of Pisces, south of Triangulum.
It may be seen evenings from late
September into April, and culminates on December 14. The
sun passes through it from about
April 16 to May 13. This should
not be confused with the dates
given for the zodiacal sign, which
due to the precession of the
equinoxes is now occupied by the

constellation Pisces. Its bright stars are: alpha, Hamal; beta, Sheratan; gamma, Mesarthim.

AURIGA (THE CHARIOTEER). Probably originally a shepherd located among the stars to watch over both his own flocks and those on earth. Later stories are connected with either a charioteer or a goat, but in narratives the man is not identified with both at the same time. When or why he became the driver of a chariot remains a mystery. Most tales extant have come from Greek sources. In one the deity is said to be Hephaestus, crippled smithy who was god of the anvil fire and maker of useful things, such as armor, arrows, and chariots, for the deities. In another he is Erichthonius, virgin-born son of Atthis, daughter of the king of Attica, or the boy who was formed from the spilled seed of Hephaestus. The infant was deformed, and Athena placed him in a closed box which she gave into the care of the sisters Agraulos, Herse, and Pandrosos, with instructions that it was not to be opened. Agraulos and Herse disobeyed and found the infant folded in the coils of a snake (an earth symbol). The frightened nurses threw themselves down the precipice of the Acropolis, but the infant lived and became the fourth king of Athens. To hide his snake-like feet he invented the chariot, for which he was rewarded by Zeus with a place in the sky. Another identification is with Myrtilus, a son of Hermes, and charioteer to Oenomaus, king of Ellis. Pelops, a grandson of Zeus, wished to marry Hippodamia, a daughter of Oenomaus, who objected to the match. To win the favor of Pelops, Myrtilus, in December, pulled the linchpin of the king's chariot and thereby caused his death. Ungrateful, Pelops, who had married the king's daughter, threw Myrtilus into the sea. Before he drowned, the charioteer placed a curse on the house of Pelops. Like Oenomaus, Pelops and his descendants died in December. Thus Myrtilus personified frost which caused the death of agricultural or sun deities.

Biblical scholars suppose the stars represent the Good Shepherd and symbolize the coming of Christ; Jacob deceiving his father with the flesh of his kids; or Saint Jerome, who extracted a thorn from a lion's paw.

In Greek art shown as a powerful man, perhaps a shepherd, seated. A goat in his left arm rests against his shoulder; in his left hand he holds two kids, and in his right a bridle. Presumably he drives a chariot which remains invisible. Variations of this illustration have come down through the ages and one similar to it appears on sculptures found in the Euphratean Valley, but whether it applied to the constellation is not known. Actually, a word for wind may have been misunderstood to be goat. On a French map of 1650 the man is Adam who kneels on the Milky Way, resting one foot on the right horn of the Bull. A she-goat is on his shoulder. Modern illustrations show the chariot drawn by a goat. An Arabian planisphere makes a mule of these stars.

Additional designations: Carter; Ploughman and His Oxen; Wagoner (Waggoner); Wainman.

Arabian: Al Dhu al 'Inan; Al

Masik al 'Inan; Al Mumsik al 'Inan, Mumassich Alhanam.

Biblical Scholars: Good Shepherd, who laid down his life for the sheep; Jacob; Joseph, son of Jacob; Pastor, also used for Bootes; Saint Jerome.

Egyptian: Lora (Reins); Roha (Wagoner).

French: Cocher (Coachman).

German: Fuhrmann (Carman). Voluyara.

Graeco-Babylonian: Rukubi (Chariot); perhaps some Taurus stars were included in the figure.

Greek: Erechtheus, an agricultural hero and brother of Bootes; Erichthonius, grandfather of Erechtheus.

Italian: Cocchiere (Coachman).

Latin and Low Latin: Agitator currus retinens; Arator (Ploughman), probably in error when used here, as it is also used for Bootes; Aurigator (Driver); Collarium (Harness); Custos Caparum; Habenifer (Charioteer); Habens Capellas; Habens Haedos; Habens Hircum; Habens oleniam capram; Heniochus (Rein-holder); Mavors, a poetical term for Mars, father of Romulus, who had been raised by a shepherd; Mulus Clitellatus (Mule with Panniers); Oleniae sidus pluviale Capellae, from Olenus, father and birthplace of the goat nymph Amalthea who had suckled Zeus; Tenens Habenas (Rein-holder); Trochilus (Running).

Medieval European barbarous names from the Arabic: Alanac,

Alanat; Alhaior; Alhaiot; Alhaiset; Alhajot; Alhajoth; Alhatod; Alhojet; Alioc; Althaiot. These were used for both the constellation and lucida; probably degenerate forms of Al 'Ayyuk, which figured as desert ibex.

Medieval European classical names: Absyrthe (Absyrtus, brother and pursuer of Medea); Bellerophon, rider of Pegasus; Cillas, driver for Pelops; Hippolytus, son of Theseus; Myrtilus, charioteer of Oenomaus; Pelethronius, a Thessalian driver; Phaethon, fatal rider of the sun chariot; Trethon (probably Triton who drove a chariot over the sea).

Portuguese: Mafurtius.

It is in the north, largely involved in the Milky Way between Perseus and Lynx and attached to Taurus by the star El Nath. In early autumn it may be seen in the east, remains in the night sky throughout the winter and in spring twilight may be seen in the west. Culmination is about February 4. Its alpha star is Capella; its beta star, Menkalinan. The Kids are represented by three stars.

BOOTES (THE PLOUGHMAN). The origin of this constellation, like that of Auriga and others, is lost in time. Its present title, pronounced Bo-ō'tez, appears in the Odyssey, but it originally may have been Arcturus, now given to the constellation's lucida.

Athenians believed these stars constituted the celestial appearance of Bootes, priestly leader of the people, brother of Erechtheus, the secular leader. After Erechtheus robbed him of

his wealth, Bootes wandered off.
He suffered extreme poverty and
hardships, laboring as a hunter,
herdsman and itinerant tiller of
the soil until he conceived the
plow, to which he yoked two oxen.
With his invention he was able
to ease his labors and he became
one of the great benefactors of
mankind.

Sabazius Bacchus also is
credited with being the first
to yoke oxen for plowing. While
he was still an infant, the Titans
lured Bacchus with golden apples,
knuckle bones, rhombus, and
other toys, and then tore him
into seven pieces. Man sprang
from his body, his blood creating
man's soul. Inasmuch as he
was a deity he was immortal and
reappeared each spring simply to
be cut into pieces again when he
reached maturity (the harvest).
Bacchus in this manner acquired
the titles Sabazius (derived from
words for beer and health) and
Zagreus (horned or torn). A
drama was performed annually
at the Sabazia, nocturnal
orgiastic mysteries, in which a
royal or fertility child was killed
and eaten. In later rites a bull
or goat became a surrogate for
the child, which supposedly was
resurrected each year by Demeter
(Mother Earth).

Early Greek myths likewise
recognized Icarius, Dionysus (an
aspect of Bacchus), Lycaon,
and Arcas in these stars.
Icarius was an Athenian who received Dionysus, disguised as a
beggar, in his home, and to
reward the hospitality the god
taught him vine cultivation. The
generous Icarius, wishing to
bestow a boon upon his fellow
men, gave a band of shepherds
some wine. They drank too
freely and became drunk. Believ-

ing they had been poisoned they
killed Icarius and buried his
body under a tree. Erigone,
daughter of Icarius, searched
in vain for her father until the
howls of his dog Maera led her
to a grave. When she un-
covered the body she hung herself
for grief. The unfortunate man
who had brought trouble upon
himself by his practical disposition of the idea of Dionysus was
exalted into the sky as the
constellation Bootes or the star
Arcturus; Erigone was made into
the constellation Virgo, and the
faithful hound into the star
Procyon or Sirius.

Lycaon, king of Arcadia,
doubted the divinity of Zeus, when
the god paid him a visit. To test
his guest, he served a dish containing human flesh, that of his
grandson Arcas. The angry god
upset the table, turned Lycaon
into a wolf, and with a flash of
lightning killed all those present,
except Arcas, whom he re-
stored to life. This myth, like
that of Icarius, also is associated
with the star Arcturus.

Bootes was probably the
Egyptian Hippopotamus, a form
of Apet or Ta-urt, a benignant
mother goddess, whose duty was
to move around the heavens and
keep a perpetual watch on the
circumpolar stars. These most
northly stars which did not set
were evil, and the Hippopotamus,
although gentle, was strong, and
therefore expected to keep the
sinful ones from doing harm.
This constellation also has been
related to the Osiris narrative,
the torturous dismemberment of
Osiris originating in the pro-
tracted successive setting of its
stars.

Early Christians assumed

Bootes to be Saint Sylvester, a pope; later Christian writers identify it as the prophet Amos herdsman and figdresser; the Good Shepherd, harvester of souls. A medieval flatterer of royalty called it The Three Swedish Crowns.

The Shepherd identification is undoubtedly connected with its proximity to the Pole, which Arabs assumed to be a sheepfold. They called the constellation Pastor, meaning Shepherd. This corresponds to the title Sibzianna which appears on a Chaldean star chart, and which means Shepherd of the Life of Heaven. Pertinent to its relationship to agriculture and the vine, it is construed to be Noah who, after the flood, invented agricultural implements and became a husbandman. When he discovered the vine he became drunk on its juice and in that condition visited his wife's tent. His youngest son Ham told his brothers about the nakedness of their father, and they turned their heads and respectfully covered him (conveyed him to the land of night). Noah cursed Ham for his disrespect and made him a servant of his brothers. The Noah-Ham myth implies the mutilation motif of the Uranus-Cronus and other father-son myths. In the original version, Noah may have been made drunk by his viniculture son and then castrated. The castration symbolizes the harvest or death of fertility.

Various allusions that treat this group as well as others just outside the rim or fence of the North Pole as a dog or wolf seem to confirm the Arabian idea of a polar sheepfold.

A classical representation is that of a tall man who, while he runs, grasps a spear, club or pastoral staff in his right hand and in his uplifted left hand the leash of his two hunting dogs, Asterion and Chara. The dogs seem to be barking at the Great Bear. Usually shown to be a young man, occasionally as a mature one. Always equipped with weapons of the hunt or with agricultural implements. In his earliest form probably carried the winnowing fan of Dionysus. A Venetian piece of 1488 has the Wheat Sheaf (Coma Berenices) at his feet. Stars that now compose Corona Borealis probably once represented the arm he held high. On some sky maps the drawing is of a vine.

Additional designations: Arrow Bearer; Atlas, because of his closeness to the Pole in a posture that is said to suggest he might be holding up the heavens; Bear Driver, because he seems to be driving the Great Bear before him; Bear Guide; Bear Watcher; Driver (of the Wain); Herdsman; Herdsman who Guides the Wain; Lance Bearer; Ploughman of the Triones; Shepherd, presumably of the sheep within the fold (Ursa Minor); Spear Bearer; Vintager, inasmuch as its rising in the morning twilight coincided with the autumnal equinox, season of grape harvest; Vociferator (Vociferous); Wagoner.

Arabic: Ahava; Al Aulad al Dhibah (Whelps of the Hyenas) for the stars theta, beta, gamma, delta and mu; Al Awwa (The Barker); Al Bakkar (The Herdsman); Al Hamil Luzz (Spear-

Bearer); Al Kameluz or Kolanza; Aramech or Archamech; Nekkar or Nakkar (Tearer or Digger). Female Wolves is an Arabic designation for a trapezium formed by gamma, beta, mu, and delta.

Assyrian: Riu-but-same, Ox-driving Ploughman.

Egyptian: Orus (Horus), a title also connected with Orion.

French: Bouvier, transliterated from Homer's Odyssey, so the title has been in use for at least 3,000 years, doubtless at first applied to its prominent star Arcturus.

Bootes, usually said to be derived from a Greek word meaning ox or one meaning drive, and translated as Ploughman or Herdsman; according to some it comes from a word meaning clamorous or shouting, i.e. the shouts or encouragements to the hounds or to the oxen, the Triones or Seven Principal stars of Ursa Minor.

Hebrew: Caleb Anubach or Kelebh hannabah (Barking Dog). Nimrod, the mighty hunter before the Lord, is also applied.

Italian: Arator; Boote.

Latin and Low Latin: Arator (Plow); Arctophylax, from two Greek words signifying bear keeper and bear driver; Arcturi Custos; Arcturus Minor (Arcturus Major being the Great Bear); Bubuleus or Bubulus (Peasant Ox-driver); Camans, which suggests shouting; Canis (Dog); Canis Latrans (Barking Dog); Carman; Clamator (Clamorous, Brawler); Custos Arcti (Bear Keeper); Custos Boun (Keeper of Oxen); Custos Erymanthidos Ursae; Lanceator; Pastinator, signifying a digger or trencher in a vineyard; Philomelus, identifying the constellation as the son of Philamela, who sometimes is said to be the southern neighbor Virgo; Plaustri Custos (Keeper of the Wain); Plorans (Loud Weeper); Portitor Ursae; Septemtrio, from its nearness to the North Pole and related to a title applied to the Bears; Venator Ursae (Hunter of the Bear); Vociferans.

Polish: Ogka (Thill)

The rising and setting of these stars, which take place near the equinoxes, portend great tempests. The constellation lies in the northern sky between Corona Borealis and Asterion and Chara (Canes Venatici), the dogs it drives in its chase of the Great Bear around the Pole.

In the latitude of New York it is visible from March to November. It rises horizontally, almost all of its stars come from below the horizon at one time. It is slow-moving, a sluggish or tardy driver that turns until it is in a nearly upright position, and when it finally sets more than eight hours are required for it to sink into the northwest. On June 16th it reaches culmination, and its bright stars are: alpha, Arcturus; beta, Nekkar; epsilon, Izar; eta, Muphrid; mu, Alkalurops.

BRANDENBURG SCEPTRE or Brandenburg Eagle was a small asterism in the northern sky between Equuleus and Aquila. It first appeared on sky maps in 1688 to honor the royal German family, but has disappeared from 20th century atlases. The name

Brandenburg Eagle also has been applied to Aquila, a few of whose stars once were included in this smaller asterism.

CAELUM (GRAVING TOOL). Constellation in the southern sky located below Lepus and between Eridanus and Columba. Pictor and Dorado form its southern border. Designed in the 18th century it was named, as others in that period of mechanical awareness, to honor an implement or tool. Other designations are: The Chisel, Sculptor's Tool; French: Burin (Graver or Graving Pin); German: Grabstichel; Italian: Bulino; Latin: Caela Sculptoris (Sculptor's Chisel), which occasionally is incorrectly written Cela Sculptoria. It comes to the meridian about January 15, and is entirely visible from the 40th parallel. No bright star has been located within its borders.

CAMELPARDALIS (GIRAFFE or CAMEL). This name, derived from the Greek, had been given to it because it is formed like a giraffe or camel and spotted like a pard. Long, faint, and straggling, like its namesake, with hind quarters in the Milky Way. Jacobus Bartschius, who first described it in 1614, said it represented to him the Camel that brought Rebecca to Isaac. Other names by which it is known are: Camelopardus; Camelpardalus; Camelus; Noah's Ark; French, Girafe; Italian Giraffa.

It lies in the northern sky between Auriga and Ursa Minor. Westerners have considered it dull and uninteresting; one German astronomer combined it with the constellation Auriga to form a configuration he called French

Lilies. In China, on the other hand, seven asterisms are defined within its boundaries: Hwa Kae (State Umbrella); Luh Kea (an anatomical term); Shang Chin (Higher Minister); Shang Wei (Higher Guard); Shaou Wei (Minor Guard); Sze Foo (four official supporters of the throne); Yin Tih (Unostentatious Virtue).

Without any bright stars it culminates about February 6.

CANCER (THE CRAB). Although the most inconspicuous of all zodiacal constellations, it since earliest times has been the subject of many notions. Dimness has won it the appellation Dark Sign, it has been described as dark without eyes. Chaldeans gave it the name Cancer because the crab walks backward or obliquely, and the sun upon arriving in this sign begins an apparent retrograde and descends deviatively.

I was born, sir, when the
Crab was ascending,
And my affairs go backward.
(Congreve).

Chaldeans and Greeks both believed that the Gate of Men, the gate by which souls supposedly descended into human bodies, was located in this constellation. The correlative gate through which souls reentered heaven upon death was Capricorn, on the opposite side of the sky.

It was the Egyptian Power of Darkness over which Anubis, the pathfinder, opener of the ways to the afterworld, was said to rule. Anubis also is assigned to Sirius.

The foot of Heracles while he was fighting the Lernean

Hydra, a neighboring constellation, was seized by this crab.
Heracles finally crushed the
crustacean under his heel, but
Hera, who detested Heracles,
placed the crab in heaven as a
reward. In another legend,
Dionysus, afflicted with insanity,
set out for the temple of Zeus
(sky) to obtain a cure. (The
sun in its scorching aspect is
said to be mad.) On his way
he came to an immense marsh.
One of two asses grazing nearby
carried Dionysus across. For this
favor the sun god transformed
the animals into stars, the
Aselli, which now graze in Cancer. The Aselli also had been
of service to the Gods (forces
of light and growth) in their
war with the Titans (forces of
darkness and frost). In the battle
one stood by Dionysus, the other
by his foster-father Silenus. The
loud braying of the asses added
to the shouts of the deities, who
were cultivators of the vine and
noted for their noisy carousing,
frightened away the giants. Silenus, too intoxicated to walk, supported himself against the ass.

In gospel mythology seen as
Issacher (literally hire), whom
Jacob likened to the "strong
ass;" the Breastplate of Righteousness; the Manger of the
infant Jesus with an Ass and Ox
presumed to be standing by; or
as Saint John the Evangelist.

Arabians combined these stars
with those of Leo for the Mouth
and Muzzle of the Lion, part of
their mammoth Great Lion.
Brihaspati, Hindu divine mediator,
priest and teacher of the gods,
who developed into Brahma of
the third triad, presided over
these stars. Cancer marked one
of the residences of the Chinese
Red or Southern Emperor,

whence it was known as Red
Bird. A Yucatan temple was
dedicated to this sign because
when Cancer was the solar mansion, the sun in the form of a
bird of fire swooped down at
noon to consume the sacrifice
on the altar.

In Babylonia and Egypt, Cancer was represented by a tortoise
rather than by a crab. Later in
Egypt the scarabaeus or beetle,
emblematic of immortality, replaced the tortoise. In any
event, the crab, tortoise, and
beetle resemble each other in
several respects. They are
hard shelled, insignificant in
appearance, sluggish in their
movements, and this latter attribute typifies what appears to
be the sun's motility at its entrance into this constellation.
While a crab appears in the
round Egyptian zodiac of
Denderah, its location is in Leo
Minor. In Eastern zodiacs it
is typified by two asses, which
may represent the pair Aselli.
The Hindus illustrated with a
crescent or an arrow head. Greeks
delineated as a beetle with its
nestball of earth in its claws or
as Silenus, the fat intoxicated
old man, riding an ass. For
ages in all parts of the world
an ass has transported casks or
bags of wine. Druids, who
picturized the sun as a horse in
all signs, here has a crab as
the horse's companion. In
medieval drawings the slow moving crayfish is used, also a
waterbeetle or a lobster with a
shrimplike object as fellow
traveler. The pictorial symbol
of the zodiacal Cancer is ♋,
understood to be the Crab's claws.

Additional designations: House
of the Moon, from an early
belief that the moon was located in

Cancer at the time of creation. Tropic Crab.

Accadian: First cuneiform inscriptions indicated that it was the Sun of the South, perhaps from its position at the winter solstice in remote antiquity; later shown to be the sun's northern gate associated with the month Duzu or Tammuz (June-July), whence the solar ball commences its retrograde movement. Other inscriptions were Nagar-asagga (Workman of the Waterway); Nangaru; Puluk-ku; Xas (Division, probably the solstitial colure as a dividing line).

Anglo-Saxon: Crabba.

Arabian: Al Liha (The Soft Palate); Al Saratan (The Cancer).

Chinese: Kwei (Cloud-like) for gamma, delta, eta, and theta, one of the Hsiu. Shun Show, one of the kung or solar mansions.

English, Middle: Cancre; Canser.

French: le Cancre; l'Ecrevisse (the Crab or Crawfish).

German: der Krebs; die Krippe.

Hebrew: Sartan (Cancer).

Hindu: Karka; Karata; Kulira, from the Greek Kolouroi, docktailed, and the English colure; Pushya (Flower) a lunar station; Sidhaya (Prosperous).

Italian: il Cancro; Granchio (Crab or Cramp)

Latin and Low Latin: Aselli, also a name of a pair of its stars. Astacus (Crab or Lobster); Cammarus (Crab or Crayfish);

Carcinus; Lernaeus (of Lerna, the marsh in which a crab pinched Heracles); Litoreus (Shore Inhabiting); Nepa (Crab or Lobster); Octipes.

Persian: Chercjengh, Kalakang (Cancer).

Peruvian: Cantut or Cantua Pata (Terrace of the Cantut or Cantua Flower).

Singalese: Kathaca.

Syrian: Sartono (Cancer).

Tamil: Karkatan (Crab).

Turkish: Lenkutch (Cancer).

Third century B. C. records indicate earth would be submerged when all planets meet here and consumed by fire when they meet in Capricorn. Occult philosophers of the middle ages reversed this rule for they only assigned good fortune to this rare conjunction. However, Cancer generally, to which they attributed the color red and control of the human breast, was in their opinion possessor of malign influences. A feminine, unfortunate sign, it was capable of causing violent death or accident by fire. It determines the fate of those born between June 21 and July 22. These persons usually have a placid disposition, adore their home and family, but are fond of social pleasures and quickly respond to the mental condition of those around them. They are however slow to change their ideas. With Scorpio and Pisces, Cancer formed the Watery Trigon, the container of all the world's waters. Romans of the fourth century B.C. judged it to be a fruitful, therefore auspicious, sign, under the guardianship of

Mercury and called Mercurii Sidus (Mercury Star), with the colors of foliage, green and russet, attached to it. However, when the sun was within its boundaries it was feared that each thunderstorm might cause commotions, famine, or locusts.

Its position in the northern sky is between Gemini and Leo above Hydra's head. It comes to the meridian about March 16. The sun, which was furthest north here about 2,000 years ago, travels through the constellation (not to be confused with the zodiacal sign) from about July 18 to August 7. The solstice, which formerly was here and gave it the name Tropic of Cancer, is now about 33⁰ degrees away in Gemini. Here, in this corner of the heavens, a comet was observed in 1531. It reappeared in 1607 and 1682. Halley accurately predicted the comet's return in 1758, and it has since been known as Halley's comet. In June of 1898 all planets except Neptune were here. The glory of Cancer is its great star cluster Praesepe (manger) which appears as a single star or comet to the naked eye, and supposedly is the Manger where the two asses feed. Other of its named stars are alpha, Acubens; gamma and delta, the Aselli; lambda, Al Tarf, none of which are greater than fourth magnitude.

CANES VENATICI (THE HUNTING DOGS). This asterism is a modern one, formed in 1690 out of scattered unattached stars in the northern sky in the vicinity of Ursa Major. It represents two dogs held in leash by Bootes, who pursues the Great Bear as it circles the Pole. The name of the northerly dog is Asterion,

that of the southerly one is Chara, both small clusters. In Chara's neck is the lucida of the constellation, the third magnitude Cor Caroli (Charles's Heart). The designation was made to honor Charles I, not Charles II, as is at times erroneously indicated. Charles II deserved the honor for he had founded Greenwich Observatory. Cor Caroli is one of the four stars forming the figure known as the Diamond of Virgo. North of Cor Caroli can be seen the star La Superba, which has a superb flashing brilliance. To the east of Canes Venatici can be seen the famous Spiral Nebula, sometimes called Whirlpool Nebula.

The usual illustration is of two greyhounds held by a leash in the hand of Bootes, ready for pursuit of the Bear around the Pole. On some 17th century maps, stars in this part of the sky are shown as a stream called the River Jordan (Jordanis, Jordanus).

Additional designations: Greyhounds; The Hounds.

Arabic: Al Karb al Ibl (Camels Burden).

Chinese: Chang Chen (A Seat). Three stars near the head of Asterion they called Three Honorary Guardians of the Heir Apparent.

French: Chiens due chasse; Levriers.

German: Jagdhunde (Sporting or Hunting Dog).

Italian: Lebrieri (Greyhounds).

Latin: Catuli (Puppies).

Canes Venatici comes to the meridian in the night sky on about July 22.

CANIS MAJOR (THE GREATER DOG).

From very early times this Dog has been called the Hound that accompanies Orion when he goes hunting, or the Hound that constantly preys on the Hare at Orion's feet. On hunting trips it has attacked Taurus, the Bull, and thus a great antagonism exists between them. Notwithstanding the watchfulness of the Dog, in this role called Custos Europae, the Bull succeeded in carrying off the maiden Europa. In other early classical works the constellation was known simply as Canis, representing Laelaps (furious wind), which Artemis (moon) had given to one of her nymphs, Procris (dew). This Hound while pursuing wild boar (drought) was metamorphosed into stone and then lifted into the heavens. Laelaps likewise was the name of one of the fifty hounds of Actaeon, the hunter who came upon Artemis while she was bathing. For gazing upon the naked goddess he was turned into a stag, whereupon he was torn to pieces and devoured by his own dogs. Canis Minor also is identified as one of the dogs that belonged to this hero. In still another Greek legend, Eos (dawn) gave a dog (wind) to Cephalus (rising sun), the husband and slayer of Procris (dew). He was the swiftest of his species, and Cephalus raced him against a fox, fleetest of all animals. They ran for some time and neither was able to obtain a lead. Zeus, fascinated by the dog's speed, gave him immortality by placing him among the stars.

As Janitor Lethaeus (Hell's Keeper) he is a form of Cerberus, surly, formidable dog who guards the lower heavens, the realm of fire, and giver, through Sirius, of canine madness. He is said to be the celestial form of Maera, faithful pet of Icarius, but usually Maera is identified with the star Procyon in Canis Minor.

In a Hindu fable the constellation is Sarama, messenger of Indra and keeper of his cows (clouds), which she rescues from the night robbers, the Panis (air and drought demons). Sarama in the form of a greyhound aids those who are lost in forests, grottoes, or dark places. Later the constellation became the realm of Lubdhaka, hunter guise of Rudra (lightning and storm god), who shot Prajapati (lord of light) with an arrow when Prajapati assumed deer form to pursue his daughter Rohini (fertility), who had taken an antelope shape to escape her father's advances. The giant Prajapati did not fall from the skies, but his body pierced by the arrow remains revolving endlessly in space in a position midway between his daughter (the star Aldebaran) and Lubdhaka. Intermittently his light covers the earth. At night the three-pointed arrow (Belt of Orion) can be seen in Prajapati's side, and in honor of this exploit Lubdhaka is called Mrigavyadha (Deer-slayer).

All legends probably were attached originally to the lucida Sirius; when the constellation was formed at some unknown later date the attachments were transferred.

On illustrated maps it usually

appears as a spotted short-haired
dog that stands on his hind legs
ready to spring at the Hare at
Orion's feet. In some configurations the blazing Sirius is held in
his open jaws. The figure was
known anciently and appears on
an ivory disk found on the site of
ancient Troy and on an Etruscan
mirror. A Dog of the Sun appears on Euphratean remains
of temples, but whether the constellation or the Star Sirius was
intended is unknown. In fact
the importance of the constellation is overshadowed by the fame
of this brightest of all fixed
stars.

Additional designations:
Larger Dog; Orion's Hound.

Arabian: Al Kalb al Jabbar
(The Dog of the Giant); Kalb-al-
akbar (Greater Dog).

Christian: Appointed Prince;
David; Dog of Tobias.

French: Grand Chien.

German: Grosse Hund.

Hindu: Lubdhaka (Hunter);
Mrga (Wild animal); Mrigavyadha
(Deerslayer); Sarama (Dog).

Italian: Cane Maggiore.

Italian and Low Latin:
Candens Canicula (Shining Puppy);
Canis Australior (Southern Dog);
Custos Europae (Europa's
Guardian); Erigonaeus (from the
Maera story); Icarius (likewise
from the Maera story).

Medieval corruptions of the
Arabic combined with Latin:
Alcheleb Alachbar; Elchabar
(probably Al Kabir, the Great);
Elscheere; Elseire; Elsere;
Sceara; Scera; Scheereliemini.

Persian: Kelbo Gavora (Dog
of the Giant).

Portuguese: Caes.

Scandinavian: Greip, a dog
attached to the sun-hero Sigurd
and a name associated with fire.

Farmers of ancient Rome
were instructed to sow beans
and millet at its heliacal setting
on May 1. It now comes to the
meridian in the evening sky
about February 16. Its location
is south of the zodiac, just below the heels of Orion, and it is
separated from Canis Major by
the Milky Way. Its center is
pierced by the Tropic of Capricorn, and its bright stars are:
alpha, Sirius; beta, Murzim
(Mirzim); delta, Wezen;
epsilon, Adhara; zeta, Furud;
mu, Aludra.

CANIS MINOR (THE LESSER
DOG). The legends associated
with this constellation are also
associated with its alpha star
Procyon, a name at one time applied to the whole group. In the
Euphratean valley it seems to
have been described as a water
dog, from its position along the
edge of the Milky Way, which
ancients called a river in the
sky.

Inasmuch as it rises shortly
before Sirius, at once loved and
dreaded by the Egyptians and
other Mediterranean peoples because it foretold rains, much
needed for life, but frequently a
cause of widespread death,
Canis Minor was praised as a
watchful animal, a trustworthy
sentinel which warned that the
Dog-star was about to appear.
It had been made out to be the
dog-headed Anubis, but the star
Sirius was more often associated

with this divinity.

As the second hunting dog that accompanied Orion, the mighty hunter, it has been called "Canis Orionis" and confounded with Canis Major. It has been said to be the loyal Maera, which belonged to Icarius and which has also been placed elsewhere in the heavens. Again it is Arigon or Argus, the dog which recognized Odysseus when he returned home after an absence of twenty years. Others have called the constellation the hound of Artemis (Diana), who was renowned for her love of the chase, or one of the fifty belonging to Actaeon that tore their master into pieces and then devoured him when he had been transformed into a stag by Artemis. In this myth, Actaeon personifies the late afternoon sun destroyed by the presence of the moon. It has been presumed to be the favorite of Helen. When it drowned in the Euripus Strait, she prayed to Zeus to lift it to the sky where it might have immortality.

Commentators on the Scriptures saw it as the Paschal Lamb or the dog that was the constant companion of Tobias.

Traditionally it is portrayed as a shaggy house or watch dog with its tail up, in contrast to the wild and fierce short-haired hunter Canis Major. Its figure is derived from its function as lookout or warner that conveyed to ancients the approach of sorching heat, the dog days. The Canis Minor group composed the contracted foreleg or paw of the Great Lion of the Arabs; the extended paw appeared in Gemini.

Additional designations: Felis, the Cat, also assigned to a constellation no longer recognized; Fovea (Pit), the explanation for which appears to be lost; Morus (Mulberry Tree); Smaller Dog. A Greek term which means "rising before his companion Dog," was transliterated into Procyon by the Romans, and in medieval Europe this became Prochion or Procion and was applied to the constellation.

Arabic: Al Ghumaisa, also a name for Procyon; Al Jummaiza, the Sycamine or Mulberry Tree; Al Shi'ra al Shamiyyah (Bright Star of Syria), named because the constellation disappeared from view when it set beyond that country.

French: Le Petit Chien.

German: der Kleine Hund.

Greek: Prokunos (First, or Before, Dog).

Italian: il Cane Minore.

Latin and Low Latin: Antecanis (Anticanis); Antecedens Canis; Antecusor; Canis; Canis Minuculus; Canis Parvus, alluding to its brightness, which was inferior to that of Canis Major; Canis Primus, because it rose first; Canis Sinister because it was on the left, Canis Major becoming Canis Dexter; Catellus or Catulus (Puppy); Praecanis; Procanis; Procynis; Septentrionalis Canis, referring to its position northerly of Canis Major.

Medieval: Strange titles became attached to the constellation in the middle ages, the explanation for several being

lost. Most are derived from
the Arabic and combined with
Latin. Alcheleb Alasgar; Al
Ghamus; Al Kalb al Asghar (The
Lesser Dog); Al Kalb al Mutaka-
ddim (The Preceding Dog), that is
the Dog that precedes Sirius; Al-
sahare alsemalija; Alsehere; As-
cemie Algameisa; Kelbelazaguar.

Astrologically Canis Minor
foretells wealth and renown.
The history of the constellation
is uncertain; when its configuration was first formed is unknown.
Located in the northern sky at
the feet of Gemini, it is separated from Canis Major by
Monoceros and the Milky Way.
It culminates February 28,
and its heliacal rising is about
July 19th. Its bright stars are
alpha, Procyon; beta, Gomeisa.

CAPRICORN (THE HORNED
GOAT). The numerous deity offspring of the chaos demon Tiamat
and her spouse Apsu, Sumerian
lord of the nether sea, defied
their parents and attempted to
establish order in the universe
to provide for the mortals they
had created out of clay. The
parents, who not only dispised
order but wished to wipe out
the handiwork of their children,
stole the tablets of human destiny
and then conspired to destroy
their disobedient children. Ea,
selected by his brothers and
sisters to defend them, castrated
his father, severed his sinews,
tore off his crown, and imprisoned the pieces in a house
(earth) built around his body. The
mother was more formidable;
fear prevented Ea from destroying
her, and she remained leader of
demon hosts (forces of darkness
and decay) that beleaguered her
offspring, the deities (forces of
light and growth). Once Ea had
disposed of Apsu, he donned his

father's crown and established
his abode in the frozen waters
beneath the earth which he
made into fertile streams. Ungrateful mankind failed to offer
the due sacrifices, and Ea's
brother Bel, supreme sky lord,
decreed that a deluge should
destroy all people. Ea still
cherished hopes for the human
race he had helped to mold and,
opposed to total destruction,
warned the sage Pir-na-pishtim,
who saved his family, his field
laborers, his servants, and a
seed of every kind of life by
building an ark, which tossed
about on the turbulent flooded
seas until the torrential rains
subsided. Ea, in the role of
preserver of the human race,
was given the title karubu, borrowed by the Hebrews as kerub
(cherub). This spring fertility
god, who taught men how to be
victorious over destructive forces
of nature, had a snake form,
which became the serpent in the
Adam legend. Wherever Ea
went verdure followed him, and
to roam the earth he assumed
the shape of a goat, large-
eared that he might be all-hear-
ing, wide-eyed that he might be
all seeing. He battled Kusariq-
que, a destructive fish-man in
Tiamat's train, for the right to
govern this celestial mansion
once located in the tenth zodiacal
station of the same name. Victorious, he rose to take up his
residence in the heavenly sea,
and a fish tail developed on his
goat body to facilitate his movement in the water when he triumphantly carried the sun through
the station he had won. At the
horizon, the great cosmic ocean
in which he swam can be seen
flowing into the waters from which
he rose and which encircle the
earth. This fable appears to
be the source of merfolk, and

probably traces back to the time primitive tribes first migrated on rafts or small boats, but appeared to land dwellers as monsters, men and women with fishtails. The poles they used as oars may have been identified as fins.

Babylonians believed the world's destruction would occur by a great conflagration when all the planets meet here; when the sun appeared the Goat was worshipped. Priests wore a sacred robe of goatskins and in festivities designated the animal to be Father of Light, a rite that seems to be exceedingly ancient, probably dating back 15,000 years, when the sun appeared in this section of the sky at the time of the summer solstice. The Scapegoat, which bears the blame or burden that should be placed on others, descended from this worthy beast. Among Jews of antiquity a goat was selected by lot and over its head on the Day of Atonement the high priest confessed the sins of all the people, thus placing them on the goat, after which it was driven into the wilderness as propitiation to Azazel. A demon was expelled from a man by placing his head next to that of a goat, which breathed in the sin or demon.

The stars which composed the Goat-Fish, sometimes called Horned-Goat to differentiate them from Iku, the Goat (Capella) are essentially those which form the modern constellation Capricorn. Because the goat typifies foolishness in the valley and wisdom, surefootedness, on a mountain or promitory, the Chaldeans identified Ea as the Wild-Goat, animal that climbs high jutting rocks without fear

or difficulty and feeds on the growth that appears on hills. The title seems especially fitting inasmuch as the sun once entered the constellation Capricorn and still enters Capricorn, the zodiacal house, at the winter solstice, the season in which it begins to mount the slope of the sky.

To the Egyptians the configuration was the ram-headed cataract deity Chnoumis or Khnemu, who wore a crown of rays and guarded the waters coming from the lower world to flood the Nile; or it was the goat-god of procreation Min (Mendes), who in festivals was represented by the phallus, and who tended the celestial herds (rain-giving clouds), prototype of the Greek goat-god Pan.

Lusty, full of fun and mischief, Pan, a man with goat's legs, whose name means all and implies plenty or all nature's productive powers, spent his days rambling in the woods or dancing over the fields and hills while he sang on the syrinx, the reed pipes which he had invented. One day, as he and some companions feasted near a river bank, the giant Typhon, monster who belched flames and smoke (hurricane), came upon them. Each, to escape Typhon's fury, fled in a different direction; Pan plunged into the river, and his goat-like rear, which sank into the water, miraculously developed a fishtail, while the upper part of his body transformed into that of a goat. Zeus, to commemorate this miracle, conveyed Pan, the Goat-Fish, to the skies, and from this high realm Pan sent winter's fertilizing rains. The fear which caused the revelers along the

river bank to flee became
known as panic.

In another Greek legend,
the stars outline the figure of
Amalthea, who suckled the infant Zeus. Zeus was born at
the winter solstice on Mount
Ida in a cave where his mother
Rhea (earth) hid to protect him
from his father Cronus (time),
who desired to consume him. In
the cave the she-goat Amalthea
nourished the child until he grew
strong and brave; then, like Ea,
he emasculated his father, fought
off revolting giants (night and
frost demons), and became chief
of the Olympian deities, god of
the day sky and dispenser of
justice, for which he used thunder
as his voice. Zeus honored his
old nurse when she died by making one of her horns a wonder
which provided peace and prosperity, and by turning her body
into the nocturnal form Capricorn. Sometimes Amalthea is
said to be a beautiful princess
who fed Zeus with milk from her
pet goat. Whether goat or
princess, she apparently personifies a fertile strip of ground in
Crete, land to the east, which
had the form of an animal's
horn and from which light seemed
to emerge. The fable, like that
of Ea, in which light and heat
emerged from a cold, dark subterranean recess, undoubtedly
developed from one of prehistoric origin in which light
rises from the nether regions to
reign over a celestial mansion
at the time of the winter solstice.
It appears in various parts of the
world as a resurrection story.

Accadians called these stars
Cave of the Rising Sun, oriental
nations called it Gate of the
Sun. Platonists referred to it
as Gate of the Gods and held

that men's souls, released from
their bodies at death, ascended
to the hereafter through its
stars; the stars of Cancer being
the road of descent.

Cabalists gave it to the
tribe of Naptali, a "hound let
loose," that is the hound that
chased the deer or antelope.
Among biblical writers it was
Matthew, the evangelist, or the
Tower of Gad, which at first appears to be from the Hebrew,
but is more likely a medieval
bungled translation from the
Arabic of the word Burj, which
means both constellation and
tower or fortress. It probably
has no connection with Gad, the
Hebrew tribe.

The Hindus saw it as Makara,
a sea-monster steed of Varuna,
the water-god, and of Vishnu,
the solar-god. Makara was a
wonder dragon, half bird, half
crocodile, or half fish, half
goat. This creature influenced
art throughout the Far East
and perhaps across the Pacific
Ocean. Wide-mouthed faces and
bodies with upraised tails that
frolic on Chinese arches and
temple roofs and on temple
sculptured walls and pillars as
far away as Mexico and Peru
resemble this queer beast and
quite likely are its lineal descendants. However, the
Tamil people of Southern Indian
were not influended by Makara;
they conceived these stars to
be an antelope.

Peruvian Indians celebrated
their New Year, which began
in the month of Capricorn with
the December solstice festival
to which they gave the appellation Nucca (Beard), which is
derived from a myth widespread
in the southern hemisphere that

the sun was a goat, a bearded one. The beard was emphasized in their rites and performers in ceremonial dances wore masks with beards that resembled those of a goat. Romans said the constellation was Neptune's offspring and thus preserved its nautical influence.

On illustrated maps it generally has been shown with the head and body of a goat or ibex ending in a fishtail, which conforms to its amphibious character. Occasionally it has been shown as a complete goat; on an Egyptian zodiac it appears as an ibis-headed man mounted on a goat. In Buddhist art it is an elephant; on a Brahmin bowl it is a fish without any part a goat. On an Aztec calendar it appears as Cipactli, the Great fish from whose body earth was made. This conforms to one Greek conception, which shows it as a swordfish. When seen on a clear night the constellation resembles an inverted cocked hat or an arrowhead. Its symbol ♑ is thought to be from ♈♂, the first two letters for the Greek word for goat; a second idea put forward is that it was inspired by the creatures twisted tail.

Tropic of Cancer was applied to it when it was the station of the winter solstice, but that title now refers to the zodiacal mansion Capricorn where the solstice occurs 33° west of the constellation.

Additional designations are: The Goat; Goat-Fish; Sea-Goat; Semi-Capran Fish.

Accadian: Su-tul (Goat-Fish), also known as a Double-Ship.

Anglo-Saxon: Bucca or

Buccan Horn.

Arabic: Al Jady (Goat); Giedi (Ibix).

Assyrian: Munaxa (Goat-Fish); Niru (Yoke); Shah or Shahu (Ibix).

Euphratean: Makhar (Ship-of-the-Rope). Some astronomers say this should instead apply to Delphinus. The stream around Earth was sometimes compared to a rope.

French: Capricorne.

German: Steinbok (Stonebuck or Ibix).

Hindu: Akokera (Horned-Goat), which comes from the Greek; Makara (Sea-monster); Mriga or Mrga (Wild animal) and occasionally shown with a goat's head on a hippopotamus body to suggest its amphibiousness, in which character it was called Shi-shu-mara or Sim-shu-mara (Crocodile), although this originally was marked by stars in Draco, last in order of all zodiacal signs in India as on the Euphrates.

Italian: Capricorno.

Latin: Aegoceros (Horned Goat); Aequoris Hircus (Sea Goat); Caper or Capra (She-Goat); Capra Illa Amalthea; Flexus Caper; Gelidus; Hircinus Sidus; Hircus Corniger; Imbrifer (Rain-bringing One); Neptuni Proles (Neptune's Offspring); Pelagi Procella (Ocean Storm); Signum Hiemale.

Medieval Latin: Oxirinque, from the Greek word for Swordfish when it was considered the cause of the inundation.

Medieval monstrosities com-

bining Arabic and Latin: Al-
cantarus or Alcaucurus, intended
to mean Horned Goat; Azazel,
the scapegoat and a symbol of
sacrifice or atonement; Elgedi;
Elgeudi; Gadio.

Pahlavi: Nahi (Goat).

Persian: Bushgali, Bahi,
Vahik, or Goi, all meaning goat.

Singalese: Makra (Antelope
or Wild Animal).

Syrian: Gadjo (Goat).

Tamil: Makaram (Antelope).

Turkish: Ughlak (Goat)

Astrologically it is a
feminine and therefore unfortunate
sign, and with Taurus and Virgo
formed the Earthly Trigon. Once
it was a Mansion of Kings, undoubtedly referring to it as
the natal sign of Gaius Octavius
Augustus. Inasmuch as Augustus
was born under this sign Roman's
exalted its virtues. It was
under the care of Vesta, custodian of the sacred fire; hence
Vestae Sidus, protector of
state and home. Romans also
associated it with the burning
south wind Auster. Arabians
regarded it as favorable, but
generally in astrology it expresses storms and symbolizes
mourning. Those born under it
will suffer much tragedy; a
man, although he will be gallant,
will develop eight illnesses and
succumb to one of them at the
age of sixty. Some combination
with a fortunate sign, known only
to the initiated, may make it
auspicious, in which those born
under it will be rich, well
loved, and long lived. In classical times when coincident

with the sun, it was a harbringer
of storms and as such ruler of
the waters. Horace called it
"tyrannus Hesperiae Capricornus."
A number of poems indicate
storms when the Goat coincides
with the Sun, which enters the
zodiacal sign about December 21
but does not reach the constellation until January 18. The sun
remains until February 14.
Black, russet or a muddy brown
were the colors assigned to it.
In the 14th and 15th centuries its
design, struck on medals, was
worn as a lucky charm. It is
located in the southern sky between Sagittarius and Aquarius,
and reaches the meridian about
September 22. Its bright
stars are: alpha, Giedi; beta,
Dabih; gamma, Nashira; delta,
Deneb Algiedi.

CARINA (THE   KEEL, i.e.
of Argo). This group, a subdivision of the constellation Argo,
contains the star Canopus,
second only in brilliancy to
Sirius, and eta, an unnamed
star, irregularly variable,
which is surrounded by the noted
Keyhole Nebula, itself a variable
and situated in one of the Milky
Way's most brilliant sections.

Babylonians referred to the
occasional faintness of the eta
light. Oriented to it was the
temple of Oannes, Lord of the
Waves, who revealed to man the
arts of agriculture, healing, and
writing. The Tree of Life was
located in the grove of his
temple. Each night and each
year at the harvest he was
swallowed by Tiamat, but reappeared each morning and each
spring. In this way, the hours
of light and warmth he lived
among men, the hours of darkness and cold he spent in the

depth of the sea. In later myths, Oannes is merged with Ea, also a mysterious human fish.

In formation the cluster is that of the ridge-shape on a bird's breast. Located entirely in the southern hemisphere, south of Vela, between Columba and Crux, its stars cannot be seen from the latitude of New York. However they can be observed from the Gulf States, and reach culmination in the night sky about March 17.

CASSIOPEIA (LADY IN THE CHAIR). Wife of the Ethiopian king Cepheus, Cassiopeia was a woman of flawless beauty, but as vain as she was fair. One day the Nereids, nymphs renowned for their beauty and grace, who frequented the waves along the shore and bubbling streams in the hills, overheard her boast that she was not only lovelier than any woman in her own land, but was more beautiful than any in heaven, even more comely than the nymphs themselves. The Nereids, who attended Poseidon, complained to this great master of the sea and he rose in anger, plunged his trident deep into the waves and created a monster which terrorized the Ethiopian people, demanded human sacrifice, and further punished Cassiopeia by placing her on a chair that revolved around the heaven's north pole. The circumpolar motion of these stars places her at times in the undignified position of standing on her head. By means of this giddy whirl was she taught humility. Cassiopeia belongs to the so-called Royal Family of stars, being the wife of a king, the mother of the princess Andromeda, and the mother-in-law of the hero

Perseus.

Don, queen (later the name was masculinized and the question of whether the deity was male, female, or bi-sexual was thus raised) of Celtic fairies made her home here. She was the ruler of heaven, life, and light, and her tribe was in constant conflict with that of Llyr, whose realms were the sea, darkness, and death. Her children were Gwydion, the sun, and inventor who built the Rainbow and resided on the Galaxy, and Arianrhod, the moon, whose mansion was the Northern Crown.

Religious astronomers of the 17th century saw the cluster as Bathsheba, mother of Solomon; Deborah, the prophetess; or Mary Magdalene. Deborah, who dwelt under a palm tree on Mount Ephraim sent for Barak and promised him victory if he would attack Sisera. He refused to undertake such an expedition unless she accompanied him. She agreed to this but warned him victory would be imputed to her, and so it was.

On sky maps drawn as a regally groomed woman seated on a gem-studded throne, drawing her robe over her shoulder with her right hand and raising a palm branch, symbol of victory, or an ear of corn to her head. On Alphonsine tables the figure holds the consecrated palm; here it is a symbol of martyrdom.

Egyptians conceived it to be a deer. Some place The Leg, an evil constellation here. An Arabian picturization was that of two dogs, of a kneeling camel, or of a large hand

stained with henna (blood), perhaps Fatima's Hand, a symbol
of rank, power, divine province,
the five principal Moslem com-
mandments, and used as a charm
to ward off the evil eye.

These stars have been
portrayed as a key variously
perceived to be the sickle-
shaped one in the wardrobe door
of Penelope; the Laconian Key
invented by the people of ancient
Laconia; or the Carion Key invented by the people of Samos in
Caria in 730 B.C. Locks and
keys appear to have been invented
even earlier. Such articles were
found on the site of Trojan
ruins, in Egyptian catacombs,
and mentioned in the biblical book
of Judges.

Additional designations:
Aethiop's Queen; Bagdei, given
as a name to help memorize
the order of the chief components,
beta, alpha, gamma, delta,
epsilon, iota, the last being the
uppermost when the figure is on
the horizon, hanging head down-
wards; Cassiepea, Cassiepeia,
Cassiope; Celestial M, when
below the Pole and the Celestial
W when above it; Hand of the
Pleiades; Lady in the Chair;
Lady of Corn, giving the constellation fertility significance; She
of the Throne; Troubled Queen;
Unhappy Cassiopeia.

Arabian: Al Dhat al Kursiyy
(The Lady in the Chair); Al
Thurayya; Dath Alcursi; Kaff al
H'adib (Tinted Hand, the bright
star marking the finger tips).

Biblical: Cushiopeia (Queen
of Cush or Kush).

Celtic: Llys Don (Home of
Don).

Chinese: Ko Taou (Porch
Way); Wang Liang, a celebrated
charioteer of the Tsin kingdom.

Eskimoan: Ibrosi, the three
rocks which support a celestial
stone lamp, for the stars alpha,
beta, gamma, which form an isosceles triangle.

Latin and Low Latin: Canis,
from the Arabic illustration;
Cerva (Roe); Harnacaff;
Inthronata; Jostandis (a Girdle);
Mulier Sedis (Woman in the
Seat); Sedes; Sella; Siliquastrum
(The Tree of Judea, referring
to the branch in the Queen's
hand); Solium.

Persian: Shuter (Camel).

Astrologers attribute to it
the nature of Saturn, a protector
of the treacherous, a bringer
of perfidy and mourning, and of
Venus, charming and gay, who
presided over motherhood and
love.

The head and body of the
queen are in one of the brightest
spots of the Milky Way, her
foot rests upon the Arctic Circle.
She sits surrounded by her
royal family and reaches the
meridian about November 23.
Because of the manner in which
it revolves around the North
Pole the constellation acts as
a luminous sidereal time piece.
It is above Polaris at noon;
when in the west at right angles
to the first position, the time is
six in the evening; at midnight
it is on the northern horizon,
and at 6 A.M. is due east.
Sidereal time naturally differs
from civil time in that the day
has its beginning at noon instead
of at midnight. The sidereal
clock agrees with the mean

solar clock on or about March 22 and gains at the rate of two hours a month. The bright stars in the constellation are: alpha, Schedar; beta, Caph; delta, Ruchbar. Al Aaraf is a temporary star.

CENTAURUS (THE CENTAUR). In Vedic mythology, Gandharva, a solitary steed, guarded the rainbow and carried the sun across the skies. Agile and swift, he moved with grace in and out of or mingled with rose and gold tinted clouds, measuring the space as he traveled from east to west. When caught in a strong wind he strained every sinew, but never slackened pace. He was not merely a horse, he was a celebrated bard, and his song blended with that of the wind. Because the upper half of his body was that of a man while his lower half was that of a horse, his voice had the tones of a mortal. From him came a class of beings called the gandharvas, who, when days were calm, frolicked and cantered in playful groups or wandered here and there in search of a pasture on the plains of the sky. In a wind before a storm these unbridled swift steeds strained every muscle in a mad race or relentlessly jostled each other in their efforts to escape to pleasanter woods or fields. They were skilled in music, dance, the medical arts, and were overly fond of women. In the first days of a marriage and gandharvas appeared as rivals to a husband, who was forced to display great love to hold his bride.

The Greek counterpart of the Gandharvas was the Centaurs, from whom the constellation received its name in classical times. Ixion, the scorching midday sun, desired Hera, celestial queen. To protect his wife, Zeus gave a cloud her likeness and, by cohabiting with the cloud, Ixion became the father of Centaurs (mists). In another version the race of Centaurs was born when Cronus, to prevent his jealous wife Rhea from recognizing him when he visited the sea nymph Philyra, changed himself into a horse. The Centaurs, like the Gandharvas, although they might outrage a bride or break up a marriage feast, became educators and protectors of men to whom they imparted knowledge and wisdom. One of their number was Pholus, noted for his hospitality; another was Chiron, musician, physician, prophet, and tutor of Achilles, Asclepius, Heracles, Jason and other renowned heroes. Chiron's favorite instrument was the lyre, whose notes were heard among the leaves of trees on Mount Pelian, where he roamed at night and studied the stars, which he charted that they might serve as a guide to deities and mortals. Before he did this no one knew how to determine where celestial alleys or lanes might be found. His student and friend Heracles accidentally struck him and his brother Pholus with an arrow. Pholus died immediately, but Chiron, being immortal lingered in racking pain. When his agony became intolerable he exchanged his immortality for the mortality of Prometheus, who then became mankind's benefactor and continued the astral studies of Chiron, stating when stars rose and when they set. After Chiron's death Zeus desired to lift him into the heavens, but in mapping the skies Chiron had used up the space and stars

in the northern and central sections. In addition, when he had
laid out the zodiac (path of the
sun) to guide the Argonauts on
their quest for the Golden Fleece,
he had designed one figure, Sagittarius, in his own image. In
spite of this Zeus was determined
to place this noble soul above
and found a place far to the
south, where he rarely is seen.
The homicide of Pholus and
Chiron led Demeter, who felt
their warm blood (rain) on her
body (earth), to institute the
Mysteries (rituals supplicating
for the renewal of green things).

Historically the Centaurs may
have been savage hairy Thes-
salians who hunted the bull and
went to war on horseback. Primitives they attacked imagined
them to be half man, half beast.
Mythologically they were cloud
masses, of which the head was
lit up by the sun, the rear in
the shade. They died when
pierced by arrows (rays) of the
sun. Also typified by them were
the two natures in man, the
spiritual, reason or wisdom;
the bestial, cruelty, cunning and
lust.

Both the Gandharvas and the
Centaurs appear to be descendants
of the double-headed figure with
the body of a beast in Babylonian
art. This may have been an
early sign for Sagittarius, a
constellation with which Centaurus
often is confused. Apothecaries
of the middle ages acknowledged
the Centaur's skill in curing,
and various medicinal herbs were
named Centaurea, Centaury,
Chironeion.

In classical works portrayed
as a horse to the waist, a man
above. He faces the east and
points with his left hand to the

nearby Lupus and Ara. In some
sculptures the hind quarters are
those of a bull, indicating at
one time this stellar figure
may have been the feared Minotaur. Arabs made the hind part
that of a bear, but adopted the
Greek title Al Kentaurus, which
degenerated into Taraapoz. In
the middle ages the portrait was
given various attributes, a hare
on the spear in his outstretched
hand and a canteen at his waist;
Lupus held by the forefoot in
his left hand and the thyrsus in
his right; a Bacchic wand and a
spear; a shaven face and heavy
mustache; holding the spear from
which a hare dangles and extending the other hand towards
Ara, to which he offers a kid;
holding a canteen from which
he is about to drink, undoubtedly
the usual libation; ready for
attack with a spear in his right
hand and on his left arm a
shield which is engraved with the
thyrsus and libation vase; or in
repose with Lupus.

Various designations are:
Centaure Chiron; Chiron; Great
Centaure; Handy One; Horseman
Beast; Phililyrides or Philyrides,
alluding to the sea nymph Philyra,
mother of Chiron by Cronus;
Well Disposed, alluding to
Pholus.

Arabic: Al Kadb al Karm
(The Vine Branch); Al Kentaurus,
from the Greek; Al Shamarih
(The Broken Off Palm Branch),
which the Centaur may have
carried.

Latin: Acris Venator (Fierce
Hunter); Centaurus; Geminus
Biformis; Minotaurus; Pelenor
or Pelethronius, from the
mountain home of the Centaurs
in Thessaly; Semi-Fer (Half-
Beast); Semi-Vir (Half-Man)

Sonipes (Noisy-Footed).

Medieval biblical adherents; Abraham with Isaac; Nebucha-drezzar, when he did eat grass as oxen; Noah.

Medieval hybrids of Arabic and Latin: Albeze, Albezze, Albizze, all unintelligible; Asemarik or Asmeat, degenerate forms of Al Shamarih; Birdun (Pack-horse); Taraapoz.

Located deep in the southern sky between Hydra and Southern Cross. Most of its stars are unseen by those in the northern hemisphere. Although Centaurus is the only constellation save that of Orion that can boast of two stars of first magnitude, they remain unnamed in European lore except for the joint epithet Southern Pointers. These brilliant stars, close together, make a striking pair and point straight at the Southern Cross, which makes them helpful in navigation. In Arabia these two stars are Hadar (Ground) and Wazn (Weight) because of their seeming inability to lift themselves from the ground. Desert nomads call them Khaiyal (Cavalier) and Zammal (Mule-driver), two riders that come face to face across the lonely fields of the southern sky. To Australian natives they are the Two Brothers who speared their enemy Tchingal to death, using the eastern stars of Crux as the spear. Bushmen called the pair Two Men that once were Lions. In South China they are Nan Mun (South Gate of the Sky). Culmination of Centaurus is about May 14.

CEPHEUS (KING, MONARCH). The ancestry of Cepheus remains a mystery; he is said to be identical with Cush, son of Ham, or with Cheops (Khufu), builder of the Great Pyramid at Gizeh, an Egyptian who seized the throne and became king of the Fourth Dynasty. The burden of taxes he imposed was so intolerable hundreds of thousands were forced into slave labor. The hatred for him lasted several centuries until his tomb was raided and his mummy torn to pieces. The people refused to call the pyramid he built by his name and called it after Philitis, a shepherd who grazed flocks near it. He supposedly composed a religious work called the Sacred Book, which is used by mystics. To intimate that he descended from the god Khnumu, he was called Khnumu-Khufu. Cheops was the Greek form. Then again Zeus was the ancestor of Cepheus. One point all concede: he was king of Ethiopia, a valiant warrior who accompanied the Argonauts on their quest for the Golden Fleece. Upon his return he married the enchanting beauty Cassiopeia, but when he settled down to enjoy connubial bliss, he discovered his queen was vain and arrogant. He was unable to escape the eventual calamity that accompanies rare beauty. The misfortune that befell him and his realm is told where the story of his daughter Andromeda is related. Inasmuch as he is king of the Royal Family of luminaries, consisting of Cassiopeia, Andromeda, Perseus, his stars never set; because of the weakness he displayed in his marital affairs, his configuration is dim. Notwithstanding, a fire burns within him. This is revealed by mu Cephei. Although small it is the reddest naked-eye luminary to be seen and celebrated as the Garnet Star.

In Christian lore the outline
delineates the coming of the
Redeemer as King.

Chinese imagined these
stars to be Tsao Fu (Tsau-fu),
charioteer to the 10th century
emperor Mu Wang. Mu Wang
set out with his charioteer for
a visit to the Western Paradise
on the slopes of Mount K'uen
Lun in the center of the land
of immortality. Many varieties
of trees beautified the garden,
some had flowers or fruit composed of pearls, jade, and other
precious stones. The innermost
court was that of Hsi Wang Mu,
queen-mother, and there she
cultivated the peach tree of everlasting life, Shen t'ao, which
bore fruit every 3,000 years.
Each thirty centuries, when the
fruit ripened, Hsi Wang Mu invited all the gods and a rare
mortal who possessed great
virtue to partake of the peaches
which possessed the essence of
infinity. Mu Wang had resolved
to enjoy this magic nourishment
when he had instructed Tsao Fu
to harness his eight magnificent
steeds to the chariot. With
great pomp they set out, but
neither the emperor nor his
horses nor his driver were ever
again seen on earth. It is assumed they did indeed reach
the court of Hsi Wang Mu and
were rewarded for the exploit by
a gift of a peach, a bite of which
made them lose all sense of time
as well as a desire to return to
their native land. Tsao Fu, as
the less self-seeking of the two,
was lifted up and provided a
residence among the stars of
Cepheus. In a simpler explanation for this name, the Chinese
Inner Throne of Five Emperors
stood within this constellation's
boundaries. One of the
emperors ordered some of the

stars to be called Tsao Fu after
his favorite charioteer.

The likeness of Cepheus is
that of a seated figure in royal
robes with one foot on the pole,
the other on the solstitial colure.
He wears a crown of stars and
in his left hand holds a scepter
extended toward Cassiopeia, who
is nearby; with his right hand
he holds a scarf or part of his
robe above his shoulder. He
also is shown as the Celestial
K, open towards Cassiopeia.
Arabs drew these stars as a
dog, a companion of Cassiopeia,
also drawn as a dog.

Some claim the name is derived from Hyk, Ethiopian for
king, but this is questionable as
the constellation appears to be of
ancient Euphratean origin. One
designation is Little Diamond in
contradistinction to the Big
Diamond (Pegasus). Probably
in an effort to connect Cepheus
with Cheops (Khufu) unusual or
erroneous transcriptions of his
name appear in the Arabic, such
as: Kankaus, Kifaus, and Kikaus.
In Persian in some peculiar
manner these became Fifaus,
Fikaus, Ficares, Phicares,
Phicarus, or Pirchaeus, all intended to mean Fire-kindler,
which seems closer to the Arabic
Kidr (Pot).

Superbly situated with nights
resplendent with stars and in a
climate ideal for star gazing,
the Arabs let their fertile
imaginations drift into the mystery
of nocturnal hours. On the hills,
where they lingered, they wove
heroic or rustic tales around
the figures they conceived. Like
Euphrateans, who listed these
stars as "numerous flocks," the
Arabs were a pastoral and
nomadic people. Quite naturally

stars close to the North Pole became the Fold, and the Cepheus grouping converted into a Shepherd with his dog watching sheep at pasture. Inevitably the names Al Aghnam (The Sheep); Kelds or Kalb (Shepherd's Dog); Raar or Rai (Shepherd); San or Sham (Dog) attached to it.

Other designations are— French: Cephee; Hindu; Capuji, adopted from the Greek. An earlier name may have been Sugriva, the Ape-god who was son of the sun and became king of monkeys. Italian: Cefeo.

Latin: An early confusion with Bootes brought Cantans, Sonans, and Vociferans (sound, noise). Titles that suggest the fiery and inappropriate for such a faint figure unless they are connected with the fable that the Table of the Sun, which ministered to the wants of all, the bad as well as the good, was spread in Ethiopia, the land Cepheus ruled while on earth, are: Dominus Solis, Flammiger, Incensus, Inflammatus. These were translated by Arabians into Al Multahab. Other Latin epithets are: Iasides; Juvenis aequoreus; Nereus, because he was aged; Regulus or Vir regius, because of his royal position; Senex aequoreus.

Medieval biblical appelations: King Solomon; Saint Stephen; Zerah, Ethiopian king overthrown by King Asa.

Medieval Latin derivatives: Caicans, Ceginus, Ceichius, Chegninus, Chegnius, Cheguinus, Chiphus, some of which also are attached to Bootes.

This constellation appears in the night sky of autumn and reaches culmination about November 13. Its bright stars are alpha, Aldermain, which will be the north pole in about 5,600 years; beta, Alfirk; gamma, Er Rai.

CERBERUS. Formerly an adjunct of Hercules; now entirely disregarded by astronomers. Stars that had been assigned to it lie between Hercules' head and the head of Cygnus. Also called Rameau at Cerbere (Branch of Cerberus).

CETUS (SEA MONSTER). One of the largest constellations in the heavens, it appeared among early configurations. In antiquity some of its stars may have represented Tiamat, the bloodthirsty serpent of the abyss. It has consistenly represented the chaos of the deep and has been presented as a monster that rises from the dark nether sea with ravenous appetite for humans. On occasions, to the consternation of those who beheld it, Cetus enjoyed swimming in the Eridanus, or river Po, the cosmic stream into which Zeus, with a bolt of lightning, hurled Phaethon, when the rash youth lost control while driving his father's sun chariot and set the fire in the heavens that scorched the skin of the Ethiopians. In Greek mythology he is Cetus, the hell-dragon sent by Poseidon to devour Andromeda. In his encounter with Perseus, who came to the rescue of the maiden in distress, Cetus became a victim of the petrifying powers of the bleeding Medusa head carried by the hero and belched a blood-red stream that gushed into the air like a fountain; then he turned into stone. Many have corroborated the story that its fossilized skeleton over forty feet in length

with a vertabrae six feet in circumference had been preserved.
Saint Jerome claimed he saw the
monster's bones at Tyre. Pau-
sanias, 2nd century A.D. Greek
traveler and geographer said that
he saw a fountain red with its
blood. Fundamentally Cetus
signified the wild dark waves that
rose from the depths in the
season of high winds, lightning,
and torrential rains to devour
long stretches of beaches or
fertile fields, and symbolized the
demons of famine and hunger
which accompany inundations.
Cetus is the prototype of every
fiend that ever threatened a
virgin maid in fairy tales.

Seventeenth century biblical
writers have variously claimed
the stars to be the Leviathan,
which the Lord told the patriarch
Job, the Messiah will catch and
divide among the faithful for
food at the end of the world;
the Whale that swallowed Jonah;
the serpent form of Satan; the
Dragon of Saint George; Saints
Joachim and Anne.

Depicted as a ferocious marine
creature, the like of which never
has actually been seen by anyone
on earth, its head, facing the east,
resembles that of a dinosaur,
walrus with a single tusk rising
above its nose, or a greyhound.
Its two front paws are immersed
in the river; its scaly body ends
in the tail of a fish. On certain
manuscripts it appears as a
mutilated hand, a kite, and
an inverted bowl, somewhat
larger but otherwise resembling
the so-called Milk Dipper in
Sagittarius.

Additional designations: The
Dusky Monster, The Easy Chair,
alluding to the arrangement of
its principal stars, which are
visible from October to February
and suggest a lounge or reclining
chair.

Arabian: Al Ketus, from the
Greek Cetus, which corrupted
into Elkaitos, Elkaitus, Elketos;
Al Kaffal Jidhmah (The Part of
the Hand) for stars in the head
lying above the equator; Al
Na amat (Hen Ostriches) for
stars in the body of the figure;
Al Nitham (The Necklace) for
four stars in a straight line in
the tail.

French: Baleine (Whale).

German: Wallfisch (Whale).

Greek: One title incorporated
the meaning to blow or sprout,
a habit of the mammal.

Italian: Balaena.

Latin: Pristis or Pristix
(Sawfish).

Medieval Latin: Belua (Beast),
Canis Tritonis; Cete; Chien de
Mer; Gibbus (Humped); Monstrum
Marinum; Orphas, Orphus,
Ursus Marinus.

Because bad seas frequently
accompany the appearance of
Cetus, mariners despise it, in
fact look upon it as an enemy.
Astrologically it is a bringer
of misfortune.

Close by Andromeda, adjoining Pisces, the head of the
Whale is above the equator, the
body below it. Culmination is
about November 29. Principal
stars are alpha, Menkab; beta,
Deneb Kaitos, which has become
the lucida; omicron, Mira, the
Wonderful, a variable situated
in the neck.

CHAMAELEON (THE CHAMELEON). Because this lizard has the power of changing its shape at will by inflating itself with air and also of changing its color, it typifies that which is unpredictable or capricious, especially fickle persons, a character somewhat applicable to this group of uncertain stars. In African lore this is an unlucky animal, the embodiment of departed spirits and associated with the entry of death into the world. In Biblical lore this cluster was combined with Apus and Musca and called Eve.

Although designed in the middle ages, the title comes from the Greek. Additional designations: Chamaeleon with the Fly (or Flie) when combined with Musca; Chameleon (Lion on the Ground); French: Cameleon; German: Chamaleon; Italian: Camaleonte.

This was first figured in the 15th or 16th century from observations by navigators in southern waters. It is small and unimportant, without bright stars, and lies in the southern-sky below Carina, separated from the Pole by Octans. Culmination is about April 15.

CIRCINUS (PAIR OF COMPASSES). A configuration of the 19th century, when astronomers tended to name their discoveries after mechanical instruments.

Additional designations - French: Compas; German: Zirkel (Pair of Compasses); Italian: Compasso.

Located in the southern sky south of Lupus and Norma close to the feet of Centaurus. Without bright stars, it culminates about June 14.

COLUMBA (THE DOVE). On a Eurphratean planisphere of unknown date a dove appears and early in Christian times the title was used, but doubt exists that either described these luminaries, which are quite faint. Official acknowledgment was not given to this constellation until the latter part of the 17th century, and the stars assigned were strays outside the frontier of Canis Major.

The name refers specifically to the dove-shaped receptacle used for sacrament in medieval churches or to the bird sent forth by Noah from the ark. When the dove returned with an olive branch in its mouth, Noah knew the waters had abated, and he again released the bird, which did not return. Noah understood it had found land. Into the middle ages seamen released birds to determine in which direction land lay. For thousands of years the dove has been esteemed as a herald of heavenly news. In its body a departed spirit, especially a friendly one, reappeared. In nature worship it is closely associated with rain clouds. Doves were substituted for humans when offerings were made to a deity. In Christian tradition it denotes the Holy Ghost, symbolizes annunciation and baptism, and is an emblem of an apostle or saint divinely inspired. In Christian art it is identical with the winged disc of Pagan art as a symbol of eternity, immortality, soul, and as such issues from the mouth of dying martyrs. The dove was sacred to people of ancient Egypt, Greece, Phoenicia, and

152   Outer Space

other places. In early Mosaic
law it was clean and sacrificed
in rituals of expiation, principally by the poor, particularly for
atonement for the impurity of
childbirth; similar offerings were
brought by Virgin Mary to the
temple at Jerusalem after the
birth of Christ. This seems
to echo its function as an emblem
of love and fertility deities. In
Hebraic-Christian culture the
dove compares with the Buddhist
white swan. It is one of the ten
animals in the Moslem Heaven.

Additional designations are:
Columba Noachi; Columba Noae;
Noah's Dove. French: Columbe
de Noe; German: Taube; Italian:
Colomba.

Seen in the southern winter
sky below the Hare, between
Puppis and Caelum, it culminates
about February 1, and its bright
stars are alpha, Phaet; beta,
Wezn; theta and kappa the Arabs
call Al Kurud, the Apes.

COMA BERENICES (BER-
ENICE'S HAIR). Berenice is
from a pure Greek word meaning
victory bringer, which in low
Greek became a word for amber.
In the Old Testament it was the
name of the infamous daughter of
Agrippa I, who became the wife
of her uncle Herod of Chalcis
and mistress of her brother, the
younger Agrippa. Noted for her
beauty, and ambition, she left
her brother to become a mistress
of Titus.

The constellation usually is
attached to the legend of Berenice, sister-wife of Ptolemy III,
Euergetes, who vowed to sacrifice
her magnificent amber tresses
to the goddess of beauty if her
husband were brought home safely
from a war against the Assyrians.

Upon his arrival she suspended
her hair in a temple and, when
the locks disappeared, the king
was pacified by a priest who informed him that winds had lifted
them to heaven. Probably this
group was the one known to
Egyptians as Many Stars.

Actually the right of these
stars to be termed a constellation remained unsettled for
about two thousand years; the
argument was not resolved until
1602 A.D., when they were so
catalogued in a star list. Previously they had been identified
as an asterism by itself, as
part of the great Arabian Lion,
as part of Virgo.

Sometimes the hair sacrificed
was turned into a comet or hair
star, and this group was said
to be the hair or thread (light
ray) that Ariadne gave to Theseus
to enable him to find his way out
of the labyrinth (dark other-
world), which he as the sun was
forced to traverse throughout
the night.

The wistful legend of Veronica,
who offered her sweat cloth to
Jesus that he might wipe his
brow, found his image imprinted
on it when he returned it to her
and in this way was converted
to Christianity, is affixed to
these stars. The association
comes from the resemblance of
her name to that of the Latin
Beronica, Greek Berenice.
In other Christian interpretations
the stars were Samson's Hair,
the Scourage of Christ, and
Absalom's Hair. Absalom, the
rebellious son of David, attempted
to usurp his father's throne.
While being pursued by government troops in the oak forest of
Ephraim his long flowing hair
became entangled with the branch

of a tree, and he was caught, cut down, and slain. This situation parallels many in mythology, where the old sacred king (old year or sun) is in conflict with the prince (new year or morning sun); also where the hero is emasculated and his sacred heel is saved from touching the ground by his hair. When the heel of the sun touches the horizon, death must follow.

It appears on illustrated manuscripts not only as a beautiful strand, but also is shown as a sheaf of wheat, that held by Virgo (Ceres), which is nearby.

Additional designations: Berenice's Bush; Berenice's Hair; Berenice's Locks; Berenice's Periwig; Beronice's Hair. (The name Berenice has been the source of the English word varnish, French vernis, Italian vernice, Spanish barniz, all in kinship with the color of the lady's hair). Caduceus, which indicates these stars once had been a part of Virgo, when Virgo was in the astrological house of Mercury; Ivy Wreath; Virgin's Distaff.

Arabic: Al Atha or Utha (The Mixture); Al Halbah or Al Darfirah (The Coarse Hair or Tuft, i.e. in the tail of the Lion, a figure that extended far beyond its present termination); Al Haud (The Pond) into which the Gazelle (Leo Minor) sprang when frightened by the lashing of the great Arabian Lion's tail; Al Huzmat (The Pile, i.e. of fruit, grain, or wood).

French: Chevelure (Head of Hair).

German: Haupthaar (Head Hair).

Italian: Chioma di Berenice (Blonde or White Berenice).

Latin and Low Latin: Capilli (Hair); Cincinnus (Curl); Comae (Hair) Berenices; Crines (Hair); Crines Berenices; Rosa (Rose or Wreath); Tericas, Trica, Tricas, Triquetras, all from low Greek for tresses or three fold.

Medieval: Flagellum Christi (Scourge of Christ).

Above Virgo in the northern sky it contains the northern Galactic Pole, which is directly opposite the southern pole in Sculptor. It comes to the meridian about May 17, and although it has no bright stars it has many admirers who on a clear spring night seek a view of its irregular delicacy that is lovely and fairy-like to the naked-eye and even more beautiful through glasses.

CORONA AUSTRALIS (THE SOUTHERN CROWN). Latin poets thought it the crown Bacchus placed to honor his mother Semele or one that commemorated the fivefold victory of Corinna over Pindar. Semele, Greek goddess of green earth, was the mistress of Zeus. When she pleaded with her lover to show himself to her in his greatest heavenly splendor (clothed in lightning), he was unable to resist her entreaties and she, unable to survive his burning light, perished. At the time she was pregnant and Zeus quickly absorbed his unborn son (the sun) into his own body where the fetus remained until the time had come for birth, and then he burst from the leg of his father (horizon). Poetry contests between Corinna and Pindar were held in the 5th century B.C. at

Thebes, where Corinna in-
structed Pindar in lyric poetry.
Five times they contended and
on each occasion she was a-
warded the laurel wreath.

Also this cluster has been
identified as the bunch of arrows
shot by the Archer, or presumed
to be the wheel of Ixion, a sun
hero and king of Lapithae in
Thessaly. Ixion married Dia,
daughter of Hesioneus, to whom
he promised rich gifts for his
bride, but once married Ixion
failed to send them, whereupon
Hesioneus stole the immortal
horses which drew the flaming
chariot of Ixion across the sky.
To regain his horses Ixion invited his father-in-law to visit
him and select gifts. When
Ixion opened the door of the
treasure house he told Hesioneus
to look in. Bending over the pit
the older man fell in and was
consumed by fire. Famine followed the crime as the dead
Hesioneus, a river deity, was
unable to supply fertilizing waters.
Zeus purified Ixion and invited
him to a banquet, where he made
love to Hera. Zeus substituted a
cloud in his wife's shape and by
the cloud Ixion became the father
of the Centaurs. For his crimes
Zeus ordered Hermes (wind) to
bind Ixion to an eternally revolving four-spoked wheel, i.e. a
fiery cross (sun) throwing rays
into four directions.

Gospel interpretors saw it as
the Crown of Eternal Life in the
New Testament or as the Diadem
of Solomon.

Depicted as a typical wreath,
but without the streaming ribbons
of its northern counterpart, or
as a heart-shaped object, which
has no resemblance to its name.

Additional designations:
Corona Austrina; The Southern
Crown.

Arabic: Al Fakkah (The Dish);
Al Hiba (The Tent); Al Iklil al
Janubiyyah, their equivalent for
our title, which was corrupted
back into Latin as Alachil,
Aladil, Algenubi, and Elkleil
Elgenubi. Al Kubbah (The
Tortoise, which also means
Woman's Tent or Traveling
Apartment); Al Udha al Na'am
(The Ostrich's Nest), the birds
themselves being close by in
what we call the Archer and the
Eagle.

Chinese: Pee (Tortoise).

French: Couronne Australe.

German: Südliche Krone.

Greek: The Hellens knew as
Caduceus or Herald's Wand of
Peace; Centaur's Crown, the
idea undoubtedly originated from
the way sunrays spread out in a
crown-like form around the
Centaurs (clouds). It thus was
appropriately associated with the
centaur Sagittarius and was given
the title Corona Sagittarii by
the Romans. Another Greek
name was the Southern Wreath;
early Greeks knew only Corona
Borealis as a crown.

Italian: Corona Australe.

Latin: Coelum; Coelulum;
Corolla (Little Crown); Corona
Sagittarius; Orbiculus Capitis;
parvum Coelum (little Sky, i.e.
Canopy); Rota Ixionis (Wheel of
Ixion); Sertum Australe (Southern
Garland); Spira Australis (South-
ern Coil); Uraniscus (Wand of
Mercury).

Although inconspicuous it was

discovered before Christian times and listed by Greek astronomers. Without bright stars it is located in the southern sky along the rim of the Galaxy, near by Sagittarius, in fact it is almost within the Sagittarius frame. It may be seen at culmination about August 14.

CORONA BOREALIS (THE NORTHERN CROWN). No other stellar crown was known to early Greeks and, like its later named southern counterpart, they called it A Wreath. When successors located Corona Australis, additions were made to the original stellar group to distinguish its preexistence. In very early astronomy these stars may have been the upraised arm of Bootes.

When Ariadne was deserted by Theseus, whom she had saved from a labyrinth, she sat forlornly on the rocks along the coast of Naxos. There Dionysus (Bacchus) came upon her and overcome by her entrancing beauty, he stopped to comfort her. When he asked her to become his wife, she informed him she was disillusioned with mortal men and wished to be left alone. He assured her he was a god, whereupon she instructed him to prove it. Pleasantly he chuckled, and then tossed the crown of gold he wore up into the skies. There it hung, and one by one seven bright stars danced around it, until the whole band was shining overhead. "That is your wedding gift," he said, and pulled it down. "You are to wear it as an everlasting token of your beauty." After the death of Ariadne it again was placed in the heavens.

Persephone (Proserpina) has been identified with the constellation, and this may have come about through a Chaldean title, Persephon, taken from Phe'er (Crown) and Serphon (Northern). If Charles Francois Dupuis, an 18th century French writer, who is responsible for this hypothesis is correct, the origin of the figure as well as the name may date back before Cretan times. An Italian astronomer of the 17th century, Francesco Grimaldi, attaches this asterism to the high priest's crown which appeared on Mithraic tablets.

The castle of the Brythonic moon goddess Arianrhod, a purgatory which was the abode of lost souls, was built of these stars. Although called one of the three White Ladies of Britain, she consented to the fraud of being introduced to Math, king of the sky, as a virgin after being seduced by her brother Gwydion. When she stepped over a magic rod owned by Math he discovered the deception, and she retreated to her mansion in the darkness of night.

Also, the four-square castle of glass, Caer Sidi that swirled in the winds, and where the souls of dead kings and perfect heroes resided, was situated here. It spun around so that no one might find its entrance, which was a dark door on the side of a slope. The structure was pitch black except for the twilight made by a lamp that burned before its circling gate. Feasting and revelry went on inside, and it contained the choicest of riches, the pearl-rimmed caldron of nine Celtic pythonesses, so that oracles might be sent forth. Its walls were lined with archers who shot so vigorously no armor could withstand their falling arrows (spikes or spokes of the zodiac).

In Grail legends it became
the Sacred Chalice or Holy Grail.
In modern Britain the revolving
castle survives in Easter maze
dances.

Bible spokesmen theorized
it was Mazzaroth, diadem that
the Persian king Ahasuerus
placed on the head of the Jewess
Esther when she became his wife;
that it was the golden crown of a
talent's weight worn by Ammonite
kings; that it was the Crown of
Thorns worn by Christ.

In various North American
Indian tales it is the Cave into
which the Great Bear retired
when he fled from the world and
hibernated for the winter. For
Shawnee Indians it shines as
twelve comely sisters who came
down to earth to dance on the
velvety grass of a wide prairie.
One day Algon (White Hawk), the
hunter, chanced upon them as they
left the magic basket in which
they had come down. He hid
nearby, entranced by their grace
as they danced within the boundary
of a magic circle they had outlined. To enjoy their fairy-like
elegance he returned day after
day. Gradually he fell in love
with the youngest and fairest,
and possessing supernatural
powers he transformed himself
into a field mouse and crept into
the magic circle, where he was
concealed by the grass. When
the youngest maiden danced above
him, he suddenly resumed his
own shape, leapt up and seized
her firmly in his arms. Her
sisters all rushed back to their
silver basket, while she struggled
to free herself, but her lover
held her so tightly she was unable to escape. At last the
others permitted themselves to
be lifted back into the air. Only
then did the maiden look at the

man who held her, and seeing
how handsome, tall, and strong
he was, she returned his love.
In his village of painted tents
they were married and lived
happily for several years until
finally she was moved with an
irresistible longing to see her
old home of white tents and her
sisters. While her husband was
on a hunting trip she made a
silver basket, which she transported to the fairy circle. Her
small son in her arms, she
stepped into it, and sang a fairy
chant. Algon returned home
across the fields just as the
basket rose to the tree tops,
and hearing the music he understood that had happened. Up
high in space the star maid
was not happy; she longed for
the man she loved. To see his
daughter smile once more, her
father invited Algon to make his
home among them. The hunter,
anxious to bring gifts with him,
gathered some token of every
kind of living thing in the land,
a feather from a bird, a horn
from the buffalo of the plains,
a cast-off skin of a prairie
snake, a squirrel's tail, which
he distributed upon his arrival.
The star-folk who took them
immediately became identified
with the bird, animal, or fish
whose token they accepted. In
this way each one became a
patron of some creature as well
as the tribe which had that
creature as its totem. Algon
and his wife and son held on to
the feathers of a white falcon or
hawk and in that guise constantly
hover between heaven and earth.
Free to roam, they follow the
wind, and travel at will either
in the land below or the one a-
bove. The star sisters now
dance at night in the circle called
Corona Borealis. It is not quite
complete, the gap caused by the

youngest one that left their group.

On illustrated maps it appears as a laurel wreath; as a jeweled tiara; as a wreath of birds, flowers or leaves held together by an undecorated three-quarter circle, not at all like a diadem. In mid-18th century, to honor the bishop of Salzburg, a member of the Firmian family infamous for his persecutions, the crown was labeled Corona Firmiana and was engraved with a stag's antlers from the family's crest of arms.

Additional designations: Ariadne's Crown; Ariadne's Tiara; Adriane's Crown; Adrian's Crown; Coiled Hair of Ariadne, a duplicate of the streaming tresses of Berenice; Crown of Amphitrite, probably from its proximity to the Dolphin, an attribute of that goddess; Crown of Seven Stars; Crown of Vulcan; Northern Crown; Wreath of Flowers.

Arabic: Al Fakkah (The Dish); later this title appeared for Corona Australis. Al Fakkah appeared on European lists as Alfacca, Alfecca, Alfelta, Alfeta, Alphaca, Alphakkaco, Alphena, Foca, and Phecca. Al Iklil al Shamaliyyah, from the classical title, which degenerated into Acliluschemali, Aclushemali, Iklil, Pupilla. Al Malf al Khatar (The Loop of the Wreath) for stars at the crown's junction. This deteriorated into Al Milaff al Kurrah and Al Malif al Kurra. Al Munir al Fakkah (The Bright One of the Dish), which became Malphelcane. Kas'at al Masakin (The Pauper's Bowl). Kas'at al Salik.

Australian: Woomera (Boomerang).

Brythonic: Caer Arianrhod or Arianrod (House of Arianrhod). This name bears a unique resemblance to the Greek owner of the crown. Arianrhod signifies silver wheel or circle.

Celtic: Caer Sidi (Revolving Castle).

Chinese: Kwan Soo (A Cord).

Christian: Crown of Thorns.

French: Couronne Boreale.

German: Nordliche Krone.

Hebrew: Ataroth (Crown), perhaps that of the Semitic Cushiopeia (Queen of the Cush) who is said to be none other than Ashtaroth (Astarte).

Italian: Corona; la figliuola di Minoi.

Latin and Low Latin: Ariadnaea Corona; Ariadnaea Sidus; Corona Audnae; Corona Ariadnes; Corona Borea; Corona Borealis; Corona Cretica; Corona Gnosida (Gnosos was the birthplace of Ariadne); Corona Gnossis; Corona Septentironalis; Cressa Corona; Gnosia Ardor Bacchi; Libera, derived from Liber Bacchus. Liber was an Italian god of fructification who became attached to Bacchus. Maera (The Shining One); Malfelcarre; Malphelcarre (Circle of the Pupil of the Eye), which may have had a connection with the name Pupilla, a title for Persephone. Minoia Corona; Minoia Virgo; Naxius Ardor, from Naxos where Ariadne was deserted; Oculus, a poetic term for any celestial luminary; Parma (Shield); Prosperpina (Persephone); Vichacca.

Onodaga Indians: The Bears'
Den (Den of Ursa Major, where
the celestial bear-hunt story is
told).

Persian: Kasah Darwishan
(Dervish's Platter); Kashah
Skekesteh (Broken Platter),
because the circle is not closed.

In the northern sky it is surrounded by Serpens, Bootes,
Draco, Hercules, and culminates
about July 3. Its alpha star is
Alphecca.

CORVUS (THE CROW). A
bird appears on one of the most
ancient carvings of celestial signs
ever excavated. As a matter of
course each cosmic bird configuration has been claimed to be the
original, the model for that design. Thus Corvus may be the
after-life form of mortals, whose
souls passed into the hideous
feathered monsters that followed
in the train of Tiamat and
caused storms, especially on
the desert. The prominent stars
have likewise been given the
character of the Accadian Kurra
(Horse).

The most popular association
is that of the crow in Greek
mythology. Apollo sent him with
a cup to get water at a fountain
quite a distance away. Over-
hanging the fountain the crow
noticed the branch of a fig tree
heavy with green fruit. Unable
to resist the temptation he
perched among the leaves and
waited for the fruit to ripen.
After he had eaten, troubled by
a guilty conscience, he carried
back with him not only the drink
but a water-snake he had seized
and explained to Apollo that he
had been delayed by this creature's
attack. The wise, all-seeing
Apollo knew this to be untrue.

Angry that the bird had the audac-
ity to lie to him, Apollo placed
the crow, cup (Crater), and the
snake (Hydra) among the stars
and so arranged them that the
serpent guards the brimful cup
and the hapless bird, try as he
may, cannot get close enough to
quench his thirst. This may be
why in early folklore the crow
is the only bird that does not
carry water to its fledglings.
The bird-snake conflict is an
essential part of the Tree of
Life legends. No matter how
he tried to win favor, the poor
crow or raven was in disrepute.
Coronis, loved by Apollo and by
him the mother of Asclepius,
was unfaithful to the god, taking
as her lover the Thessalian
youth Ischys (strength). A
crow brought Apollo news of
her infidelity, whereupon the
handsome deity killed her. While
she was on a flaming bier he
tore his infant son Asclepius from
her and gave the child to Chiron
to raise. Reflected here are
the countless instances in which
the sun, the ceaseless traveler,
is faithless to his love or she
to him. Asclepius is born at the
moment of his mother's flaming
death inasmuch as dawn cannot
survive the birth of the infant
sun. The name Coronis, which
means sea-gull as well as dawn,
is related to crow, the bird
which spied on her. Apollo was
so hurt by the newsmonger,
he turned its silvery or gray
plumage into black. Even Lepus,
the Hare, which always detested
the crow's croaking voice any-
way, would not have anything to
do with such a miserable creature
and set soon after Corvus came
above the horizon. In spite of
being hurt by the bird, Apollo
held Corvus sacred, for in
this shape the deity had not
only carried out his prophetic

functions, but escaped with his life during the conflict the Gods had with the Giants. The bird likewise was sacred to Athena, and when Coronaeus, daughter of the king of Phocis, who was pursued by Poseidon, appealed to the goddess of wisdom to save her, Athena translated the girl into a crow.

Among ardent biblical writers Corvus is the Bird of Doom, the white raven sent out by Noah to see if land were exposed anywhere. The bird found a corpse (Hydra) floating on the water and when it began to eat the body its plumage turned black. Affiliation with the Ark links it with others that are part of a graphic account of the Deluge. As the Cassiopeia-Cepheus-Andromeda-Perseus clan compose a serial story, so does the group of Crovus-Crater (or Argo, the Ark)-Hydra-Centaurus (biblical Noah)-Ara (altar built by Noah when the waters subsided), from which rises the Cloud of Smoke (Galaxy). On the other side of the Ark or Argo is Columba, a Dove. Significant is the arrangement in this locale, a region referred to as a sea. A sea yarn relating to the whale also appears in the Erdianus-Aquarius-Pisces-Cetus combination. Others of the middle ages thought that Corvus represented Elijah's (Elias's) Raven. Elijah, who burst upon the scene without previous notice, was accepted as a divine messenger. He provoked the wrath of Ahab and Jezebel with his threat that Israel would suffer several years of drought for its sins. When famine came he took refuge on the banks of the brook Cherth and was miraculously fed by ravens. In a contest with prophets of Baal, Jehovah answered Elijah by sending fire (lightning) from heaven, whereas Baal remained deaf to the cries of his priests. His work completed he was forewarned of the approach of his removal from earth, and, after he cast his mantle on Elisha, whom he had anointed prophet in his stead, he crossed the Jordan miraculously and was borne to heaven in a fiery chariot (sunset hues) by the whirlwind without tasting death. Early in the 17th century these stars were combined with those of Crater and called Ark of the Covenant.

Pagan Arabs used these stars to compose part of their immense Asad (Lion).

Hindus also utilized them for a tremendous figure, that of Prajapati, cosmic principle and lord of light born of the Golden Egg produced by the waters by means of tapas (heat). The bright Corvus stars composed the hand. A stella raven, Eorosch, is mentioned in the Avesta, but how or if this coincides with our stars is not known.

Corvus was part of the great stellar division of the Chinese Red Bird, which ruled or rode upon the wind. It also was the Crossbar or Threshold over which the Chariot of the Year must pass before entering the new year, and some of its stars composed an Imperial Chariot for emperors in the after world.

Early in the 19th century, under the influence of industrialism, a German astronomer endeavored to prove that Corvus-Crater-Hydra reflected the petroleum wells of Baku, the long extended serpent with

coils and folds stood for the slow
oily flow of crude oil, the Cup,
the oil's receptable or reservoir;
the Crow, the oil's inky blackness.

On ancient maps the bird
is on the coils of the water-
snake Hydra, obviously pecking
at him.

Additional designations:
Raven.

Arabic: Al Ajmal (The
Camel); Al 'Ajz al Asad (The
Rump of the Lion); Al 'Arsh
al Simak al 'Azal (Throne of
the Unarmed One, i.e. the star
Spica in Virgo) for its four bright
stars; Al Ghurab, from the
Greek, a late title; Al Hiba or
Al Chiba (The Tent); Al Hiba
Yamaniyyah (The Southern Tent).

Euphratean: Bird of the
Desert; Bird of the Great Sea;
Storm Bird; Storm Wind.

French: Corbeau.

German: Rabe.

Hebrew: Orebh or Orev
(Raven).

Italian: Corvo.

Latin: Avis Ficarius (Fig
Bird); Avis Satyra (Bird of
Satyrs); Emansor (One who
stays beyond his time); Phoe-
beius Ales; Phoebo Sacer Ales;
Pomptina, from the victory of
the Roman Emperor Valerius,
when he supposedly was aided
by a raven on the Pontine
Marsh.

Persian: Vanant, marker of
the western quarter of the earliest Persian heavens.

Corvus is a bird of spring
in the southern sky; it comes to
the meridian about 9 P.M. on
May 12.

For, lo, the winter is past,
The rain is over and gone;
The flowers appear on the
    earth;
The time of the singing of
    birds is come.
    (Solomon's Song)

Bright stars in the constellation are alpha, Alchiba; gamma,
Gienah; delta Algorab.

CRATER (THE CUP).
Originally it stood for the great
vault of heaven wherein clouds,
rain and winds were mixed by
Tiamat for the great storm
bird Corvus. It became the
pot of Mummu Tiamat, who succeeded Tiamat as ruler of the
chaotic sea and became queen
of heaven and earth. Ishtar,
great mother of the Assyro-
Babylonian pantheon inherited
it for the brewing of fertility.

No allusion to these stars by
Egyptians has been found and the
source not known of a verse
inscribed on an old vase in the
Warwick collection, which reads:

Wise ancients knew when the
    Crater rose to sight
Nile's fertile deluge had
    attained its height.

Icarius, to whom Dionysus had
entrusted the secret of wine making, stored his fermented beverage (fertile rain) in this urn.
This compares with other vessels
which gave man an inexhaustible
supply of good things, such as
the Caldron of Bran, Goblet of
the Sun of Jemshid, Horn of
Amalthea, Lamp of Aladdin,

Ethiopian Table; Well of Apollo Thyrsis, Wishing Quern of Frodi.

During the period a fashion existed to attach biblical significance to the stars it became the Cup of Christ's Passion; Cup of Joseph, found in Benjamin's sack; Cup of Wrath of the Revelations; Elijah's Cup, which the Hebrews fill with wine in the Passover service, ready for the prophet when he comes as an invisible guest to herald the Messiah's coming; one of the stone water pots of Cana, the scene of Christ's first miracle; the Wine Goblet of Noah. Combined with Corvus it made the Ark of the Covenant.

In Asia Minor this was the bowl in which human blood was mixed with wine, and in India Soma's Cup. Initially Soma was the Hindu cosmic tree. Its wine, ambrosia of the gods, was offered in libations. A draught of ecstasy with a magic power that cured all ills and provided immortality and poetic inspiration, it was one of the two chief Rig-Veda sacrifices, the other being fire. As time went on Soma was personified into an axis god, ruler of the moon, who bore a thousand shafts (rays) or was a thousand-eyed (stars) bull who fertilized the cows (clouds), gave light, and healed the ill.

Probably these stars were the frame of T'ien Kou, the Chinese Heavenly Dog shot by Chang, divinity of the Hsiu of the 26th day of each month. Its more conspicuous stars formed I (Yh, Yi, Yih, Yen), the Wings or Flanks, Hsiu of the month's 28th day.

Commonly shown to be a large urn elaborately ornamented

with two handles opposite each other and extending above the rin of the bowl, which is poised insecurely on the coils of Hydra.

The name Crater comes from the Greek. Additional designations are: The Bowl; Cinerary Urn, from a Greek term; The Cup; Goblet; The Mixing Bowl; Two-handed Pot; Waterbucket.

Arabian: Al Kas, a shallow basin; Al Ma'laf (The Stall), figured like the Manger; under Greek influence they called it Al Batinah or Batiyah, an earthen vessel for wine.

Euphratean: Bowl of the Snake.

French: Coupe.

German: Becher.

Hebrew: Cos (Cup)

Italian: Tazza

Latin and Low Latin: Calix; Cratera; Creter; Elvarad; Gratus Iaccho Crater, a mystical name of Bacchus, the wine drinker, in poetry; Patera; Poculum (Goblet), variously of Achilles, Apollo, Bacchus, Demophoon, Dido, Hercules, and Medea, an association which brings it into the Argonaut expedition, and only Hyrda separates it from the ship Argo; Pharmaz; Scyphus (Cup); Urna; Vas; Vas aquarium (Water-vase).

Medieval: Alhas, Alker, Elkis, all from the Arabic Al Kas.

Persian: Badiye, an earthen vessel for storing wine.

Astrologically its portends eminence to those born under

its influence.

Next to Corvus, and like that constellation, it is in the southern sky resting on the back of Hydra, the water-snake. For centuries Hydra et Corvus et Crater were listed as a threefold constellation, but modern astronomers catalogue it separately. It reaches the meridian about 9 P.M. on April 26, and its bright stars are alpha, Alkes; beta, Al Sharasif.

CRUX (THE CROSS). The region girdling the South Pole lacks the bewitching glamor of its northern rival; a scarcity of luminaries causes the area to remain shadowy and dim. The lack of a central or pole star makes navigation perilous and mariners have accepted the Southern Cross which glistens like small diamonds on ebony velvet as a substitute. This has given the cluster a romantic reputation far beyond anything it deserves. It symbolizes the world below the equator, warm tropical nights, luxurious life in southern climes, tender sentiments inspired by mysterious glimmerings in the far reaching darkness. "Under the Southern Cross" conjures up the love and adventure associated with the South Seas. Its poetic reputation has let down many a traveler. Most seeing it for the first time are disappointed; its illusion is for those who have not beheld it. Destitute of sweeping majesty, the clarity, the refulgence of the northern Cygnus is more like a perfect cross.

About 3,000 B.C. natives along the Baltic Sea, mainly savages, were able to see all its stars approximately 7° above the horizon. It was last seen on the Jerusalem horizon in the first days of Christianity. Although not catalogued until 1679 A.D. it appeared on a celestial globe of 1592, and had been described at least a century before that. Since early times poets of southern latitudes alluded to it. Ancient Persians celebrated a feast in its honor, but their descendants lost it in the precession and observed their feast under the Dolphin. Pliny honored Emperor Augustus by alluding to it as Thronos Caesaris (Caesar's Throne). Although invisible in Italy, he may have seen it from Alexandria where it was plainly in sight.

To others the four largest stars probably once were part of the Centaur, which now fences it in on three sides. Pious Christian Portuguese and Spanish seamen were among the first to recognize this cluster as a cross. They accepted the shape, imperfect though it is, as a sign from above, sent not merely to guide them through uncharted seas and measure distance, but as a time piece by which they might count the hours of the night.

Longfellow ascribed the four principle stars to the cardinal virtues, Justice, Prudence, Fortitude, Temperance, which Cato, the fervent Roman patriot of blunt speech displayed when, after death, he was made Guardian of Purgatory.

Five of its stars provide the design for a Brazilian postage stamp, Camoes Realms of the Holy Cross. Twenty-one additional stars surround the central design to symbolize the 21 states. Some coins carry the same figure.

The constellation was an emblem of Australia when drawn as five silver stars and of New Zealand when formed by four five-pointed red stars with silver borders.

Chaco Indians of Paraguay interpret the stars to be hunters and dogs in pursuit of a rhea. The conception of the Conibos of Peru is that it is the skeleton of a manatee.

Additional designations: Crus Australis; Four Stars of the South; Pole Star of the South, so designated because it is the most prominent constellation in the Pole's vicinity; Southern Celestial Clock, and as such has served a useful purpose for nearly 4,000 years; Southern Cross; Southern Triangle; Veil of the Fishes (Dante's designation).

Chinese: Shih Tsze Kea, equivalent to our title and probably derived from it.

English of 17th century: Croisade.

French: Croix.

German: Kreuz.

Hindu: Shula.

Italian: Croce; El Crucero; Mandorla (Almond), used in art for the vescica piscis, the oblong glory that surrounds the bodies of saints ascending to heaven.

Latin: Crosers, Crosier, Crosse, Crossiers, Crucis, Crusero, Crusiers.

Pareni Indian: Bahumehi, a fish.

Persian: Sataves, or Çatavaeca, one of the leaders of the four quarters of the sky, the others were Vanand or Vanant (Vega), Haptok Ring or Haptoiringa (Ursa Major), Tishtrya or Tistrya (Sirius).

Portuguese: Cruzero.

Spanish: Cruciero.

In the Southern sky, it lies in the Milky Way hemmed in by Musca and Centaurus. Its appearance is more like an inexpertly made kite than a cross. Partly within its boundaries is the Coal-Sack or Soot-Bag, an ink-black pear-shaped spot more formally titled Black Magellanic Cloud. Culmination is about April 26. Its alpha star is simply designated Acrux. This seems to be the one India termed Sula (Beam of the Crucifixion), which led to Shula and claimed by Hindu astronomers as the South Pole. Sula may have been a more general designation before Cross or Crux.

CUSTOS MESSIUM (HARVEST KEEPER). In 1775 J.J.L. de Lalande published this configuration of his globe, made up of inconspicuous stars scattered in a field close to the North Pole, fenced in by Camelopardalis, Cassiopeia, and Cepheus. It had a short life for astronomers soon ceased to recognize it.

Lalande's alternate title, Le Messier, has been said to be a "poorish punning compliment to his friend, the 'Comet Ferret,'" inasmuch as Louis XV had so called Charles Messier, who for 30 years had been a gatherer and keeper of the harvest of comets. Perhaps the title had been induced by the fact that

two royal neighbors ruled agricultural nations and the Giraffe,
nearby, was an animal that
ruined grain fields; or it may
have been selected because the
Phoenicians supposedly imagined
a large Wheat Field in this area.

The indefatigable and enthus-
iastic Lalande spent evenings on
the Pont Neuf over the Seine,
and to all who would listen he
would explain how wonderful was
the variable star Algol. With-
drawal into his observatory while
the French Revolution raged enabled him to "thank his stars"
that he had escaped the fate of
many of his friends. He lived
until 1807 and died in his 75th
year after cataloguing nearly
5,000 stars.

In 1751 the French Academy
had sent the youthful genius,
then only 19 years of age, to
Berlin to determine the moon's
parallax. When he organized
this constellation, the Germans
courteously acknowledged it and
gave it the name Erndtehuter.
Italians followed the Germans
and called it Mietitore (Reaper).

CYGNUS (THE SWAN). A
bird is shown on Euphratean
stellar tables, one that may
have been the pattern for the
Roc, Phoenix, and other fabulous
feathered creatures, but nothing
has been found to link it to these
particular stars. Undoubtedly
its present figure was invented
before the Greeks recorded it,
but its original myths have not
been uncovered, and we are unable to indicate what they might
have been.

The great Zeus, who wished
to remain undetected by his
scolding wife Hera, changed
himself into a swan when he

visited Leda, wife of the Spartan
king. As a result of this amour,
Leda, whose name denotes
oblivion of night, produced two
eggs. From one emerged Caster
and Clytemnestra, from the
other came Pollux and Helen.
As the swan that accounted for
two heroes who accompanied the
Argonauts, it sometimes is confused with the bird Corvus, which
is associated with the Argo, or
said to be another aspect of the
sacred crow.

Orpheus has been dressed in
these stars. When Eurydice,
his wife died, Orpheus moved
Aides to pity with his music,
and the underworld deity consented to release the musician's
bride on condition he should not
look upon her until they reached
the upper world. Just before he
stepped out of Hades he glanced
back and she vanished, thus
dawn disappears with the full
emergence of the sun over the
horizon. The prolonged grief of
Orpheus (failure to provide the
warmth needed for fertility) enraged the Thracian maenads and,
while engaged in a Dionysiac
orgy, they tore him to pieces.
The fragments of his body were
collected by the Muses and
placed nearby his beloved harp
(Lyra).

This constellation also involves
the myth of Phaethon, a son of
Helios. When Phaethon, the
original hot-rodder, drove his
father's chariot with such reckless-
ness it set the heaven's afire and
made a desert of Lybia, Zeus
struck him with lightning, he
fell, and was drowned in the
river Po. Phaethon's faithful
friend Cycnus (Cygnus) came to
the river to search for him,
but all that was left were a few
charred fragments in the water's

depth. Again and again Cycnus dived to bring up the meager remains that Phaethon might have a proper burial. When he dived he looked a bit ridiculous, like a fowl in search of food, but the gods on Mount Olympus, in spite of being moved to laughter, were touched by his devotion. Their compassion moved them to transform him into a swan and place him along the heavenly stream into which he seems to thrust his head occasionally.

Another Cycnus, a son of Poseidon, also was the Swan. This one was invulnerable to attack from blows or missiles, and in the Trojan War, Achilles, an enemy strove in vain to wound him. Finally Cycnus was smothered, and as Achilles was about to rob his victim he was changed into a swan and lifted up into the air.

This was the original of the Arabian and Persian Roc (Rukh), the fabulous bird of enormous size and marvelous strength which provided a great adventure for Sindbad the Sailor. Desert Arabs conceived it to be a Little Hen, not a tame barnyard type, but a splendid bird with swift wings that carried her along the Galaxy, the river of heaven. Whether swan or hen, no celestial bird is more magnificent, flying continuously high in space with wings outstretched.

Universally the swan has been a vehicle for the soul's journey into paradise, thus a symbol of resurrection, and many fables have been constructed around it. In Lohengrin one is the magic steed of the hero; it is said to have the ability to distinguish the essential from the non-essential

the pure from the dross, because it supposedly separates milk from water when the two are mixed; it accounts for the divine heritage of man in swan-maiden themes.

Quite consistently shown as an imposing long-necked bird in full flight. A star-spangled swan with wide-spread wings in full flight down the stream of the Milky Way toward the southwest is another common representation. On some old maps the bird is just springing from the ground. Greeks pictured as a bird or hen.

Additional designations: The Bird; Cycnus; Flying Swan; The Hen; An Ibis; Northern Cross, and it actually makes a more perfect cross than Crux; Phaethon's Bird; Swan.

Arabic: Al Fawaris (The Riders); Al Katat (A Pigeon), which became Katha; Al Ridhadh, perhaps a sweet-scented flower. This degenerated into El Rided, perhaps the original of Arided, sometimes used for the lucida Deneb. Al Ta'ir al Arduf (The Flying Eagle or Partridge), which became Altayr, and then was further corrupted into Al Radif or Al Dajajah (The Hen), which in turn became Adige, Adigege, Aldigaga, Aldigagato, Degige, Edegiagith, Eldigiagich.

Christian: Christi Crux; Cross of Calvary; Crux cum Saint Helena.

Euphratean: Urukhga (Bird of the Forest). Some doubt exists that this applies to Cygnus.

French: Cygne.

German: Schwan.

Greek: Potamos (River).

Hebrew: Timshemath (Horned Owl).

Italian: Cigno.

Latin and Low Latin: Ales (Bird); Ales Jovis; Ales Ledaeus; Avis (Bird); Avis Veneris; Eurisim; Gallina (Hen); Hierizim, Hirezym, Hyresym; Myrtilus, a title given to the bird because it was sacred to Venus as was the Myrtle tree; Olor (Swan); Orpheus; Phoebi Assessor, the bird being sacred to Pheobus Apollo; Vultur cadens, a title more correctly applied to Lyra.

Spanish: Cisne.

It flies in the northern sky and seems to be in pursuit of Aquila, a natural enemy. Following it is Cepheus. From May to December it is visible in the night sky and reaches culmination about September 13. Its bright stars are: alpha, Deneb, also called Arided; beta, Albireo; gamma, Sadr; epsilon, Gienah; pi, Azelfafage. Within its borders are the Lace-Work Nebula, the North America Nebula, named from its resemblance to a map of the continent, and one of the most remarkable black gaps in the Milky Way, the Northern Coal Sack, a seemingly bottomless abyss in whose depths are hidden the profound mysteries of interstellar space. Coincidently the Southern Cross also contains a celebrated Coal-Sack.

DELPHINUS (THE DOLPHIN). The dolphin was translated into a constellation by Poseidon after one of these gentle, frolicking fish, which had served as his mount, persuaded Amphitrite, one of the Nereids, who had made a

vow of perpetual celibacy, to become the sea-lord's queen.

In Greek mythology the dolphin was one of the forms under which Apollo was worshipped. He assumed the form to agitate the waters of the Corinthian Gulf, and then led Cretan mariners of a ship in distress to the safety of the shore, whence he departed in the form of a brilliant star. The seamen followed him to Delphi, and there founded a temple in his honor and became priests devoted to his worship. This far-famed oracle became the only shrine in the world not exclusively national. It was consulted by Etruscans, Lydians, Phrygians, Romans, etc.

Others support the theory that the constellation is one of the dolphin's enchanted by Arion, the poet and musician who left his native Lesbos at the invitation of Periander, the tyrant, to visit Corinth. So great was his talent he was presented with honors and riches, but he longed to visit his native land. On shipboard he became aware that the sailors were resolved to murder him and divide his wealth. Arion tried to soften their hearts with his songs, but they remained immovable. When it became obvious they were growing impatient, Arion begged permission to play on his harp which produced wonderful music (songs of the wind) before he should be put to death. His plaintive melody attracted a school of dolphins and they gathered around the ship. Just before the sailors reached for him, he jumped overboard, and one of the dolphins swam close, raised the singer onto its back, and in this manner he was car-

ried safely to Taenarus, a
promontory of the Peloponnesus,
whence he traveled to the court
of Periander, who ordered the
sailors crucified. This fable
is a variation of an early
Semitic myth of the sun-god
Baal Hamon or Baal Ammon. On
another occasion dolphins acted
as life-savers in the rescue of
Taras, founder of Tarentum in
Italy. The city struck a coin
in memory of this event.

The dolphins performed
many friendly services in the
cause of justice. Hesiod,
Greek poet of the 8th century B.
C., father of didactic poetry,
was slain and his body tossed into the sea. Dolphins supposedly
recovered it and conveyed it to
shore, where it was discovered
by friends, who aided by the poet's
dogs, located the assassins and
drowned them in the waters into
which they had cast Hesiod. This
rather curious incident corrobor-
ates a belief that the dolphin
bears souls of the departed to
the Island of the Blessed, provides
preservation to a corpse, and is
a benevolent messenger of the
sea-god. A popular name for
this constellation is Job's Coffin,
and in Christianity a dolphin is
symbolic of resurrection and
salvation, indeed it is an aspect
of Christ the Savior. An early
Christian sect thought it was the
Cross of Jesus placed in the
skies after the crucifixion. Later
Christians claimed it to be the
fish that swallowed Jonah, also
maintained for Cetus. A tendancy
prevails to give mythological
figures more than one abode or
form in the sky, and so gospel
interpretors have placed here
as well as elsewhere the
Leviathan, Great Fish that
Swallowed Jonah, and the Water-
pots of Cana.

Orientalists say the Greeks
borrowed from the Hindus; Oc-
cidentalists claim the reverse.
Be that as it may, Indians
gave these stars a porpoise
shape and located here their
remarkable nakshatra the Sravish-
tha (Most Favorable) or Dhanish-
tha (Richest), whose regents
were the Vasus. The Vasus, literally the bright or good ones,
were the eight divine children of
Aditi. Personifications of
natural phenomena, fire, wind,
water, earth, the pole star,
dawn, light, and the moon,
they accompanied Indra as
his attendants. The mount of
these and other divinities was
Makara, which here may have
a porpoise form and at Capricorn that of a strange hybrid.
Makara probably derives from
the Euphratean Makhar, also
worshipped as Capricorn.

The original outline of the
constellation probably had been
designed by a coastal or sea-
faring people, and from time
immemorial it has been drawn
as a dolphin or porpoise. According to one theory the name
comes from the Delphinia, a
Greek spring festival celebrated
to commemorate "the genial
influence of the spring sun on the
waters, the opening of nagivation,
and the restoration of life to
creatures of the waves.

Additional designations: Bended
Dolphin, Vector Arionis.

Arabic: Al Kaud (The Riding
Camel); Dulfim, a marine animal
friendly to man and attending
ships to save sailors from a
watery grave, adopted from the
Greek.

Chinese: Kwa Chaou (A
Gourd) for the four principal

stars in the diamond-shaped head.

Euphratean: Makhar (Ship-of-the-Rope). This may apply to Capricorn.

English of middle ages: Delphyn, Dolphyne.

French: Dauphin.

German: Delphin.

Hindu: Shi-shu-mara or Sim-shu-mara, later known as Zizumara (Porpoise).

Italian: Delfino.

Latin and Low Latin: Acetes, after a pirate-pilot who protected Dionysus (Bacchus) when he traveled to Naxos to claim Ariadne as his bride; Apollo; Curvus, applying to its form, which due to a typographical error has been written Currus; Delphin, Delphis; Hermippus, an Attic dramatic poet who lived about 430 B.C.; Musicum Signum; Neptunus; Persuasor Amphitrites; Smon Barbaris, Smon Nautis, which seems to be from the Greek Simon (Flat-nosed), an old-time marine designation; Triton, a sea-god.

Astrologically it stands for philanthropy, not only because of the classical stories built around it, but because of the fish's devotion to its young. In the 16th century its stars were believed to be aware of human births and had a genethliacal influence which swayed the nature or character of those under its control.

Now one of the smallest of constellations this may once have contained many more stars, including those of Equuleus. All astronomical literature refers to Delphinus, which is in the northern sky east of Aquila, close by Sagitta and Vulpecula, in a section known as the sea or water. It culminates on September 14, and its alpha star is Sualocin.

DORADO (THE GOLDFISH). First published early in the 17th century, the title was derived from a Spanish word and refers not to the exotic little species we place in bowls and train as pets, but to the large dolphins or porpoises that swim about in the open tropical seas and are noted for the brilliant change of color they undergo when at the point of death after being taken from the water. In early Christian astronomy these stars were combined with those of Volans for the figure Abel the Just.

Additional designations are: Craver; the Fish Dorado; Gilthead Fish, a type that appears off the British coast; Gold Field; The Swordfish.

Chinese: Kin Yu (Goldfish), undoubtedly under Jesuit influence.

French: Dorade.

German: Dorado, Schwerdtfisch.

Italian: Dorado.

Latin: Doradus; Polus Doradinalis, because the head of Dorado marks region of the south pole of the ecliptic; Xiphias.

It is in the southern sky surrounded by Pictor, Reticulum, Mensa, and Volans. One of the most extraordinary bodies of outer space is located in the fields that separate Dorado and Mensa, the True Lovers

Knot or Great Looped Nebula.
This is Nebecula Major, the
Large Magellanic Cloud, which,
like the Small Magellanic Cloud
or Nebecula Minor in Tucana,
once was thought to be a detached portion of the Milky Way,
but has been discerned to be a
distant and distinct Galaxy.
Dorado's stars are not bright
and remain unnamed. The constellation comes to the meridian
about January 31.

DRACO (THE DRAGON).

Wherever a dragon or serpent
appears in the sky, the first per-
sonality with which it is associated
is Tiamat, ancestress of all fic-
tional evil characters or instiga-
tors of friction and conflict. Each
one of these obnoxious, can-
tankerous scoundrels has been
overcome in time by a hero with
the courage to face them. After
Marduk defeated Tiamat, the
north wind carried away her blood,
which shows as streaks high
in space from time to time. The
victor split her skull and tore
her skin into pieces, and from
these he molded heaven and earth.
In the upper regions he set the
mansions of the gods, created the
stars, dictated the paths they
should follow or cut paths among
them, outlined the constellations
and placed them to serve as
signs to designate the days,
months, seasons, and years. He
fixed the dome of heaven in place
with a strong bolt and set a
watchman, a many-headed dragon,
to guard it, that it might not be
carried away or collapsed. Once
the constellations were organized,
he surveyed the skies and engi-
neered the zodiacal track. Then
he rested from his labors.

The Babylonians alluded to a
Snail that appeared at the tail
of a Dragon near the Pole. The

reference may have been to this
constellation. Also among the
inscriptions, Sir or Tsir (Snake)
was deciphered, but to which sky
serpent it applied is unknown.
It may have been the snake overcome by the kneeling Izdubar
(Gizdhubar or Gilgamesh), our
constellation Hercules, whose
foot is upon it.

Some of the stars of this
cluster appear on the Denderah
planisphere as part of the immense Egyptian Hippopotamus
or its variant the Crocodile,
both forms of Ammit, who
devoured the dead whose hearts
were heavy with misdeeds. The
goddess also is known as Hes-
mut or Shesemtet (Raging Mother).
An object somewhat like a
ploughshare held in her paw has
been identified as the neighboring
Plough. The lady was separated
from her husband earth by the
intervention of the atmosphere
god, who wished to give breathing space to all forms of life that
had been created. When she was
first lifted off her husband, her
broad star-speckled body was so
heavy a ladder was required to
fix her in place. The hieroglyph
of this Hippopotamus stood for the
heavens in general, and the constellation as an emblem of Hathor
(Athor or Athyr), the cosmic
mother, personification of the
great power of nature, perpetually
bringing forth, rearing, and
destroying old things, whose husband was Horus, male ruler of
the skies. She is said to be
the mother of Isis and, in early
myths, identical with Isis. The
name of Set, the evil monster
destroyed by Horus, also has
been associated with these stars,
as has been that of Tanen, a
gigantic earth deity. Tanen is
not unlike the Aramaic Tannin
and Hebrew Tannim, and they

perhaps had the same significance. In fact Tanen may have
been derived from them.

A ten year struggle, the
Gigantomachia, the war of the
Gigantes, a monstrous serpent-
legged race that sprang from
Gaea (Earth) when the blood of
the multilated Uranus fell upon
her, and the Olympian Gods, led
by Zeus, raged from the mountains of Greece to the valleys
of Egypt. Among the forces to
assist the Giants was the many-
headed Hydra, who lived in a
swamp and ravaged the land,
and other dragons who spat
volcanic fire, earthquakes,
typhoons, and other catastrophic
upheavals that resounded throughout the universe. As the struggle
reached a crisis, one of the
Giants rushed against Athene, but
the goddess of wisdom, fully
arrayed in heavy armor, was
not easily frightened. She seized
her foe, lifted him from the
ground, swung him around her
head, and with all her strength
hurled him into space, and there
he remains sprawled around the
North Pole with which his coils
are inextricably entangled. Other
Giants also were lifted from
the ground and forced onto their
backs. Once their feet were off
mother-earth, upon which they
depended for strength, they
weakened, and the Gods were
the victors. The Hydra, who
aided the Giants, eventually met
Heracles (Hercules) in single
combat.

The nickname of Thebes in
Boeotia was City of the Dragon,
that its inhabitants might never
slacken their vigilance because
they had forgotten the ferocious
monster who once had occupied
the site and devoured all the
original natives. Cadmus, who
had located his sister Europa,
after she had been abducted by
Zeus, at Delphi, stopped at the
shrine and was instructed by the
oracle to follow a heifer that
stood outside and, where it lay
down to rest, to sacrifice it
and establish a city on the
site. The cow chose Thebes,
but, before Cadmus was able to
approach the animal a dragon
offspring of Ares sprang between
them. Cadmus after a trying
struggle killed the dragon, and
a downpour flooded the earth.
When the waters subsided Cadmus
sowed the earth with the dragon's
teeth and a harvest of armed
men, the Spartoi, sprang up.
These barbarians killed one
another until only five were
left, but these five became the
progenitors of the local families.
For slaying a descendant of a
god, Cadmus was forced to become a bondsman. After eight
years of servitude, Ares forgave
him, and Cadmus, now king of
Thebes, married the beautiful
Harmonia, daughter of Ares and
Aphrodite. The dragon is
interpreted to be drought, the
heifer fertility, the Spartoi clouds
of gloom. The servitude of
Cadmus resembles that of Jacob,
who also married the daughter of
his master. Harmonia is the
progeny of the marriage of
opposites, war and love, ugliness and beauty.

As the "emblem of eternal
vigilance," in that it never sets,
the constellation is Ladon, the
ever-watchful dragon that assisted
nymphs who guarded the Garden
of Hesperides, a paradise which
lay at the western extremity of
the world, bordering on the
region of eternal darkness,
where grew the Tree (Pole)
bearing three golden apples.
Heracles, to pluck these apples

was forced to overcome Ladon.
Hence the sun, to obtain the
fruits of fertility, had to dispense
with the estuary that encircled
the garden. Some identify these
stars as the Lernaean water-
snake on which Hercules holds a
foot, but this dragon is more
often placed at Hydra.

Python too is seen here. The
treasures of fertility he had
snatched from the Deluge, Python
held for himself. Warned in a
prophecy that he was doomed
to die at the hands of Leto's
son, he tried to kill Leto, but
was frustrated by Zeus. Apollo
fulfilled the prophecy by killing
him near Delphi at the foot of
Mount Parnassus; then the sun-
god distributed the wealth Python
had hoarded. In symbolism the
dragon often has been confounded
with rivers, hence Apollo, the
sun may have suffocated a death-
dealing river.

After the enormous Midgard
serpent, which in Norse legend,
squirted poison (darkness) over
the air and land, had been captured, it was placed before Odin
in his heaven of Asgard. The
father of the gods lifted the
slimy sinuous beast and flung
him over the walls of his realm
beyond the outermost boundaries
of earth and into the great river
along the edge of the universe.
There, in the water's depth,
it lengthened until it could no
longer lie without curling up, so
it took its tail in its mouth and
formed a rim of darkness around
the world.

Among the fearless who
dared to come face to face with
this malefactor was Beowulf, sun-
hero of an ancient Anglo-Saxon
epic. He was the bravest and
strongest of the Swedish tribe

and, when Heorot, palace of
the Danish king Hrothgar, was
raided nightly by Grendel (darkness), who destroyed those sleeping (knights of light) in the
palace hall, Beowulf undertook
the beast's destruction. Grendel's
dam attempted to avenge her
son's death, but Beowulf pursued
her to her cave under the sea
and killed her with the magic
sword Hrunting (sun rays on
water), that he found there. He
then returned to his own people
and ruled as king for fifty years,
at the end of which time he was
attacked by a dragon (winter),
which possessed an immense
hoard of wealth (riches underground). With his magic sword
Naegling (rays) Beowulf killed
the dragon, but was sprayed
with its poisonous venom. He
was deserted by all his tribe except Wiglaf (gloaming), and in
his death agony he gazed upon
the treasures he had won for his
people (budding verdure).

Zealous Christians ignored its
former nature and presented it
as the Holy Innocents of Bethlehem;
those not indifferent to its past
saw these stars as the Old
Serpent; the Dragon slain by
Saint George; Dragon of the
Inferno; the tempter of Eve; or
the dragon with whom the Assyro-
Babylonian Bel battled. An effort
was made to give a moral concept to this ever attentive,
ever watchful one. It gazed
down from its throne in the
highest realm of space in a
continual search for a remedy of
original sin. On the alert for
knaves, it was a perpetual menace
to evil-doers.

Rabbis traced the Crooked Serpent mentioned in the Book of
Job. A suggestion has been
made the constellation we know

as Ophiuchus was the Crooked
Serpent, but Draco, ancient
possessor of the Pole Star,
seems the more likely.

In the Arabian Nights, Sindbad, a Bagdad merchant set out on
a trip and experienced a number of
marvelous adventures. On one
occasion he came upon an old
man who asked to be carried
across a brook. Once mounted
on Sindbad's shoulders he clung
until the merchant contrived to
make him drunk. He had become so heavy and breathed so
hard, Sindbad realized the aged
rascal was none other than the
Old Man of the Sea, who had his
mansion in Draco.

Its form almost consistently
has been that of an animal con-
cerned with both land and water.
Hindus conceived it to be an
alligator. In both the East
and West it symbolized darkness,
the dread powers that opposed
mankind and pulled them into
the afterworld, but at the same
time guarded vast buried riches
(fertility), unseen by those who
walked on earth.

The heroes who have over-
come this dragon are countless.
Susa-no-wo, Shinto Swift-
impetuous-male, being among
them. One of a trinity with his
sister Amaterasu, sun-goddess,
and his brother Tsuki-yomi,
moon-god. A fierce-tempered
deity, with excrement he laid
waste his sister's rice garden
and by other deeds caused her
to hide in the cave Ame-no-
Iwato, with the consequence
the world was thrown into darkness (suggesting an eclipse). For
his mischievous acts he was
expelled to Idzumo (Japan),
where he saved Kushi-nada-hime,
a rice goddess by slaying the

dragon Koshi (tides), which
yearly devoured a beautiful
maiden. In the tail of the
dragon he found Kusanagi, the
magic sword from which Amaterasu created deities. Later
he was expelled to the underworld, and his descendant O-kuni-
nushi-no-kami became Idzumo's
ruler. Susa-no-wo, a sea-god,
was gloomy, furious, impetuous,
strong, an agent of darkness and
death as well as a destroyer of
the wicked. He appeared in the
rain, thunder, whirlwinds, and
was invoked against pestilence
and shipwreck. Of miraculous
birth, he was born from the
nose of Izanagi, whose wife was
Izanami, a dreaded dragon.
Izanami had been a beautiful
woman, the sister-wife of Izanagi,
with whom with a jewel-spear
(phallus) she churned the primeval sea and begat many
children, islands, forests, winds,
etc. When giving birth to Kagu-
tsuchi, fire, her vagina was
burned and she died. Izanagi
traced his wife to the underworld, where she informed him
that she had partaken of food and
therefore was unable to return to
earth. In any event, her monstrous shape frightened him, and
he fled as fast as he was able.
Humiliated and angry, she
gathered a company of demons
(storm spirits) together and pursued him, but he tossed peaches
(a fruit of phallic significance),
to those who followed and when
they stooped to pick up the fruit
he escaped. Upon reaching this
world he performed purifying
ablutions and Amaterasu was
born from his left eye, Tsuki-
yomi was born as he washed his
right eye, and Susa-no-wo came
from his nose. In the realm
of after-life without Izanagi,
Izanami also produced deities,
but these were all evil and came

from her feces, urine, and vomit.

Configurations. Its Chaldean likeness doubtlessly bore the scales, which denoted stars, horns for authority, claws for protection and ferocity, and wings for aspiration, all attributes of early traditional dragons. The original constellation was much longer and folded both Bears within its coils. The customary figure is a combination of bird and reptile, or winged reptile, symbol of the forces that control the elements, the giver and taker of the waters of life or fertilizing moisture, whose emblem is a jewel or pearl.

Additional designations: Baltic Sea, which a Swedish naturalist, around 1700, said the stars symbolized. The Quiver, an unusual title.

Accadian: Dayan Esiru (Prospering Judge or Crown of Heaven); Dayan Shisha (Directing Judge, as having the highest seat among the host of heaven).

Anglo-Saxon chronicles: Denier of the Gods; Dragon-wing of Night; Fire Drake; Terrible Enemy of Man; Unsleeping Poison-fanged Monster.

Arabic: Al Hayyah (The Snake), also applied to Serpens; Al Shuja (The Snake), also applied to Hydra; Al Thuban or Al Tinnin, both translations from the Greek for dragon, which degenerated into Aben (Abeen) or Taben (Taeben), Alanin, Attanino, Daban, Etabin.

Chinese: Tsi Kung (Palace of the Heavenly Emperor).

Egyptian: Tanen, a name

retained by the gamma star.

French: Dragon.

German: Drache.

Greek: Pytho (Rot).

Hindu: Kalli Nagu, meaning banishment of Vishnu, a solar deity; Shi-shu-mara (Alligator or Porpoise), also given to Delphinus.

Italian: Dragone.

Latin and Low Latin: Aesculapius, whose emblem was a serpent; Anguis, Coluber, Python, Serpens, all used elsewhere; Arborem Conscendens; Arctoe et Draco (Bear and Draco); Audax (Bold); Coluber Custos (Serpent Custodian); Hesperidum (Watcher of Hesperides); Maximus Anguis; Monstrum; Monstrum Audax; Monstrum Mirabile; Palmes emeritus (Exhausted Vine Branch) Sidus Minervae et Bacchi.

Medieval hybrid of Arabic and Latin: Alghavil Altannin (poisonous Dragon), probably an allusion to an accepted astrological belief that when a comet appeared here it spread poison over the world.

Persian: Azhdeha (Man-eating Serpent) translated into Hashteher.

Turkish: Etanin.

Once the design of the twelve zodiacal signs had been deciphered, the illuminated northern skies received attention, and the Dragon, probably the next constellation mapped out, was placed to guard the cold north.

Although loathed and feared by mortals, it quite appropriately became the crown of the heavens. If the Dragon destroyed fertility with a breath that alternately scorched and frosted earth, it also guarded the wealth buried in dark recesses of the universe, a portion of which some hero periodically forced it to release for the benefit of mankind. When it first guarded the Pole, around which the universe pivots, it boasted the Pole Star, but in the course of time the precession of the equinoxes forced Draco off the pole and possession of the North Star went to Ursa Minor. In Christian lore the stalwart Michael had taken this honor away from the dreaded dragon, which not sprawls south of the Little Bear and north of Hercules, Bootes and Ursa Major. It never sets, but reaches culmination in the night sky of July 8, and its bright stars are alpha, Thuban; beta, Rastaban, gamma, Eltanin.

EQUULEUS (THE LESSER HORSE). Exactly which mythological horse was responsible for this constellation is in doubt. It was said to be the celestial Celeris, brother of Pegasus, given by Hermes (Mercury) to Castor; Cyllarus, gift of Pollux to Hera (Juno); or the animal which Poseidon (Neptune) brought to life. In a quarrel with Athena over a city's name, Zeus decreed it should be called after the deity who conferred the best gift on mankind. Poseidon produced the horse, symbol of war, by shattering a rock with his trident, but lost to Athena, producer of the olive tree, symbol of peace and prosperity, and the city was called Athens. Poseidon, himself, changed into a horse on occasions. Once he pursued the

earth goddess Demeter, and when she fled from him in the shape of a mare, he assumed that of a horse and covered her, thus the sea covered the shore. The offspring of Cronus who, to prevent his wife from recognizing him, visited Philyra in the guise of a horse, is sometimes placed here, sometimes placed at Centaurus.

Romans used an instrument called the Equulus to torture confessions from accused persons. Christians had a diversified opinion. It was recognized as the horse Haman, chief minister to the Persian king Ahasuerus, hoped for, as told in the Book of Esther; the horse of Saint George; the Mystic Rose.

Symbolically the horse stands for endurance, force, freedom, generosity, grace, gratitude, intellect, motion, solar energy, science, speed, time, triumph, understanding, and conversely, obstinacy, pride, war. A mount of the gods, it typifies clouds, lightning, rays, waves and wind. When the mount of a devil, its significance is phallic. Where the horse was venerated, a tabu was placed on eating its meat except at the sacred autumn festival, and this survives as a strong repugnance. Among Pagan Chinese it carried the sun through the seventh of the twelve terrestrial branches of the zodiac. Druides used a horse in twelve different ways to represent the progress of the sun through the months.

Usually on illustrations only the head is drawn and, like Pegasus, it appears in an inverted position.

Additional designations are: The Colt, The Foal, the Horse's Head, The Lesser Horse, The Little Horse.

Arabic: Al Faras al Awwal (The First Horse), an allusion to its rising before Pegasus; Al Faras al Thani (The Second Horse), an allusion to its inferior size or to the time of its adoption as a constellation; Al Kitah al Faras (Part of a Horse), which on European charts became Kataat Alfaras and Kitalpha; Hinnulus (Young Mule), which degenerated into Elmac Alcheras.

French: Petit Cheval.

German: Fullen (The Filly).

Greek: Ippou protones (First, or Before, Horse).

Hindu: Asvins, Aswini or Açvini (The Horsemen), although their figure, copied from the Occidental, was the fore-part of the horse. The Asvins are associated with other stars as well.

Italian: Cavallino.

Latin and Low Latin: Eculeus; Equi Caput (Horse's Head); Equi Praesectio, Equi Sectio, Sectio equina, Sectio Equi Minoris, Semi-perfectus, Praesegmen, all references to it as a bust or part of an animal; Equiculus; Equulus; Equus primus or prior, as rising before Pegasus; Equus Minor, referring to its size, which is inferior to that of Pegasus; Praecisio Equi; Rosa Mystica, a Christian reference.

Composed of stars which form a rectangular shaped figure, it probably was devised by the Greeks shortly before the Chris-

tian era from part of the earlier and larger Dolphin. It lies slightly north of the zodiacal ecliptic between Delphinus and the head of Pegasus. Culmination is about September 22, and Kitalpha is its most prominent star, although it is not brighter than fourth magnitude.

ERIDANUS (THE RIVER). This word first was seen in Hesiod's work for the river Phasis, the modern Aras, which flows along the Russo-Persian frontier. When these particular stars were designated a stream is unknown. This section of the sky, associated as it is with the rainy season, has always been regarded a vast deep, and two streams, conjectured to be the Euphrates (Udkipnunki, King of the Plain of Eridu, i.e. Life of the Land) and the Tigris (Masguga, The Currents, i.e. Life of the Land) have been found on conical stones dating back to the cradle of civilization, and another has been located on Egyptian carvings, here unquestionably intended for the Nile. Both the Euphrates and the Nile had once long ago been given the epithets Pura (water) and Ioma or Iauma (Sea). They resemble each other as meandering streams that connected heaven, Paradise or the realm of the Gods, and earth, the realm of man, and were is some way involved with the overthrow of a sun-deity. Perhaps this accounts for the location of their double in space between Orion, a sun-hero, and Cetus, a sea monster. Allusion to the Euphrates and the Nile brings to mind a wide-spread belief that they were branches of the same stream, and in the Authorized Version the name Sihor appears for the Nile as

one of the four great parts of
the River of Paradise. The
Eridanus seems to conform
more to the Nile than to any
other, inasmuch as the Nile is
the only great river that flows
from south to north as the Eridanus appears to do when it comes
into view above the horizon.

The river which forms our
modern constellation seems to
have been first celebrated in
Greek mythology as the river
that flows into the Euxine Sea near
the spot where the Argonauts obtained the Golden Fleece. Later
it became the celestial extension
of the brook under the Acropolis,
which was important only because it watered the Gardens of
the Gods. The Granicus,
where Alexander the Great won a
decisive victory, was transported
to the afterworld with the warrior
that he might reminisce along
its banks. Heracles on his quest
for the Golden Apples of
Hesperides asked for directions
from the nymphs of this river.
Greek navigators revered it as
the Iberus (Ebro) in Spain,
where they came upon a people of
small stature who buried their
dead in tombs.

Romans saw it as a continu-
ation of the Ligurian Bodencus in
western Italy, also as the Po,
anciently called Padus, in
northern Italy. The Po, the
country's largest river has the
title Rex Fluviorum and is noteworthy for the role it played in
the Phaethon story. When
Phaethon lost control of the
horses which pulled the sun
chariot he was driving, the
heavens were set ablaze by the
runaway team, and to save the
world, Zeus struck the youth
with lightning. With his hair
on fire like a meteor, Phaethon

dropped from the sky vault into
the stream's depth. While his
devoted friend Cycnus dived to
recover the charred remains of
his body, the Heliades, his sisters,
wept, and their tears as they
fell into the water turned into
amber (sunlit particles of water).
The gods could not prevail upon
the nymphs to leave the river
and, pitying them, turned them
into poplars. This Stream of
Tears was noted for its commerce and was an early artery
in the amber trade. The fable
of Phaethon may hint of an
extraordinary period of heat and
drought suffered in some remote
time.

To Teutons it was the Rhenus
(Rhine), where the mist folk
Nibelungen hid the treasures
(fertility) they had robbed from
earth; to the Franks it was the
Rhodanus (Rhone); to biblical
scholars the Gihon, river in
Genesis "that compasseth the
whole land of Cush," and is identified as one of the four rivers
of the Garden of Eden; the River
Jordan, or the Red Sea, which
parted to permit the Israelites,
who had the Egyptians close on
their heels, to pass over dry
land. Once the Israelites had
reached the other side safely the
sea closed on the Egyptians, who
drowned. The safe passage of
the Israelites coincides with
baptism, purification, rebirth.

Far to the north the stream
was the Nowhere Existing Sea,
the waterway that flowed around
the earth in a clockwise direction, marking the ultimate rim of
the world. On it a golden bark
carried Sun to his home in the
East after his day's labors
were done.

In addition to conceiving these

stars as a river, Arabs of the desert imagined them to be a group of young and old ostriches, eggs or egg shells.

Orion claimed the river as his own because it terminates at his star Rigel.

Configurations. Illuminated manuscripts have placed a hoary river-god along with an urn, aquatic plants and a row of stars on the stream's surface. Artists of the 15th century substituted a beautiful nude woman with stars along the lower bank or the monster Cetus with his fore flippers in the water. One design has reeds and sedge on the margin.

Additional designations: King of Rivers, River of Ocean, River of Heaven, the River Po.

Accadian: Aria-dan (Strong River); Erib-me-gali.

Arabic: Al Nahr (The River), appeared on European uranometries as Alvahar, Nahal (also probably a derivation of Nile), Nahar, Nar. Wadi al Kabir (The Great River).

Egyptian: Khem (Black), a reference to the color of the fertile deposit left by the Nile on the shore.

French: Eridan.

German: Fluss Eridanus.

Greek: Nereus, Oceanus, Poseidon.

Italian: Eridano.

Latin and Low Latin: Amnis; Eridanus; Flumen, Fluvius; Melo, an early name for the Nile;

Mulda, from a Greek word for black, which connects it with the Egyptian Khem; Neptune; Nilus; Padus; Vardi, from the Arabic Wadi.

Medieval: Gyon (Gihon), Red Sea, River Jordan, River of Judges.

Moorish: Guad, from the Arabic Wadi.

Spanish: Guadalquivir (Great River).

Turkish: Fasch, a general appellation for all rivers, perhaps from the Sanscrit Phas (Water) still found in the German Wasser.

The river curves irregularly through the southern sky. Its path is so far-reaching it has been divided into a northern and southern stream. The former extends from the foot of Orion to the paws of Cetus; there it is lost on the horizon to those in the northern hemisphere for it turns sharply south passed the Whale's head to follow an erratic course until it disappears at a point close to Hydrus, not far from the southern pole. Although the longest constellation in the sky, it has only one star greater than third magnitude, and that is Achernar. Its beta star is Cursa, its gamma is Zamack (Zaurak). Culmination is about December 25.

FELIS (THE CAT). In 1799 Lalande said, "I am very fond of cats. I will let this animal scratch on the chart. The starry sky has worried me quite enough in my life, so now I can have my joke with it." However, he did not put it on a map until 1805, when he placed it in the southern sky between Antila and Hydra. Literally the name means happy, fortunate, prosperous. Additional designations are: Faelis, Faulx, Felix, Gatto, Katze (German). Since late in the 19th century it has been discontinued in catalogues and on planispheres.

FORNAX (THE FURNACE). Formed in France by Nicolas Louis de Lacaille in 1763 from stars within the southern loop of the River Eridanus, it still is recognized by astronomers. Its shape, however, is more like a baton or wand than an oven or furnace.

Fornax was the Roman goddess of the oven and a patroness of bakers, her name being a generic term for furnace. Additional designations: Apparatus; Chemical Furnace; Chemicus; Chemique, a later alteration to honor the chemist Antoine Lavoisier, director of the French gunpowder works in 1779, and who was guillotined; Chemische Apparat; Chymische Ofen; Fornax Chemica; Fornax Chymiae; l' Apparat. The Chinese knew it as Tien Yu (Heaven's Temporary Granary).

Without bright stars it reaches culmination about December 17.

FOX. A constellation which appeared on an Egyptian sphere. Nothing is now known about it except that it was charted along the northern borders of Scorpio, perhaps from stars now in Ophiuchus.

FREDERICI HONORES (HONORS OF FREDERICK). Formed in 1787 by Johann Elert Bode to honor his monarch

Frederick II of Prussia, who had died the year before, from stars in the northern sky in the space between Andromeda, Cassiopeia and Cygnus, where the Lacerta of Johann Hevelius had been placed more than a century earlier. Bode was no more successful in dispossessing Lacerta than Augustine Royer had been in 1679, when he attempted to place his Scepter and Hand of Justice here. Royer for his form also had borrowed from the northern hand of Andromeda, which he moved to a more easterly position, entirely unconcerned that the lady had squatter's rights, having rested her hand in one locale for three thousand years.

A description of Bode's figure was "Below a nimbus, the sign of royal dignity, wreathed with the imperishable laural of fame, was a sword, pen, and olive branch, to distinguish this ever to be remembered monarch as hero, sage, and peacemaker."

Frederici Honores has been disgarded and is so seldom mentioned it is almost forgotten, while Lacerta maintains its position in this much desired area. Other names by which the Bode design were once designated are Frederick's Glory, Gloria Frederica, Gloria Frederici, Gloria Frederika.

GENINI (THE TWINS).
     By turns they visit this
          etherial sky
     And live alternate and
          alternate die.
                    (Homer)
After the moon, two bright stars along its path were the first objects in the night sky that seemed noteworthy. Although never conclusively identified

they appear to be the bright
stars of Gemini, which about
4,000 B.C. served as indicators
of the first new moon of the year
as the star Capella was to 2,000
years later. In any event, two
stars and a crescent appear on
a Babylonian boundary stone, one
of the small oblongs anciently
used to keep a record of land
owned. The symbol, known as
the Triad of Stars, had been
repeated over and over on cones
and pillars. Consequently since
earliest antiquity these stars seem
to have been recognized as a
pair and it is apparent the Triad
of Stars, the earliest record of
an astronomical event to find its
way to modern man, is nothing
more than a simple report of
what herdsmen saw year after
year in the sunset sky 6,000
years ago. Gradually the two
bright stars of the design became
eyes in a configuration composed
of other stars in their neighborhood. Quite possibly at the
beginning the constellation was
conceived to be a couple of
kids, an animal vital in the daily
life of shepherd-astronomers,
and a popular sacrifice to the
gods. In later texts twins are
named Etalak and Latarak,
the sun-god Ninurta as the opener
of the morning's double-gate;
Ningishzida and Ninsubur, who
guarded the gates of Anu (Sky);
and Umunlua and Umunisiga,
the beneficent and hostile aspects
of the giver of light. These
last names signify lord who
gives plenty and the cruel lord.

Early Egyptians saw Two
Sprouting Plants in these stars;
later they represented Horus the
Elder and Horus the Younger,
two phases of the sun, or as
Shu and Tefenet, twin brother
and sister as well as husband
and wife, who stood for ethereal
space separating heaven and
earth.

Until the Greeks thousands of
years later attached their twin
heroes, the Dioscuri, to the
configuration with two bright
eyes, no fables were associated
with it. The Dioscuri were
Castor and Polux, twin sons of
Zeus and Leda. Originally
Spartan heroes, they were such
outstanding exponents of heroic
virtue and valor, their worship
was imported by the Athenians.
So deep was their affection for
each other they became divine
guardians of friendship. Castor
was the greatest charioteer of
his time, Pollux the greatest
pugilist. They accompanied the
Argonaut expedition and took part
in other gallant adventures.
Castor taught Heracles the art
of armed warfare. When Castor
was killed in a battle Zeus
offered Pollux immortality, but
he refused to accept the gift unless allowed to share it with
his brother. Touched by this
devotion Zeus granted the wish
but decreed they were to live
alternately and placed them in
the heavens. The death and
rebirth of these brothers typifies
the recurring motions of light
and darkness. Pollux appeared
in the east in the morning to usher
in light, Castor in the west in
the evening, the escort of darkness. They were dawn and dusk,
morning and evening stars, day
and night, sun and moon, riding
white horses. Etymologically
Pollux is identical with bollux
or bollix, to mix up; Castor
means crocus, is akin to the
Sanscrit kasturi (musk), and
may be the source of castrate,
the act of offering the phallus
to the love goddess.

While returning home after

obtaining the Golden Fleece, with power over wind and waves they had supposedly received from Poseidon, they saved fellow mariners from shipwreck and routed pirates that overran the Hellespont. A claim has been made that Orpheus with his stirring music prevailed upon the Gods to aid them, and that the Twins, who had failed to take any action, received all the credit because two bright stars, later assigned to them, lighted in the heavens directly over their heads. Thereafter men in peril prayed to the brothers and their fame spread as the friend and protector of sailors. Seamen said of Saint Elmo's Fire, if one flame showed itself the worst of the storm was yet to come and was a visitation from a sister of the twins, Helen; if two or more luminous flames appeared they called them Castor and Pollux or Ledean Lights and predicted weather would soon be fair. The history of the Twins seems to connect them with electrical phenomena common in heavy weather at sea and more treacherous to the small craft of ancient shippers than to modern liners. The lights are now generally known as Composant, Corposant, or Corpusant, from the Italian Corpo Santo. It also has been dubbed Saint Anne's Light and Saint Electricity. To Christian seamen of the Mediterranean area in modern times the light is known as Saint Peter and Saint Nicholas, the former from his miracle of walking on water, the latter because he stilled storms at sea when he voyaged to the Holy Land and restored life to a sailor drowned in the Aegean Sea. Pollux, the star, still is used by navigators in taking lunar observations. Now and then Castor and Pollux have been re-

placed by such pairs as Heracles and Apollo, Triptolemus and Jason, Achilles and Patroclus, Theseus and Pirithous, Amphion and Zethus.

The Romans borrowed Castor and Pollux from the Greeks and worshipped them as bringers of victory, helpers in time of need.

Castor and Pollux first in
    martial force,
One bold on foot, one re-
    nowned for horse.
                    (Virgil)
At the battle of Lake Regillus they surprised the Romans by appearing when the weary warriors were hard pressed by the Etruscans. Overwhelmed by the sight of these dazzling immortals, the Etruscans hesitated, broke their ranks, and were lost. While the victorious Romans were busy routing their foe across the plain, the two white-clad horsemen rode silently away. A temple was built to the Twins on the very spot they had bathed their horses before riding into battle, and they became patron deities of the city. July 15, when they had appeared at Lake Regillus, was kept sacred in their name.

After these two had ceased to mark the equinox they were still believed to possess their original potency. The title of Gemini (Twins) dates from Roman times, and they continue to be invoked in: By Jiminy (Jimminy), O Gemini, O Gemony.

A common practice was to place effigies of the Twins in the prow and, Saint Paul, who had been shipwrecked and brought to Malta, sailed from there to Syracuse in an Alexandrian vessel with a figurehead of the Twin Brothers.

Impassioned biblical writers linked these stars to Adam and Eve, Isaac and Ishmael, Jacob and Esau, Zarah and Perez, David and Jonathan, and placed Saint James the Less as their ruler. Rabbis generally ascribe to Simeon-Levi, the Brethren; some accredit to the tribe of Benjamin, brother of Joseph.

For the Arabs they were Two Peacocks, gorgeous with their tail-coverts opened into a large semicircular fan. Nomads of the desert believed that the stars were one of the fore paws of their great ancient lion Asad.

The Hindu twins, the Asvins, parallel the Greek and no doubt derive from the same source. They are beautiful young horsemen, one fair, one dark, whose steeds are the rays of the sun not yet seen above the horizon and the tints that linger after the sun has been lost in the west, but Aries rather than Gemini belongs to them. Aditi, the visible infinite, primal mother who has many sons, including the twelve who, in the course of a year, alternately ride in the sun cart, has claimed Gemini to serve as her lunar inn. She is hailed as a cow and is implored for freedom from disease and forgiveness from sin. One of her sons, Marttanda, had been encased in an egg Aditi thought dead, so she let it roll off across the sky to the very edge, away from the beautiful mansions of the gods. One who was mortal was unfit to have a place among immortals. Marttanda revived each morning and crept back among the divinities, but each evening, along the rim of the

outer world, in view of all, he died. His daily rejuvenation won the admiration of the gods, and they finally acknowledged him to be one of their own.

Before the 16th century Jesuit influence, Chinese figured these stars as an Ape; under the Jesuits they became lovers, the Yang-Yin, the eternal opposition in nature. Yang, the active, male, or positive principle, who stood for celestial breath, action, fire, light, vigor, warmth, and heaven, was born when the Tai-kih, the Great Monad, moved. When the Yang moved to the utmost, he created the Yin, the passive female, or negative principle, symbolic of submissiveness, weakness, darkness, coldness, the moon, and earth. The Yang is represented by odd numbers because they cannot be broken, even numbers, which are easily broken, represent the Yin. Yet, one without the other is nothing; together their dual natures achieve dynamic balance or harmony.

Australian aboriginies state that the year opens when Two Young Men, Turree (Castor) and Wanjil (Pollux) chase Purra, the kangaroo (Capella). All through the spring the pursuit continues, but they overtake Purra annually at the beginning of intense heat and kill him. The raging fire on which the kangaroo is roasted sends up the smoke which causes the Coonar Turung (Great Mirage), which can be seen each summer.

To Peruvians they were Manco Capac, the sun, and his wife, Mama Ogllo, the moon, a conception akin to that of several Asiatic nations, and further

confirming the suspicion of a
contact between the two continents
at some time in the far distant
past. The couple's symbol
was a Pile of Bricks, memorial
to the founding of Cuzco by this
pair. Strangely enough the
Sumerian name for the month
May-June, ruled by Gemini,
signified bricks. The Eskimos
see in these stars the two door-
stones of an igloo.

A concept of lovers here inspired the Babes in the Woods
tale.

Configurations. The representations are many and varied.
A Euphratean drawing which
shows a couple of naked male
children, feet to feet, one standing on its head, probably is of
the sun and moon, one up while
the other is down. A variant
of this in which the boys are
clothed may apply to the two
bright stars of Gemini, and
designs for the two stars later
applied to the whole constellation.
Phoenicians illustrated these
stars as Two Kids or Gazelles.
In Rome, the Twins were simply
symbolized by two stars over a
ship or as two horsemen with
oval caps topped by stars, the
halves of the egg-shell from
which they supposedly emerged
at birth nearby. On most
western maps they are shown as
two sturdy youths standing side
by side, each wearing a bright
star and watching the conflict between Orion and the Bull. In
Christian art the configuration
is of Two Angels. A 15th century Venetian piece has two
nudes, a boy and a girl, seated
with their arms over each other's
shoulders. The Leyden manuscript shows two unclad youths
with Phrygian caps, each surmounted by a star and Maltese

cross, one holds a club and
spear, one holds a stringed
instrument. Another map copies
the Leyden except a sickle replaces the musical instrument.
On modern eastern atlases,
especially those of India, the
pair is composed of a man and
a woman. A Buddhist zodiac
has a single figure, a woman
holding a golden cord.

Additional designations:
Familiar Twins; The Giant's
Eyes; Ledaen Lights; Ledaen
Stars; Spartan Twins; Twin
Laconian Stars; Twins; Two Kids
or Two Gazellas, from the
Phoenician.

Anglo-Norman: Frere.

Anglo-Saxon: ge Twisan.

Arabic: Al Burj al Jauza
(The Constellation of the Twins),
a desert designation which came
from Jauza (Walnut), which is
a divided circle, and which in
Europe became Algeuze, Elgeuzi,
Gieuz, Jauzah, for the center,
as these stars long designated
a region believed to be the
center of the sky, either because they composed a zenith
zodiacal constellation or from
the brilliancy of this section of
outer space. Al Tauaman (The
Twins). Ell, a measure of
length, $4-1/2^o$, by which the
Twins are separated.

Australian: Turree and
Wanjil (The Young Men), where-
as the Pleiades were the Young
Girls.

Biblical: Twin Sons of
Rebecca.

Chaldean: Tammech (Twins).

Chinese Shih Chin (Ape);

Yang-Yin (Male-Female).

Egyptian: Harpichruti, whom the Greeks knew as Harpocrates. Harpichruti in Egyptian mythology was Horus, the child, who sat on a lotus flower with a finger in his mouth. Symbolically, the hero (humanized deity) places his finger in his mouth after roasting the dragon (foe of mankind); in effect he eats the slain dragon to acquire his victim's knowledge and strength. The constellation also is known as Horus the Elder and Horus the Younger.

French: Gemeaux.

German: Zwillinge or Zwilling.

Greek: Dii Samothraces, from the ancient seat of worship of the Cabiri, sometimes connected with these stars; Dioscuri.

Hebrew: Teomim (Twins).

Hindu: Asvins (Açvini, Ashwins, Aswins); Mithuna (Boy and Girl).

Italian: Castore et Polluce; Gemelli; Nido di Leda.

Khoramian: Adhupakarik (Two Figures).

Latin and Low Latin: Alter Castor; Anaces, a reference to Sparta; Astor, the starry one, and Polyleukes, the lightful; Castores; Castor fraterque; magni Castoris; Claustrum Hori, an allusion to Horus the Elder and Younger; Cycno generati, a reference to the swan shape in which Zeus visited Leda, mother of the Twins; Dii Germani (Brother Gods); Gemini Lacones; Gem-inum Astrum; Ledaei Fratres; Ledaei Juvenes; Ledaeum Sidus (Leda's Stars); Oeballi or Ocbalidae, from their grandfather, king of Sparta; Phoebi Sidus, being under Apollo's protection, Pueri Tyndarii, Tyndaridae, Tyndarides, Clarum Tyndaridae Sidus, all from Tyndareus, their putative father; Spartana Suboles, from their mother's home.

Medieval: Alioure, a corruption of the Arabic: Duo Pavones (Two Peacocks), a medieval Latin title which seems to have influenced the Arabic conception.

Persian: Du Paikar or Do Paikar (Two Figures).

Polynesian: Na Ainanu, the two Ainanus, one above, one below. The two stars were Pipiri or Tu and Rehua, the heaven proppers, who lifted heaven off earth because the two were in constant cohabitation and the creatures they had created had no room in which to breathe.

Tamil: Midhunam (Jituma, Tituma, from the Greek title, Twins.

Tyrian: Tome (Twins).

Astrologically it is a masculine, fortunate sign of the House of Mercury. Due to the precession of the equinoxes the sun no longer enters the constellation at the same time it enters the zodiacal sign, by which fortunes are controlled. Those born between May 21 and June 20 are the natives of the sign, that is are under its influence. They will be tall and straight, have dark eyes, brown hair, and active ways. In character they will be dual or versatile, contradictory, fickle, at the same time unselfish and tending toward genius, Mercury here governs the health of arms and legs. Chinese star readers claimed that when Gemini is invaded by Mars war and a paltry harvest will ensue. Symbolized by a couple or pair, especially two circles, eyes (a pair of spectacles), or wheels. The gnostic symbol is AA, and the pictorial emblem for Gemini is ♊ .

It is in the northern sky, the highest of the zodiacal twelve, with the feet of the heroes on the brink of the Milky Way, the river of heaven, as if to confirm that these heroes were the favorites of Poseidon (Neptune) as well as of Zeus (Jupiter). In an old fable the sea god as well as the sky god rewarded these brothers for their love for each other by providing them the ability to walk over the waters of his kingdom. It is noticeably conspicuous above the setting Orion in April. The two bright stars culminate about eleven minutes apart in the night sky of February 19. Auriga, Lynx, Cancer, Canis Minor, and Orion surround it. Among its named stars are: alpha, Castor; beta, Pollux; gamma, Alhena; delta, Wassat; eta., Propus. The two bright stars lie side by side and no other pair of equal brilliance are so close together in northern latitudes; for this reason they have always been spoken of together.

GLOBUS AEROSTATICUS VEL AETHERIUS (THE BALLOON). Formed by Lalande in 1798, but like most of the stellar groups he named so enthusiastically, it was scarcely recognized by fellow astronomers. It appeared in one catalogue as the Luft Ballon, in another as the Luft Ball. In the middle of the 18th century it appeared on an Italian map as Aerostato and on a French map as Ballon Aerostatique. Since then it has been ignored. Lalande had placed it east of Microscopium, between the tail of Piscis Austrinus and the body of Capricorn.

GRUS (THE CRANE). This title is peculiarly appropriate for in Egypt the crane was symbolic of a star observer. First published by Johann Bayer in 1603, the only mythology attached to it has been by religious astronomers, who imagined it to be the Stork in the Heaven of Jeremiah (a Crane replaces the Stork in some verses) or combined it with the Phoenix to form Aaron, the High Priest. Arabs included its stars in the Southern Fish.

Cranes are haughty and imposing in appearance, among themselves amiable and sociable, but suspicious and wary of others. These birds correspond to persons in fashionable society who are distant to those outside their circle, vying within their set in display and presumptuousness, scornful of underlings to whom they express themselves loudly and vehemently. From their V formation the angular form of letters was taken. Standing in water, they are the first to welcome Dawn as she rises. An aerial steed of immortals, they are sacred to deities in many parts of the world. In China the crane acts as a guide of the deceased and is displayed at funeral processions. During the middle ages the stork was a symbol of adultery and this may be why some translators of the Bible replaced the stork with a crane.

An alternate title, Phoeni-
copterus or Phoenicopter (Flamingo) is now rarely, if ever,
used. Additional designations
are - English: Bittern, a small
heron; French and Italian: la
Grue; German: der Kranich;
Spanish: Flamenco.

The components compose a
zigzag in the southern sky below
Piscis Austrinus and above
Tucana. Its alpha star is Al
Na'ir and culmination is about
October 12.

HERCULES (THE LEGENDARY
STRONG MAN). The adventures
ascribed to this constellation began with Gilgamesh, a solar hero
and legendary king of Erech,
capital of Shinar (Sumer), whom
the Chaldeans called Izdubar and
considered the celestial prototype
of Nimrod. Gilgamesh ruled
with such unrelenting severity
(scorching aspect of the sun),
the gods fashioned Enkidu (wind),
also called Eabani, a savage
man to punish him. Instead the
two became friends and traveled
together. Enamored of Gilgamesh's beauty and strength, the
goddess Ishtar offered him her
love and, when he scorned her,
she called upon her father Anu
(sky) to avenge the insult. Anu
sent a bull (rain withholder) to
Erech, and together Gilgamesh
and Enkidu severed the leg
(masculated) the bull and threw
the phallus against the goddess,
an incident probably derived
from the rite of self-emascula-
tion which had been practiced
in honor of Ishtar. The goddess
thereupon killed Enkidu and smote
Gilgamesh with the disease. To
cure his leprosy and win back
his friend, Gilgamesh sought his
ancestor Utnapishtim who,
with his wife, had survived
the deluge and who possessed the

secret of immortality. Utnapishtim showed Gilgamesh the plant
of life at the bottom of the sea
beneath the earth. Gilgamesh
dived for it and, as he stopped
to rest on the way back to the
upper world, a sea serpent, sent
by jealous gods, devoured it;
thus the serpent (darkness)
gained immortality, and Gilgamesh, by losing it also caused
man, whom he represented, to
remain mortal. Pitying gods
granted Gilgamesh the privilege
of visiting Enkidu in the underworld. The Gilgamesh epic appears to be a combination of
popular tradition, history, and
mythology. As a time myth it
has been related in twelve tablets
corresponding to the transit of
the sun through the twelve
branches of the zodiac. The
first tablet probably corresponds
to March or April, which would
place the visit of Gilgamesh into
this section of the sky in late
autumn or early winter. The
tablets show: 1-Gilgamesh named
tyrant of Erech, and Enkidu
created to oppose him. 2-
Enkidu is civilized by a shamkhat
(joy maiden from Ishtar's temple),
who yields herself to him for
seven nights and six days. Gilgamesh and Enkidu meet in single
combat, after which they become friends. 3-Enkidu deserts
the harlot and with Gilgamesh
sets out to slay the monster
Humbaba. 4-Gilgamesh and
Enkidu on the way to the forest
of Cedars of Lebanon, the haunt
of Humbaba. 5-The head of
Humbaba is cut off (fertility is
released). 6-Ishtar becomes
enamored of Gilgamesh, who
rejects her love. Gilgamesh
and Enkidu slay the bull sent to
destroy them. 7-Gilgamesh is
stricken with leprosy; Enkidu is
slain by the gods. 8-Gilgamesh
wails for his friend. 9-Gilga-

mesh visits Utnapishtim. 10-
Utnapishtim reveals to Gilgamesh
the plant of immortality is deep
in the sea. 11-Gilgamesh is
robbed of the plant. 12-Gilga-
mesh visits Enkidu, i.e. the
sun sinks into the underworld.

Those who succeeded Gilgamesh were the Babylonian
Tammuz, who in turn developed
into the Phrygian deity of vegetation Attis, whom the Greeks accepted as Adonis. Another successor was the Phoenician
Melkarth, or Melqarth, a savior
deity, by the Greeks called
Melicertis, and who at the end
of each day plunged into the sea.

Another Greek sun-hero whose
history has been derived from
that of Gilgamesh is Heracles,
known to Phoenicians as Harekhal
and to Romans as Hercules.
Early Greek astronomers probably
did not know this star group by
the hero's name, but simply as
The Kneeler. Although one of
the oldest, when this constellation
was formed remains a mystery.
Likewise, when the adventures of
the solar hero who engaged in
twelve battles was first placed
here is not known; a guess has
been ventured that makes 500
B.C. the date, in an effort on
the part of the Greeks to intro-
duce another of the Argonauts into the heavens. Heracles was the
son of Alcmene by Zeus, who
visited her in the guise of her
husband Amphitryon. Shortly
before the child's birth, Zeus
boasted to Hera that the first
child born that day to the family
of Perseus, grandfather of
Amphitryon and Alcmene, should
rule over his race. Hera,
aided by Ate, spirit of mischief,
hastened the birth of Eurystheus,
another grandchild of Perseus,
and preceding Heracles in birth

he became entitled to the honor
Zeus intended for Heracles,
who was doomed by Hera's
action to serve his kinsman, and
he was assigned twelve labors,
which were: 1-Strangle the
Nemean Lion, who spread frost;
2-Kill the Lernaean Hydra, a
drought demon; 3-Slay the
Arcadian stag, which consumed
vegetation; 4-Capture the
Erymanthian Boar, which he
caught in deep snow; 5-Clean
the Augean Stables in which
3,000 oxen were housed, a task
he accomplished in one day by
diverting the river Alpheus
through the stalls; 6-Scatter
the Stymphalean Birds (storm
clouds), which he frightened
off with a rattle; 7-Capture the
Cretan Bull, which had an insatiable appetite. When Eurystheus, master of Hercules,
refused to accept it, the hero
released it, and it roamed until
it finally settled at Marathon.
8-Kill the Diomedes' Mares,
which ate human flesh. 9-
Obtain the girdle of Hippolyta,
queen of the Amazons. 10-Slay
the purple oxen (storm clouds)
of Geryon, a winged giant with
three heads, six hands and six
feet. 11-Obtain the Hesperian
Apples of love and fruitfulness.
They were located in the Garden
of Hesperides, and to get them
Heracles was forced to slay
the many-eyed Ladon (night).
12-Bring from the underworld
the dog Cerberus, which guarded
the entrance to the infernal
regions. In addition to his
twelve labors, Heracles assisted
the Gods in their war against
the Giants, accompanied the
Argonauts to Colchis, pillaged
Troy when Laomedon, the city's
king, cheated him, reestablished
his friend Tyndarus on the
throne of Sparta, shot Nessus,
when the licentious centaur

tried to abduct his wife Deianeira, and engaged in many other daring and dangerous adventures, which made him the most renowned hero of ancient times. Nessus, before he died, gave Deianeira a shirt, saying that, if she ever were in danger of losing the love of Heracles, she had only to place this gift on him to win her husband back. In appreciation of his many victories, Heracles wished to offer a sacrifice to Zeus, and asked Deianeira for his best robe. Believing that he intended to visit another woman, she decided to test the efficacy of the love-charm of the robe given to her by Nessus. Hot flames that rose from the altar heated poisons in the robe, and in agony he implored friends to set his body on a funeral pyre. The body of Heracles was borne to Olympus by Athene in a chariot drawn by four horses, and Hebe, a cup-bearer to the gods, was made his celestial wife. The death of Heracles is an astronomical allegory, representing the end of the year, when the sun reaches the most westerly point in its annual journey at the time of the winter solstice. Even after death, as a constellation, Heracles can be seen in the winter sky trampling on the Dragon. The Roman Fabian gens, men who were superior physically and intellectually, claimed this model of fearlessness as an ancestor.

The various evil spirits that Gilgamesh, Heracles (Hercules) and other heroes had been forced to battle on earth followed them into space, and there the conflict of the year continues. Until the valiant one is able to overcome the Bull, he holds his place in the winter sky; the Scorpion, which once bit the hero, has its pincer-like claws ready for attack; sea-serpents, water-snakes, dragons, a lion, and other wild animals, all keep peace from reigning in the heavens.

Kneeling, a posture usually assigned to a knight in the presence of his king, seems a bit absurd for a deity or a hero in the act of overcoming a dragon (Draco, the next constellation), and no satisfactory explanation has been found for it. It probably has some religious significance for heroes are portrayed in this position on extremely ancient monuments. One fable states that Hercules found himself among the Ligurians, against whom he had to defend himself. He looked about in vain for something to throw at his foes. Jupiter noticed the danger to his son and sent a rain of round stones, with which Hercules repulsed his enemies, and the Engonasis is said to be the giant bending over to pick up the missiles.

Christians turned away from Pagan lore and delivered these stars to the first Adam, beguiled by the serpent and doomed to a life of toil; while Ophiuchus has been entrusted to the second Adam (Christ), who is triumphant over the serpent. The Hercules cluster also is given to the Three Wise Men of the East, and more fittingly to Samson.

This section of the sky is the great meadow of the Arabs. Here a shepherd pastured his flocks and the various rows of stars are fences to protect the sheep from hyenas and jackals. The unfenced side of the meadow is guarded by two dogs, the stars alpha Herculis and alpha Ophiuchi.

Configurations. Portrayed as a nude young man kneeling; as one with a lion's skin tossed over his shoulder who kneels with his right foot on a twisting serpent's (Draco's) head while he brandishes a club with his right hand and holds either Cerberus or a branch in which serpents are entangled in his left; as a young boy carrying a short star-tipped shepherd's crook and a lion's skin and head; a strong young man clothed in the lion's skin and holding a brazen club and an apple branch, with his right hand on the edge of the Milky Way; a young man holding in his left hand the branch with two vipers, a reminder of the almost forgotten stellar Cerberus with serpent's tongues; a strong man with an ass's jawbone, undoubtedly Samson; or, as on a Venetian illustration, an apple tree with a serpent twisted around the trunk, which may have been a medieval attempt to emphasize the adventure of Hercules when he overcame the guardian dragon Ladon to get the Golden Apples of Hesperides or to connect these stars with the Garden of Eden.

Additional designations: Adam, undoubtedly a reference to the tree and serpent drawing; Bended Knee; Bender on His Knee; Inexplicable Image; Kneeler; Kneeling One. Man Who Kneels; One Who Bends Down; Orpheus, a sun-hero; Phantom; Samson; Theseus, a sun-hero; Unknown Image.

Arabic: Al Jathiyy a la Rukbataihi (One Who Kneels on Both Knees), which decayed into Alcheti (or Alchete) hale rechabatih, Algethi, Algiethi, Elhathi, Elgeziale rulxbachei, Elzegeziale. Al Rakis (The Dancer) from the

classical Saltator or Leaper. Rasaben, from the neighboring Al Ras al Thuban (Draco). Raudah (Pasture), which also included stars of Ophiuchus and Serpens. Part of the Pasture was Nasak Shamiyyah (Northern Border), part was Nasak Yamaniyyah (Southern Border). The section now known as the Club of Hercules was the sheep in the pasture.

Euphratean: Gilgamens or Gilgames, whose most popular attitude on monuments is resting on one knee with a foot upon the Dragon's head. Lugal or Sarru (King).

French: Rameau et Cerbere (Branch and Cerberus).

German: Zweig (Branch).

Greek: Engonasi, Engonasin, Engonasis (Kneeling One).

Italian: Cerbero, the three-headed porter or dog who guarded the afterworld entrance; Ercole, an abbreviation of Hercules; Ramo (Branch); Ramo e Cerbero.

Latin and Low Latin: Alcides, a poetical title either from a Greek word for strength or from Alcaeus, Heracles' paternal grandfather. Amphitryoniades, from the hero's putative father; Aper, the wild boar slain by a hero at Elis, holy land of the ancient Greeks. Caeteus, Ceteus, or Cetheus, a son of Lycaon, and thus brother of Callisto (Kallisto), who was transformed into Ursa Major. Celticus or Almannus, from two heroes, one Celtic, one German, noted for strength and daring, who supposedly descended from Hercules. Cernuator (Wrestler) from the hero's skill. Clavator or Claviger (Club-

Bearer); Defectum Sidus (Defective Star); Desanaus, Desanes, Dorsanes, Dosanes, of Sanscrit origin. Effigies defecta labore. Geniculatus, Genuflexus, Ignota Facies, Imago, Ingenicla, Ingeniclus, Ingeniculatus, Ingeniculus, which are a combination of the Greek and Latin, and all seem to refer to kneeling or the shame of kneeling. Imago laboranti similis. Incumbens in genibus, Incumbentis genubus, Incurvatus in genu, which are related to the Greek and suggest incumbent or kneeling. Ixion, who labored at a wheel, perhaps because Heracles did likewise at the Omphalos. Lycaon, who kneels to weep over Callisto's misfortune. Maceris, from Libya. Malica, Melica, Melicartus, or Melicerta, who became the sea-goddess Palaemon. Mellus, from Malum or apples in the Hesperides adventure. Nessus, who caused the hero's death. Nisus, eponymous hero of the harbor of Nisaca. Oetaeus, from the Thessalian mountain range whence Heracles descended into the funeral pyre. Ovillus, from Ovine, the sheep driven by Heracles. Pataecus and Epipataecus are blends of Egyptian and Latin, meaning unexplained. Procidens, Prociduus,Procumbens in genua. Prometheus bent in chains. Qui in genibus est. Ramus pomifer (Fruit Branch). Saltator (Leaper). Sanctus, incorrectly written for Sancus, ancient Italian god of hospitality. Thamyris, who challenged the Muses to a music contest, and bent in dejection when his lyre was broken. Tirynthius, from the traditional early home of the hero.

Persian: Ber zanu nisheste (Resting on His Knee); Ternuelles which might be from a mistaken orthography of the name Hercules.

Phoenician: Harekhal (Traveler).

Syrians included stars of Serpens and called the asterism a Row of Pearls.

The constellation is in the northern sky surrounded by Draco to the north, Corona Borealis, Ophiuchus to the south, and Lyra. In 4667 B.C. it culminated on the northern meridian at midnight of the spring equinox, and never since that time has it commanded such an important position in space. Culmination date now is about July 28. Through the summer and autumn he is seen in the rather undignified position of hanging downward, his lower extremities uppermost. The stars of the group are faint; alpha is named Ras Algethi, beta is Korenephorus.

HOROLOGIUM (THE CLOCK). Introduced in 1751, it is a small constellation in the southern sky without bright stars, enclosed by Eridanus, Hydrus, Reticulum, and Dorado. Although it continues to appear on maps it rarely is mentioned. Additional designations are: Clock of Argo; Horoscope; Pendulum Clock. French: Orloge; German: Pendeluhr; Italian Orologio; Latin: Horologium Oscillatorium (Pendulum Clock). Culmination is about December 25.

HYDRA (SEA SERPENT). On a stone uranograph of 1,200 B.C., a water-snake appears which has been identified as one of the several sky symbols of the great Tiamat or one of the monsters of her court, and may be intended for this configuration.

Tiamat's cohort Mushussu, a
raging power of darkness and evil
eventually overcome by Ninurta
(Aquila) has been put forward.
Ereshkigal and Ningishzida also
have been mentioned. Ereshkigal,
a sister of Ishtar, was the fearful goddess of the underworld
and death. In love with Tammuz,
she forces him to spend half of
each year with her underground.
Although she receives her sister
Ishtar in anger, she permits her
to enter the underworld mansion
and rescue Tammuz each spring.
She is beneficient inasmuch as
she permits the wealth in her subterranean vaults to rise to the
surface with her lost love.
Ningishzida was the son of Ereshkigal. A serpent-dragon, he
was one of the watchmen at
the gate of Anu (Sky), and ap-
portioned vegetation. Also a
patron of herbs and medicine,
his emblem was a snake coiled
around a staff, and into the present day this remains a symbol
of physicians.

The same figure that appears
on the uranograph is seen on a
boundary stone with a scorpion
by its side. An ancient Accadian
hymn makes mention of a storm
and ocean monstrosity that bears
a yoke on its seven heads. An
analogy between a curling or
flowing stream and a swiftly
gliding snake was obvious to our
primal ancestors, and so they
arrived at the River of the
Snake, which, with its several
branches (heads), poured out
water that created the ocean
stream along the limits of the
universe. In Egypt the River of
the Snake was the celestial
section of the Nile.

No definitive identification
can be made; the ancient skies
held three other sea-monsters,

Draco, on which Hercules treads;
the one in the hands of Ophiuchus;
Cetus. We can only conjecture
which myths apply to each.
Hydra was the Greek notion.
The offspring of Typhon and
Echidna, a beautiful woman whose
body was that of a snake below
the waist. Hydra was nine-
headed, lightning flashed from
his eyes, he stirred the whirlwind. A demon of drought
and darkness, he dwelt in the
Lernean swamp near the well of
Anymone, withheld its waters,
and ravaged the surrounding
country of Argos. As his
second labor, Heracles was
directed to slay it, but its middle head was immortal, and
every time Heracles cut it off,
it grew on again, until, with the
assistance of his nephew and
charioteer (fire which accompanies
the sun) Iolaus, Heracles burned
the head and buried it under a
rock. By dipping his arrows
(rays) in the Hydra's blood,
Heracles rendered them fatal.
After its death the Hydra was
made whole again by the gods
and placed in the southern skies.

Hera, jealous of Heracles,
sent a sea-crab (Cancer) to bite
the hero's foot while he was
finishing off the serpent, but
the crustacean was easily disposed of, much of Hera's morti-
fication.

Sceptics have denied the
Lernean freak was a snake, al-
leging it was an octopus that
lived in the swamp waters, its
writhing tentacles giving it the
appearance of one with many
heads.

This asterism was connected
with the Argonautic constellations
when it was said to represent
the dragon Aetes set to safe-

guard the Golden Fleece.

In the middle ages, Christian astronomers, disregarding each other as well as Pagan writers, claimed these stars for the Devil in the Garden of Eden, the Flood, Noah's Wine Cup, Noah's Raven, and the River Jordan. This latter includes Crater and Corvus as well.

Norwegians believed this was their marine monster Kraken, said to be a mile and a half in circumference and to cause whirlpools when it dives.

For an unknown period its meandering course symbolized that of the moon, especially in the Orient. For this reason, lunar nodes were called the Dragon's head and tail, as the Hindu Rahu and Ketu. When these parts held a comet, poison was squeezed from it and scattered over the world. These fanciful ideas have now been transferred to Draco. In India, Vrtra (Vritra), whose name means obstruction, and who consumed Indra's cows (fertile rains clouds), covered the earth with darkness and caused drought, was placed here as well as on the Rainbow.

A kindly Chinese god, Chang Hsien lived among these stars, a neighbor of Tien Kou, the evil Heavenly Dog, which lived on the stars of Crater. The baneful dog was not only responsible for eclipses, but prevented the birth of males in families which fell under his influence. A man must have an heir, a son to take his turn as head of the family or he is less than nothing, scorned in this world and the next, a useless being who cannot assure his dead ancestors of

proper offerings or receive them himself in the afterlife. Unfortunate women, who failed to provide their husbands with sons, invoked the white bearded and haired Chang Isien to intercede for them. Chang Hsien who warded off calamities, had been known to go as far as to lift his magic bow and arrow and shoot the Dog of Heaven. The beings of the sky are immortal so he could not kill the Dog, but the painful wound of his arrow usually drove home his viewpoint and many a family was saved from a sonless fate. Chang Hsien was sometimes simply called Chang, the Glorious Chang meaning to draw a bow. While he was helpful to women who wished to have sons he usually was unlucky in any enterprise.

After the formation of Hydrus in 1603 A.D., Hydra was made the spouse of the younger constellation.

Configuration: The Hydra wriggles across the zodiacal equator, his ferocious head and fangs dangerously close to the Lesser Dog, while the Crab seems to lie in wait to grip him with his vice-like claws. On Hydra's back are the Cup and two birds, the Crow, which picks at its folds because Hydra prevents his access to the Cup, and an Owl, for the Noctua, a constellation, probably invented in the 19th century, which has been disgarded. A drawing of Hydra dated 1488 shows the serpent's head resting in tree branches, simulating the Hesperides dragon, although the legend is more correctly attached to Draco.

A portrait of Chang Hsien

holding a bow and arrow and accompanied by a little boy is a popular conception that often hangs above the altar in a Chinese home. The bow is made up of stars of Hydra's second coil, and he points toward the Dog (Crater).

Until the 18th century, Corvus and Crater, its riders, were often spoken of as if they were part of Hydra; examples are Hydra et Corvus, Hydra et Crater, Continuatio Hydrae.

Additional designations: Draco, a confusion with the more northerly dragon; Nepa and Nepas, originally African words for the terrestrial Crab and Scorpion; The Water Monster; The Water Serpent; The Water Snake.

Accadian: En-te-na-mas-luv or En-te-na-mas-mur (Tail Up). Perhaps stars in Hydra's Tail and Libra, rather than all of Hydra.

Arabian: Al Hail (The Horse), an early desert figure. Al Hayyah (The Snake), which became El Havic on maps of the middle ages. Al Shuja (The Snake), which collapsed into Alsugahh, Asiua, Asuia, Asvia, as only late medieval astronomical writers were able to turn Arabic into low Greek and Latin.

Assyrian: Etsen-tsiri (Tail-Up). Probably the same stars that made up the Accadian Tail.

Chinese: Lieu (Willow Branch) or Liu (Circular Willow Garland). This was worn on Chang Hsien's head and composed the 24th Hsiu. It formed the beak of the great Chinese Red or Vermilion Bird. The appear-

ance of Liu was a good omen, a lucky period for herds and flocks. The constellation governed the planets and was worshipped at the summer solstice festival as a giver of immortality.

Egyptian: Nile.

French: Hydre.

German: Grosse Wasserchlange.

Italian: Idra.

Latin and Low Latin: Asina, meaning She Ass, probably from a typographical error in the barbarous Asiua, which came from the Arabian. Coluber (Snake); Echidna (Viper), also used with the adjectives Furiosus, Magnanimus, Sublimatus. Hidra, Hydros, Hydrus, these latter two, after the 16th century, used for the new southern figure which became the mate of Hydra. Idra or Ydra; Idrus aquaticus; Serpens aquaticus.

Norwegian: Kraken or Kraaken (Dragon).

The figure curls from Cancer in the northern sky to Libra just out of the Scorpion's reach in the southern sky. About April 29 it can be seen at culmination. Alphard is the alpha star.

HYDRUS (THE WATER SNAKE). This constellation invented in 1603, almost immediately was dubbed the mate of the ancient and much longer Hydra. In legend it is a hater and destroyer of the crocodile, a symbolic form of the devil or evil.

The Chinese formed four clusters from these and a few

neighboring stars: Shay Show (Serpent's Head); Shay Fuh (Serpent's Belly); Shay We (Serpent's Tail), Foo Pih (significance unknown).

The French title was l'Hydre Male; the German, der Kleine Wasserchlange.

From this, combined with some of the stars of Tucana, a biblical figure, Raphael, was made.

Without named stars, it is deep in the southern sky, its head close by the polar Octans, its tail almost reaching to the beautiful star Achernar. Other clusters around it are Mensa, Reticulum, Tucana. Culmination comes about December 10.

INDUS (THE INDIAN). A modern constellation, formed in 1603, the name comes from the Persian for a river. However, it generally is portrayed as a rather civilized American Indian, nevertheless nude, with arrows in both hands but lacking a bow.

Julius Schiller joined it with Pavo and presented the patriarch Job.

The Chinese knew its lucida as the Persian, a title supplied by Jesuit missionaries. Previously they had known it as Pe Sze, of uncertain significance.

A title, Triangle Indien, most likely came from its general outline. To the French it is Indien; to the Germans, Indianer; to Italians, Indiano.

Situated in the southern sky, it is below Miscroscopum, between Grus and Pavo. None of its stars are named, and culmination is about October 1.

LACERTA (THE LIZARD). This asterism was introduced in the middle of the 17th century. The original figure was a "strange weasel-built creature with a curly tail," which Johann Hevelius, the designer, placed at the head of the list of offerings to Urania. Before the Lizard was formed, the Sceptre and the Hand of Justice to honor Louis XIV was introduced here, but this title, like Frederici Honores to glorify Frederick the Great a century later, has been forgotten. Hevelius gave an alternate title, Stellio, from Stellion, a newt with starlike dorsal spots found along the Mediterranean coast. A drawing made after the death of Hevelius is more like that of a greyhound.

Early Chinese combine these stars with several in Cygnus for their Flying Serpent. The French title is Lizard; the German, Eidechse; the Italian, Lucertola.

Located in the northern sky it extends from a foot of Pegasus into the Milky Way to a point close to the head of Cepheus. Few bright stars are located in this area, and none of the luminaries of Lacerta have more than a 3.9 magnitude. Culmination is about October 12.

LEO (THE LION). Stars that sent humid nights in which breathing was difficult and everyone tossed and turned, scarcely able to sleep, seemed to people, who resided between the Euphrates and the Tigris, to be in league with a power that during the day burned crops, ravaged flocks, and spread fever and death. Naturally, a period such as this was ruled by one who had the strength and boldness to scorch earth and leave it charred. Who but the lion had the necessary ferocity! Its very red mane suggested curling flames of fire. It was symbolic of action, authority, beastliness, pride, stealth, vigilance, superhuman and subhuman (divine and animal) force. Time and again deities appeared dressed in its skin or in war utilized the lion as a steed or throne, and at the height of the summer heat the celestial beast revelled in its glory, for it was host to the sun, the greatest potency of the skies. Humans down below engaged in magic, offered choice sacrifices, and prayed; each one sought to beguile the Lion into sending relief.

The original Leo may have been one aspect of Humbaba (Khumbaba), the demon with a beard that resembled human entrails and guarded the cedar forests of Lebanon in much the same manner that the dragon Ladon later watched over the Garden of Hesperides. This hideous creature was slain by Gilgamesh and Enkidu. However, more often it is said to be Ugallu, one of the demons in Tiamat's train. The fore part of the group, now known as the Sickle, the Sumerians knew as the Curved Weapon, and may once have regarded this section as an asterism in its own right.

That the lion figure was designed when the summer solstice was in this constellation seems to be beyond doubt. Around the time the constellation was wrought the sun entered this area of the sky about a month earlier than it now does, and a connection between the constellation and a return of the sun

to its highest realm is obvious. If the Lion was feared, his superiority was respected; no one disputed that he was king of beasts, and who but the king of beasts had the right to entertain the king of divine regions at the most crucial time of the year, when he stood for a moment at the apex of the arch of heaven.

During this midsummer period the Nile overflowed and brought life back to the cracked, arid land, but the season's intense heat may have compelled mortal lions of the desert to leave natural haunts for the banks of the river, where waters of the inundation provided them with relief. To the fanciful, the lions had come not for comfort but to pay homage to their celestial ancestor. A lion's head was carved on gates that opened the Nile for irrigation, presumably the source of the figure that has become popular the world over, the lion from whose open jaws a fountain gushes. In ancient judicial proceedings a water-clock was used that had a lion's shape, and its name signified Guardian of the Stream. Coincidentally an Assyrian base relief has water streaming from a ring-shaped vessel on either side of which stands a lion guard. So, the lion was not merely host to the sun, but sentinel of the waters.

Although some Egyptologists maintain the Androsphinx at Gizeh has the head of an early king, or perhaps that of Harmachis, god of the rising sun, on a lion's body, a theory persists that the head on the great idol belongs to the Virgin, the adjoining configuration, and the next to entertain the still hot summer sun. The ancient Egyptian

stellar lion embodied only a part
of the one with which we are
familiar, and some of the stars
were shown as a Knife.

In 243 B.C. the Lion lost
the magnificent tuft which had
beautified his tail. At that time
the Pharaoh undertook a
hazardous campaign against the
Assyrians, and his devoted queen
Berenice vowed to sacrifice her
auburn hair to the god upon her
husband's safe return from the
expedition. The gods provided
the Pharaoh with victory and, to
make a place for her tresses in
the heavens, the lion's adornment
was cut off and Coma Berenices
created.

To the Greeks this cluster
typified the Lion which originally
fell from the moon in the form
of a meteor and landed on the
Isthmus of Corinth, where it terrified the inhabitants, destroyed
herbs, wasted the land, and appropriated the Nemean (Nemaean)
forest for its lair. Heracles,
as the first of his labors, was
commanded to slay this lion. Inasmuch as it was invulnerable
to arrows, Heracles strangled
him to death. Thus the arrows
(rays) of the spring sun were
not strong enough to kill a
drought or winter demon. After
the beast's death, he was carried
back to the heavens with his
conqueror, who was permitted
to wear a lion's skin as a token
of his victory. To keep Leo
from falling down to earth again,
he was tacked to the heavenly
vault with star-studded nails,
and the Nemean Festival of
funeral games celebrated the
slaying of the Lion. Parsley
wreaths were awarded to con-
testant winners.

The chief Druid in Britain

was dubbed a Lion. Whether
this had a connection with rites
that were held when the summer
solstice was among these stars
and the sun had a higher position here than anywhere else in
the sky is not known. The lion
also is significant to Freemasons.
The Lion's Paw Grip supposedly
raised to life man's spirit, long
buried in material existence,
and entitled a builder or mason
to become a master mason. In
Egyptian mysteries the priest
who offered the Lion's Paw Grip
wore a lion mask.

Rabbis claim Leo to be the
tribal emblem of Judah, avering
that it was allotted to the son
from whose name the word Jew
was derived, when Jacob said,
"Judah is a lion's whelp." To
further this contention, this
constellation supposedly was
Judah's natal sign, and the
signet ring he gave to Tamar,
his son Er's widow, by whom
he conceived children, had a
lion etched on it. According to
another theory, although Judah's
emblem was a lion, he ruled
Sagittarius and his brother
Ephraim, whose emblem was a
grape, governed Leo.

To the apostolic school Leo
was governed by Doubting Thomas,
the saint who refused to believe
in the resurrection of Christ
until convinced by sight and
touch, or it was ruled by John
the Baptist. Christians of the
middle ages and those who later
placed biblical characters throughout the heavens called it one of
the lions in the den into which
Daniel had been thrown.

Our figure is composed of
stars that were only a small number of the stars that made up the
ancient Asad of Arabia, which

extended from Gemini over Cancer, Leo, Virgo, Libra, into
Corvus, with parts of other
constellations both north and
south of the ecliptic. When later
Arabians adopted the Greek form,
they simply condensed their own
Lion (Asad). Some of these
stars the Arabs viewed as a
pond, its water aglow in the sun
and over which the Gazelle,
formed of the stars which now
are known as Leo Minor, leaped
to safety when frightened by the
swishing of the Lion's tail.

The device of the National
banner of Persia was the sun
among the stars of Leo, and a
lion couchant with a rising sun
at his back is sculptured on public structures. Among these
stars appear three Hindu lunar
stations, the tenth, which is
represented by a house; the
eleventh, a bed; the twelfth, a
couch.

In most parts of the world
a gigantic feline was deciphered
here, but on early Chinese
zodiacs, these stars were first
part of the Red or Vermilion
Bird, then became the Quail's
Fire, or Horse, and after the
16th century, the Chinese
adopted our sign. With the stars
Leo Minor the Chinese recognized another form, that of a
Yellow Dragon mounting steps
of heaven on the way to the
land of the gods. Mexicans
worshipped the lion. Among
Peruvians the form was that
of a Puma springing at its prey.

Configurations: The familiar
Lion is perhaps the most famous
of all zodiacal designs. It generally is shown standing, alert,
ready to spring, or in fatal conflict with the Bull, to suggest
the constant battle between light

and darkness. On the Denderah
planisphere he stands on an outstretched serpent, perhaps Hydra,
an instinctive enemy, and thus
portrays the victory of light over
darkness. The section which
once composed the Egyptian
Knife is now well delineated on
some illustrated maps as a
Sickle. Its pictorial symbol ∂l
supposedly is a likeness of the
animal's mane, but seems more
appropriate to the opposite
extremity. Others maintain
it is the crouching lion, the
conspicuous stars which form
the Sickle, or a corruption
of $\wedge$, lambda, the initial of
the animal's name when written
in Greek. A hieroglyph of a
lion appears among symbols of
Mithraic worship, but we have
no records to indicate if this
agreed with ours.

Additional designations: The
Lion; The Sickle, for stars
forming the forepart of the
animal.

Accadian: Gis-mes (The
Curved Weapon), formed by the
stars now designated to be a
Sickle.

Anglo-Norman: Leun.

Arabic: Al Haud (The Pond);
Asad (Lion), a constellation
which extended far beyond the
boundaries of the present constellation.

Assyrian: Pa-pil-sak (Scepter
or Great Fire), identified with
the month Abu, our July-
August, the fiery hot.

Babylonian: Aru (Lion).
Maru-sha-arkat-Sharru (Fourth
Son or Four-Year Old Son behind the King) for rho star,
the 16th ecliptic constellation.

Chinese: Shun Ho (Quail's Fire); Sze Tsze (Lion).

Coptic: Titefui (Forehead).

Euphratean: Gisbar-namru-sa-pan, variously translated but most often given as The Shining Disc which precedes Bel (Ursa Major) or is in some other way intimately connected with him.

French: Lion.

German: Fahne (Banner), a long forgotten asterism that lay in Leo and Virgo as a distinct configuration in a 15th century manuscript. Lowe (Lion).

Hebrew: Arye (Lion).

Hindu: Asleha, Sinha.

Italian: Leone.

Khorasmian: Khamshish (Scimetar), for the stars of the Sickle.

Latin and Low Latin: Bacchi Sidus (Stars of Bacchus), the deity being associated with the lion, either because he assumed its shape in his numerous transformations or because the lion skin was a frequent costume. Cleonaeum Sidus (Cleonae Star, Cleonae being the Argolic town near the Nemean forest). Domicilium Solis, an emblem of fire and heat which derived from the philosopher Petosiris, attached to the court of the Egyptian king Necepsos, who taught that at creation the sun rose near Denebola, which thus became its domicile. Hercleum Astrum; Hercleus; Herculeus Leo; Jovis et Juonis Sidus, that is stars under the guardianship of Jove and Juno, quite appropriate for

the king of beasts. Nemaeo truculento; Nemeaeum Monstrum; Nemeaeus; Nemeas Alumnus; Nemees Terror; Violentus Leo.

Medieval corruptions of the Arabic Asad influenced by Latin: Alasado, Alasid, Alatid, Aleser, Alezet, Asedaton, Asid, Asis, Assid, Ellesed.

Persian: Ser, Shir.

Syrian: Aryo (Lion).

Tamil: Leya, Leyaya (from Leo); Simham, from the Sanscrit for Lion.

Turkish: Aratan (Lion).

On talismans the lion is a symbol of health, and as a zodiacal sign its quality of influence is masculine and therefore fortunate. When the constellation is the house of the sun, from about August 7 to September 14 (these dates do not correspond to those of the zodiacal sign, which is from about July 23 to August 23), it rules the human heart and is responsible for its well being or diseases. Ancient physicians feared the time the sun spent here, for during this period all medicines were believed to be poisonous, even a bath was harmful. The weatherwise said that thunder here foretold sedition and death to great men, and that these stars were in charge of the wind from the north by a third northwest. Natives of the sign are said to be magnetic, proud, generous, faithful, chivalrous, high-spirited, pleasure-loving, opinionated.

One of the most graceful and striking constellations in the northern sky, it contains over a hundred stars visible to the unaided eye. Cancer, Hydra, Virgo, and Leo Minor surround it. Culmination is in the night sky about April 15. Among its many bright stars are alpha, Regulus; beta, Denebola; gamma, Algeiba; delta, Zozma (Duhr); epsilon, Algenubi; theta, Chort; lambda, Alterf; rho, Maru-sha-arkat-sharru; chi, Al Minhar al Asad.

LEO MINOR (THE LESSER LION). This cluster first appeared in 1690 on a posthumous work of John Hevelius, who had died in 1687. Hevelius had formed it from eighteen stars scattered in the northern sky between the Greater Lion and Bear. This title was given, he said, because it partook of the same nature of its more magnificent neighbor.

The Crab of the Denderah zodiac is located in this figure, and this area of space was reserved as sacred to the Egyptian god Ptah, father of the beginning, architect of the universe, who emerged from an egg laid by the Chaos Goose. In one tradition, Ptah shaped everything from mud; in another he called into existence each thing he willed to create, thus the embodiment of mind from which all emerges. He was a lame dwarf after whom the European elf was patterned, and his assistants were earth spirits called Khnumu (Molders).

The Chinese placed two clusters here, Nuy Ping (Inner Screen) and Seaou Wei (Small Tail). These stars with those of Leo were used for their Yellow Dragon.

Additional designations: Leaena (Lioness), an arbitrary

title of the 19th century, which made it the mate of Leo. The Small Lion.

Arabic: Al Haud (The Pond), with stars of Leo and also a designation of Coma Berenices when Asad, the Great Lion, occupied almost a third of outer space. Al Thiba wa Auladuha (The Gazelle and Her Young).

French: Petit Lion.

German: Kleine Lowe.

Italian: Leoncino.

Without stars greater than fourth magnitude, Leo Minor culminates about April 9.

LEPUS (THE HARE).

Below Orion's feet the Hare
Is chased eternally, behind him
Sirius ever speeds as in pursuit.
(Aratus)

The hare has been sacred to the moon as the cock has been to the sun into the distant past. It has been found with the satellite on Euphratean cylinders, Syrian agate seals, Chinese coins, Central Asian crescent cakes, and tales of its adventures, which lead to the moon, have been told by widely separated races and savage tribes. The Khoikoin Hottentots and the Bantus were two of the African peoples who allied the hare and the moon in worship and story, declaring that the hare, ill-treated by the moon, retaliated by scratching her face and the scars are still there.

In a Bushman legend the hare was to deliver a message for the

the orb of night in which a promise is made to people on earth that they will rise again after death as the moon does. Because the messenger falsified the intelligence, man does not rise again and is mortal. The moon, thus frustrated, hit the hare across the mouth and split its lip.

The experienced wisdom and shrewd benevolence of the African hare or rabbit crossed to the New World and, for American Indians, burrowed away in the soil and released the primeval race from under ground. This great American Indian Spirit was variously called Glooscap, Ioskeha, Manabozho, Messou, Michabo. Among the Nahuatl tribe, the hare was Totochtin, god of drunkeness and idleness. Eventually the animal found his way into the Uncle Remus stories as Brer Rabbit, witty trickster who overcomes the superior strength of Brer Fox and Brer Wolf.

Sasin (Çaçin) or Sasanka (Marked with the Hare) is one Hindu name for the moon, from the story told about the Buddha Sakyamuni. In an early stage of his existence this Buddha was a hare, who had an ape and a fox for his companions. One day as they roamed they met a beggar who was none other than the god Indra in disguise. The god wished to test their hospitality. When he asked for food they all went off in search of some; the hare alone returned empty-handed. That he might not be remiss as a host, he informed his guest to enjoy a hot meal he was about to prepare; then he built a great fire and plunged into it. Indra rewarded him with a place in the moon. In other Sanscrit, Singalese and Oriental fables, the palace of the hare is on the face of the moon. In the Chinese and Japanese version, there the Hare pounds with mortar and pestle the elixir of life and, in addition, carries the sun through the house of Scorpio.

The constellation is said to be a duplication of the Moon, put to flight by the Sun (Orion), who pursues and vanquishes the timid Hare. The mighty Orion delighted in hunting this swift-footed destroyer of vegetable gardens, and routed it with the hounds he held on leash, a problem that perplexed mythologists. Why should a rugged hunter find gratification in the chase of such an insignificant creature? Among the solutions they have offered are that Orion, the solar type, and Lepus, the lunar type, are instinctive antagonists, the solar being far the stronger, or that Sicily once was overrun by hares that devastated farms and that the animal finally was placed in the heavens near the hunter who had saved the land. The Hare also is the enemy of Aquila, the Eagle. The hatred between the bird that adores the sun and the rodent attached to the moon is so great, the latter will not rise until the former has left the sky. It likewise detests the voice of the Crow and drops out of sight, sets, when this bird comes into view.

Early Egyptians beheld in these stars the Boat of Osiris, in which he travelled through space. Later in Egypt and in Persia, the figure is a serpent on zodiacs beneath a bird of prey (Orion), suggesting the elements in conflict.

Among biblical astronomers the constellation stands for Gideon's Fleece; Magdalen in Tears; Judas Iscariot; Cain driven from the face of the earth to the face of the moon; it is the Easter symbol because it typifies the church or a pursued Christian. In art sometimes placed at the foot of the Virgin Mary to indicate her triumph over lust.

Arabs believed four of these stars were the Chair of the Giant (Orion) or Throne of Al Jauzah (The Maiden). They also described the four stars of the quadrilateral as Four Camels Quenching Their Thirst in a nearby river, Al Nahr (Eridanus).

Classical writers are uncertain about the history or influence of the constellation. While in Africa it was held to be so unlucky the hunter would return home if one crossed his path in the morning, in the Americas it was a giver of luck in the chase.

Additional designations: The Hare.

Arabic: Al Arnab, adopted from the classical title. In medieval Europe this degenerated into Alarnebet, Elarneb, Harneb. Al Arsh al Jauzah (The Throne of the Maiden); Al Kursiyy al Jabbar (The Throne of the Giant, i.e. Orion). Al Nihal (The Thirst-Quenching Camels), for the four brighter stars.

Chinese: Tsih (A Shed).

Egyptian: Boat of Osiris, who has been identified with Orion.

Euphratean: Udkagaba (Smit-

ing Sun Face); also assigned to Sagittarius.

French: Lievre.

German: Hase.

Hebrew: Arnebeth.

Italian: Lepre.

Latin: Lepus, frequently qualified by the descriptive Auritus (Eared), Dasypus (Rough-footed), Levipes (Light-footed), Velox (Swift).

Portuguese: Lebre.

Lepus is located in the southern sky surrounded by Eridanus, Columba, Canis Minor, and Orion. Most of the constellations in this area of the sky, close to the ecliptic, are much more distinct, and its fame seems to rest on its affinity with Orion. An imaginative writer has said its dimness has come about by its attempt to escape Orion's notice. Alpha star is Arneb, beta is Nibal (Nihal). Culmination comes about January 28.

LIBRA (THE SCALES). Of the twelve zodiacal signs this is the only one to honor an inanimate object. The configuration may have been the original Altar or Altar Censer or Lamp, which for centuries was forgotten, and when revived placed further south as Ara. Bir (or Mer), the Assyrian god, known as the father, feeder, fire, and great light, seems to have owned these stars. To further support an association of offerings to the light god with this group, the Hebrew 7th month, whose emblem was the Holy Mound, Tul Ku, which designated

the Tower of Babel, was surmounted by an altar. One interpretation of Tower was that it
had been built to bring offerings
up to the god of the day sky.

On boundary stones a lamp is
shown held in the Scorpion's
claws, which mythologically symbolizes light held by darkness.
During the period light was lost,
the Claws were left behind and
perhaps extended, until they in
turn gave way to the Scales.
When this small and inconspicuous
constellation was first conceived
to be a Balance is not known.
The likelihood is that Egypt, to
give holy significance to the
instrument that measured and,
through its magic equalizing
powers, abated the swelling
sacred waters of the Nile, portrayed here a beam. Or the
object may have been the Scales
of Justice on which the human
heart was measured after death
against the Feather of Truth under
the supervision of Osiris, who
was attended by the dog-headed
Anubis. When the heart was
lighter than the feather, the man
was admitted to the land of light,
where dwelt the gods; when it was
heavier, he was condemned to the
dark underworld. At the autumnal
equinox this cluster balanced the
sun at the horizon between the
upper and lower world as well
as the symmetry of day and
night, although the Scales in art
rarely appear on an even balance.
The Romans applied the name
Libra to these representations,
and as Libra these stars are
best known.

In a poem, Virgil hails
Augustus, whose birthday coincided with the sun's entrance among
the Claw stars as the dispenser
of Justice. He petitioned the gods
to place the soul of Augustus
here, a fitting resting place for
the emperor when, after death,
he should be inscribed on the
roll of the gods. In this way
he implied the encloser had no
occupant, the Scorpion having
contracted his Claws to make
room for a neighbor. On medals still in existence, Augustus
holds the Scales, a token of
his infinite wisdom and justice.
Both the Claw designation and
Libra seem to have been respected in Virgil's time.

Julius Caesar too has been
given a place here. A luminary,
undoubtedly the comet of 43 B.C.,
probably the same one that appeared in 531, 1106, 1680, and
may return in 2255, was named
the Julian Star. Its appearance
a few months after Caesar's as-
sassination in 44 B.C. prompted
Augustus, heir and great nephew
of Caesar, to assert the star
came in consequence of the slaying and for the purpose of bearing Caesar's soul to its rightful
place aloft. Romans claimed
that originally Libra had eleven
stars and they added a twelfth
at the time of the formation of the
Julian calendar, which Caesar,
as pontifex maximus, ordered
organized.

Astraea, starry virgin of justice, soon expelled both Augustus
and Caesar. In the Golden
Age, she refused to unite with
the Titans against Zeus and came
down to dwell on earth. In the
Silver Age, she left her mountain
home only in the evening, and in
the Bronze Age, she left the
abodes of men forever. She was
the last of the immortals to linger
on earth, and Zeus placed her in
the heavens as Virgo. As an
impersonation of Justice, who
weighed the fate of mortals,

her emblem was a Balance, the
next constellation, with which she
also indicated to ancient tillers
of the soil the proper time for
sowing winter grain.

> But when Astraea's Balance,
>   hung on high
> Betwixt the nights and days,
>   divides the sky,
> Then yoke your oxen, sow
>   your winter grain,
> Till cold December comes
>   with driving rain.
>   (Virgil)

A chariot black as night
pulled by coal-black horses
harnessed with golden reins sometimes was seen in these stars.
This chariot belonged to Aides,
who used it when he abducted
Persephone (the adjacent Virgo).
Through a cleft in the earth they
descended in this season to subterranean lands over which Aides
was king, and there he enthroned
the maiden as his queen.

The Rabbis assigned various
rulers, some placed it on the
banner of Manasseh; some on
the banner of Asher, to whom
others entrusted Virgo.

Early Christians gave these
stars to Apostle Philip, later
Christians identified with the
Balances of the Book of Daniel
on which Belshazzar had been
weighed and found wanting, or
with the Altar Noah erected after
the Deluge, although this latter
is usually placed at Ara.

This seems to be identical
with the Mayan asterism which
was oriented to a temple where
dwelt a priest whose business
was to administer justice and
foretell the future by means of
information obtained from spirits
of the dead residing in these

stars.

The Peruvian group which included Libra was entitled Rainbow, Lightning, Celestial or
Divided River, Earth, all titles
which to a degree indicated the
tempestuous character of
weather when the sun was in the
sign as well as the union of the
Earth Mother with the Male
Principle. The sun here was a
signal to perform ceremonial
bathing at the junction of two
streams, that is, where they
branched off from each other.

Configurations. Ancient round
altars, censers, and lamps
figured on tablets and gems are
believed to represent these stars.
The Beam or Nileometer, an
instrument used by Egyptians
when they measured the Nile's
inundation, or Two Feathers
were additional models for
early illustrations. The Atef,
headdress worn by certain gods,
had astronomical significance
that related to Aries, Capricornus, Cancer, and Libra. It
was decorated with the horns of
a ram and a goat, a disc that
enclosed the uraeus or scarabaeus, and flanked by two plumes.
The feathers stood for the equal
weights of the Scales of Justice.
Eventually the figure of a man
holding a pair of scales was
used. Frequently a scale-beam
or pair of scales appear alone.
In India a man bends on one
knee while he holds a balance
or the stars are represented by
an arrow touching an eye. In an
early Chinese solar zodiac the
asterism was a Crocodile or
Dragon, the national emblem;
after the 16th century Jesuit influence it became a Balance.
Its pictorial emblem ═══ may
represent the beam of a balance
in equilibrium, or it may

represent the top of an archaic
Euphratean altar. A Persian
sphere depicts a human figure
with the scales in one hand a
lamb in the other, the lamb
anciently being a form of weight
in the East.

Additional designations:
The Balance; The Claws; Life-
Maker of Heaven; Lofty Altar;
The Scales; Weigh-Beam,
Weight, both from the Greek.

Accadian: Mulu-izi (Man of
Fire), a lunar asterism composed of alpha and beta stars
and ruled by Laterak.

Anglo-Norman: Peise (Scales
or Weight).

Anglo-Saxon: Pund (Scales);
Waege (Weight).

Arabian: Al Kiffatan (The
Trays of the Balance) with
Roman influence; Al Mizan
(The Scale-Beam), which may
have come from the Hebrew and
which corrupted in Europe into
Almisan, Almizcn, Midsanon,
Mizin. Al Zubana (The Claws)
or Al Zubanatain, which in the
west degenerated into Azubane.
Wazn (Weight), which became
Vazneganubi, Vaznegenubi,
Vazneschemali.

Chinese: Show Sing (Star of
Longevity); Tien Ching (Celestial
Balance). A Chinese law which
regulated weights annually was
believed to have been enacted
under the influence and during
the reign of this sign.

Euphratean: Sugi (Chariot
Yoke), probably for stars alpha
and beta.

French: Balance.

German: Waage, Wag, Wage
(Weight).

Greek: Chelon (Claws).

Hebrew: Mznaim or Moznayim
(Scale-Beam); also the letter
Tau, the shape of the beam.

Hindu: Juga or Juka, which
seems to be from the Greek.
Tola, Tula, Tulam, all meaning balance; also called a Fire,
perhaps a recollection of an
early altar form.

Italian: Bilancia; Libra.

Khorasmian: Sara-fasariva
(One Next to the Leader, i.e.
the preceding moon station composed of stars in Virgo).

Latin and Low Latin: Astraea;
Chelae Scorpionis (Claws of
Scorpion); die Lampe als
Nuru (The Solar Lamp); Jugum
(Yoke), which may refer to the
yoking of oxen for sowing winter
grain. Applied by Cicero in an
attempt to disclaim Caesar's
contention that these stars had
any connection with the Julian
calendar. Mochos, a supposed
inventor of weights and measures;
Noctipares, to suggest night in
even balance with day; Veneris
Sidus (Venus's Star); Vulcani
Sidus (Vulcan's Star).

Ninth Century Codices from
the Greek: Zichos (Yoke or
Beam of the balance).

Persian: Terazu or Tarazuk
(Pair of Scales).

Sogdian: Fasariva (One Next
to the Leader).

Syrian: Masatha (Pair of
Scales), which degenerated into
Masathre.

Tamil: Tulam (Balance).

Ancient husbandmen regarded
this sign as an indication that
the time had come for sowing
winter grain. Astrologers give
some evidence in favor of Chaldea
as the origin of this constellation. They claim ancient records indicate that when the Sugi
stars, or Northern Scale, was
clear, the time was eminently
fortunate and fruitful and crops
would be good. The reverse
held for the Southern Scale. Libra also held influence over commerce as Ben Jonson wrote in
the Alchemist:

> His house of life being Libra;
> which foreshadow'd
> He should be a merchant,
> and should trade with bal-
> ance.

In modern times its quality
of influence is masculine, therefore fortunate. When it is the
house of Venus those born under
its control are amorous, humane,
intellectual and pleasure loving,
and it regulates the well being
or disease of the reins.

About twenty-two centuries
ago the constellation coincided
with the zodiacal sign, but
owing to the precession of the
equinoxes it has advanced on the
ecliptic and is now within the
boundaries of the sign Scorpio.
It is located in the southern
sky between Virgo and Scorpius.
Culmination is about June 23,
and its bright stars are: alpha,
Zuben Elgenubi; beta, Zuben
Eschamali.

LOCHIUM FUNIS. A con-
stellation formed in the 18th
century from stars in Argo,
and now in disuse. Also written
Logleine (Log Line).

LUPUS (THE WOLF). The
first lord of these stars seems to
have been Uridimmu, a gruesome
lion in the service of Tiamat.
Greeks conceived it variously
as the wolf into which Lycaon
had been changed by Zeus when
the king set a dish of human
flesh before the god, or as
a wine-skin in the hand of
Centaurus, from which he was
about to pour a libation. A
she-wolf was the mother of the
Roman heroes Romulus and
Remus.   As such it was
Rome's guardian and appeared on
the military ensign. In biblical
lore it was the wolf to which
Jacob likened Benjamin or Jacob
himself.

The wolf has been sacred to
sun or fire gods, such as
Apollo and Mars, its role being
that of drought-scorching rays.
Satan's messenger was a wolf,
and Satan himself sometimes
appeared as one. Christian
art depicts the animal as an
attribute of Saint Francis, because the saint supposedly re-
formed one. In German folklore
the wolf stands for time, which
swallows six little goats (days
of the week). The six kids are
rescued as the children of
Cronus were gouged up, and
stones substituted for them be-
for the seventh kid is swallowed
or before the week runs out and
is unable to repeat itself. Finno-
Ugrians believe the dead hunt the
living in wolf shape. In parts
of Europe the woman who binds
the last sheaf of wheat is a
wolf, i.e. corn spirit; she
bites the farm mistress and can
only be placated by meat, the
booby prize. Among North A-
merican Indians the wolf stands
for man's maliciousness, his
questioning of fate, his restless-
ness. Like the Hare he was

one who released the primeval race from the underworld by scratching away the soil. Later he appears as a trickster who counsels heroes and steals the tornado with which he introduces death. Frequently in mythology he appears as a spirit of winter darkness, of storm, or wind. He usually is bloodthirsty, covetous, cowardly, cruel, and cunning.

Additional designations are: The Wolf.

Accadian: Urbat (Beast of Death or Star of Dead Fathers).

Arabic: Al Asadah (The Lioness), which European astronomers spelt Asida. Al Fahd (The Leopard or Panther); Al Sabu (The Wild Beast), which became Al Subahh. Al Shamarih (The Palm Branches), a desert name for some of the smaller stars, for which Kadb al Karm (Vine Branch) sometimes was substituted.

Euphratean: Kakkab Su-gub Gud-Elim (Star Left Hand of the Horned Bull), probably a reference to a centaur and may have involved only the alpha star. Zibu (Beast); association with this constellation is conjectural.

French: Loup.

German: Wolff.

Greek: Theriou (Beast).

Italian: Lupo.

Latin and Low Latin: Belua (Monster); Hostia (Victim), Hostiola. Martius, the wolf being sacred to Mars. All the following relate to beasts or wild animals; Bestia, Bestia Centauri, Canis Ululans, Deferens Leonem, Equus masculus, Fera, Fera Lupus, Leaena, Leo Marinus, Leopardus, Lupa, Lycisca (Hybrid of wolf), Panthera, Quadrupes vasta, Victima Centauri.

Persian: Bridemif or Birdun (Packhorse).

The constellation is located in the southern sky directly below Libra, between Scorpius and Centaurus. It has no named stars and can be seen at culmination about June 23.

LYNX (THE LYNX). This constellation first appeared on a star map in 1690 . Johannes Hevelius, who placed it there, accounts for the title with this statement, "It is so inconspicuous a star group, only a lynx-eyed person is able to discern it." Besides its acute vision, the lynx is known for its ferocity, furtiveness, and intense individualism, characteristics also of the Tiger, an alternate name now in disuse. Actually the reason given for the tiger title was the resemblance of its many little stars to the spots of the animal. During earlier years of the 17th century some of these stars were first known as The Tigris; then as the Polish Bull, also a designation of Ophiuchus, and subsequent to these titles the Little Fox with the Goose.

Additional designations are: French, Lynx; German, Luchs, Linx; Italian, Lince; Latin, Lynx sive Tigris (Lynx or Tiger).

Notable chiefly for the beauty and number of its double and triple luminaries, it is a rather extensive but dim constellation located in the northern sky between Ursa Major and Auriga. Without named stars it culminates about March 5.

LYRA (THE LYRE). At the time this constellation was fabricated, Vega, its brightest star, may have been near the North Pole and therefore appeared to have a motion as slow as that of a tortoise, an animal associated with Hermes (the wind), who a few hours after his birth in a cave on Mount Cyllene in Arcadia, wandered out to the shore and, seeing some oxen (clouds), stole them. On his way back to his cave he found a turtle, which he killed and, by piercing it with several holes and stretching seven strings across the empty shell, he invented the Lyre. To appease Apollo, who owned the oxen, and who came after him in a fiery rage, he gave him the lyre and the two became fast friends, Apollo, in return giving Hermes a winged shepherd's staff, the famed caduceus, capable of uniting in love those divided in hate. Apollo also permitted Hermes, whom the Romans called Mercury, to have full dominion over flocks, herds, horses, and wild animals, and taught him to prophecy by dice and signs, but forbade him to use speech when prophesying. In time the Lyre was placed in the sky near Heracles (Hercules) to alleviate the drudgery of his labors.

Orpheus, Apollo's son, also played this instrument. With its golden tones he tamed wild beasts and moved stones and trees (rain clouds). While an Argonaut he saved his shipmates by drowning out the sirens' song with his lyre as they passed the island of these sweet singing witches. After his death, nightingales sang over his grave, and his head, buried separately, continued to sing and prophesy, a conception that probably had its origin in the ancient practice of skull divination. His irresistible music reappeared in that of the Pied Piper of Hamelin.

The constellation seems to have a history pre-dating the Greek, in which the Phoenician Harekhal (Traveler), probably derived from a Euphratean deity, and prototype of the Greek Heracles, was attacked by three birds, one of which was this constellation. The bird, by drawing in his wings, let himself fall as far as earth, if he desired, and from this supposedly came the conception of the Falling Grype.

Christians, as usual, disassociated these stars from Pagan influences. They saw them as King David's Harp; The Manger, birthplace of Christ; Praesepe Salvatoris. According to the Old Testament, Jubal, a descendant of Cain, was the inventor of the harp and shepherd's pipe or lyre and flute. His name literally is blast of trumpets or music, and he probably was a wind deity who resembled Hermes or Pan. The pious believe these stars symbolize the rejoicing in heaven at the final victory over the powers of evil.

Arabs conceived Lyra as the Swooping Eagle to distinguish it from Aquila, the Flying Eagle. The Far East, China, Korea, and Japan, place a touching story about a Herdsman and a Spinning Maid in this section of the sky; inasmuch as it is usually connected specifically with the star Vega, we tell it there.

Configurations. A coin from Delos, claimed to be Apollo's birthplace in the Cyclades, has a lyre engraved on it. A drawing of the middle ages is of an instrument that neither any ancient nor any modern person has ever seen. On a Dresden globe a circular vessel with a flat bottom and two handles called a Hazaf is figured here. A scroll known as Rabesco is shown on the Borgian globe. Arabs figured as an eagle with half-closed wings. Hindus pictured as a triangle or the three-corned nut of an aquatic plant.

The name Lyra is of Greek derivation. Additional designations: Eagle; Goose; Harp of Arion; King Arthur's Harp; Kite; Little Tortoise or Shell, a reference to the legendary origin of the instrument, which was made from the tortoise's empty case found on the shore with tendons stretched across it. The Sitting Vulture; Vulture; Wood Falcon.

Accadian: Urakhga, a great storm bird, later applied to Corvus.

Anglo-Saxon: Georgii Hearpe, Harpa, Hearpe (Harp).

Arabic: Al Bagh (The Mule), which was translated Albegala and Albegalo. Al Iwazz (The Goose). Al Lura, which reflects Greek influence, degenerated in Europe into Alchoro, Allore, Alloure, Alohore. Al Nasr al Sakit, which corrupted into Nessrusakat and Nessrusakito. Al Nasr al Waki, refers to the sweeping Stone Eagle of the Desert, and shows the bird with half closed wings.

In Europe this became Alvaka. Al Sanj, from the Persian, which degenerated into Alsanja, Arnig, Asange, Asanges, Asangue, Asenger, Aznig, Mesanguo, Sangue. An Orientalist of the 17th century thought these medieval European titles were from the Arabic Azzango (Cymbal). An unlikely translation of Sanj has been given as Brinek. Nablon or Nablium (The Phoenician Harp). Salibák, Shalyak, Shelyak, and Sulahfat, all words for tortoise, which turned into Azulafe, Schaliaf, and Zuliaca. Uthfiyyah, used by the nomads, probably came from a Greek word for tripod.

Bohemian: Hauslicky na Nebi (Fiddle in the Sky).

English, Early: Talyn Arthur (Arthur's Head).

French: Lyre.

German: Leier.

Greek: Chelys (Tortoise); Herme's Lyre.

Italian: Lira.

Latin and Low Latin: Amphionis, Apollinis, Lyra Arionis, Mercurii, Orphei, Orphica, all from skillful players. Aquila Cadens (Swooping Eagle); Aquila Marina (The Osprey); Aquilarius, inasmuch as the lyre was shown hanging from the claws of the Eagle; Baoavos, probably a mistranslation of Testa; Belua aquatica, an indefinite water object. Canticum (Song); Chirka (Hornstone or Grinding Stone), an error for the Hazaf on the Dresden globe. Cithara. Clara, Cyllenea, Mercurialis, all derived from divinities who

played the instrument. Decachor-
dum; Deferens Psalterium;
Falco Sylvestres (Wood Falcon).
Fides (Fidis), Fidicen, Fidicula,
from a supposed Lyrist. Jugum
(Yoke) incorrectly applied here.
Lura (Thong); Lutaria (Mud-
inhabiting); Lyrae Testudo;
Marina; Mus, Musculus, for a
marine creature, probably the
mussel. Pupilla, a blunder for
Aquila. Testa (Upper or Outer
Shell); Testudo (Shell); Tym-
panum. Urcuchillay, intended
for the ram in charge of the
heavenly flocks of ancient
Peruvians. Vultur Cadens
(Swooping Vulture), popularly
translated Falling Grype and portrayed with an upturned head
carrying a lyre in its beak.
Xelus.

Persian: Dik Paye, from a
Greek word for tripod; used
by the common people. Lyre
of Zurah; Sanj Rumi, translated
from the Greek and alluding to
it as the first stringed instruments of Greek bards.

Spanish: Galapago (Turtle?)

Teuton: Harapha (Harp).

Lyra lies in the northern
sky on the rim of the Milky Way
between Cygnus and Hercules.
The Lyraids, meteors identified
as the Swiftly Moving Comet of
1861, radiate near it, and their
maximum is reached about
April 19 and 20. Culmination
of the constellation is about
August 18. Its bright stars are
alpha, Vega; beta, Sheliak;
gamma, Sulafat.

MACHINA ELECTRICA
(ELECTRICAL MACHINE). In
1790 Johann Bode introduced
this constellation south of the
central portion of Cetus under

the name Elektrisir Machine
or Machine Electrique. Italians
gave it the title name. It now
is omitted from sky maps and
catalogues.

MALUS. Mast of the Ship
Argo in the southern sky. A
constellation name abandoned.

MENAT. An immense Egyptian
constellation that extended from
Arcturus in Bootes in the northern sky to Antares in Scorpio
in the southern sky. The
menat was a whip amulet worn
for conjugal happiness; it supposedly gave strength to the
reproductive organs, promoted
fruitfulness and health and drove
evil away.

MENSA (THE TABLE MOUN-
TAIN). Nicolas Louis de
Lacaille, the first astronomer
to measure a South African arc
of the meridian and who had
made observations of approximately 10,000 southern stars,
invented this constellation, which
is located close by the southern
Pole. He formed the figure
from stars under Nubecula Major
or Greater Cloud. Astronomers
abbreviated his title Mons
Mensae, which had been suggested by the fact that the Table
Mountain near Cape Town, "which
had witnessed my nightly vigils
and daily toil," are frequently
capped by a cloud.

Additional designations:
French, Montagne de la Table;
German, Tafelberg; Italian,
Monte Tavola.

The constellation, which contains no named stars, reaches
culmination January 28.

MICROSCOPIUM (THE
MICROSCOPE). Another dim

constellation formed by Lacaille with a title that symbolizes investigation. It is in the southern sky below Capricornus and above Indus, and culminates on September 18. In this vicinity, perhaps including these stars, was a figure listed in a German astronomical catalogue of 1564 called Neper, the Auger, which also is referred to as Bohrer, a boring tool or gimlet. The meaning of Neper is not known; it may have been some sort of an object or instrument used in divination or fortune telling.

MONOCEROS (THE UNICORN).

No agreement exists as to the date of this figure's invention. One astronomer claims to have seen it on an ancient Persian globe; another to have seen it on a sphere of 1564, where it was called The Other Horse. Jacob Bartsch, a 17th century astronomer, generally is said to have been its designer.

The Unicorn, an attribute of solar heroes, symbolizing fearlessness, felicity, and grandeur, quite appropriately lies in the broad but comparatively vacant field just south of the celestial equator, between Orion, a sun hero, and his two dogs.

Additional designations: French, la Licorne; German, das Einhorn; Italian, il Unicorno or Licorno; Latin, Cervus (Deer).

Two Chinese asterisms, the Four Great Canals and the Outer Kitchen, lay in this vicinity.

Although it is barren of bright stars, having none brighter than fourth magnitude, it has many fine small star-clusters. Culmination is on February 19.

MONS MAENALUS.

Maenalus, mountain haunt of the Greek god Pan, was honored when this constellation was designed in 1679. It was placed at the feet of Bootes, and occasionally recognized until the 19th century, when an impressive likeness of Bootes, the husbandman, with a sickle and staff, standing on this mountain, was painted. The title also is spelled Mons Menelai or Menelaus. The German name was Berg Menalus; the Italian, Menalo. It no longer appears on maps.

MUSCA AUSTRALIS (SOUTHERN FLY).

This figure first appeared on a uranometria of 1603, and has been identified as the gadfly which stung Bellerophon, when he attempted to fly to heaven on his winged horse Pegasus, and caused him to fall to earth. Broken in spirit, Bellerophon wandered alone on the Aleian Plain until he died. The fall of Bellerophon is the rapid late afternoon descent of the sun on the plain or broad expanse of somber twilight. On another occasion this gadfly had been sent by Hera to sting Io. Io had been made pregnant by Zeus, and to save her from the jealous Hera, he transformed her into a white heifer. Gaining possession of the heifer, Hera placed her in the care of Argus Panoptes, the hundred-eyed. Hermes, at Zeus's bidding, rescued Io by putting Argus to sleep with a flute, whereupon Hera tormented Io with a gadfly, which drove her from land to land. She journeyed through Thrace, across the Bosphorus (Heifer's ford), she visited the Graeae (Fog) and the Gorgons (Night) until she finally reached Ethiopia (land of the well of the sun), where she returned to her original shape

and gave birth to her son
Epaphus (Touch). The metamor-
phosis of Io is that of the moon,
which is subject to changes,
suffering, and wandering. She is
the virgin of heaven upon whom
the sky (Zeus) looks with love,
but upon whom the queen of daylight (Hera), looks with hate and
jealousy; she is placed under
the care of the night sky (Argus),
whose eyes (stars) open according to the revolution of the
heavens and is finally put to
sleep by the whisper of the morning breeze. The shapes of Io
are those from the full moon
through those of the various
stages of the horned moon and
back to the full. She is finally
released from the watchful eyes
of the stars as is the moon each
morning when it lingers in the
sky after dawn.

In the middle ages the gadfly
was identified with Beelzebub,
originally a Philistine deity worshipped as a destroyer of flies.
His name Baalzebul meant lord
of the high house, which Jews
interpreted to be Solomon's
Temple. Misunderstanding his
name, they called him Beelzebub,
i.e. fly lord, and looking upon
him as the chief representative
of false gods, he was placed
among the demons. In the New
Testament he is referred to as
the prince of devils. He appears
in Mumming plays, and in
Milton's works is next in rank to
Satan.

Additional designations:
Abeille (Bee); Apis (Bee); Apis
seu Musca; Biene (Bee); The
Fly; Musca Apis; Musca Aus-
tralis vel Indica (Southern or
Indian Fly). French, Mouche
Australe ou Indienne; German,
Sudliche Fliege; Italian, Mosca
Australe.

Uniting it with the nearby
Apus (Bird of Paradise) and
Chamaeleon it became Mother
Eve. It lies in the Southern
Sky partly in the Milky Way be-
low Crux and above Chamaeleon.
Culmination is about May 14.

MUSCA BOREALIS (NORTH-
ERN FLY). A dim constellation
above the Ram in the northern
sky, it frequently is omitted
from sky maps. This probably
was designed early in the 17th
century, at which time it was
called Vespa (Wasp), although
it did not appear on atlases
until 1781, and there given as
Musca.

Additional designations: Apis
(Bee); Beel-zebul (God of Flies)
from Baalzebul (or Baal-zebubu),
this insect being the deity's ideograph, varied sometimes by the
scarabaeus; titles also used for
Musca Australis.

Arabic: Na'ir al Butain
(Bright One of the Little Belly).
Probably No. 41, a 3.6 magni-
tude star, and the 2nd manzil.

Chinese: W'ei or Oei (Belly),
the 17th Hsiu.

Coptic: Koleon (Belly or
Scabbard).

French: le Fleur de lis, the
lily shown with the French
coat of arms; Mouche.

German: Fliege.

Hindu: Barani (Bearer), 2nd
lunar station.

Italian: Mosca.

Khorasmian: Farankhand
(Forerunners).

Persian: Pish Parvis, the
2nd lunar inn.

Sogdian: Barv.

Located in the northern sky
south of Andromeda, north of
Aries, its culmination date is
December 17th.

NOCTUA (THE NIGHT OWL)
This had been added in modern
times to the already over-
burdened Hydra. It was shown
roosting on the tail-tip, en-
croaching into the boundary of
Libra. In the 18th century
the site was first occupied by
Solitaire or Turdus Solitarius
(Solitary Thrush). Neither of these
asterisms is now recognized.

NORMA (THE SQUARE). A
constellation composed of unformed stars of Ara and Lupus
was introduced to exalt the
builder's T-Square, a symbol of
exactness, planning, and survey-
ing. In 1603 it was dispossessed
to make room for the Southern
Triangle. Late in the 18th century it was reestablished along
one of the streams of the Milky
Way in the southern sky directly
above the asterism that had
usurped its position and made a
companion of Circinus, the Pair
of Compasses.

Additional designations:
The Level, Quadra Euclidis,
The Rule.

French: l'Equerre et la
Regle (The Square and the Rule);
Libella or Niveau, both signify-
ing Level.

German: Lineal (Linear);
Winkelmass (Rule).

Italian: Riga e Squadra
(Rule and Square).

Norma is so far south it is
visible only in low altitudes.
Culmination is about July 3.

NUBECULAE MAGELLANI.
The most prominent objects in
space seen by navigators as
they near the Cape of Good
Hope in Southern Africa are
the Two Cape Clouds, usually
called Nubeculae Magellani
(Little Clouds of Magellani) to
honor Ferdinand Magellan, early
16th century navigator who first
described them.

They also have been called
Magellan Patches and Sacks of
Coal, although this latter title
applies more correctly to dark,
vacant patches in the Milky Way
near the Northern and Southern
Crosses. W.W. Gill in stories
about natives of the Hervey
Group called them Nga Mau,
which seems to come from the
Polynesian name Mahu (Mist).
Polynesians distinguished them
simply as Upper and Lower.

Together they help mariners
locate the Pole inasmuch as
they mark two angles of nearly
equilaterial triangles, of which
the polar point is the third.
This cloud-like mass is composed of galaxies, regular
and irregular nebulae, and
nebulous streaks and blis-
ters. Around them the sky is
blank, so black, especially in
the case of the Minor, it is "as
if all cosmical material in the
neighborhood had been swept up
and garnered in these mighty
groups."

The Nubeculae Magellani are
individually called Nubecula
Major and Nubecula Minor.

NUBECULA MAJOR (THE
GREATER CLOUD) is located

20⁰ from the South Pole in the Milky Way between the constellations Dorado and Mensa. Strangely enough, the intensity of its light is inferior to that of the Minor and is obliterated by a full moon.

Additional designations: Nubes Major (Clouds Major); Oxen of Tehama, which is a province along the Red Sea. This title probably includes Nubecula Minor. In biblical lore, combined with Dorado and Piscis Volans, it became Abel the Just.

Arabic: Al Bakr (The White Ox). This title must have been given by southern Arabs as it is invisible from Baghdad and other northerly areas.

French: Grand Nuage (Great Cloud).

German: Grosse Wolke (large or Great Cloud).

Italian: Nube Maggiore (Major Cloud).

NUBECULA MINOR (THE LESSER CLOUD). This lies across the borders of Hydrus and Tucana in the southern sky. The space around it is so devoid of stars, Sir John Herschel wrote, "...most oppressively desolate and access to it on all sides is through a desert."

Additional designations: Nubes Minor; French, Petit Nuage; German, Kleine Wolke; Italian, Nube Minore.

OCTANS (THE OCTANT). Another constellation that pays tribute to the mechanical age. Formed in 1752 in admiration of the octant invented by John Hadley

it has the shape of a straight line with a short strip that goes off at an angle, almost like the top of a cane. It contains the stars closest to the South Pole, in fact it almost crosses the Pole, an illustrious position. Mythological references to the South Pole were infrequent; however the Romans have Phoebus allude to it when he gives instructions to Phaethon. Pagan Arabs apparently were aware of one for they fancied the luminaries here, like those close to the North Pole, exercised a healing power on afflicted persons, and the Hindus had given it a name, Dramasa.

Saint Peter of Verona, Peter Martyr, a member of the Spanish Inquisition, who was killed near Como, Italy, in 1252, wrote, "They have no starre there (South Pole) lyke unto this pole (North Pole), that might be decerned aboute the poynte." Navigators of the 15th and 16th centuries commented correctly on the emptiness of the skies, and scarcity of stars in the region.

Additional designations: Octans Hadleianus (Octant of Hadley); French, l'Octans Reflexion; Octant; German, Oktant; Italian, Ottante.

Because it is circumpolar Octans is always visible to those in the southern hemisphere. It contains no bright stars.

OFFICINA TYPOGRAPHICA (THE PRINTING OFFICE). Quite appropriately, in a period when laurels were being awarded to various tools, instruments, and other contrivances, a device for printing should be glorified. In 1799 this asterism was formed

in the southern sky from uncharted stars above Puppis and
below Monoceros. It no longer
is placed on maps, nor is it
recognized by astronomers.
Germans called it Buchdrucker
Presse (Printing Press) or Buchdrucker Werkstadt (Workshop).
The Italian name was Tipografia.

OPHIUCHUS (THE SERPENT
HOLDER). This constellation may
have been invented about 3,500
B.C. in a latitude of 35° north,
when this star group and sun were
in opposition to each other at
the spring equinox. With it,
for generation upon generation,
primitive man chronicled the
defeat of evil powers, for it
exemplifies the triumph of the
messenger of light (Ophiuchus)
over darkness, the scorpion
(Scorpius), on which the hero
treads, and the serpent he
crushes with his hands. The serpent held may also be a record
of reptile idolatry, which was
very ancient. It was the earliest
of phallic totem beasts, the re-
embodiment of deceased mortals,
and as such assigned to earth,
river, and subterranean deities.
If, in his jealousy of the living,
he was merciless to his descendants, those who offered him the
proper sacrifices and paid him
fitting homage were often rewarded. If he withheld light,
warmth, rain, and the riches
of fertility, in certain seasons
he might be prevailed upon, by
force, or trickery when necessary, to yield these treasures.
If his sting was poisonous, he
also possessed magic secrets,
especially as to which were
the proper herbs needed in the
cure of dread disease, which
any able medicine man or snake
charmer was able to extract
from him.

The most notable legend connected with these stars is that
of Asclepius, of whom James I
said in his poetry, "a medi-
ciner after made a god."
Asclepius, whom the Romans
called Aesculapius, was the
Greek deity of healing, an
aspect of the sun as healer.
His mother Coronis (dawn)
was seduced by Apollo (sun).
During her pregnancy, Coronis
was unfaithful to her lover,
who directed that she be slain
by a thunderbolt. From her
body on the funeral pyre Apollo
rescued their unborn child,
and then left him exposed on a
mountain. In one version of
the myth the child was guarded
by a dog until rescued by the
goatherd Aresthanas, who called
him Aiglaer (Shiner). Eventually
he was placed with the centaur
Chiron, who taught him the art
of using herbs and consulting
oracular serpents in his search
for the proper plants. Asclepius
was the ship's surgeon on the
Argonaut expedition, and in time
became more proficient than
his teacher; he even restored
life to several youths after
they had died, among them
Hippolytus, son of Theseus.
When Aides (Hades) complained
his underworld realm would become desolate, Zeus permitted
the healer to be slain. Apollo
was so overcome by the tragedy,
Zeus placed Asclepius with the
serpent that had been helpful to
him in the heavens as Ophiuchus.
His shrines were located at health
resorts on hills near springs.
The cock, as a sun emblem,
was, along with the serpent,
sacred to this great physician,
and one of the last acts of
Socrates was to offer Asclepius
a cock.

Hercules (Heracles) also is

celebrated as these stars, a confusion that may have come about because the boundaries between the two stellar heroes were at first ill defined and the stars seemed to intermingle. Since each now has his place clearly marked, they form an unusual pair, like Siamese twins joined at the top. The head of Ophiuchus, who is upright clutching the serpent, meets that of Hercules, who, although he stands upside down, treads a dragon underfoot. The bodies of the serpent and dragon extend so far into opposite directions they stretch almost from the North Pole to the Equator. Whereas Hercules finally slays his antagonist, Ophiuchus (Asclepius) merely wrests the secret of health or immortality from his.

A sacramental communion with snakes, children of earth, givers of nourishment, was not uncommon. In some mythological conflicts the victors were unfair to the vanquished, thus Hercules, after a fight at the river Sagarinus (or Sagaris) in Asia Minor, usurped the medicinal springs of his serpent enemies and thus plagiarized his role of healer. Quite appropriately, veneration was shared by the man and the reptile or shifted fron one to the other as can be seen from the stories associated with various rulers of this constellation, such as Triopas, legendary king of the Perrhaebians, an agricultural lord whose form was that of a snake. Triopas was slain by Carnabus (Carnabon, or Carnabas), king of Getae in Thrace. Carnabus also killed one of the dragons that drew the chariot of Triptolemus, whose name signifies triple ploughing. Triptolemus, son of Dysaules (Double Furrow), had

been designated by Demeter to be the first priest in her worship. The sacrilegious acts of Carnabus caused his downfall, and he was replaced by his son Phorbas, who freed Rhodes from snakes.

Aristaeus, who introduced the cultivation of bees and the olive, found these stars a refuge. While pursuing Eurydice, faithful wife of Orpheus, across a field, she was bitten by a snake and died. In the sky he found some alleviation from his sense of guilt by warding off the effects of Sirius, the dog-star, and acting as protector of herdsmen and hunters.

Cadmus, who was changed into a serpent, existed among these stars, as did Glaucus, a sea-monster. Until he ate a magic herb growing along the shore, Glaucus was a simple fisherman. The herb endowed him with a gift of prophecy, and thereafter he made the sea his home. He instructed Apollo in the art of soothsaying and aided other deities. When he fell in love with Scylla, Circe became jealous and turned Scylla into a miserable rock perilous to mariners. As the prophecies of Glaucus usually foretold evil, fishermen dreaded the visits he made each year to the waters into which they steered their boats and fasted and prayed to avert the misfortunes he prophesied. He sometimes took the form of a mermen and also was known as Pontus, lover of the sea youth Melicertes. His frantic horses were the stormy waves.

This constellation also was intended for Laocoon, son of Priam and priest of Apollo. He warned his fellow Trojans against the colossal wooden horse left by Greeks on the plains outside the city walls. The fall of Troy had been decreed by the gods and, in consequence of his eloquence, as he and his sons were about to offer a sacrifice to Apollo, two enormous serpents rose from the sea and strangled the three. The Trojans interpreted their fate as punishment. The wooden horse, they decided, was consecrated, admitted it to their city, and were destroyed.

Impassioned Christians, who would wipe out Pagan ideologies, placed here Aaron, whose staff became a serpent; Moses lifting the Brazen Serpent; Saint Benedict, the great physician; Saint Paul with the maltese viper. Remarkable comets appeared here in 1495, 1523, 1537, 1569, and descriptions of them inspired Milton to compare the fires of this asterism with Satan.

In Sanscrit lore, Krishna occupied these stars. He stood with one foot on the serpent's head and held the rest of the body up by the tail, which is a reduplication of the Ophiuchus and Hercules conceptions. King Kamsa of Mathura, warned that the eighth child born to his virgin cousin Devaki and her husband Vasudeva would being about his death, had each of her first six children killed at birth. The seventh Balarama was saved by the goddess Bhavani, who removed him from Devaki's womb to that of Rohini, another wife of Vasudeva. Krishna, the eighth child, was saved by Vasudeva, who carried the infant across the Jumna River, normally deep and dangerous, but which receded to his knees as he carried the child. He

deposited the infant as well as Balarama in the land of cows (clouds) with the cowherd Nanda and his wife Yasoda, and in exchange took their infant daughter. The tiny girl was slain by Kamsa, who, when he discovered he had been deceived, issued an order to destroy all male children. In contrast to the order given by Pharaoh, the order was ineffectual. At an early age Krishna and Balarama displayed marvelous strength. They sported with the gopis (herdmaids), and the Rasa or Hallisa dances performed in honor of Krishna down to the present day celebrate their gambols. When they grew to manhood they put Kamsa to death and placed a new king on the throne. Krishna then established his own capital at Dvaraka (City-of-Gates), organized the people, the Yadavas, and set out to destroy evil demons and impious kings. At the request of Indra he visited Naraka Loka, the underworld to retrieve Aditi's earrings (light), which had been stolen. By Rukmini he became the father of Pradyumna (love) and grandfather of Aniruddha (egotism). Satyabhama, one of his 16, 000 wives (stars), requested him to bring back the Parijata tree. To obtain it, he had to battle Indra. After a fierce struggle Indra permitted him to have the tree. However, catastrope overtook his people; his brother was slain, the Yadavas killed one another to the last man. Krishna outlived them all and finally perished when he was wounded in the heel by the stray arrow of a hunter. Krishna was fourarmed at birth, suggesting the four directions or winds. The color assigned to him usually was blue; his name means

black, suggesting wisdom and
eternity, the white Balarama
signifying time. In one legend,
Balarama was torn from his
mother in the form of a white hair,
Krishna in the form of a black
hair. This explains the fact
that in early phases of the waxing moon (Devaki being a moon
goddess), a thin arc of light,
which may be likened to a white
hair, appears to the right, and
when the moon begins to wane,
a thin rim or shadow appears,
which may be likened to a single
black hair. Krishna's struggle
with Kamsa symbolizes the defeat of the old and victory of the
new spirit of vegetation. Like
another Hindu god, Vishnu,
Krishna took three steps, i.e.
his going down, his period of
darkness, his rising again, and
his name incorporates the syl-
lable ish, meaning light. His
physical character suggests fire,
heaven, lightning, storm, sun.
He was joyous and voluptuous, a
hero invincible in love and war;
although brave, also crafty.

The discarded Polish Bull or
Bull of Poniatowski (Poniatovski)
was contained in these stars.
The Poniatowskis were a Polish
princely family of Italian origin,
tracing descent from Giuseppe
Torelli, who about 1650 married
an heiress of the Lithuanian
family of Poniator, whose name
he assumed. The first of the
Poniatowski to distinguish himself was Stanislaus (1677-1762),
an adopted son, being the
natural child of Prince Saphieha
and a Jewess. Stanislaus became a noted warrior and states-
man. His second son Stanislaus
Augustus became king of Poland.

Configuration. Although
most often portrayed holding or
strangling the serpent, western

catalogues and maps invariably
give the stars as two distinct
constellations, the second one
being Serpens. Old maps
depicted a venerable man, both
hands clenched in the folds of
a huge snake, which writhes its
head close to Corona Borealis,
on which account the snake is
said, "to be licking the Crown."
The figure of an old man may
have been copied from the
celebrated statue of Asclepius
at his temple on the outskirts
of Epidarus. On the Leyden
manuscript the figure is that of an
unclad boy with the serpent in
his hands standing alongside
Scorpion. A Turkish plane-
sphere illustrated as a crane
or stork, which led to the title
Grus aut Ciconia. The stork
or adjutant bird was prominent
in moon worship; it was a
form in which the moon traveled
or used as a mount on which to
travel.

Ophiuchus was not a name;
this title was a description
which derived from two Greek
words meaning the man who holds
the snake. Additional designations are: Asclepius; God of
Medicine; Poniatovski's (or
Poniatowski's) Bull; The Serpent Bearer; Serpent Charmer;
Serpent Holder; Snake Charmer;
Taurus Poniatowski; Toiling
(from the Greek).

Accadian: Mulubat (Man of
Death) for the stars epsilon and
zeta, which marked a lunar
station. Tsir or Sir (Snake) for
stars eta, theta, and xi.

Arabic: Al Hawwa, a translation from the Greek, which appeared in medieval Europe as
Al Haur, Alhava.

Babylonian: Kash-shud Sha-

ka-tar-pa (significance undetermined) for star theta which
marked the 25th ecliptic station.

Coptic; Aggia (Magician);
Tshio (Snake).

Euphratean: Nu-tsir-da (Image
of the Serpent), a title shared
with the neighboring Serpens.
Sa-gi-mu (God of Invocation).

French: Serpentaire.

German: Schlangentrager.

Italian: Ofiuco.

Khorasmian: Markhashik
(Serpent Bitten); Sardhiwa (Head
of the Evil One) for stars zeta
and eta.

Latin and Low Latin:
Aesculapius; Anguifer (Snake-
like), Anguiger, Anguitenens;
Grus aut Ciconia (Crane or
Stork). Ophiulchus, Ophiulcus,
Ophiultus, Ophiulculus, all from
the Greek. Ophiuculus, diminu-
tive of the foregoing. In the
16th and 17th centuries these
degenerated into Afeichius,
Afeichus, Alpheichius. Ophiuchus
vel Serpentarius. Psylle from
Psylli, snake-charmers of
Lybia noted for their skill in
curing snake bites. Serpens
(The Serpent); Serpentarius
(Serpent Bearer); Serpentiger,
Serpentinarius, Serpentis Lator,
Serpentis Praeses.

Moorish: Al Hague, from the
Arabic Al Hawwa, which early
European astronomers turned
into Alange, Alangue, Hasalangue,
probably combining with the
Turkish Yilange.

Persian: Garafsa (Serpent
Tamer) for some of the stars.

Sogdian: Bastham (Bound),
i. e. The hero enveloped in the
coils of Ophis (Snake). Wajrik
(The Magician).

Turkish: Yilange, probably
from the Latin Anguis (Snake).

Astrologically Ophiuchus is
believed to be dangerous to
mankind, bringing about death
by poison.

It is situated almost exactly
half-way between the two Poles
and midway between the vernal
and autumnal equinoxes, which
provides the constellation with
a suggestion of equalizing power.
Crossing the celestial equator
it is above Scorpius in the southern sky and below Hercules in
the northern sky. Bright stars
are alpha, Ras Alhague; beta,
Cheleb; delta, Yed Prior;
epsilon, Yed Posterior. Culmination comes about July 26.

ORION (THE HUNTER).

Orion

Mighty hunter, who warms
my dreams, drop your trophy,
the mangled royal beast;
unleash your tired hounds;
release your girdle, set
with kingly jewels that
bedazzle at your bend;
lay away your blood-soiled
blade; unlace your buskins;
loosen your coarse tunic.
Torment me not, transplace
your gaze from the Virgin
and let the Butler fill
your goblet. Stain my lips
with your wine; pleasure me
the pain of your embrace.

In all historic time this stellar group, the most brilliant to
the naked eye, has been the most
greatly admired, and, after the

Great Bear, the most widely known of the constellations. With the Pleiades, with which it sometimes is linked in legend, this asterism is one of the most intensely interesting mythologically.

In Sumer the stars were personified as Ninsubur, a messenger of Ishtar and one of the guards of Anu, the high one. Much doubt and mystery surround its titles and fables. Robert Brown is of the opinion that the name comes from Uru-anna (Light of Heaven), a Eurphratean Valley title of the supreme god. Orion has been identified with Nimrod, "mighty hunter before the Lord." Nimrod, king of Babel, has been said to be the mortal form of Marduk. In the old Testament, he is a grandson of Ham and a son of Cush, who presented him with the garments that God had furnished Adam and Eve upon their leaving the Garden of Eden. These clothers rendered the wearer invincible, and Nimrod became the world's first mortal ruler. He set up idols and enthroned himself for worship as the supreme deity. To display his powers he ordered an altar, the Tower of Babel, erected that would reach into the skies. For his rebellion against Him, Jehovah revealed His strength. Nimrod was placed in bands or fetters (girdle), and the tower became a place of tumult and confusion. As Nimrod must serve a term in Sheol, he disappears from the horizon every winter. Proverbial from earliest times as a mighty hunter, the name Nimrod became a synonym for daring or outstanding hunter.

In certain versions of the Book of Job and Amos, the word Orion appears in place of the Hebrew Kesil, which means Fool in the sense of godless, impious, inconstant, self-seeking. Etymologically Kesil is connected with Kislev, the ninth Hebrew month, the blustery November-December. Storms or 'inconstancy' were usual at the constellation's autumnal rising. In Scriptures it also is associated with Kimah, a word which refers to the Pleiades, that are likened to a flock of doves. This bears out the myth that a mighty hunter (the godless Nimrod), who tramples on the timid Hare, pursues a flock of inoffensive Doves. Thus the Hebrews designated a Fool the constellation their neighbors, the Babylonians, had deified as their supreme god and styled Mighty Hunter.

The Egyptians converted this asterism into the mansion of Unas, a pharaoh who became a sun-god and lord of the constellation by devouring his predecessors. With Lynx, Cancer, Hydra, and other carnal companion stars, he continued to hunt deities as humans chase wild beasts. Those who were unlucky enough to be captured were boiled in fiery caldrons and then consumed. Their livers, hearts, and entrails, the most potent portions of the body, were relished that the qualities of courage and wisdom contained in them might be absorbed by the banqueters. Uncertainty exists whether the identification of a Pharaoh with the configuration is a later evolution, an effort to insure that the dead monarch partake of the revels of the star-deities and imbibe virtues and valor to insure him immortality, or whether it is the echo of some prehistoric cannibalistic religion in which the personification of this constellation is a form of contagious magic, a tribute to the superior virtues of an adversary. The flesh and blood consumed becomes an innate part of the diner. Thus, if a man feeds on a stag, some measure of the animal's swiftness becomes a part of his own skill; if he drinks the blood of a warrior, he acquires the warrior's power and strength. For this reason a meal of the timid rabbit is tabu among many cannibal tribes. A feast composed of other deities might be attributed to star groups (deities) lost to sight when Orion appeared in the fiery late afternoon sky.

Quite naturally a constellation that held so high a place in Egyptian belief ultimately became a focal point in the legends of greater gods. Horus, personification of the over-reaching sky, with a name literally meaning He Who is Above, and the supreme god of early Egyptian immigrants, was believed to appear in the night sky in the form of this asterism. The portrayal was that of a man fleet of foot with a wide step looking back over his shoulder as he ran. He held in his right hand either a star or the hieroglyph of life. Later Horus was the splendid young sun of morning and evening, the terrible slayer of monsters of darkness and drought which appeared among the stars as Scorpio and Serpens. As Horus the Elder he was the hawk-headed son of Hathor and a brother of Osiris and Isis. As Horus the Younger he was the son of Osiris and Isis. While he was still an infant his mother placed him in a barque which she sent down the Nile to save him from the fury of his pursuer Set, demon of darkness, aridness, and slayer of his father. He was rescued

and raised by the serpent earth-goddess Uazit. Later he waged war against Set, whom he mutilated as Set had mutilated Osiris. When Ra became the supreme god he replaced Horus as lord of this star group. His portrait was that of a man in a boat surrounded by luminaries and followed by the star Sirius, shown as a cow, also in a boat.

An early title Sahu is connected with the Osiris story. Sahu means mummy, around which the ba (soul) of a man hovers in the form of a bird with a human head until it is able to reenter the body and protect it from decay. These stars are specifically the Sahu of Osiris. Set built a magnificent box of scented pine wood and invited each of his brothers to step into it, promising to present it as a gift to the one who seemed to fit it most perfectly. Pine was the sacred plant of Osiris, consequently the measurements of the box were his, and when he stepped inside, Set slammed down the lid and Osiris smothered. Thus darkness closed over light. Isis found the coffin and went for aid. While she was gone, Set, who realized Isis had discovered what he had done, cut the body of Osiris into fourteen pieces, which he threw here and there. The distraught Isis was able to locate thirteen of the pieces, but the fourteenth, the phallus, had been eaten by fish. Without all parts of his body intact, Osiris would be denied immortality, so Isis carved a phallus from pine and wrapped the entire body in linen; then she breathed life into his nostrils. His sahu or mummy became the most illustrious constellation in the skies.

The Masai, a fierce African tribe regard the three stars that compose the Belt as well as those that hang from it as three old widows pursuing three old men. To the Basuto tribe the three Belt stars are Three Pigs. The Khoikhoi, a Hottentot agricultural people, paid little attention to stars beyond those essential to the cultivator. Accordingly they have few myths and designated these stars as Zebras.

In a Greek myth, Orion was the son of Poseidon, who governed the waters, by Eurale, one of the Gorgons who inhabited the Western Ocean near the region of night. He was the most magnificent man of his time and of so great a stature, when he walked along the floor of the sea, his head extended beyond the waves, a description which coincides with the fact that half the stars are above and half below the celestial equator or ocean that ringed earth. After clearing Chios of wild beasts, Orion asked the country's king Oenopion for the hand of his daughter Merope. When the king refused him, he attempted to abduct the princess. Oenopion, enraged at this and other improper conduct, made Orion drunk, put out his eyes, and left him on the seashore. The blinded hero followed the sound of a hammer and made his way to the forge of Hephaestus, where he besought assistance. In pity, Hephaestus gave him one of his assistant blacksmiths, the lame Cyclops Cedalion, to lead him. Orion lifted Cedalion onto his shoulders and he directed the blind man to the top of a mountain and set him so that he faced the rising sun, whose healing rays replaced the lost sight. This is a time myth in which the evening (or autumn) sun is brought back to health by the young sun.

When Orion profanely boasted that earth was unable to produce any animal he could not conquer, Hera decreed that a huge scorpion rise out of the ground and bite him. The scorpion's poison (frost) caused his death. At the request of Artemis he was placed in the sky in such a location that he might escape in the west each time his slayer, Scorpius, also lifted into the heavens, rose in the east.

In another story, Orion was the hunting companion of Artemis who fell in love with him and would have become his wife had not her jealous twin brother Apollo opposed their marriage. One day Apollo persuaded Artemis to try her skill at archery by shooting at an object shining in the sea. Artemis hit the mark, which was the head of Orion, who was wading at a distance from shore. The heart-broken Artemis prevailed upon Zeus to place him in the sky as the most beautiful of all stellar objects. Thus an aspect of the early sun prevails upon the moon to destroy the late sun whose brilliance is reflected on water. This story had another version: Artemis destroyed Orion when she discovered he had become the lover of Eos, the dawn.

One reason given for his everlasting conflict with the Bull is his pursuit of the Pleiades, described both as virgins and doves, and to whose rescue Taurus had dedicated himself. This contest demonstrates the enmity between two phases of light. In folklore, the Hare is frequently associated with the Moon. Instinctively Orion, the sun, would resent the moon, which causes him to sink into the afterworld. Thus, when he stands on the timid creature, he symbolizes the perpetual strife between the powers of light and darkness in which the former is the stronger and prevails.

Among the Norse, these stars were the giant Orvandel, known as the valiant sea wanderer. His abode was on the borders of Jotunheim, and Thor frequently rested there after his battles with giants. The relationship between the gods and the giants is somewhat confused. Probably the giants existed first, were worshipped as gods, and were driven from their high office by the newcomers brought over from another land; yet their worlds continued to exist side by side and they regularly visited each other. The gods of light went into the lightless regions at night or in the autumn, and the giants, who controlled darkness and frost, were admitted into the palaces of the gods, that is the palaces became theirs during the season they spread darkness or frost. The gods had no compunction of taking song mead (wind) or anything else they desired from the giants. They even took things that were useless to them and tossed them into the sky simply for the fun of creating twinkling stars; sometimes they threw up whole giants. Orvandel apparently originally was a hero with solar and wind attributes. He was a mighty archer of a tribe certainly older than the gods. Once when he was in danger, although he counted among the giants, his friend Thor lifted

him onto his shoulders and carried him to safety. On their way they had to pass through twelve frozen rivers that flowed underground in the realm of frost giants. Although Thor lifted Orvandel high above the dangerous waters, Orvandel slipped and one of his big toes touched the ice and the toe became stiff. Thor snapped it off and pitched it far into the northern sky where it became the star Alcor or Orvandel's Toe. The Anglo-Saxon name for Orvandel was Earendel, who may have been identical with Horvendillus, father of Amleth (Hamlet).

In medieval biblical lore the constellation is said to be Jacob Wrestling with the Angel; Joshua, the Hebrew Warrior; Saint Joseph, husband of Mary. The three bright Belt stars were defined as the Three Magi; also as Jacob's Staff, an allusion to his wanderings.

In an Arabian myth the constellation composes Al Jauzah (The Maiden). When Suhail (Canopus) came up north to woo her, she not only spurned him, but kicked him back into the southern sky. In another version, they married, Suhail slew her, and then fled south. The Arabs, who on religious grounds do not draw the human figure, rarely assign a human form to any of the stars.

Certain stars of the constellation were adopted by the Khorasmians as a figure of their zodiac in place of Gemini.

The Hindu Prajapati had transformed into Mrga (Stag or Wild Beast) to run after his daughter, Rohini, our star

Aldebaran. Tishiya, the deer-slayer or avenging hunter, our star Sirius, transfixed Prajapati by a three-jointed arrow, the Belt stars, and so he cannot move from this section of the sky. Rohini became one of the wives of Soma, the moon deity, although as Soma's wife her father's name is given as Daksha.

The Chinese hsiu Tsan, Shen, or Shi Ch'en was made up of conspicuous stars in the shoulder, belt, and knees. Three of these, anciently called Sal are described as side by side, Three Stars, or Three Kings. They are the Belt, and may have been the original hsiu.

Australian natives believe the Belt stars are young men dancing. Eskimos called the Belt, Tua Tsan. The resemblance to the Chinese title may indicate that the Eskimos came from China, which many maintain to be a fact. The Eskimos thought these stars represented three steps cut into a steep snowbank by some celestial ancestors who wished to reach the top, or they were bear-hunters with a sled who had lost their way. Greenland Eskimos believed the Belt stars were seal hunters who had become bewildered when they were lost at sea and were transferred to the skies.

To the Blackfeet the triangle formed by the stars is a sacred symbol. It is the arrowhead of the great hunter Bull of the Hills, the balance of the constellation. Medicine men wore earrings made of shells from the Pacific Ocean in the form of a triangle as charms. The Cherokees and the Micmacs revered the Belt stars. They believed they are Three Magicians or Little Men, in-visible wonder-workers possessed of superhuman power. The idea is so suggestive of the Three Magi of Catholic tradition, a strong suspicion of missionary influence prevails.

Configurations. On classical atlases of the heavens, Orion is shown as a colossal giant that tramples on the frightened Hare, while he holds his ground glaring heroically at the infuriated Bull that, with long golden horns, is rushing toward him. A lion's hide hangs over his left arm and serves as a shield which dangles at the Bull. With his raised right hand he swings a knotty club as if he were about to strike the forehead of the beast. A sword or hunting knife hangs from his jeweled Belt. Sometimes he is represented with his back turned toward earth, his face in profile, armed with a club or sword and protected by a shield. He also is shown as a lightly clad youth with a short curved staff in his right hand, the Hare in the background. On medieval globes figured as the Roman two-headed eagle, Christ's seamless coat, and a chalice.

Additional designations: Aorion, Argion, Arion, Urion. The derivation of the word is in doubt, probably from the Accadian Uru-anna. Cock's Foot, which relates to a 16th century uranologia, which likens the constellation to a strutting cock. Foot-turning Wanderer or Roamer, which touches on the myth that tells of his roaming about in blindness until miraculously restored to sight by the rising sun. Slayer. 19th century titles: Hunter, Napoleon, Nelson. Ell or Yard; Golden Yard-arm; Our Lady's Wand;

Rake; Three Bands; Three Magi;
The Three Marys; Three Mowers;
Three Sisters, all for the Belt.

Accadian: Uru-anna (Light of
Heaven), a sun deity who appeared in Chaldeo-Assyrian
mythology as D'umuzi, a sun
god and fifth antediluvian king of
Sumer, later known as Tammuz.

Arabian: Al Babadur (The
Strong One). Al Jabbar (The
Giant), debased into Algebar,
Algebaro, Algebra, Algibbar.
Al Jauzah, a term used by
desert Arabs for a black sheep
with a white spot on the middle
of its body and, perhaps the
designation for the heaven's middle figure, which has always been
a center of attraction. Also a
female name. Erroneously Al
Jauzah has been translated giant.
Jauzah also means Walnut, and
the Belt stars, which lay in the
figure's center, had been styled
Golden Walnut. Al Jauzah
degenerated in the middle ages
to Elgeuze, Geuzazugar, Geuze,
Jeuze. Al Nasak or Nusuk (A
Line or Row) applied to the Belt
and intended for a string of pearls.
Al Shuja (The Snake) corrupted
into Asugia (intended for Mad-
man), Sugia. Ragulon (Hero).

Blackfeet: Magsi-satis
(Hunter's Belt), probably for
the Belt.

Celtic:Caomai (Armed King).

Chaldean: Niphla, meaning
unknown.

Chinese: Tsan (Three).

Egyptian: Horus; Sahu (Mummy), a title about 3,285 B. C.
Smati-Osiris (Barley God or Barley Giver Osiris).

Hindu: Mrga; Praja-pati;
Trisanku, which relates to some
triform god, undoubtedly a sun
emblem.

Latin: Audax (Bold); Bella-
tor (Male Warrior); Bellatrix
(Female Warrior); Comesque
Bootae; Dianae Comes or
Amasius (Diana's Companion
or Lover); Fortis or Fortissimus
(Strong); Furiosus (Furious);
Gigas (Giant); Hyriea proles,
which relates to the sheid of
rawhide or the lion's or bull's
hide on his arm, and which
caused him to be described as
"the verie cutthrote of cattle."
This last became Hyreides,
Hyriades. Jugula or Jugulae
(The Joined) referring to
jugulare (throat cutter) or to
the two bright stars in the
shoulder as if connected by the
jugulum, or collar bone.
Saturnus, probably descended
from the Uru-anna legend.
Sublimatus (Sublime, i.e.
raised to a great height). Tri-
pater (Triple Father). Venator
(Hunter of Men).

Norse: Orvandel (Orwendil).
The Belt stars were Frigg's
Distaff or Spindle.

Old Testament: Gibbor (Giant),
that is Nimrod. Kesilim, which
appears in Isaiah and rendered
constellations in some versions,
is assigned to Orion as well as
to other sky figures. Rahab
(Proud Helpers), also said to
have the significance of arrogance,
rebellion, strength, violence.

Saxons: Ebioring or Ebuorung,
which Jacob Grimm thought was
connected with Iringe or Irmin
of the Milky Way.

Syriac: Gabbara (Giant).

Astrologically the constellation generally is dangerous to navigation. Mariners are warned to avoid the perils of the sea when the Pleiades, fleeing from Orion, are lost in the waves. The Belt however portends good fortune and public honors.

Classical writers alluded to Orion as a calendar sign, for its morning risings indicated the beginning of winter. Hesiod in his Works and Days instructed the husbandman to:

> Forget not, when Orion first
>   appears,
> To make your servants
>   thresh the sacred ears.

His midnight rising marked grape-gathering; his evening appearance the approach of winter. Orion appears above the north-eastern horizon, south-east of Taurus, in a reclining posture from which he rises slowly until he reaches the meridian, when he is in an upright position. As he approaches the western horizon he appears to be more and more inclined. On frosty nights this illustrious constellation dominates the sky and is visible from late October until May. Culmination is about January 27.

On account of its evening rising taking place late in autumn, Orion in all parts of the world has been regarded as a somewhat stormy constellation. Early Hindus referred to this characteristic. Roman sailors composed songs on the subject. The loss of the Roman fleet in the first Punic War two centuries before Christ was attributed to its having sailed just after Orion's rising. In the 17th century Breeches Bible marginal rendering in the Book of Job states "which starre bringeth in winter."

Its bright stars are: alpha, Betelgeuze; beta, Rigel; gamma, Bellatrix; delta, Mintaka; zeta, Al Nitak; kappa, Saiph. Delta and zeta are in the Belt.

PAVO (THE PEACOCK). Invented early in the 17th century and designated as the bird which symbolized immortality and watchfulness, because its stars, located close to the southern pole, are enduring. This bird has wide mythological significance. Ancients made blasphemous oaths by it. In some localities it was worshipped as the phoenix and believed to be a destroyer of serpents, thus a releaser of fertilizing moisture. Its starry tail rendered the peacock sacred to many deities, and it was the mount of the Buddhist Amitabha, Mahamayuri, and Sarasvati; the Etruscan great mother Uni; the Greek Hera; Hindu Maya; Japanese Benten; Roman Juno. Except for Amitabha, Buddha of the present world, the others are all great mother goddesses. It was an emblem of a Byzantine empress and, in Christian art, of the ever-vigilant church. Under the Chinese empire the peacock's feather was a distinction awarded to mandarins for public service. In a Greek myth, Argus, builder of the ship Argo, upon death was metamorphosed into a peacock by Hera that he might become one of her pets in the sky. His vessel likewise was lifted into the heavens. Biblical scholars of the middle ages saw these stars as Saint Job.

Additional designations:

Anglo-Saxon, Pawa; Chinese, Joo Tseo, a translation of our word; French, Paon; Greek, Taos; German, Pfau; Italian, Pavone; Persian, Tawus. All mean peacock.

It lies in the southern sky close to the Pole. None of its stars are named, and culmination is on August 29.

PEGASUS (THE WINGED HORSE).

When Perseus cut off the head of Medusa, Poseidon, her lover, commanded that Pegasus spring from her blood as soon as it mingled with his sea-foam, and the name is said to signify eighter Springs of Water or Strong. Snowy-white (sea-foam), he was when he rose from the depths the mount of Poseidon, later he became a favorite of the Muses. While romping with them he kicked Mount Helicon and caused the fountain Hippocrene to flow. Athena (wisdom), who had helped tame Pegasus, provided Bellerophon (sun) with a golden bridle (rays) with which to catch the horse (clouds or vapors which rise from the sea), and he became the steed of the hero whom he aided when Bellerophon was ordered by the king of Lycia to destroy the Chimera, the three-headed, fire-breathing drought monster, part goat, part lion, and part serpent. The Chimera vanquished, Bellerophon hoped his mount, which had developed wings, would carry him into the highest heaven. Zeus, incensed by his presumption, sent a gad-fly to sting the horse and dismount the rider, who fell to earth (set). Rid of his burden, Pegasus continued his upward flight and was employed to carry thunder and lightning for Zeus. His spirit broken, Bellerophon roamed alone on the Aleian plain until he died. Erroneously, Rubens and other artists of the middle ages identified Pegasus with Perseus and the horse became part of the Perseus legend. Even Shakespeare in Troilus and Cressida mentions Perseus's horse.

The figure of a winged horse appeared on Euphratean, Hittite, and Etruscan tablets, coins, and vases. Asva, Sanscrit word for mare, is the root of Asvins, Vedic twins of dawn light who filled a hundred vases with sweet liquor (dew or fertile moisture, an allusion related to Hippocrene), from which may be gathered the constellation is a very ancient one. Indeed, the name Pegasus may be compounded of the Phoenician words Pag or Pega and Sus, meaning the Bridled Horse that made up the figurehead of a ship. This certainly would account for the half figure, the head and fore quarters shown on illustrations, or it may come from the Egyptian pag (to cease) and sus (a vessel), thus symbolizing the cessation of navigation when the Nile began to overflow. In an old work, Destruction of Troy, Pegasus is a ship built by Perseus and likened to a flying horse. A ship in this section of the heavens, anciently called The Sea, is proper. Reduplication plays an important part in constellation designs. Inasmuch as other equine figures exist, Centaurus, Equuleus, Sagittarius, quite possibly this was intended to be a ship; companion or duplication of Argo.

In biblical lore the constellation was Nimrod's Horse; one

of those of Jeremiah, that were "swifter than eagles;" the Ass on which Christ rode triumphantly into Jerusalem; the Archangle Gabriel; or the Messenger of Glad Tidings. In medieval heraldry it became the Luneburg Horse to honor dukes of Hanover in Prussia.

Longfellow, in Pegasus in Pound, placed this "wonderful winged steed with mane of gold," in a pound in a quiet New England village, but he found his quarters uncomfortable, escaped, and soared up to the stars again.

An asterism called Al Faras al Tamm (The Complete Horse) now virtually lost to modern viewers and rarely mentioned was surrounded by the stars of Pegasus, Equuleus, Cygnus, and Lacerta, and probably drew its components from the last three.

Configuration: Usually shown as the fore half of a winged horse in inverted position, his feet pawing the sky. If he were turned about he would be close to the water-jar of Aquarius, the source of the great stream that flows down the steep southern sky, and which might be equated with the fountain on Helicon. Descriptions indicate the horse was without wings until after middle classical times. It was characterized as cut in two, the rear part of the body hidden by dark clouds.

Additional designations: Demi Horse, Flying Horse, Half Horse, Winged Horse.

Arabic: Al Dalw (Water-bucket); Al Faras al Thani (The Second Horse), which debased into Alfaras, Alathem, Alphares, Alpheras. Amphora,

from Latin and more correctly applied to the Aquarius Urn.

Chinese: Pik (Partition or Wall, i.e. between the Old and New Years).

Egyptian: Servant or Jackal.

French: Pegase.

Greek: Divine; Half-visible Lybian Horse; Ippou (Horse); Melanippe, after a daughter of Chiron who had been changed by Artemis into a black mare; occasionally incorrectly written Menalippe.

Italian: Pegaso.

Latin: Bellerophon, Bellero-phontes; Cornipes (Horn-footed); Ephippiatus (Caparisoned); Equus (Horse), Equus Ales, Equus Pegasus; Equus posterior, Volans aereus dimidiatus (Latter Horse Flying in Air and Cut in Half); Fontis Musarum Inventor, from the fountain Hippo-crene he caused to flow on Helicon; Pegasides; Pegasus Equus alatus; Sagmarius Caballus (Pack-horse); Sonipes (Noisy-Footed), Sonipes Ales.

Spanish: Alatus (Winged), Secundus sometimes added to distinguish it from Equuleus.

A starless region in the constellation was called Al Baldah (The Fox's Kennel).

Those born under its influence are said to soar on the gift of poetic heights.

Situated in the northern sky, it is surrounded by Pisces, Andromeda, Equuleus, and Aquarius. Its chief object is a large quadrangular stellar

form called Great Square of
Pegasus or the Big Diamond,
which marks the horses body.
It has a number of named
stars, including: alpha, Markab;
beta, Scheat; gamma, Algenib;
epsilon, Enif (Enir); zeta, Homan;
theta, Baham. Culmination comes
about October 16.

PERSEUS (THE CHAMPION).
As a result of the visits of
Zeus (sky) to Danae (dawn) in
the form of a shower of gold
(rays), Perseus (sun) was born.
Acrisius, king of Argos and father
of Danae, advised by an oracle
that his grandson would kill him,
set his daughter and the child
adrift in a boat. Fishermen of
Seriphus rescued them. For
years, Polydectes, king of the
island, tried to persuade Danae
to become his wife. He thought
he might have more success with
Perseus out of the way, so
he sent the youth on the hopeless
task of obtaining the head of
Medusa, the mortal one of the
three Gorgon Sisters who lived
at the edge of the Western
Ocean (Night). So hideous were
her features, with enormous
tusk-like teeth, brazen claws,
and hissing serpents for hair,
that anyone who looked upon them
turned to stone. The gods, who
favored Perseus, provided him
with the necessary equipment;
Hades gave him a helmet of
invisibility, Athena a shield,
Hermes winged sandals and a
magic wallet in which to carry the
head once it had been severed
from her body. Perseus found
the sisters asleep and, not daring
to gaze at Medusa lest she should
awaken and petrify him with her
glance, he looked at her image
reflected in the polished shield,
then with a backward stroke of
his magic sword he cut off the
head and with it started for home.

On his way he rescued Andromeda from a sea-monster and
then married her. At Seriphus,
he turned Polydectes into stone
by showing him the Medusa head
he had demanded, and released
Danae from the prison in which
the king she continued to reject
had placed her. At Larissa,
he took part in some funeral
games and accidentally hit his
grandfather, who was among the
spectators. Unwilling to occupy
the throne of the man he had
killed, he exchanged Argos for
another kingdom. Eve'ntually
he founded the city of Mycenae
and presented the Medusa head to
Athena. Many great heroes
descended from Perseus and
Andromeda, the most renowned
being Heracles, their great
grandson. Perseus's labors
symbolize the career of the sun.
He is parted from his mother,
dawn, in the morning; in the
evening he finds her imprisoned
in darkness by the king of
night. The fulfillment of the
prophecy signifies the death
of the old year or sun by the
new year or young sun.

The name Perseus appears
to be derived from the Hebrew
Parash, a Horseman. This may
be the reason he sometimes is
mentioned instead of Bellerophon
as the rider of Pegasus, the
horse that adjoins Andromeda in
the northern sky. Perseus may
be of the same group of stars
called Parsondas in Babylonia.
The constellation, or some of its
stars, seem to correspond to
the Egyptian asterism Khem.
The Egyptian Khem is identical
with Ham, son of Noah, and
Ham, according to some interpretors of the Bible, stands
roughly for the south western
division of the world as known to
the Israelites, a division re-

garded as the natural sphere of influence of Egypt. Literally Khem is black; also it was a name of Egypt. In the Bible, Ham played the villain, thus in Egyptian lore Ham (Khem) would be a hero.

The constellation also corresponds to the Persian sun hero Mithra, which was the name of the constellation in that country. Conversely, Perses (a name which means destroyer, thus sun in destructive aspect), son of Perseus and Andromeda, supposedly gave his name to Persia, whose people previously were the Chephenes, descendants of Chepheus, whose lineage traced back to the Babylonian Belus (Baal). Chepheus has been identified with Cepheus, king of Ethiopia.

The biblical school regarded the asterism as David with the Goliath Head; Apostle Paul with his Sword and Book; or Saint George and the Dragon he killed to save Cleodolinda, daughter of the king of Lydia. The Saint George legend, undoubtedly adopted from that of Perseus, is an allegory that expresses the triumph of Christianity over evil. He is called the everlasting green one, inasmuch as his conflict with evil is everlasting.

Configurations. Early illustrations show a nude youth wearing talaria or winged sandals with a light scarf curled around his body. In his left hand he holds the Medusa-head and in his right the enormous sword he received from Hermes. Later illustrations picture him in a flowing robe or in hero's attire.

Additional designations: The Champion, The Horseman, the Rescuer.

Arabic: Bershawish, Fersaus, Siaush, all from the Greek. Hamil Ras al Ghul (Bearer of the Demon's or Spectre's Head), which became Amirazzual in Moorish Spain.

Christian: Redeemer of Mankind.

French: Persee.

German: Perseus, Perseus et Caput Medusae. Trager des Medusen Kopf, a title that compares to the Arabic.

Hindu: Prasiea, a transliteration from the Greek.

Italian: Perseo.

Latin and Low Latin: Abantiades, Acrisioniades, Inachides, names which allude to his father and grandfather and an earlier ancestor, the first king of Argos. Canis (Dog). Cyllenius. Hermes, who aided the hero, was born on Mount Cyllene. Deferens caput Algol; Deferens Cathenam; Gorgonifer; Gorgonisue; Victor Gorgonei monstri, which express connection with Medusa and the chain of Andromeda. Pinnipes, referring to the talaria. Portans caput larvae, a translation from the Arabic. Profugus (Flying One).

Lato-Arabic: Celeub, Cheleub, Chelub, probably from the Arabic Kullab (Hero's Weapon) or from Kalb (Dog).

Astrologically its influence was evil; the astrologers' name for it was Cacodaemon (Bad Demon).

A well known meteor shower,

the Perseids, radiates from this group with its maximum about August 10. The shower also is called Larmes de Saint Laurent (Tears of Saint Laurence), whose martyrdom upon a red hot gridiron took place on August 10, 258. The meteor stream has been observed since the 9th century. The constellation itself, among the most extended in the heavens, is described as very tall. One of the Royal Family, it lies in the Milky Way, north of the Pleiades, between Auriga and Andromeda, below Cassiopeia, which is not far from the North Pole. Perseus is said to be "stirring up the dust in heaven," the dust being the section of the Milky Way around him, which he stirs up in his hurry to reach Andromeda. One mythologist has contended that his connection with Andromeda in legend may have come about because Perseus rises before the maiden he hastens to deliver from the monster night.

Perseus culminates on December 22; its bright stars are; alpha, Algenib, also called Mirfak; beta Algol.

PHOENIX (THE PHOENIX). Fabulous Arabian emblem of solar or fire worship. A bird that supposedly lives to a great age, at which time it burns itself to ashes, and then after three days comes to life again. It appears alone, without mate or companion, and symbolizes a cyclic period, a person of superlative excellence, resurrection, self-immolation. Because alchemists used it as an emblem of their vocation it has become a chemist's shop sign. The bird evolved from the conception of Bennu, Egyptian bird of the rising sun. Sometimes portrayed as an eagle or griffin.

Additional designations: Arabian, Al Nahr (The River); Al Rial (The Young Ostriches), which has been incorrectly written Al Zibal; Al Zaurak (The Boat). Chinese, Ho Neaou. French, Phenix. German, Phonix. Italian, Fenice. Medieval Christian, Aaron the High Priest.

Formed at the turn of the 17th century, Phoenix is located in the southern sky between Eridanus and Grus, south of Sculptor. Culmination is about November 18. The constellation has no bright stars.

PICTOR (THE PAINTER'S EASEL). A constellation formed in the middle of the 18th century. Located in the southern sky below Columba, above Dorado and Volans.

Additional designations: French, Chevalet du Peintre; Palette. German, Malerstaffelei. Italian, Pittore. Latin, Equuleus Pictoris; Pluteum Pictoris.

Although none of its stars are bright, one is the swiftest known in the skies, and for this reason is called Flying or Run-away Star. It is of eighth magnitude, of orange-yellow color, with an estimated speed of 185 miles a second. The constellation culminates about January 30.

PISCES (THE FISHES). The original asterism probably was only one fish, symbol of the Assyrian great mother Derceto (Derke), a fish or mermaid goddess, female counterpart of Dagon, an extremely ancient god. Dagon appears to be one of the names under which

Ea was worshipped, and he was among the deities who sat in judgment on the souls of the dead in the lower world. These names account for some of those in low Latin.

The Greeks corrupted Adir (Great) and Dag (Fish) into Tar-ata, which led to Atargatis, bisexual goddess, which was born of an egg found by a fish and thrust ashore. A defender of cities, she fixed the fates of mankind, in which role she wore a turreted crown. As fertility mother she was portrayed as a mother nursing a child. Her temple included a pond of sacred fish. At Rome worshipped as Dea Syria. In inscriptions her name has been translated Aphrodite, of whom as sea-born she is indeed a counterpart. In one myth, Aphrodite and her son Eros (spring sun) or Adonis (spring vegetation) were strolling along the banks of a river where the sudden appearance of the terrorsome giant Typhon, who belched flames and smoke (lightning and clouds) alarmed them, and to escape hím they plunged into the water and were transformed into fishes. This legend descended from that of Astarte, who parallels Derceto and Atargatis, who percipitated herself with her son into the Euphrates when pursued by a monster. Latin writers who tell essentially the same story about Venus and Cupid made Pisces the fishes that carried mother and child to safety. This escape legend is analogous to that of Pan, who is associated with the constellation Capricorn.

In Egypt the sign betokened the approach of spring, the season for fishing, for when the sun entered Pisces, fishes were fattest and most desirable.

In Christian faiths, a fish, symbol of Christ the fisher of souls, was used in the eucharist until replaced by bread. Biblical scholars say these fish represent those with which Christ fed "about five thousand men, besides women and children, or was a symbol of Saint Matthias.

A story told in the Old Testament relates that the pious Tobit when in captivity at Ninevah evaded decrees and buried the Hebrew dead. Because of his position, this act made him ritually unclean, and when he fell asleep outside his courtyard he was blinded by sparrow dung. His son Tobias cured him by applying fish gall to his eyes. Tobias personified dawn or spring, who drove off night or winter and with the aid of the sea gave renewed sight to Tobit, the sun, that is dawn helped the sun rise from water.

Within the boundaries of Pisces three distinct conjunctions of Jupiter and Saturn took place in the year 747, these phenomena strikingly agreeing in some details with Saint Matthew's account of the Star of Bethlehem that guided the Magi in their visit to the infant Jesus. Rabbis in the 15th century recorded that a similar conjunction took place in Pisces shortly before the birth of Moses and that they anticipate a repetition of the conjunction at their Messiah's advent. Thus the Fishes were considered an emblem of the Jews as well as a tribul emblem of Zebulun.

Among Peruvians the month of Pisces was represented by

two star groups: 1-The Terrace of the Granaries or Doves, a name also given to the Pleiades, and strangely enough also a form of Derceto and Aphrodite. From its illustration, a net with numerous meshes, the Granaries seem to be connected with the sea. Again strangely, the name like that of Dagon, signified grain as well as fish. 2-Pichu (the Knot), a name by which the month also was known. It was figured by a net enclosing fish.

Configurations. On atlases two fishes widely separated are shown. A ribbon is attached to the tail of each, and the ends are tied in a knot, which is marked by the star Al Rischa. The north eastern fish is headed toward Andromeda, the south-western fish is headed toward Aquarius and Pegasus. A Chaldean drawing of a fish with the head of a swallow, the bird of spring when the sun is in this region of the sky, may refer to this star group. The bird-fish, which typifies the eternal conflict within nature, may well symbolize the flight of the fertility goddess and her son, who personifies sun and or verdure, from the demon of destruction. Some astronomers are of the opinion one fish originally marked the sign; the dual form came into existence to indicate the double month inserted every six years to adjust the Babylonian calendar. Others claim the sign is a reduplication of the nocturnal sun, the fish-sun (sun after setting in water) concealed in the sea, an interpretation which may be applied to celestial beings associated with the constellation. Its pictorial emblem is ♓.

The name is believed to have been derived from its coincidence with the sun during the rainy season. Additional designations are: Dolphin, Exaltation of Venus, Tunny.

Anglo-Norman: Peisun.

Anglo-Saxon: Fixas.

Arabic: Al Hut (The Fish); Al Risha (The Cord); Al Samakah, Al Samaktain, a dual form; Batn al Hut (Belly of the Fish). In Europe these corrupted into El Haut, Elhautine, Haut, Sameh.

Assyrian: Dagon, also applied to Piscis Australis, Derceto, Derke.

Babylonian: Nunu (Fish).

Chinese: Koei, K'uei, Kwei (Striding Legs); Shwang Yu (Two Fishes); Tseu Tsze (Pig).

Euphratean: Fishes of Ea (Hea or Ia), Ea being lord of the deep, who as the constellation Piscis Australis was the father of the twins. Nuni (Fishes).

French: l'Hirondelle (Swallow); Poissons (Fishes).

German: Fische.

Graeco-Babylonian: Zib, which signifies boundary, that is the end of the Fishes, Water, or Zodiac.

Greek: Atargatis; Ichthues, Ichthus, or Ichthys (Fish, and a word which resolves into ik-theos, i.e. great god), which in the middle ages degenerated into Echiguen, Ichiguen, Ittha. Urania, Greek Muse of astronomy.

Hebrew: Dagaim (Two Fishes).

Hindu: Revati (Abundant or Wealthy).

Italian: Pesci.

Latin and Low Latin: Aquilonaris, Aquilonius, alluding to Aquilo, the wind that brings rain from the northeast. Bambycii, Bombycii Hierapolitani, from Bambyce and Hierapolis, seats of Derceto worship. Dagiotho; Dea Syria; Dercete; Dercetis; Dercis; Dii Syrii; Dione; Gemini Pisces (Twin Fish); Imbrifer Duo Pisces; Neptuni Sidus (Neptune's Star, suggesting it was under Neptune's care); Phacetis; Pisces Borealis; Piscis Gemellus (Fish Twins); Proles Dercia (Offspring of Derceto); Veneris Mater; Venus cum Adone; Venus et Cupid; Venus Syria cum Cupidine.

Persian: Mahik (Fish).

Spanish: Pesces.

Syriac: Nuno (Fish).

Tamilian: Anta, Jitu, Mina, Minam.

Turkish: Balik (Fish).

Astrologically the influences of the sign were dull, treacherous and phlegmatic. Egyptians and Hebrews abstain from eating sea-fish out of their dread and abhorrence. A fish represented the odious in hieroglyphics. A comet here was particularly dreaded as a bringer of war and pestilence; later this became the reputation of comets wherever they appeared. Hindus held a contrary opinion; to them the sign portended plenty.

Astrologers say that its quality of influence is feminine and unfortunate, and that it influences the health of the feet. It is called the zodiac's hell. It is ruled by Neptune, who provides its treacherous character. When it is the house of Venus, those born under its influence are sensual, sensitive, psychic, unaggressive, restless, and obstinate.

Located in the northern sky northeast of Cetus, south of Andromeda and Pegasus. The constellation is important only because of its position in the precession of the equinoxes. It is now the twelfth zodiacal sign and the first zodiacal constellation, which lies in the sign of Aries. Within its boundaries is the vernal equinox or point where the sun crosses the equator on its way north each spring. This point is known as the Greenwich of the sky, and for this reason The Fishes are called the Leaders of the Celestial Host. From it the right ascension of all stars is reckoned. The southwestern Fish culminates about November 11, the northeastern late in November. It has no particularly bright stars; among those named is: alpha, Al Rischa. Various of its stars formed lunar stations, usually the 28th or for the last day of the month, as the following: Arabic, Batn al Hut (Fish's Belly) or Al Risha (The Cord); Babylonian, Kullat Nunu (Cord of the Fish or Dwelling of the Fish); Coptic, Kuton (Cord); Hindu, Revati (Rich); Khorasmian, Zidadh; Persian, Kaht or Kahtsan (Cord); Sogdian, Rewand.

PISCIS AUSTRALIS (THE SOUTHERN FISH). In early legend, parent of the Twin

Fishes in the northern sky. The conception of a fish drinking a stream is very ancient. In deluge stories a fish saves the world by pulling a vessel to safety or consuming the excess water. This fish is the sky form of Dagon, an androgynous creator and male counterpart of Derceto. Half man, half fish, Dagon appears to have been one of the names under which Ea, lord of the deep, was worshipped, and he was among the deities who sat in judgment on the souls of the dead in the world beyond. Oannes, lord of wisdom, who lived among men during the day and retired to the depths of the sea at night is assigned to this constellation as well as to Aquarius.

In Egyptian lore the fish is Oxyrhynchus, which became sacred when it swallowed the phallus of Osiris. To Hebrews it represented the Barrel of Meal belonging to the widow of Sarepta. Christians pronounced it to be the fish taken by Saint Peter with a piece of money in its mouth.

Configurations. Generally depicted as a fish in an upright position with mouth agape, drinking the stream that pours from the Aquarius water-jug. In older illustrations the fish floats on his back showing the stars on his belly. In modern drawings he is in the water in normal position.

Additional designations: Golden Fish, probably because it is more conspicuous than Pisces; Greater Fish; Piscis Austrinus.

Arabic: Al Hut al Janubiyy (The Larger Southern Fish),

probably a translation from the Greek. In late medieval literature this distorted into Ahaut Algenubi and Haut elgenubi.

Assyrian: Dagon.

Egyptian: Oxyrhynchus.

French: Poisson Australe.

German: Sudliche Fisch.

Italian: Pesce Australe.

Latin and Low Latin: Oxyrinque, from the Egyptian; Phagre; Piscis Aquosus; Piscis Capricorni, alluding to its position; Piscis Magnus; Piscis Solitarius.

Astrologers instructed beekeepers to gather honey when Piscis Australis was high in the night sky.

Located in that part of the southern sky known as the Celestial Sea, south of Aquarius, north of Grus. Its lucida Formalhaut is the only bright star in this comparatively starless region and is visible from August until the end of December, reaching culmination about October 9.

PSALTERIUM GEORGII (GEORGIANUM). This constellation, formed in 1781, was named to honor King George II of England. It lay close to the celestial equator between Taurus and Eridanus. The name, from the Latin, means George's Lute or Harp. On various planispheres its name appeared as George's Harfe, Georgs Harffe, Harpa Georgii. Psalterium no longer is recognized by astronomers.

PUPPIS (THE POOP). A

subdivision of the ship Argo, which see. It lies in the southern sky surrounded by Carina, Vela, Pyxis, Canis Major, Columba. It has no bright stars and comes to the meridian about Feburary 22. Other designations are: The Deck, the Stern, i.e. of Argo.

PYXIS (THE MARINER'S COMPASS). Like Puppis, a subdivision of the ship Argo. It was formed from stars of the sky's mast, so its name is something of an anachronism. Located in the southern sky between Puppis and Vela, below Hydra. It has no bright stars, and other names by which it is known are: The Compass (of Argo), Nautical Box, Pyxis Nautica. It is at culmination about March 21.

QUADRANS MURALIS (THE MURAL QUADRANT). This asterism was formed in 1795 from stars in the northern sky that are surrounded by Hercules, Bootes, and Draco, by Joseph Lalande. In this manner he made of stars a souvenir of the instrument he and his nephew used to observe them. On other planispheres it appeared as Mauer Quadrant or Quadrante. These stars come to the meridian about June 19. The constellation is now ignored by astronomers, its stars having been distributed among other constellations.

RETICULUM (THE NET). Formed by the 18th century astronomer Isaak Habrecht of Strassburg as a memorial of the instrument he used in making celebrated astronomical discoveries, and by him called Rhombus. Lacaille, who adopted the asterism, became its reputed inventor. Also called

Reticulus Rhomboidalis (Rhomboidal Net). The French term is Reticule or Rhombe; the German, Rhomboidische Netz; the Italian, Reticolo. It is located deep in the southern sky between Dorado and Hydrus and reaches the meridian about January 3.

ROBUR CAROLINUM (CHARLES' OAK). Published in 1679 by Edmund Halley to commemorate the Royal Oak in which his patron, Charles II Of England, had lain hidden for twenty-four hours after his defeat by Cromwell in 1651. The stars had been taken from among the most brilliant of the ship Argo, but astronomers ceased to recognize the asterism within fifty years after it had been formed. In Germany it had been known as Karlseiche and in Italy as Querica.

SAGITTA (THE ARROW). Universally the arrow has been symbolic of divine judgment. Ancient priests shot arrows into the air and, from their positions when they returned to earth, read the will of the gods. In the possession of a hero, an arrow invariably had magic properties that aided the owner, thus a sun hero's arrow had the qualities of rays; one who had an ungovernable temper or was bloodthirsty might have a dart which contained the nature of hurricane or lightning.

In Greek mythology this particular weapon is said to have served several gods. It was used by Apollo, the sun, to exterminate the Cyclops who forged thunder and lightning; by the mischievous god of love Eros (Cupid) to pierce human hearts; by the enemies of Zeus,

great ruler of the skies, to kill
his pet eagle and bearer of his
weapons (wind, thunder, and
lightning); by Heracles when he
slew the vulture (storm demon)
that gnawed at the liver of
Prometheus and again when he
attempted to slay the Stymphalian
Birds, who devoured crops and
mortals. It never reached the
Birds and remains suspended in
space as a constellation. All of
these legends treat the Arrow as
a ray of the sun. It also is said
to be the dart of Sagittarius,
which had strayed from him. In
classical times it was thought to
represent the Reed from which
arrows were formed. In biblical
lore it was said to be the Arrow
shot by Joash at Elisha's command; the one sent by Jonathan at
David near the stone Ezel; or the
Nail of the Crucifixion.

Configurations. Usually
portrayed simply as an arrow or
dart overlying a bow. Occasionally the dart is feathered or is
shown in Eagle's talons, inasmuch
as the bird was Zeus's weapon
bearer.

Additional designations:

Arabic: Al Hams or Hamash
(The Five, i.e. stars), which
was corrupted into Alahance. Al
Sahm (Arrow), which corroded
into Alsoham, Schaham, Sham.

Christian: Nail of Cruci-
fixion; Spear.

French: Fleche.

German: Pfeil.

Hebrew: Hes or Hets
(Arrow).

Italian: Saetta.

Latin and Low Latin:
Arrow of Cupid (Eros); Calamus,
Canna, Harundo, all signifying
reed from which arrow-shafts
were made. Herculea; Istiusc;
Jaculum (Javelin); Missile
(Weapon). Missore, to indicate
arrow-shooter; Musator, which
may be a barbarism for Missore
or from the Arabic Satar
(Straight Line). Obelus,
possibly Obelisk. Telum (Dart);
Temo meridianus (Southern
Beam); Vectis (Pole); Virga
(Wand); Virgula jacens (Falling
Wand).

Lato-Arabic: Albanere;
Alchanzato.

Persian and Armenian:
Tigris (Arrow).

Spanish: Istusc.

Turkish: Otysys Kalem (A
Smooth Arrow), which degenerated into Orfercalim.

Astrologically the natures
of Mars and Venus have been
ascribed to it, for which reason
it was given names which reflect
the characters of these deities:
Daemon, Feluco, Fossorium.

This constellation is located
in the Milky Way directly above
Aquila and below Cygnus, point-
ing eastward. Although ancient,
Sagitta is insignificant, having
no star brighter than fourth
magnitude and none interesting
enough to bear a name. It
comes to the meridian about
August 30.

SAGITTARIUS (THE ARCHER).
Nergal (Nerigal), Assyro-
Babylonian great archer or war
god, with the titles Giant King
of War, Illuminator of the
Great City, Strong One, was

guardian of this constellation.
From the summer solstice to the
winter solstice he was lord of
the fires of the underworld, the
unseen portion of the southern
sky, and judge of souls of the
dead. When he returned to the
upper world he was at first
benevolent, but in summer he
became the burning agent of
pestilence and war, in which
role he also commanded the
planet Mars. He appeared in
lion form or as a man holding
a sword in hand and a head cut
off from a body in the other,
an aspect later given to Perseus
with the Medusa head.

When the constellation was
assigned a satyr form it
characterized Enkidu (Eabani).
a wild hairy monster, half man,
half beast (violent winds), who
had been created to destroy
Gilgamesh, King of Shinar, who
ruled with unrelenting severity
(scorching aspect of the sun).
To the consternation of the gods,
Enkidu and Gilgamesh became
friends and traveled together.
One of its brighter stars is
believed to be the one known to
Chaldeans as "Star of Proclamation of the Sea," because it was
the herald of winter and the wet
constellations that were to come.

In India the satyrs developed
into the Gandharvas, assigned to
the constellation Centaurus. The
counterpart of the Gandharvas
among the Greeks was the
Centaurs, some of whom were
cruel and barbaric, some of
whom were enlightened and kind.
Chiron, the wisest of them all,
was not only adept in the arts of
gymnastics and hunting, but a
skilled herbalist, pharmacist,
diviner, lyre player, and com-
poser of music. He laid out a
path among the stars and, to

guide the Argonauts on their
expedition to Colchis to obtain
the Golden Fleece, he mapped
out the zodiac, placing among
them a group of stars called
Sagittarius, which he intended
to be in his own image. Instead, the asterism emulated the
disposition of another Centaur,
Crotus, who was cruel and
ferocious (fabricated winter inasmuch as he held the sun during
November-December). So wild
and fierce was Crotus and so
deadly was his arrow, even
Scorpio, himself with a lethal
sting, shrank from him. The
bull Taurus, on the other side
of the sky, fled across the
horizon as soon as Crotus-Sagit-
tarius first appeared. This confirms an ancient belief that the
Centaurs were bull slayers.
When Chiron exchanged im-
mortality for mortality to escape
the pain he suffered at the time
Heracles accidentally shot him
with a poisoned arrow, Zeus,
who honored Chiron, wished to
lift him into the heavens. To
dispossess Crotus would be useless, that constellation's character
was not suitable for Chiron. In
making his map, Chiron had used
up all the space and stars along
the ecliptic, so Zeus was forced
to place him far to the south
where he rarely is seen. The
constellation is called Centaurus.

Christian scholars, as is their
habit, assigned the stars to
more than one biblical character.
It represented Joash, king of
Israel, who was directed by the
dying Elisha to shoot arrows
eastward out of the window, that
is toward Syria. Joash did as
he was commanded and achieved
a great victory. Other identifications were with Ishmael, James
the Great, and Matthew the
Apostle. The stars that form

the curve were the Bow of Promise set in the Cloud (Milky Way) that followed the Deluge.

Desert Arabs worshipped two clusters of its stars, one just inside the Milky Way, one just outside, as ostriches going to and from the celestial river in which they quenched their thirst. Those on the west were going to the stream, those on the east were departing from the stream. Their keeper was one of the central stars; their nest was located in the nearby Southern Cross. Why non-drinking animals should be placed here in connection with water is inexplicable. Some mythologists say pasturing camels were intended; others that the title more correctly signifies the beam over the mouth of a well to which pulleys are attached. A third explanation is that a true reading renders an Overturned or Empty Chair, a probable reference to the barren season in which the sun appeared within its boundaries. The Medians identified these stars with Ahura, great creator, who generally was represented as holding a ring or crown (Corona Australis).

Hindus believed the Asvins, who in stellar nomenclature appeared at various celestial stations, were the rulers here. In earlier belief, the stars of the bow and the human part of the figure typified the fan of the lion's tail twirled by Mula, the pampered and vain wife of Chandra Gupta, who ruled an Indian kingdom in 300 B.C.

Configurations. The constellation undoubtedly was conceived in the Euphratean Valley. Exactly which stars were included is unsolved, and the figure seems to have undergone several changes. The first known drawing is that of a Satyr, probably derived from the Sumerian Enkidu. On an Assyrian standard appears the figure of an archer (autumn) above that of a galloping bull (summer), which might date back to 6,000 or 4,000 B.C., in which period the constellation marked the autumnal equinoctial point. An ancient Egyptian drawing of an arrow held in a human hand is believed to illustrate this asterism or a number of its stars. Other Egyptian representations were an Ibis or Swan or an Archer with two heads, one of a man, one of a lion. Some Asiatic maps symbolized this group with a bow and arrow. Early European illustrations gave the face savage features, later art depicted the face as gentle and intelligent. Some late manuscripts have provided the figure with a flowing robe, a crown near his fore feet, and in his hand an arrow which he aims at the Scorpion. A frequent representation is that of a Centaur, with the head and shoulders of a man and the body and legs of a horse, in the act of shooting an arrow which is aimed at Scorpius. In India figured as a Horse, Horse's Head, or Horseman. The sign's pictorial emblem is ↗ .

Generally the names applied are attributed to the fact that at the time the sun entered this section of the sky the hunting season opened, and Sagittarius always has been considered a patron of hunters and the chase.

Additional designations: The Archer, The Bow, Bow Stretcher, Chiron, Drawer of the Arrow, Giant of War, Illuminator of the Great City, Light of the White

Face, On Horseback, Smiting
Sun Face, The Strong One.
Its stars zeta, tau, sigma, phi,
lambda form an inverted scoop,
anciently called the Ladle or
Milk Dipper. Another title for
these stars is Hobby Horse.

Accadian: Ban (Bow); Mul-
ban (Star of the Bow).

Anglo-Saxon: Scytta.

Arabic: Al Baldah (The
City or District), composed of
the empty space in the upper
part of the figure. Al Kaus,
which corrupted became Alkauuso,
Elkausu, Elkusu. Al Kiladah
(The Necklace); Al Naam
(Ostriches); Al Naam al Sadirah
(The Returning Ostriches); Al
Naam al Warid (The Going
Ostriches); Al Udhiyy (The
Ostrich's Nest.)

Assyro-Babylonian: Kakkab
Kastu (Constellation or Star of
the Bow); Pa or Xut (Dayspring);
Udgudua (Flowing Day or the
Smiting Sun Face); Utucagaba
(Light of the White Face).

Chaldean: Kertko (Bow).

Chinese: Jin Ma (The Man-
Horse); Ki or Kit (Sieve); Seih
Muh (Cleft Tree or branches cut
for firewood); Tew, also Dew,
Tow, Nan Tow (Ladle or
Measure). Other Chinese
epithets were Temple, Tiger.

French: Sagittaire.

German: Schutz, Schutze
(Protection).

Hebrew: Kesheth (Bow).

Hindu: Dhanu, Dhanuk,
Dhanasu, Dhanus, Taukshika, all
signifying bowman. Purva and

Uttara Ashadha (Former and
Latter Unconquered) for various
stars. These latter two were
lunar mansions.

Latin and Low Latin:
Antepes, Antepedes (Forefeet),
also applied to the constellation
Centaurus. Arcitenens,
Arquitenens, a term sometimes
applied to Apollo. Arcus (Bow);
Astronochus (Star-holder);
Cornipedes (Horn-footed).
Croton or Crotos (Herdsman).
Dianae Sidus (Diana's Star).
Haemonios Arcus. Joculator
(Jester), perhaps a medieval
court fool or minstrel. Mino-
taurus, from a fabled earlier
shape. Pharetra (Quiver).
Sagitta arcui applicata. Sagit-
tare, Sagitary, Sagittarie,
Sagittary, Sagittifer, Sagittiger,
Sagittipotens. Semivir (Half-
man). Taurus, from a fabled
earlier shape. Telum. Thes-
salicae Sagitta, Thessaly being
the birthplace of the Centaurs.

Persian: Kaman, Nimasp
(Bow).

Syriac: Keshta (Bow).

Tamil: Dhamsu (Bowman).

Turkish: Yai (Bow).

In Assyria these stars were
associated with Kislivu, the ninth
month, which corresponds to
the modern November-December,
a period with which Orion also
is related. This association no
doubt was formed when the sun
was in the sign, and those born
during these days are said to be
influenced by it. The season in
which the moon appeared in the
sign was inclined to fruitfulness
and therefore fortunate. Astrologers see its quality of influence
as masculine and fortunate. It is

ruled by Jupiter, governs the health of the thighs, and the character given to those born under it is candid, magnetic, prophetic, just, impatient, shrewd, ambitious.

This ancient constellation is in the southern sky between Capricornus and Scorpio, on the edge of the region known as the Celestial Sea, where watery constellations are found. It rises just before the stars that form the sea and accordingly warns of their approach. One of its bright stars is believed to be the star known to Chaldeans as "Star of the Proclamation of the Sea," because it was the herald of winter and the wet constellations that were to follow. Culmination of the constellation is about August 21. Its named stars are: alpha, Rukbat; beta, Arkab; gamma, Al Nasl; delta, Kaus Meridionalis; epsilon, Kaus Australis; lambda, Kaus Borealis; mu, Gau; sigma, Nunki.

SCEPTRUM BRANDEN-BURG (THE BRANDENBURG SCEPTRE). This asterism of four stars was placed on charts in 1688 by Gotfried Kirch, the first astronomer of the Prussian Royal Society of Sciences. Since that time it has passed into oblivion. The Chinese had an asterism called Kew Yew composed of these stars, which are located between Lepus and Eridanus in the southern sky.

Previous to the introduction of this figure a Sceptre held by the Hand of Justice had been placed in the northern sky in 1679 to honor Louis XIV, king of France. Both Sceptres have been forgotten.

SCORPIO or SCORPIUS (THE SCORPION). This sign had been carved on stones of great antiquity and from its inception stood for the reputed slayer of a valiant hero. Girtablili, a chaos demon in the train of Tiamat and guardian of the gateway that separated the world of darkness from the world of light, was a scorpion-man, who each night and each autumn attacked the fairer descendants of the great mother goddess, especially Anu, the bright day sky, and Marduk, the sun. With his stinger, Girtablili bruised the sacred heel of any king or hero who happened to cross his path. Gilgamesh, on his search for the plant of immortality, visited Pir-na-pishtim, the Babylonian Noah, who provided him with extra-ordinary powers. These powers permitted Gilgamesh to pass the Western Mountains, the gate of sunset, at which Girtablili stood guard, and to return at daybreak (a theme borrowed for the Cinderella story). The reappear-ance of Gilgamesh in the morning parallels that of the Egyptian Ra who battled the monster Apep each night. Mythologically, a sacred heel is that part of the sun or moon that at setting touches earth or sea. The bruise it receives is poisonous in that it causes the whole body to col-lapse or sink. Since these early times this hole-and-corner animal with a sting out of all proportion to its small body, which thrives in cold dampness and treats sunlight as if it were a natural enemy, has been a symbol of darkness, torture, treachery, and evil in general.

Egyptians lamented the death of Osiris (Orion) when the sun entered this sign, a time which fixed the commencement of the reign of Set, cruel deity of darkness and sterility.

At the command of Hera, Greek mother goddess, when Orion boasted that he could conquer any animal, a scorpion sprang out of earth and stung the great hunter's foot, of which wound he died. Hera rewarded the Scorpion with a place in the skies; Artemis pleaded on behalf of Orion, whom she loved, and Zeus, her father, answered her petition by making her lover the most beautiful of all heavenly configurations. Not only did Scorpion slay the Mighty Giant, but it stung the steeds Phaethon drove on his fatal ride in the chariot of Helios, and brought about the fall in which the youth lost his life. The heel of Harpocrates, personification of the youth of the morning sun, also was stung by Scorpion. Harpocrates sat on a lotus flower, his finger at his lips. Because of this gesture he was called a god of silence. This was the result of a mistaken notion about the Egyptian Harpichruti, of whom Harpocrates was a counterpart. Harpichruti likewise sat on a lotus; his finger was in his mouth, a gesture symbolizing the absorption of wisdom (milk which dropped from the breast of his mother).

All these legends appear to be dramatizations of seasonal peculiarities. When the sun enters the region of the zodiac dominated by Scorpio, diseases incident to the fruit season naturally prevail, inasmuch as autumn, which abounds in fruit may bring with it fevers or a variety of diseases quite fittingly attributed to a venomous creature, who, as it recedes, wounds with a stinger in its tail. Then too, the ancients saw changes from light

to darkness or from warmth to cold as a struggle for control. This strife was personified when star groups were organized. Orion and the Scorpio simply continue their battle in the boundless realm of space. There, when the ugly beast appears in the east, Orion, in fear of this foe of fertility and light, sinks into the western horizon out of Scorpio's range of vision. But the Scorpion is not let off scotfree. Sagittarius aims his dart at Scorpio, and Ophiuchus, close by, treads on him and follows him across the sky until he too succumbs.

When the constellations were originally designed, the sun at the time of the winter solstice was no doubt in the middle of the constellation and zodiacal sign Aquarius; at the time of the spring equinox in the middle of Taurus; at the time of the summer solstice in the middle of Leo. This leaves the fourth point, held by the sun at the autumnal equinox, which would appear to be where the foot of Ophiuchus, who crushes a serpent in his arms, treads on Scorpio. The precession of the equinoxes has moved Scorpio as well as the other three zodiacal constellations out of their original signs along the ecliptic.

Biblical commentators assert that the sign known to the patriarch Abraham was an Eagle, one of the forms of the Cherubim, which, in fourfold character, lion, calf, man, and eagle, appeared among the constellations. Usually the eagle is assigned to Aquila, but Antares, alpha star of Scorpio, has from remote antiquity been known in various parts of the world as one of the so-called Royal Stars,

the guardians of the four directions, and for this reason gives
credence to the argument that
Abraham saw an eagle in this
section of the sky. The so-
called Chambers of the South,
being opposite the Pleiades,
a northern station, has been
placed here, although generally
the stars of this group are said
to be the Hebrew Akrabh, and
so inscribed on the banners of
Dan as the emblem of the tribe
whose founder was a "serpent by
the way, an adder in the path."
This group captured the imagination of medieval scriptural
interpretors, who considered it
one of the Scorpions of Rehoboam
or the scorpion or serpent whereby Pharaoh was constrained to let
the children of Israel depart from
Egypt. These stars also were
said to be a form of the Apostle
Bartholomew or simply a
Cardinal's Hat.

In China it was part of the
noble Azure Dragon, bringer of
spring, and served as the
residence of the Blue Emperor,
who commanded the heavens.
Confucians conceived it as Ta
Who, the Great Fire, a primeval
name for its star Antares.

To the Mayas it was the
sign of the death god, Yalahau,
the lord of blackness and waters,
a warrior cruel to those he captured, forcing death upon them.
The bat, dog, and jaguar accompanied him.

Like the three stars of Orion's
Belt, the luminaries beta, delta,
and pi, here, have attracted attention in all ages. On the Euphrates
this group was the celestial Tree
of the Garden of Light, forerunner
of all cosmic or world trees.
Invariably the sacred tree which
nourishes all life stands in a

garden, its branches reaching
into the firmament and overhang-
ing a pool of clear water. A
dragon, serpent, or crocodile
(water withholder) sits at its
roots, guarding the pool. Among
the leaves (stars) at the top
sits a golden cock or eagle that
frequently attacks the evil
monster at the base. Under the
cool of the tree the gods meet
in judgment and determine the
fate of mankind. In the Garden
of Eden, the evil serpent at the
roots tempted Adam and Eve,
and an eagle was one of the
four forms of the Cherubim which
acted as guards.

Lambda, mu, and nu Scorpii
were known to the Polynesians
as Maui's Fishhook. Although
the chief Polynesian culture
hero, Maui was of small stature,
caused by his being an aborted
child. Because of this birth,
his mother despised him,
wrapped him in her apron, and
then abandoning him, left him to
die. He was saved by sea-
gods and given to a sky ancestor,
who educated him. Earth and
sky were in continual copulation,
and to give the various forms of
life already conceived room in
which to breathe and move, he
raised the sky in three heaves,
first to tree tops, then to
mountain tops, finally to where it
is. When he returned to earth,
his brilliance fascinated all. His
mother identified the apron and
proclaimed he was her youngest
and favorite child. To provide
dry days for her wash, he snared
the sun (another aspect of himself) with a lasso made from
the hair taken from his sister-
wife, and forced the solar ball
to agree to slacken its pace
before he released it. He cap-
turned all the winds, except the
west wind, which eluded him.

Those caught, he imprisoned in caves to provide his people with a mild climate. He conquered his ancestress, the fire goddess, and brought fire to mankind. A trickster, he played many pranks on his stupid and older brothers. Once he stole their fishhook and, when it was lost, to retrieve it, he dove into the sea, where he found it lodged in mud at the bottom. He tugged and tugged until he thought he had loosened it, and lugging it behind him he swam back to the surface, where he saw the hook was attached to a great fish that was covered with grass and trees, and on which men were hunting, women were cooking at fires, and children were at play, for he had raised the great island Te-ika-a-maui or Fish of Maui (New Zealand). Overjoyed to have accomplished so great an exploit, he performed a dance of rejoicing, and in his dance tossed his fishhook into the sky. After his dance, he warned his brothers not to cut the fish, but to spite him they hacked out pieces that gave the land its irregular coast, and they dug into the soil, piling up the dirt removed to make it mountainous. In spite of all he gave to mankind, Maui is responsible for each person's death. With the power of shape changing (seasonal changes), in the guise of a bird he followed his mother (earth) into the underworld, where he found her with his father Tangaroa, who then gave Maui a name, but made an omission. Before he might return to the upper regions, he had to pass through the body of a goddess (night). Jealous gods, who conceived the name and soul to be identical and a source of power and strength, worked their magic and then decreed that if he passed through

her, she would die, and he and mankind would be immortal. Once he entered the ogress, a bird that sings at sunset revealed the flaw in his name. She thus discovered how to pronounce it, and that made him unable to emerge from the dark recesses of her body. Symbolically, the fishhook is not merely an implement whereby one explores the unknown or unseen, it is an emblem of experimentation, quest, and research, and also an agent of deceit and perfidy. The theme of a lost fishhook or other lost article is not uncommon in stories that treat of death and rebirth.

Configurations. When depicted as curling his sting upwards to wound Ophiuchus's heel, Scorpio is an apparent illustration of the biblical words, "I will put enmity between thee and the woman and between they seed and her seed. It shall bruise thy head and thou shalt bruise his heel." In early times the constellation, originally much larger in size than the Scorpio with which we are familiar, was portrayed in a number of ways, including a snake and a crocodile, but most frequently as a scorpion. Early Euphratean monuments contain the figure of a lamp, at the base of which and almost touching it is a scorpion with tremendous claws. Stars in the claws form a circular figure and some authorities claim they represent the aged sun or sun succumbing before the authority of darkness. A semi-human form of two Scorpion-men, the claws grasping a circular altar or lamp, may have been intended for this constellation. This design was used in the middle ages, except the Scales were substituted for other articles. In popular modern publications it is illustrated as a Kite, which the stars actually resemble. As a rule shown as a gigantic scorpion, its head facing the west, its claws toward Libra, its reverted sting about to strike Ophiuchus, who appears to be trampling on it. On the banners of the tribe of Dan, it was a crowned snake or basilisk. Its pictorial emblem was *m̃ʒ*.

Additional designations: Basilisk; Cardinal's Hat; Crowned Snake; Double Sword. Great Beast, Great Sign, both terms probably alluding to the fact that the slayer of Orion was able to overcome him because he actually was of greater size than the hero. Place where One Bows Down, indicating the creature's dangerous character.

Accadian: Girtab (Seizer or Stinger).

Anglo-Norman: Escorpiun.

Anglo-Saxon: Throwend.

Arabic: Al Akrab (The Scorpion), which degenerated into Aakrab, Alacrab, Alatrab, Alatrap, Askrab, Hacrab, Hacerab.

Chinese: Ta Who; Tien He.

English, Middle: Scorpioun.

Hebrew: Akrabh (Serpent).

Hindu: Ali Viçrika, Ali Visrika, or Vrouchicam (Scorpion).

Italian: Friddo Animale, an allusion to its rising in the freezing hours of dawn. Un Secchione.

Latin and Low Latin: Forficulae (Scissors); Graffias, a term applied to the claws; Martis Sidus (House or Stars of Mars); Nepa or Nepas (Walking Backward); Scorpio, Scorpios, Scorpius; Scorpius cum Chelis (Scorpius with Scales, i.e. of Libra).

Persian: Ghezhdum or Kazhdum (Scorpion).

Singalese: Ussika.

Syrian: Akreva (Scorpion), corrupted into Acrobo.

Tamil: Kaurpya (Scorpion), which deteriorated into Kaurba. Vrishaman (Scorpion).

Turkish: Khoirughi (Tailed); Uzun Koirughi (Long Tailed).

The weather-wise of antiquity thought that its setting exerted a malignant influence that was accompanied by storms. Alchemists held it in high regard inasmuch as they believed iron could be transmuted into gold only when the sun was in this sign. Although astrologers respected the constellation as active, eminent and fruitful, they despised it as an accursed source of war and discord, the birthplace of the planet Mars. It was a feminine and therefore unfortunate sign. Those under its influence were dramatic, managerial, strong-willed, self-absorbed, sarcastic, jealous. It may have received its character from the red color of its lucida or from the poisonous attributes of its earthly complement. The appearance of a comet here portended a plague of reptiles, locusts, and other insects.

A belief prevails that the first zodiac designed by Euphratean star gazers was composed of six constellations and that Scorpio, greatly extended from the figure as we now know it, was one of those six. At this time, although nominally in the zodiac, the sun actually passes through only two small northern sections near Ophiuchus, and a mere nine days is required for the journey. In its present form it stretches across the southern sky, south of Ophiuchus, north of Ara, between Sagittarius and Libra. In Babylonia the sign corresponded to the eighth month, Arakh-Savna, our October-November. This region of the sky is famous as a field in which many brilliant novae have appeared. These strange blaze stars may have been an influence when ancients condemned the constellation as malign, one that caused conflagrations and cataclysms. The constellation also is noted for the radiancy of its permanent stars, among them: alpha, Antares; beta, Graffias; gamma, Brachium; delta, Dschubba; lambda, Shaula; nu, Jabbah. Culmination is about July 18.

SCULPTOR (SCULPTOR'S WORKSHOP). A constellation, north of Phoenix in a rather dim area of the southern sky, formed in the 18th century. It contains the southern Galactic Pole, whereas the northern end of the Galaxy's axis lies in coma Berenices.

Additional designations are: French, l'Atelier du Sculpteur (Sculptor's Studio or Workshop), sometimes written Officina Sculptoria or Apparatus Sculptoris. German, Bildhauer Werstadt or Bildhauerwerkstatte. Italian, Scultore.

Without named stars it culminates about November 10.

SCUTUM (THE SHIELD OF SOBIESKI). The third John Sobieski, king of Poland, drove the Turks from his native land, and then in 1683 routed them from the walls of the city of Vienna. At the time of his triumphal entry into the city, the priest officiating at the cathedral thanksgiving service read the passage, "A man was sent from God, whose name was John." Sobieski was acclaimed hero of Christendom, and seven years later a new constellation was formed in the southern hemisphere to glorify the cross emblazoned on his shield. Four stars on the shield's border are for the king's four sons. This cross also is identified as that of John of Capistrano, a war-minded Franciscan friar, who was papal inquisitor and leader of an army against the Turks when they besieged Belgrade in 1450. A colossal statue of Capistrano is outside the Vienna cathedral.

A notable cluster resembling the flight of wild ducks lies on the dexter chief of the Shield.

Additional designations: Coat of Arms, The Shield, Sobieski's Shield.

Chinese: Tien Pieu (Heavenly Casque). In China this is an ancient configuration and includes some stars of Aquila.

French: Boucliere, or Ecu, de Sobieski.

German: Sobieskischer Schild.

Italian: Scudo di Sobieski.

Latin and Low Latin: Clipeus or Clypeus Sobieskii; Scutum Sobiescianum; Sobiesii, Sobieskii.

It occupies a small triangular space in the southern sky below Aquila, between the head of Sagittarius and the tail of Serpens in an unusually bright section of the Milky Way; in fact it is noticeable mainly from the peculiar brightness of the encompassing Galaxy. None of its stars are named, and it appears at culmination about August 15.

SERPENS (THE SERPENT). In Babylonian mythology a water-snake was the thief who stole the plant of immortality from Gilgamesh; whereas in Egypt the sun-god Ra and his boatload of souls nightly passed through the body of the gigantic serpent Ankh Neteru to be reborn each morning, thus we see the snake as an extremely ancient spirit of resurrection. Asclepius, Greek deity of healing, carried a staff around which coiled healing or oracular serpents; occasionally the god himself took the shape of the reptile. Laocoon, a priest of Troy, with his two sons, was strangled to death by pythons after he had warned his countrymen against the wooden horse. These monstrous pythons were the agents of Hera, great sky-mother, who sided with the Greeks in the war, and as such they were instruments of fate. When Glaucus, son of the Cretan king Minos, fell into a jug of honey and smothered to death, Minos shut the soothsayer Polyidos in a cave with the body and demanded that the child be brought back to life. A dragon or snake approached the corpse. Polyidos killed it with a stone and then noticed another dragon cover the dead monster with grass, whereupon it breathed and drifted away. Polyidos ap-

plied the lesson he had learned from these crawling animals and restored life to the child. The death of Glaucus typifies the death of fertility; a being of the earth, or a being symbolizing earth, showed how resurrection might be achieved. These myths exemplify that the serpent or snake was not merely one that carried the curse of death (night or frost), but also was a bestower of health or resurrection. In this dual role, Serpens appeared in the sky.

The Romans assigned this constellation to Cacus (Caecius, Caesius), a three-headed, flame-breathing crawler, who lived on the Aventine, where Rome now stands. When Hercules (Heracles) passed with the cattle of Geryon, Cacus stole several, dragging them down to his cave backwards by the tail. Unable to trace their hoof-prints, Hercules was about to go on his way when he heard them lowing. He entered the cave, and slew Cacus with his club. Thus the sun (Hercules) released fertile clouds (cows) from a dark sky (cave). The flames Cacus sent off were flashes of lightning which precede a storm. Contrary currents blow at different elevations, thus clouds (cows) appear to be going against the wind or backwards. Cacus was an aboriginal Italian fire god to whom an episode in the life of Hercules (Heracles) became attached.

Like the Roman snake, the Norse Nithhoggr spread darkness and winter. In serpent form, Satan bewitched Eve and she and Adam were forced out the Garden of Eden, where growing things were perpetually green. On the other hand a great worm, Schamir (fertility) aided Solomon in hewing the Temple stones, and a viper helped Aaron obtain salvation for the Jews. When the high priest threw his cataleptic serpent (rod) on the floor before Pharaoh, it devoured the serpents (rods) of Egyptian magicians, and the astounded Pharaoh, who accepted the defeat of his wonder-workers as prophetic, permitted the Jews to leave the land of bondage. In the wilderness, after a visitation of fiery serpents, Moses erected a brazen serpent, and those who looked upon it were cured. Christians later revered this asterism as symbolic of Christ, and within modern times Christians have observed stars in the head of Serpens as a stellar Cross belonging to Saint Patrick. Saint Paul on a pilgrimage against sin overcame an evil Maltese viper, said to be this configuration.

It also is believed to be Aido Hwedo, the Dahomey great rainbow serpent which transported Mawu, goddess-creator of the universe. Excrement left by Aido molded into mountains. In most African traditions the snake appears as a dawdler, the untrustworthy messenger of the creator-god. The god, angered by man, sent a tortoise with a message of death. Relenting, he sent a snake to overtake the tortoise. The snake loitered on the way; accordingly man must die first; then he may recover eternal life.

Zohak, a serpent in Persian mythology, was a drought bringer. The Hindu nagas appeared in every branch of learning. One of their leaders, Sesa, floated on the primeval waters and furnished a couch for Vishnu's fecund sleep. He had a thousand heads (stars), which served as a canopy for the sleeper. One head, which supports the earth, destroys it at the end of each kalpa by vomiting fire; thus he typifies eternity. With a companion, Vasuki, he served as a rope with which earth was originally churned in the primal sea. Ahi, an evil strangler and withholder of water, was overcome by Indra, who pierced him with a thunderbolt. Krishna too overcame one of these monsters by treading on him. Contrariwise, Mucalinda, Buddhist serpent king, emulated Sesa and spread his hood as a canopy over Buddha to shelter him from the elements during the period preceding enlightenment and to celebrate Buddha's victory over the demon-temper Mara.

The first of the three great legendary Chinese emperors, Fu-hsi, who was fully informed in all mysteries of heaven and earth and gave to man the knowledge of divination, had for the upper part of his body the shape of a man and for the lower part that of a serpent. He led his people out of a cave (darkness), taught them how to build, hunt, and cook, established marriage laws, divided the populace into clans, and gave each clan a name. While resting on the banks of a river trying to combine the characters of a bird's footprint into script, a dragonhorse, or unicorn, rose from the stream. On its back were signs which the emperor formed into the pa kua (eight diagrams), from which evolved the written Chinese language.

In a Maori legend, a serpent appeared to sever heaven from earth, which were in continual copulation and suffocated all who were born. The Melanesian genius which pulled dry land up from the bottom of the ocean and gave fire to mortals that huddled on it, had a snake shape. In other Pacific Island myths this creature was a destroyer of primordial land and growth.

Among American Indians, a wizard provides snake bravery to warriors. Ciuateotl, Aztec snake-woman, was the divine mother whose roaring voice betokened war. Her priests wore phallic emblems to induce her to provide good crops. Cherokees worshipped a mighty horned-serpent, the Uktena. And in a legend, the daughter of the sun was placed in the wooden box Gunesuni to preserve her body after death from a venomous snake. The Guatemalan Gucumatz was a winged serpent. He had three manifestations: lightning flash, lightning bolt, and thunder, viz; creator, dominator, fertilizer. He lived alone in darkness and stillness. Another of his names, Hurakan, was adopted into English as hurricane.

Probably no form has been as widely used in symbolism. It is the most ancient of phallic totem beasts. Primitive peoples revered it as the reimbodiment of deceased mortals. It has been assigned to mother goddesses, earth, river, sea, rainbow and underworld deities as well as to rain-withholding clouds. It is a weather controller in all tree-worshiping cultures. In desolate lands it symbolizes poverty, toil, and want. From the manner in which it sheds its skin, it stands for resurrection.

It is that which creeps and does not rise, hence lacks the ability to aspire. Fortunes good and bad are assigned to it; it stands for prophecy, prudence, redemption, renewal, salvation, wisdom, cunning, deceit, false appearance, jealousy, lasciviousness, obstruction, and treachery. It is an emblem of medicine and witchcraft, and often figured on amulets. Snake charmers are respected for their grace, skill, and powers of exorcism in many parts of the world.

Although one of four, this is the stellar snake par excellence. The outline undoubtedly was defined in ancient times and throughout the ages it had been depicted with the neighboring Ophiuchus. Once its stars were catalogued with those of Ophiuchus. Often shown as grasped by the hands of the giant, a delineation that may be intended to indicate the struggle between light or fertility (the hero) and darkness or withholder of fruitfulness (the serpent-villain); or it may be intended to show the affinity between the hero and serpent as healers. When an earth power, the serpent's role was often that of healer or fecundater. The constant battle between the sky and the underworld, between light and darkness, summer and winter, fertility and drought, good and evil, that is the forces that control the world's destiny, have since earliest times been dramatized with an eagle or other great bird in the role of benevolent hero and a serpent or dragon in the role of villain. This drama was transported to the skies with the constellations Aquila and Serpens as the cast.

Additional designations: The

Serpent, occasionally split into
Serpens Caput (Serpent's Head)
and Serpens Cauda (Serpent's
Tail), on either side of the
Serpent-holder Ophiuchus.

Arabic: Al Hayyah (The
Snake), which corroded into
Alhafa. The influence for this
title was Hellenic. Early Arabs
called it Al Raudah (The Pasture).
A part, with stars of Hercules,
was known as Nasak Shamiyy
(Northern Boundary), and with
stars of Ophiuchus, a part
was known as Nasak Yamaniyy
(Southern Boundary, i.e. of the
Pasture) and fenced in sheep were
indicated by stars now known as
the Club of Hercules. The sheep
were guarded by the Shepherd
and his Dog, alpha stars of
Ophiuchus and Hercules.

Euphratean: Nu-tsir-da
(Image of the Serpent), which
title was shared with Ophiuchus,
and by the Ophites, a 2nd century
gnostic Christian sect, worshipped
as a representative of divinity.

French: le Serpent.

German: die Schlange (The
Snake).

Greeks knew it as both a
Serpent and Eel.

Italian: il Serpente.

Latin and low Latin:
Anguilla, (Eel); Anguis (Snake);
Coluber (Serpent); Draco
Lesbius and Tiberinus; Lucidus
Anguis; Serpens Hercules;
Lernaeus (Lernaean Hydra, a
nine-headed drought dragon that
hid in the swamps of Lerna and
was slain by Heracles);
Sagarinus   (perhaps the Sagarius
river in Asia Minor). Serpent
of Aesculapius (Asclepius),

Cacus (Caecius, or Caesius),
Glaucus, Laocoon, and of
Ophiuchus.

A title from corrupted Latin
and Arabic is Serpens Alangue.

It crosses the celestial
equator, circling around Ophiuchus in both the northern and
southern skies. It also extends
into the Milky Way in both
skies. Although a long constellation it has few bright stars,
its lucida being Unuk al Hay.
It reaches the meridian about
July 21.

SEXTANS (THE SEXTANT).
This is a modern constellation
designed from twelve unclaimed
stars between Leo and Hydra in
the southern sky close to the
celestial equator. Johannes
Hevelius named it in honor of
the sextant he used successfully
in taking stellar measurements
at Danzig from 1658 to 1679.
When his house and the observatory it contained were demolished
by fire in 1679, or as he noted,
when Vulcan, the Roman fire-
god, overcame Urania, Greek
muse of astronomy, the instruments he had constructed
were destroyed. From Hevelius's
comments came such titles as
Sextans Uraniae, Urania's
Sextant.

Bible commentators saw the
Sudarium Veronicae, or Saint
Veronica's Sacred Handkerchief,
in these stars.

Without named stars, it culminates about April 8.

SOLARIUM. Little is known
about this figure. It appears on
some 19th century maps in the
southern sky between Dorado
and Hydrus as Solarium, or the

Sun-dial, but astronomers of the present day ignore it, and its stars probably have been combined with those of neighboring constellations.

TARANDUS VEL RANGIFER (THE REINDEER). In 1736, when Pierre Charles Lemonnier was 21 years of age, he assisted in measuring a degree of the meridian within the Polar circle in Lapland. In memory of this trip he formed a small asterism from unused stars in the northern sky located between Cassiopeia and Camelopardalis, and named it Renne, after the animal he had seen in the north. Later the name appeared as above and on German lists appeared as Rennthier. It had appeared rarely on maps and no longer is mentioned.

TAURUS (THE BULL). In view of the fact that from about 4,000 B.C. to 1,700 B.C., the golden age of ancient astronomy, this constellation marked the vernal equinox, the day of triumph for summer in the never-ending combat with winter, a conflict which is the underlying theme of most legends, this may have been the first asterism invented. On old zodiacs the Bull, leader of celestial hosts, indicated the year's beginning and stood for humid or passive power, while the Lion symbolized the active generative power; later the Bull symbolized the sky and fecundating sun, the supreme deity in male aspect of creator. A generative force, a bull was eaten at sacrificial feasts to give men strength.

Enlil, the bull whose goring horns ploughed the great furrow of the skies, the zodiac, who ushered in the spring, kept the cycle of the seasons revolving, and brought each season in turn to earth, was worshipped in Sumer as a god of light and fertility as well as one who battled to maintain the order he had established. Man, who was molded by Enlil, thus was conceived in this sign. Enlil's Assyro-Babylonian counterpart, Ninib, the morning and spring sun, guardian of agriculture, was furiously hostile toward fully earth-bound creatures. Another Assyrian god, Asshur, creator-preserver-destroyer, self-power or world soul, monarch of the empyrean, had four faces, those of a bull (or ox), eagle, lion, and man, to signify he was lord of the four cardinal points which constrolled the seasons. At an appeal from Ishtar, goddess of love, Anu, the high one or day sky, created a bull, Gudanna, to destroy Gilgamesh, the sun-hero, who had repulsed her advances. The intense heat of Gudanna (Taurus), although he pulled the plough stars (Triangulum), caused seven years of drought. Gilgamesh stood by patiently all those years and watched the monster destroy the land, but finally emasculated him. A class of spirits called lamassu or lamatsu were depicted as human-headed winged-bulls. With tempests or scorching heat they destroyed people but protected palaces, and their statues usually flanked entrances to state buildings. These stars are associated not only with all these animals but with the second month of the Assyrian year, A-aru, Directing Bull and conqueror of the Centaur, our April-May.

Apis, Egyptian earthly counterpart of the celestial Bull, was begotten by a ray of generative light flowing from the moon. His birth, always presumed to characterize resurrection, was celebrated with public rejoicings, and women, in an act of sympathetic magic to assure fruitfulness, exposed their sexual parts to the sacred animal, into which the soul of Bacis, Hapi, Mnevis, Osiris, or Ptah migrated. Any Apis Bull that had lived for 25 years was drowned in the temple's sacred cistern, and priests wailed he had committed suicide when he had discovered a lack of virility would make it impossible for him to spermatize the land. Whether he died of natural causes or was slain, everyone believed the godhead had passed from his body. He was buried with pomp in a mausoleum which stood at the end of a long avenue flanked on both sides by guardian stone lions. The mausoleum itself consisted of a vast arched gallery cut into rock. Each recess held a granite sarcophagus, the coffin of one of the animals, next to whom was laid a princess to serve as his bride in the afterworld. This custom is interpreted as a symbolic marriage to assure fertility.

Disconsolate believers shaved their hair off and remained in mourning until a new Apis was born. The markings that made the Bull recognizable were a white triangle on the forehead of a black beast, the outline of an eagle on its back, a circular lump, in the shape of a scarabaeus, under its tongue, and double hairs in his tail. Preferably, a fiery light should be seen hovering over his mother's head just before his birth, but this last proof of the moon's generative light was not absolutely necessary. The black of the Bull symbolized night (eternity), the white symbolized day (time), the eagle and scarabaeus were badges of the sun. That a true Apis might absorb the deity soul, he was held for four months in a building facing east and fed solely on milk and honey. At the New Moon, after the allotted time, a priest bowed before him and for the first time addressed him as a god. He was then placed on a handsomely decorated barge and taken to his temple, which had a court in which he might exercise, at Memphis, the original seat of his worship. Pilgrims came from all parts of the land. They consulted him by offerings of food. His response to a question was favorable or unfavorable according to whether he ate the offering. As a result, not only he, but the priests responsible for his wellbeing lived on the fat of the land. Every year, his birthday, a date fixed officially and corresponding to the expected rising of the Nile, was celebrated with gifts, sacrifices, and processionals. A golden cup was tossed into the river to bribe the life-giving waters, upon which Egypt depended, to flow over the thirsty land. These ceremonies were of further importance from the belief that human life was created when the sun was among the stars of the celestial Bull.

Greeks called the Egyptian Bull Serapis (Osiris-Apis or Osiris-Hapi) and believed that in it the souls of the two gods were united after death. In their own mythology, the bull was sacred in several forms. He was the Cretan Minotaur, literally Bull of Minos, a monster with the body of a man and the head of a bull or vice versa. A deity of darkness, death, and winter, he was the son of Pasiphae, the moon goddess, wife of Minos, by her lover, the sea-god Poseidon. When Poseidon presented the blood-thirsty beast to the Cretan king Minos, he dared not offend a deity by refusing to accept a gift. For safety he placed it in a labyrinth (maze of stars) and fed it on the flesh of seven maidens and seven youths, extracted every nine years as a tribute from Aegeus, king of Athens, for the slaying of his son Androgeos, Cretan prince of light. Ariadne, daughter of Minos, deceived her father, and revealed to Theseus, son of Aegeus and one of the youths sent for the sacrifice, how to slay the Minotaur and find his way out of the labyrinth. In explanation: Ariadne, the dawn, provided Theseus, the sun, with the secret of escape from the labyrinth of night. The devouring bull appears to have been derived from Moloch, to whom humans were sacrficed.

In some accounts both the Minotaur and Minos were offsprings of Europa and Zeus. Europa, daughter of Agenor, a fire deity and Phoenician king whose capital was Tyre, and of Telephassa, the far-reaching lunar rays, was gathering crocuses along a sea-shore when she came upon a handsome white bull. The animal seemed tame and playful and she stopped to pet it, whereupon the bull came down on his fore knees before her. The grace of his curtsy touched her heart, and she climbed upon his back. No sooner had she done so than the bull, who was Zeus in disguise, dashed into the sea and carried her to Crete. The heartbroken Agenor sent his sons to search for his abducted daughter. Although Telephassa accompanied the pursuers to provide them with light, for Zeus had entered a road that led into the dark reaches of the other world, and they discovered evidence of her here and there, they never again saw her face to face. After bearing Zeus several sons, Europa became the wife of the Cretan king. Europa was the dawn, personification of morning splendor, supported across the firmament throughout the day and night by the god of heaven to the east, where she is seen again for a few moments each day in all her radiant beauty. Her name, said to mean she-of-the-broad-face, is related to the Vedic Uruasi, wide-spreading, and she has become the female figure symbolic of Europe.

The bull in legend frequently is the recipient of an external soul. A white bull, such as were the forms of Osiris and Zeus, denotes cosmic energy (white) and creative force (bull). In a poem Virgil honors the Europa Bull:

When with his golden hornes
    bright Taurus opes,
The yeare; and downward the
    crosse Dog-starre stoopes.

Although these lines were written as late as the 1st century B.C., he still addresses the Bull as opener of the year. Taurus was held dear by the Romans as a favorable sign, a bringer of good fortune, whence they ornamented the pages of their books with a bull.

This Bull also is said to be one of the two with brazen feet

tamed by Jason, who then
directed the Argonautic expedition through the sign.

In the Old Testament the
emblem of a chief or prince is a
bull, one of the principal forms
by which the sun deity of early
Israelites was worshipped. It
typified an invader, a fierce foe
(scorching sun) which trampled
underfoot and from which no
one might escape. A bull-
shaped Prince of Death is mentioned. In very early Semitic
myths, the bull was the mount
or steed of the roaring rain and
thunder god; whereas the steed
of the earth-goddess was a lion,
and that of the sun-god a horse.
Medieval biblical scholars assign
it to the first animal that Adam
offered in burnt sacrifice; to
later victims in the Jewish Temple; to the tribes of Ephraim,
whose sacred animal was a wild
bull; of Issacher, whose animal,
an ass, crouched beneath its
burden and shared the toil of the
ox(or bull); or of Manasseh,
Joseph's eldest son, who was
deprived of his birthright by E-
phraim, the second son. Manasseh's sacred animal was the unicorn. Others said it appeared on
the banners of Simeon and Levi
jointly, from Jacob's death-bed
remark that they, "houghed an
ox."

In the Christian school, the
constellation was the Ox that
stood with the Ass in the
manger; Joseph the Patriarch,
or Saint Andrew.

Celtic druids esteemed the
Bull as the embodiment of spring,
herald of the New Year and
revivification of nature. Bonfires
were lighted, burnt offerings were
made to earth and fertility gods
when the sun hovered around the
Pleiades. The old Morris
Dance was a remnant of this
festival, and survives in the
May Day ceremonies. Tors,
sacred hills, may have derived
their name from Taurus and been
used for rituals of adoration of
the Bull. Bull-cakes served at
the great Tauric feasts became
the hot-cross buns of Christians. Actually, these cakes
trace back to Egyptians and
Phoenicians.

In the Taghairm ceremony
in the Scottish Highlands a seer
was wrapped in a bull's skin
and left by a running stream all
night to dream or meditate. Sir
Walter Scott refers to this
observance in Canto IV of Lady
of the Lake:

> Last eventide
> Brian an augury hath tried...
> The Taghairm called, by
>   which afar
> Our sires foresaw the events
>   of war.
> Duncraggan's milk-white bull
>   they slew....

Throughout the ages priests
and gods have been clad in the
skins of animals from which
protection and magical powers
supposedly were derived; also
they seemingly received inspiration or revelations while in certain skin coverings. The belief
in the magic exercised by
sacred clothing gave origin to
priestly robes.

A faith survives among the
credulous in certain parts of
Scotland that the Candlemas
Bull rises in the gloaming on
New Year's eve and crosses
heaven; this he does if you
locate the Bull in Taurus's rising stars. In the city of York,
which once was the Roman town

of Eboracum, the remains of a temple dedicated to Serapis are still to be seen.

The Brown Bull and the White Horned Bull in Irish legend were reincarnations of deities. Friuch, swineherd of Bodb, a corn or oak god and fairy king of Munster who lived in a magnificent underground palace and owned all the fertility held in dark recesses within the earth, due to gossip, became the mortal enemy of Rucht, swineherd of Ochall Ochne, who was lord of fertility above the ground. Able to change his shape at will and, to successfully carry on his fight, Friuch became a raven, wolf, trout, demon, stag, water-beast, and finally a worm, which was swallowed by a cow. The cow, as a result, bore the Donn or Brown Bull, and the bull in time became the possession of Daire of Cualgne. Like Friuch, Rucht changed his shape and when he became a worm he was swallowed by a kine, which gave birth to Findbennach, the White Bull, which joined the herds of King Ailill. Queen Medb, jealous of her husband, determined to obtain the Brown Bull owned by Daire, which was able to carry 150 children on its back as well as protect a hundred warriors, by its shelter, from hot or cold. Despite her evil character, on the occasion that Medb sent her army against Daire and his lord Conchobar, king of Ulster, Ailill came to his wife's aid. In the course of the war the Brown Bull killed its rival the White Bull; then, going mad with pride, dashed out its brains against a rock. Each of these two Bulls was succeeded by its calf. The war of the bulls is interpreted to be a con-

flict of the forces of light or warmth (overworld) with darkness or cold (underworld) for the wealth of fertility. All changes assumed are seasonal, Friuch and Rucht adapting themselves to the months. The march of time endures through the calves.

Kuyuta, the Moslem Bull, supports earth. He stands in the cosmic ocean on the fabulous fish Bahamut which carried the rock which braces the angel who holds earth steady. Siberians and Finno-Ugrians have an identical bull; when his horn breaks the world will come to an end.

In India, the lunar race of kings supposedly came into being under the influences of this sign, and in Indo-Iranian tradition the bull is a guise of a rain and storm deity, an allusion to the violence of storms and to the fertility which water brings to the world. Mithraic sculptures depict the solar and corn god slaying a wild death-dealing (harvest) bull; the sacred bull (or ox) had to be sacrificed to Mithra before the sun might rise again. Death in autumn assured resurrection in spring, and, as in the Marduk-Tiamat counteraction, the divisions of the year fell into place. This is the principle underlying the Japanese cosmic bull that broke the egg of chaos and established order in the universe.

Anciently the Chinese knew the constellation as the White Tiger, an aspect of the god of wealth; later they knew it as the Golden Ox. The ox often appears in mythology as the counterpart of the heavenly bull owing to its service in the cultivation of the ground, and, in South America in the Amazon country, the constellation was worshipped as this animal. However, in Mexico and other parts of Central America, the asterism was a Stag or horned Rabbit. The Rabbit had acquired the horns of the Stag, which often shared his adventures as a companion or partner. Among the Cherokees, Great Rabbit foretells the coming of the Pleiades to warn of the approach of a deluge (rainy season).

The unicorn may have evolved from the Taurus Bull. Along the Euphrates, where the four great beasts symbolized the major points of the compass and the seasons, the bull of the east and spring and the lion of the south and summer were often carved together, two giant animals on their hind legs, face to face in a tussle for the solar ball. The moment the sun passed from one to the other the loser was doomed to die. The scufflers were in profile and only one horn of the bull was to be seen. This scene was copied over and over, chiseled on walls, archways, tablets, facades, and in time the strange one-horned animal was given an identity of its own unrelated to that of the celestial bull. Into this day the lion and the unicorn are drawn together, their seasonal differences forgotten, and so they appear in the British royal coat-of-arms.

Configurations. On modern sky maps the Bull manifests the animal that Orion hunts through the heavens. To charge down on the Hunter, it must back away all across the sky. Most frequently depicted as a massive half-humped figure, a head, broad shoulders and star-tipped butting horns, so long they are out of proportion to his body. The half figure represents the bull climbing out of the sea, his flanks still immersed in waves. Almost all Euphratean figurings show him crouched, some with a lion's head. In memory of his aspect in Assyrian sculpture, the Bull on various works is winged. In rare illustrations he has a bird on his back, perhaps to indicate the Pleiades above him to the northwest, which are known as doves. The most ancient hieorglyph of Taurus 𐦜 suggests the face and horns of a bull. The Greek letter tau (𝛕) and the English T derived from this symbol in the following steps 𐦜 ૪ 𝛕 𝛕 T. The Masonic tau cross ⊥⊤ is symbolic of the vernal equinox of immortality. On zodiac charts, the pictorial sign is ♉ .

Taurus is from the Greek, which seems to trace back to the Egyptian root tau, meaning bull or cow. In Arabic, Coptic, Hebrew, and Syriac the word for bull also means coming or who cometh.

Additional designations: Bull of Light; The Bust, because he is a half figure; Crouching Taurus; Lame Taurus; Marduk; Striving Taurus; Taurus on Bended Knees.

Accadian: Gut-an-na (Heavenly Bull), mentioned in connection with rain, a reminder of the rainy Hyades; Te Te, a reference to its two clusters, the Hyades and Pleiades.

Anglo-Saxon: Fearr.

Arabian: Al Hatt, adopted from the Latin Sectio Tauri; Al Thaur (The Bull), which contracted into Altauro, Altor, Ataur, El Taur, Taur, Tur. Al Daika (Growing Small) for the relatively vacant space in the direction of the Pleiades, from its rapid setting. Another name for the space is Kalb al Daraban (Dog of Aldebaran). It was feared as a place of evil omen.

Babylonian: Alaparos, 2nd mythical antediluvian king; Shur, whose stars marked four ecliptic constellations.

Chinese: Kin Neu (Golden Ox); Ta Leang (Great Bridge).

Egyptian: Apis (the Bull); Hapi (Fertilizer), personification of the river Nile; Isis, sister-wife of Osiris; Osiris.

English, Middle: Whyte Bole.

French: l'Taureau.

German: der Stier..

Hindu: Taouri, a transliteration of Taurus, which degenerated into Tambiru. Varaha Mihira, boar incarnation of Vishnu, assumed to deliver the earth from the power of Hiranyaksha, who had carried it to the ocean's depths. After a thousand year battle, Varaha killed the demon, brought earth back to the surface, and supported it on a tusk. Earthquakes are caused when Varaha shifts his burden from one tusk to another. Vrisha, Vrishan, or Vrouchaban, a divine mediator and light deity, a name also associated with the planet Jupiter.

Italian: il Toro.

Judaean: A or aleph, coincidentally crudely resembling a bull's face and horns. R'em, now translated Unicorn, but probably more correctly Wild Ox. Shor.

Latin and Low Latin: Agenoreus, a reference to Europa's father; Amasius Pasiphaes (Lover of Pasiphae); Bos (Ox); Bubulcus or Bubulum Caput (Peasant Head or Driver of Oxen), a title more correct for Bootes, to which it also is applied; Chironis Filia (Chiron's Daughter); Cornus (Horns). Domus Veneris nocturna, Gaudium Veneris, Veneris Sidus, inasmuch as it was one of the mansions of Venus. Europae. Inachis or Juvenca Inachia, from Inachus, father of Io. Io, the wanderer, probably a sex confusion as well as of the Io and Europa legends, Io being an object of Zeus's affections whom the jealous Hera turned into a cow. Portitor or Proditor, the portage of Europa. Princeps armenti (Leader of the Herd); Sectio Tauri (Section of Taurus); Tyrius (of Tyre).

Persian: Gau, Ghav, Tora.

Singalese: Urusaba.

South American Amazon Indians: Tapura Rayoaba (Jaw of an Ox).

Syriac: Taura.

Tamil: Rishabam (Sage).

Turkish: Ughuz.

Astrologically on the whole

it is unfortunate, but to the
weatherwise, thunder, when
the sun is here brings a plentiful
supply of victuals.

Located in the northern sky
between Auriga and Orion, both
of which are close to it. In
the evening sky it is visible from
September until May, and can
be seen at culmination about
January 14. Its bright stars
are: alpha, Aldebaran; beta,
El Nath, which touches the constellation Auriga; gamma,
Hyadum I; zeta, Shurnarkabti-
sha-shutu. The Hyades and
Pleiades are noted clusters within the constellation.

TAURUS PONIATOVSKII.
Composed of uniformed stars of
Ophiuchus in 1777 to honor
Stanislaus Poniatowskii, king of
Poland. Some of the stars form
the letter V, and a fancied
resemblance to the horns of the
celestial Bull or to the Hyades
inspired another Taurus. An
asterism called River Tigris contained most of these stars, but
that constellation lost recognition
in 1679. Taurus Poniatovskii no
longer appears on star maps; its
component parts have been added
to Ophiuchus.

Additional designations:
Poniatowski's Bull; Royal Bull;
Taurus Regalis.

Chinese: Tsung Ting or
Tsung Jin (a Relative).

French: Taureau Royal.

German: Poln Stier (Polish
Star); Poniatowsky's Stier.

Italian: Toro di Poniatowski.

Its location was between the
shoulders of Ophiuchus and the

Eagle, a group of stars that
comes to the meridian about
August 10.

TELESCOPIUM (THE TELE-
SCOPE). Formed in the 18th
century in the southern sky along
the Rim of the Milky Way. Its
irregular shape encroaches on
Sagittarius, Pavo and Corona
Australis.

Additional designations:
Astronomische Fernrohr; Tubus
Astronomicus.

Its alpha star is known to the
Chinese as We (Danger); its
gamma star as Chuen Shwo, a
mythical figure.

Culmination is about August
24.

TELESCOPIUM HERSCHELII.
This asterism, which has disappeared from sky atlases, was
formed in 1781 in honor of Sir
William Herschel. It lay between Lynx and Gemini.

TRIANGULUM (THE TRIANGLE).
Curiously enough, one astronomer
of the 17th century claimed this
constellation had been invented
merely that the head of Aries
might be more readily located. It
is an old figuration and probably
was noticed more in antiquity
than now. To Assyro-Babylonians
these were plough stars, drawn
by the bull Gudanna (Taurus).
In a Greek myth, Demeter begged
Zeus to reproduce the triangle
formed by three Sicilian promon-
tories, Lilybaeum, Pelorus, and
Pachynus, where Greek colonists
had settled and identified with
the Thrinakia, mentioned in the
Odyssey as the pasture ground
of the Oxen-of-the-Sun, and in
English poetry called Mela's
Holy Ox-land. In modern times

this section of the world has become the site of the noted Palermo Observatory. Ancient titles for Sicily, Sicilia, Trinacria, Triquetra, have been applied to this group. From its resemblance to the Greek letter Delta, a name also applied to it, it has been associated with the delta of the river Nile, and this led Romans to call it Aegyptus (Egypt); Nili Domum (Home of the Nile); Nili Donum (Gift of the Nile).

Biblical scholars of the middle ages claimed these stars showed the Mitre of Saint Peter and likened it to the Trinity.

Additional designations: Northern Triangle; River's Gift; The Triangle; Triangulus Major.

Arabic: Al Muthallah, a translation of Triangulum, which has come back into western usage as Almutaleh, Almutallath, Almutlato, Mutlat, Mutlathum, Mutlaton.

English and French: Triangle.

German: Dreieck.

Italian: Triangolo.

Jewish: Shalish, a triangular shaped musical instrument or one with three cords mentioned in the Bible. This same figure also has been assigned to three bright stars of Aries.

Latin and Low Latin: Caput Trinaguli (Head Triangle); Deltoton or Deltotum (of Delta Shape); Orbis terrarum tripertitus, to represent the three known parts of the earth, Europe, Asia, and Africa. Triangulus Septentrionalis, to distinguish it from Triangulus Australe; Tricuspis

(Three-pointed); Trigon, Trigonum, Trigonus, Triplicitas, Triquetrum (Trinal Aspect, i.e. of astrology).

It lies in the northern sky, south of Andromeda, north of Aries, and culminates about December 7. None of its stars are very bright.

TRIANGULUM AUSTRALE (THE SOUTHERN TRIANGLE). This constellation first appeared on maps in 1603, but its formation is said to have taken place a century earlier.

In Biblical lore it was The Three Patriarchs, Abraham, Isaac, and Jacob, from its three prominent stars. Arabs called it Almutabet alengubi, which carries the same meaning as the Latin title. The Chinese equivalent of the title is San Kio Hung.

It lies in the southern sky, south of Norma and Ara, between the tail of Pavo and Circinus, and comes to the meridian about July 7.

TRIANGULUM MINOR. Formed from three small stars in the northern sky just south of Triangulum in the 17th century. Astronomers have since ceased to acknowledge the constellation. It also appeared as Triangula.

TUCANA (THE TOUCAN). Named to honor a Brazilian bird discovered in the middle of the 16th century, which had become a symbol of noisy chatter. This avian word may be from ti (nose) and cang (bone). Seventeenth Century English called it Brasilian Pye, which became geographically incorrect in Pica Indica. The name also has been

written Toucan, Toucana, Touch-
an. Other designations have been
American Gans (American Goose);
Anser Americanus. Chinese translated the word given to them by
the Jesuits as Neaou Chuy
(Beak Bird), quite fitting to one
that is almost all beak.

The constellation lies south
of Phoenix and Grus, bordering
the south polar Octans, and
reaches the meridian on November 1.

TURDUS SOLITARIUS (THE
SOLITARY THRUSH). Formed
in 1776 from faint stars above
the tail-tip of Hydra. The title
is said to be derived from that
of the Solitaire, a bird formerly
peculiar to the tiny island
Rodriguez in the Indian Ocean.
The generic term Turdus seems
to be incorrect, for the bird
was not a thrush but a sort of
flightless pigeon, akin to the
dodos, larger and taller than a
turkey. The bird and the constellation are both extinct.

Other names by which the
stars were known were:
Noctua (Night Owl), and the
German Drossel (Thrush) and
Einsiedler (hermit).

URSA MAJOR (THE GREATER
BEAR). The best known of all
stellar formations, and invariably
the first group recognized by
amateur astronomers. As it
strides westward, with Boötes
and his dogs in perpetual pursuit,
it always is either partly or
wholly above the horizon in
latitudes north of New York City.
The Bear's tail like an enormous
clockhand swings around the pole
every twelve hours, and if observed at the same hour every
night in the year, reveals seasons
as well as hours. Early in the

evening the tail points north in
winter, east in spring, south in
summer, west in autumn. If
sunlight did not blot it out, it
might be seen by day as well
as by night.

Ursa Major probably is the
cluster known to Sumerians as
Margidda, the Rope of Heaven
or the Wagon driven by Ninlil,
virgin sister-wife of Enlil, lord
of the upper world. When it
originally was conceived to be a
bear is lost in antiquity. Undoubtedly the hardiness of a
creature that dared to venture
into solitude and cold had something to do with the inspiration.
In one early account of unknown
origin this Bear by metamorpho-
sis gave birth to bears on earth;
in another, two bears were slain
by a mighty huntsman. Their skins
were so magnificent they were
stretched with jeweled nails
across the highest arch of the
sky vault. The manner in which
it circles the pole has been suggestive of many fanciful ideas: a
bear and her young feeding in
the meadows around the pole; a
beast perpetually driven across
snow by a hunter; a bride or
maiden robber; a chariot on a
never-ending road; dancers who
move in time to the music of the
spheres; a herd driven by its
keeper (Arcturus); a mother
prowling through the dark for
her lost children (stars that set
and so become invisible); a
mighty wanderer; a plough turning in a field; the rope that holds
all things in the heavens together;
the scepter with which the gods
rule mortals; the watcher who
guards the universe; or, with
Ursa Minor, two Bears that
restlessly prowl around their
dens (North Pole or Corona
Borealis). Its seven principal
stars linked together form the

familiar figure known as the Big Dipper.

The Egyptian Set, hateful deity of darkness and drought, appeared in these evil stars. The desert wind which brought with it a violent criminal wave came from his breath as he revolved around the pole. Of envious disposition, he yearly destroyed his brother Osiris (light and growth) and in turn was mutilated by Horus (spring sun), but never completely destroyed. Set's wife Ta-urt was the Hippopotamus shown by an adjoining cluster, which now is a part of Draco. Egyptians also applied Set as a collective term to all circumpolar asterisms, because always visible they paradoxically were believed to typify darkness. When Egypt, which once had swayed Greek thought, fell under the influence of the Hellenes, the ever-present light of these stars was attributed to the sun and they became the Car of Osiris. Stars have at times been thought of as particles chipped off from the sun. These luminaries also seem to have been known as a bear, boat, ox-leg, or thigh. In very early times they were part of a larger group known as Kapi, an Egyptian ape-god.

Among early Greeks, until it lost prestige to the Pole Star, Ursa Major, being so conspicuous and so nearly due north, was the mariner's guide as well as friendly companion during the lonely hours while on night watch. Homer, in his description of Odysseus on his journey homeward after leaving the island of the fascinating Calypso, relates how the hero used this constellation to keep sailing due east:

.... nor did sleep fall upon his eyelids, as he viewed the Pleiades and Boötes, that setteth late, and the Bear, which they likewise call the Wain, which turneth ever in one place, and keepeth watch upon Orion, and alone hath no part in the baths of Ocean. This star, Calypso, the fair goddess, bade him keep ever on the left as he traversed the deep.

Greek philosophers who tried to solve the workings of the universe concluded that Ursa Major was a mammoth whirlpool whose spinning whipped the seasons into rotation and at times sent down wind and rain. The Hellenes associated these stars with innumerable narratives, the most often told being that of Callisto, the daughter of Lycaon, king of Arcadia. An attendant in the train of the virgin-goddess Artemis, Calisto was forbidden to marry, so Zeus in the form of the huntress-goddess caressed the priestess, and Callisto became the mother of Arcas. In jealous fury, Hera turned Callisto into a bear. Arcas, while roaming in the woods, came upon the bear's trail. He aimed his arrow, when Zeus, to prevent the crime of matricide, transformed his son into a bear and transported these two he loved into the field of heaven. There they appeared more beautiful than they had on earth, and nightly, while reposing on his downy couch of clouds that hovered over Mount Olympus, he watched their rhythmic dance around the pole. Hera was further enraged. In her anger she went to her brother Poseidon and asked him to close his doors to this hateful pair, and never permit them to enter his kingdom of the sea, either to drink, rest, or bathe. For hundreds of years neither was permitted near the ocean. Perhaps Poseidon has relented slightly, for in recent times the tail of Callisto sometimes dips into the water as she whirls in space, but Arcas still goes around without rest or refreshment after his frolic.

Likewise these stars are said to be the two Cretan bears, Helice and Melissa, who nursed the infant Zeus and were raised to heaven as the Bear constellations for their devotion to their charge. Among the many Greek tales is that of Ixion, king of Lapithae in Thessaly, who was invited by Zeus to a banquet. The mortal made love to Hera, and to protect his wife Zeus substituted a cloud that looked like her, and by this cloud Ixion became the father of the Centaurs. For his impudence, Zeus ordered Hermes to bind Ixion to an eternally revolving four-spoke wheel. In some elucidations, Ixion was bound to the sun, which had spokes that sent rays in four directions. In others the wheel was the circling course of this constellation, and Ixion, whose name is akin to axis, was said to be identical with Akshivan, the Hindu driver of Aksha (the Axle). The Centaurs typified vapours which expand from a cloud. In his attempt to reach Hera, the highest point in the heavens, Ixion was bound to fail.

In legendary history, Nauplius, son of Poseidon by the river goddess Amymone and founder of the seaport Nauplia, was a famous navigator. To find his way at night he designed this constellation.

The Arthurian myths place the king's residence here, the distinct ark made by the encircling handle being the Round Table where he dined with his noble companions and instituted the first known military order of knighthood. One source of his name is given as two Welsh words, Arth, Bear, and Uthyr, Wonderful. Some of his followers actually claimed that he was an incarnation of the constellation's spirit. In one story told about him, long before he thought of becoming king he fell asleep close by the sea. A spirit came to him while he slept and led him far up into the north where the stars of the Bear were bright. There he found knights of heaven seated at a circular table. The knights, who were as radiant as perfect gems, counseled him to take the name Arthur, to pattern his life according to the rules of heaven, and return to earth to become king and in like manner rule and lead his people. So it was that he took the name Arthur, gathered around him men modeled after those he had met in heaven, gained the throne, and became known as the wisest and bravest of all men. Instead of dying, Arthur simply ascended to his stars to await the day his country would need and call upon him to return and save her once again. The stars thereafter were familiarly called Arthur's Chariot or Wain. From a similar legend about Charlemagne was derived the name Charles' Wain.

In another theory, the English, Germans, and others accounted for the long stellar appendage on the heavenly counterpart of an almost tailless animal by saying that its captor, fearful of the beast's teeth, held fast to the small projection. The bear being heavy and the distance to heaven being great, the tail stretched as the animal was drawn upward. A similar explanation applies to Ursa Minor's tail. Both Bears are still to be found on sign-boards of British inns, and have been emblazoned on the coat of arms of Antwerp, Groningen, and other European cities.

The Seven Sleepers is a world-wide theme related to sorrow or disaster (the death of one season when another comes into being). Epimenides was a Greek sleeper. A legendary Cretan poet and philosopher, he fell asleep in a cave. Fifty-seven years later he awakened to find his soul freed from the burdens of flesh and endowed with miraculous wisdom, where-upon he purified Athens from the plague. He typifies the sun slumbering during the long spell of winter. In Norse legend the sleepers are the sons of Mimer and sleep in a cave in the realm of darkness next to a golden treasure (fertility underground). Anyone who attempts to steal the treasure withers. The slumberers await the blast of the horn at Ragnarok, when they will awake and take part in the battle. If rain falls on their day it will fall for seven weeks there-after, the source of weather saints. Christians too, tell of sleepers. Seven youths of Ephesus fled the Decian persecutions in 250 A.D. and hid in a cave. After a lapse of two or three centuries they awoke faithful to Christianity. This fable may have arisen from a mis-apprehension of "They fell asleep in the Lord," i.e. died. The Koran sleepers were guarded by the dog Katmir, who aroused them to proclaim the coming of

Mahomet. The sleepers may be identified as the seven bright stars that sleep during the day. In mythology day is likened to spring or summer, the season when nature is awake.

Christians also claimed the stars to be the Ship of Saint Peter or the heavenly aspect of the archangel Michael. Few stars are named in the Old Testament; most of these few appear in the Book of Job. One, a constellation called Mezarim, seems to indicate either the Great Bear or both Bears. The clues, which are scarce, are discussed in our chapter Host of Heaven.

In Finnish legend Otava is the bear-god of the constellation and Otso, the bear, was born on his shoulders. Otso was given no teeth or claws until he pledged not to commit bloody deeds or violence. Because he did not keep his word he may be hunted. In another legend, the pole stars, especially Polaris, are young and beautiful maidens, highly skilled in spinning and weaving. This interpretation probably reflects a fancied resemblance of their rays to that of a web.

Arabian nomads saw in these stars the tracks of their Ghazal (Gazelle), which fled when the Lion (Leo Minor) swung his tail. In a fable, the children or mourners of Al Naash, the war-rior who had been slain by Al Jadi (Pole-star), nightly sur-round the murderer to make sure he does not escape. One of the daughters (Mizar) holds her newborn infant (Alcor) in her arms, while Suhail (Sirius) slowly struggles up from the south to aid them. The dreaded

northeast wind Naashi is believed
to rise from this constellation.
The title Bier or the idea of a
funeral procession is attributed to
the slow and solemn motion
around the pole. In poetry these
mourners are said to be "good-
for-nothing people whose rising
and setting do not bring rain."

The Seven Rishis, Hindu
semi-divine sages, with their
hymns caused dawn to rise and the
sun to shine. They were the instruments through whom the Vedas
were imparted to man, and when
they died their ghosts formed the
constellation Great or Seven
Bears, and those of their wives
became the stars of the Pleiades.
The Seven Bears also were said
to be the seven wise men of
India who sailed with Manu in the
Ark and escaped the Deluge, or
to be Vashishtha, a form of
Brahma (zeta star), and his six
sons, Kratu (alpha),Pulaha (beta),
Pulastya (gamma), Atri (delta),
Angiras (epsilon), Marici (eta).
That these supernaturals are
identified as bears may be due
to a confusion of sound; indeed
this confusion may have brought
about the first identification of
these stars as bears and by a
people to whom the animal is not
familiar. The Sanscrit root
word riksha (star or to shine)
when used in a different gender
means bear. Gradually the meaning transferred from Seven
Shiners to Seven Bears. To add
to the mix up the word riksha
was confounded with the word
rishi (sage or poet) and so
India had seven wisemen to form
their Bear.

Marici in Buddhism became
an emanation of Vairocana, a
goddess who made her home on
Alkaid, the star strategically
located at the tip of the tail.

She was a terrifying three-
headed monster, one of her
faces being that of a wild boar,
and when she rode across the
vast areas of space accompanied
by the demon of eclipse, her
dark chariot was harnessed to
seven wild boars, probably
stars of the constellation. In
Tibet, China, and Japan, Marici
moved in and took possession of
the whole constellation, and her
disposition became milder. In
Tibet she was Queen of Dawn,
in China Queen of Heaven,
Mother of the Rice Measure,
who measured man's life, patron
of sailors and all who drowned,
suggesting that Jesuits may have
introduced the constellation's
function as a mariner's or nomad's
guide. Although missionaries may
have acquainted the Chinese with
western notions, the stars had
long played an important part in
their religious beliefs. The seven
bright stars, known as the Dipper, together with the sun and
moon, were in remote times
called the Nine Lights of Heaven.
The constellation they imaged to
be a Balance of Jade with which
the Jade Emperor maintained
the perpetual balance of the
seasons, the balance on which
the structure of the universe
depended. It also was deemed
to be a Palace of Fate. A
potent power was presumed to
dwell in the constellation's heart.
That the earthly emperor's
destiny might be auspicious,
seven stars were embroidered
on his robe, a tribute to this
configuration.

The Chinese god of literature
also made his home here. A
young literary student, K'uei,
brilliant and witty, was so ugly
the sight of him caused a beholder
distress. In examinations conducted for the gold rose trophy which

was awarded by the emperor, he came out the winner. Proudly K'uei approached the throne, but when the emperor saw K'uei's face his shock caused the rose to slip to the floor and break. The heart-broken student felt disgraced. He ran from the palace and cast him-self into the sea. Hardly had the waves closed over his head than he sensed a sea dragon under his feet; soon he was sitting astride it ris-ing to the surface and then high in the air until he had been carried to the palace of the Jade Lord, where he was appointed to watch over the literary affairs of the world. Students and scholars hang pictures of him on their walls, hoping that he will help them in their examinations that they may eventually gain wealth and fame.

The Mongols place six demons here who kidnaped a daughter of the Pleiades, which constantly pursue them. The six have become gods of thieves. In Siberia they are seven wolves on the trail of seven horses (Ursa Minor). When they catch the horses a great dis-turbance will occur and the world will come to an end. Or they are the skulls of seven blacksmiths, who had been killed by a hero who made cups of their heads from which he gave his wife to drink. She became intoxicated and threw the cups into the sky. Thus the constellation is the protector of blacksmiths.

To the Eskimos the constel-lation was four men carrying a sick or dead friend. Some said the Dipper was a herd of reindeer.

Among North American Indians the account of a hunt was widespread. Bear (stars of the Dipper's bowl), a Great Spirit, lived in the frozen wastes of the far north, beyond the realms in which other living things dared to venture. Through-out the winter he hibernated in his den, Polaris or Corona Borealis, but in the spring he roused himself and appeared in the east. He stalked silently, his footsteps muted by the snow, but his immense body lumbered along, steadily following the circle around the sky's pole. As quiet as he was he was seen by Robin (Alioth). Too small to capture Bear, Robin appealed to his friends the Chickadee (Mizar), Moose Bird (Alcaid), Pigeon (Seginus of Boötes), Bluejay (Izar), Owl (Arcturus), and the brilliantly-feathered Saw-whet (Muphrid). In the chase some of the hunters wearied and dropped out (set) until only three remained to pursue the Bear. The spot of red on Robin's breast came from the blood that spattered when he wounded Bear with his arrow. The Moose Bird who had lingered behind finally came up when the meat was to be cut and demanded his share, and for this reason he has been nicknamed He-who-comes-in-at-the-last-moment. Sometimes the hunters were said to be three, the stars of the handle, with Mizar carrying a pot (Alcor) in which to cook Bear's meat. For months they followed the circle of prints in the snow, but Bear always out-witted and outdistanced them, but in autumn he weakened, and the hunters, whose mouths watered for his delicious meat, let their arrows fly. Hit in the side, Bear bled so profusely even the forests below him were stained crimson. The hunters cooked his meat in their pot and after a sumptuous feast started for home, but they had lost their way and circled helplessly

around until spring. The soul
of the Great Spirit meanwhile
entered another body and hibernated. When he emerged in the
spring he again tempted hunters
and so once more the cycle of
the seasons began. In some
fables Bear was only wounded,
in some he was pursued by a
man and two dogs. In a variant
tale, hunters killed a bear,
made a fire, and cooked some of
the meat. After eating they left
for home carrying what remained
of the carcass. As they journeyed
the landscape kept moving further
and further away from them. The
next evening people on earth saw
seven stars above, and for
eternity the hunters must tread
across the cold wastes high overhead carrying the carcass on their
back simply because they had lost
their way. The honeydew, which
is plentiful in autumn, comes
from the bear's fat over a fire.

The Iroquois account for the
absurd length of the tail in this
manner: in the far distant past
all bears had imposing bushy
tails. Earth-bear, however,
was vain and pretentious, and
he would show off by dropping his
tail into a hole gnawed in ice
and bring up fish with it. One
day, colder than usual, the tail
froze and fell off, leaving a
mere stump. Sky-bear, who had
been more modest, still has his
magnificent tail, and it can be
seen curling stately around the
axis aloft.

The Blackfeets tell about a
bear that is pursuer rather than
the pursued. A family consisted of a father, mother,
seven brothers, and two sisters.
All were grown except for one
boy and girl, who were left in
the care of the older sister while
the others went hunting, fishing,

or engaged in other chores.
This older sister fell in love
with and married a grizzly bear,
an animal possessed of supernatural powers. The horrified
male members of her family
slew the bear, whereupon its
ability entered the body of his
wife. One day, while her
brothers hunted, in the guise of
a bear she killed her parents
and laid waste the village in which
they resided, and then returned
to her two small charges. The
strange behavior of their elder
sister alarmed the boy Okinai
and the girl Sinopa. Sinopa, on
the pretext of going to a stream
for water, sought out her
brothers and warned them they
would be killed if they returned
to the wigwam. The brothers
held council and advised Sinopa
to scatter prickly pears on the
ground outside her tent, but to
leave one narrow lane. Late
that same night Sinopa awakened
her younger brother and together
they crept along the path she had
provided and then ran to the
brothers who awaited them.
Quiet as they had tried to be,
the elder sister heard them, but
when she rushed out of the tent
she was caught among the prickly
pears and screamed with pain.
Quickly she transformed herself
into a bear and bounded over the
burrs on the heels of the fugitives.

Okinai, also a possesser of
magical powers, shot an arrow,
which placed them all as far
ahead of bear-woman as the
arrow had gone. When the magic
wore off the elder sister gained
on them. Okinai waved a feather
and a thick clump of bushes
sprang up behind them, but she
had cleared a way for herself.
Okinai waved his hand and a tall
tree shot up beside them. The
eight terrified refugees scrambled

onto the branches. Bear-woman climbed the tree, grabbed four of her kin and was about to reach for the rest when Okinai shot his last eight arrows straight up into the blue. Each arrow lifted one of them and they were carried high into the sky, where they turned into stars. The four brothers that bear-woman had actually touched while in the tree formed the bowl of the Dipper; the four for whom she was reaching when Okinai let go his arrows lined up to create the handle. The star Alcor is the frightened Sinopa, who still huddles close to one of her brothers.

Tezcatlipoca, chief Aztec sun deity, had an obsidian mirror as a foot in which reflected all mankind's deeds, over which he judged. A defier of time, he remained eternally young, but sacrificed himself daily to assure light's resurrection each morning. His noble behavior brought him many honors until he sinned against his brother Quetzalcoatl, another aspect of the sun. For this indiscretion he was turned into a tiger, then into a puppet, and placed in the night sky where he dances on his hands around the pole. In his nocturnal form he became evil, a sender of famines, plagues, and wars, and was worshipped by thieves and witches. A handsome youth was feted for a year and then sacrificed to appease him, but his appetite was insatiable and each year he demanded another youth.

Almost everywhere the constellation has been depicted as a Bear, usually female, from its legends or from its prototype on earth, which always has been a symbol of frozen wastes. Unaccountably the Teutons did not see this shape among these stars, which they perceived to be a Wagon. On the Denderah planisphere and in other Egyptian temples it was delineated as a single thigh or hind quarter of the animal and so called in inscriptions on tombs and walls. Every now and then a cow's body with disc and horns appeared instead of the thigh.

Ursa Major is from the Latin meaning the Great She Bear. Additional designations: Beam, for the three line stars; Bear; Bier; Brood Hen; Butcher's Cleaver; Bull's Thigh or Fore Shank; Car of Boötes; Danish elephant, from heraldry; Great Chariot; Great Coffin; Greater Bear; Handle, for the three line stars; Harrow; Heavenly Plough; King Charles' Wain, a reference to English kings of this name by courtiers of Charles I and II and others; Ladle; Northern Cars; Northern Team; Plough; Plough Oxen; Screw; Seven Antelopes; Seven Bulls, these last three in India, the Seven Bulls becoming the Great Spotted Bull; Seven Champions of Christendom; Seven Little Indians (American Folklore); Seven Sages (Sanscrit); Seven Sleepers (Christian); Seven Wise Men (Greek), generally given as Bias, Chilo, Cleobulus, Epimenides or Periander; Pittacus, Solon, and the astronomer Thales; Southern Tramontane; Southern Mountain; Team for the three tail stars; Twister; Ursa; Waggon; Wagon; Waggoner; Wain Harrow; Wild Boar (Syrian). Sometimes erroneously called Big Dipper, which actually refers to the constellations seven bright stars, which form a bowl with a handle.

Accadian: Aganna or Akanna,

Lord of Heaven.

Anglo-Norman: Chaere.

Anglo-Saxon: Carles-waen
(Charles Wain), commonly
thought of as a title of the people
and often said to be derived from
the Saxon ceorl, which became
churl, a peasant's cart. Scholars
now are of the opinion Carles
refers to Charles the Great,
Charlemagne. Another title was
Irmines Wagen, Irmin being the
god of wisdom identical with the
Norse Heimdal, heaven's defender.

Arabic: Al Dubb al Akbar,
the Greater Bear, which degenerated into Dob, Dub Alacber,
Dubbe, Dubhe, Dubhelacbar,
Dubon. Banat Na'ash al Kubra,
Daughters of the Great Bier,
i.e. the Mourners, which in the
middle ages was written Benenas,
Beneth As, Benethasch, and
applied to the three stars of the
team or handle. Another title was
El Keid, The Egg-shells.

Arabic Christian: Na'ash
Laazar, Bier of Lazarus, the
stars of the tail representing
Mary, Martha, and Mary
Magdalene.

Chinese: Kwei, an object of
worship, for the center of the
square; Pih Tow, Northern
Measure or Bushel; Tien Li,
Heavenly Reason, for the square;
Ti Tche, Emperor's Chariot;
Tseih Sing, Seven Stars, also
known as the Government; T'si
Tsiang, Seven Goers; To Wei,
Jade Palace of Shang-ti, heaven's
supreme ruler.

Christian: Arcturus, which
came about in error. In the Vulgate, Saint Jerome thus translated Ash or Ayish. He probably
intended Arctus. It appears as

Arcturus in the King James edition, but in the revised editions
of the Bible has been corrected
to "the Bear and her train, the
latter represented by the three
tail stars. Waynes or Vaynes
of Heaven, used in England in
the 16th century, became Waves
of Heaven. Titles shared with
Ursa Minor are: Chariot of
Elijah; Chariot of Joseph;
Peter's Skiff; Ship of Saint Peter.

Dutch: Wagen am Himmel,
Wagon of Heaven.

Egyptian: Ark; Boat; Car of
Osiris; Dog, or Thigh, of Set;
Meskhet or Mesxet (Set).

Euphratean: Bel-me-khi-ra,
Confronter of Bel. Sugi, the
Wain, also applied to Libra,
where it had the meaning Yoke.

Finnish: Otava (Otawa);
Otavainen (Otawainen);
Seitsen tahtinen, Seven Stars.

French: Casserole, Sauce-
pan; Grand Ourse.

Gaelic: Crann, Crannarain,
Baker's Shovel; Grigirean, a
Ladle.

German: Grosse Bar, Large
Bear; Herwagen (Horwagen,
Hurwagen), with the tail stars
as draught-horses in a line;
Himmel Wagen, Heaven's Wagon;
Wagen of Woden or Wuoten
(Odin).

Goth: Karl Wagen.

Great Britain: Arthur's
Chariot or Wain; Mistress
Ursula; Wain.

Greek: Amaxa, Wagon;
Arctos megale, whence comes
Arctic; Callisto (Kallisto),

literally Fairest; Helice, from the birthplace of Callisto and later the name of one of Zeus's Cretan nymphs; Helix, Screw, which is plainly related to its spiral motion; Lycaonia, Lycaonia Arctos, Lycaonia Puella, all three alluding to Callisto's father.

Greenlanders: Tukto, Reindeer.

Hebrew: Ajala or Galta, Wagon; Ash or Ayish, a Bier. Ash referred either to the square of this constellation or to Aldebaran, alpha star of Taurus. Dobh, Bear; Pharashah, Guiding Star. One biblical translator gives Mazzaroth, by others identified as the five planets.

Hindu: Riksha, which signifies both Bear and Star, i.e. bright or to shine. This led to the title Seven Shiners. Eventually Riksha was confounded with Rishi and connected with the Seven Poets or Sages. Sugi, the Wain, also was applied to Libra, where it had the meaning Yoke. Saptar Shayar, Seven Anchorites, who were raised to a high elevation in the sky with the pious woman Al Suha (Alcor).

Irish: Camcheacta, Plough; King David's Chariot, a reference to one of Ireland's early kings.

Iroquois: Okouari (Okuari), Bear.

Italian: Carro, Car; Cataletto, a Bier, Orsa Maggiore.

Lapp: Sarw, Reindeer.

Latin and Low Latin: Arcadian Sidus, Arcadian Stars; As Ursas; Canes Laconicae, Spartan Dogs; Canis Venatica,

Callisto's Hounds; Cretaeae sive Arctoe, from the Naxian legend; Currus, a Conveyance; Dianae Comes or Phoebes Miles, because Callisto was a companion of the moon goddess; Erymanthis, perhaps the Erymanthian Boar or a Bear, symbolic of frost; Fera Major; Filia Ursae, Ursa cum puerulo; Horus Apollo, the myth of the sun deity being applied to these ever-brilliant stars; La Roue, the Wheel; Maenalia Arctos, Maenalis, Maenalis Ursa, from those mountains; Parrhasis, Parrhasia Virgo, Parrhasides Stellae, from the tribe or aboriginal people to whom Lycaon was king; Plaustrum, a two-wheeled ox-cart, which deteriorated into Plastrum, Plaustra Parrhasis, Plaustricula, Plostrum magnum; Septentriones, for the Dipper; Seven Oxen; Tegeaea Virgo, from the Arcadian town Tegea; Triones or Teriones, the Oxen that walked around the threshing floor (of the pole); Ursus, masculine form of Ursa; Virgo Nonacrina, Virgin of Nonacris, an Arcadian town.

Norse: Karl Vagn, Karl's Wagon, Karl being the god Thor; Stori Vagn, Great Wagon; Odin's Wagon.

North American Indian: Paukunawá, Bear. The constellation tail was known as: Hunter with his Two Dogs or Three Hunters.

Ostiak: Los, Reindeer.

Persian: Mihin Hapto-iringas (Hafturengh, Haptokring, Heft Averengh, Heft Rengh), Greater of the Seven Bulls or Protector of the North.

Phoenician: Chalitsa or Kalitsah, Safety, inasmuch as it was helpful to a safe voyage;

Dub, Bear; Parrasis, Guiding Star.

Polish: Woz Niebeski, Heavenly Wain.

Portuguese: Carreta, Cart; Set Flammas, Seven Flames or Stars.

Saxon: Waenes Thisl, Wagon-pole.

Siberian: Elwe'kyen, Wild Reindeer Bucks, which pursue the seven horses of Ursa Minor; when the horses are caught, the world will come to an end.

Turkish: Yidigher Yilduz, Seven Stars.

Collective names for both Bear constellations or names applied to either one: Greek: Arctos or Arctus; Latin: Arctoe or Arctoi; Gelidae; Geminae Ursae; Magna minorque ferae; Septen (Septem), Septemtrio, or Septentriones, Seven Oxen, eventually a term for the north pole and north wind, still later for the north generally.

In astrology this has always been an important constellation. Because the stars numbered the sacred seven, in Sumer they were possessed of high magic. The priests and the people searched the skies nightly for the cluster, which contained this number's special virtue, and, seeing it, knew that the gods were pleased and all was well. To Egyptians it was the monster of the sky, and therefore ill-omened. In Arabia these stars, perhaps because of their slow movement around the pole, were emblematic of inactivity and laziness. Christians have worshipped them as a sevenfold spirit, the rope which holds all

things in heaven together. In Shakespeare's time they were said to portend evil influences. The Chinese knew Ursa Major and Ursa Minor together as longevity and wealth gods.

In remote times the constellation, by reason of precession, was nearer to the pole than its is now, and in higher latitudes seemed never to set. Into modern times, to the English rustic these stars have been timepieces of the night. The Greeks used the constellation in navigation; Arabian nomads used it in crossing the deserts.

It reaches its meridian about April 25, and its bright stars are alpha, Dubhe; beta, Merak; gamma, Phad (Phecda); delta, Megrez; epsilon, Alioth; zeta, Mizar; iota, Talitha; nu, Benetnasch; omicron, Muscida, g, Alcor, a companion of Mizar. A star in the constellation, known as 1,830 Groombridge, is also called The Flying or Runaway Star from the fact that its motion, until a quite recent discovery, was swifter than that of any other star in the heavens.

URSA MINOR (THE SMALLER BEAR). In the early days of Sumer the heavens were believed to be supported by a great mountain, the peak of the world, located far in the old north. On it the gods had their mansions and about it was an ocean or abyss upon which earth floated. Directly above this mountain gleamed the lights of Ursa Minor. The south, on the other hand, the hot realm in the depth of the sea, was the abode of the prince of death and his comrades, the demons. This delightful dazzling land, where the gods held their assemblies, apparently fell into eclipse, for the Babylonians saw these stars as a Leopard, a symbol of darkness, which they shared with other circumpolar figures. The Egyptians likewise had this view; to them the figure was the Jackal of Set, regarded with fear and foreboding. For centuries these stars were dreaded, until the Phoenicians pointed out that Polaris, the star around which the others rotate, was an ideal mariner's guide. Since, it has been the most adored and exalted of the northern constellations. Many of the stories related about its nature are tied to those of Ursa Major, some of which fail to take into account the actual differences in their shapes and positions. Manilius, who noted this, wrote they:

.... stand not front to front
but each doth view
The others Tayl, pursu'd
as they pursue.

Face toward tail they may be, yet both are in a never-ending circular dance which men, widely spearated by time and space, have imitated to work the magic of keeping the seasons in their proper order. The center of the celestial dance was marked by a jeweled nail or pole, an axis, the pole-star. In time the axis swelled into something huge, and the idea of a cosmic mountain emerged from the darkness into which it had been cast.

In allegories, mountain implied meditation, a mystical realm, in contrast to the flat land of reality; light and gaiety opposed to the darkness and tears of the valley. Primitive peoples conceived it as an entrance into the other-world, and buried their dead in high caves or on slopes. Abraham

was buried in such a cave. In some comological legends the mountain converted into the stick with which the above-deity churned the primordial waters to bring land up from the bottom, or, after the deluge, to bring up land for a new world, while its peak functioned as the holy harbor of the ark. Legends still circulate about an ark on some mountain top on which deluge survivors once lived, but death comes to those who climb up and reach it. Almost every mythology has a sacred mountain thought to be connected with the umbilical cord attached to the foetus through which Earth drew her increase. It appears as the home of dwarfs, fairies, giants, the heaven's vault, the ladder to heaven, the mansion or throne of the creator god, the world-pillar that holds up the sky vault. This appears to be related to the idea of a tree of life or world tree. The summit is the scene of eternal youth, sunshine, joyous repose, place for worship, site of the waters of health, trysting spot of men and gods.

The Egyptians and others had four mountains, one at each of the four cardinal points. Virtuous souls after death traveled to the Egyptian mountain of the west. On an island in the center of a lake on the summit, the Lake of the Green Falcon, stood a tree on which grew the fruit of immortality. The souls of the pharaohs were escorted to this remarkable land on the wings of the Green Falcon, the Morning Star, that they might have ever-lasting life. That the bodies of the pharaohs might also be eternally preserved and serve as a home to which the souls might return, they were mummified and placed in pyramid tombs, the head, lying close to the west wall, faced the north. The pyramids themselves were adjusted to the compass points, the four sides squarely facing north, south, east and west. The most northerly stars, from which nothing was hidden, observed this extraordinary conduct, donned sparrow bodies, flew to the tree, and ate of its fruit. They immediately became immortal or ever-visible. These imperishable stars were also said to be the oarsman of the Barque of Ra, a vessel 1,200 feet in length which made its way across the heavens nightly to carry the sun back to the eastern horizon.

When Zeus, the Greek lord of the bright sky, was born, his mother Rhea, to save him from his cannibal father Cronus (Time), carried him to the top of Mount Ida, where he was reared in secrecy in a cave. Cynosura, sometimes called Melissa, was one of the nurses who not only cared for the infant Zeus (the child Kouros), but clashed metal cymbals and whirled in a frenzied dance to drown out the noise made when he cried, lest his father trace him. When Zeus grew to manhood he honored Cynosura with this place in the skies. The origin of Cynosura, which means Dog's Tail, is obscure, and if these stars are a tail, where is the dog? The answer may rest in one of the legends of Callisto, in which she is said to be an aspect of Artemis who often went hunting with a hound beside her. Cynosura also is applied to Polaris. Inasmuch as the pole-star is observed by all, the word has become a term to express the focus of attraction or atten-

tion; inasmuch as it points the way for seamen, it expresses guidance, sometimes facetiously. In the Callisto story, these stars are the bear form of Arcas.

The great Norse mountain was Himinbjorg, Hill of Heaven. Here was the citadel or abode of Heimdal, heaven's defender, guardian of Bifrost (Rainbow), the bridge which united earth to Asgard, literally Yard of the Ass, the garden of light in which dwelled the gods and heroes who died bravely in battle.

Christopher Columbus thought he came upon the base of the glorious mountain which he called Paria, on which Paradise was located, somewhere in the neighborhood of his discoveries in Central America. A century later an earnest reference was made to such a mountain with the name Slotus, described as the highest in the world and lying under the Pole.

The Hindu sacred mountain was Meru, dwelling place or pleasure ground of the deities. Birds on it had golden feathers, and it was the pillar that separated heaven and earth, the spine that sustained the universe.

To the Chinese all circumpolar stars were believed to be palaces of nobles and ministers of state who served at the court of the Emperor of Heaven. The administration, which kept the sun and moon in order, regulated the seasons, and in general governed the universe, was maintained here.

In Old Testament lore, Ursa Minor is said to be the Bear slain by David; the chariot sent by Joseph to bring his father into Egypt; the chariot in which Elijah was carried to heaven; one of the Bears sent by Elisha to punish his juvenile persecutors; or an angelic aspect of Ezra.

American Indians tell of a hunting party that lost its way and prayed to the gods to direct them homeward. During their dance around their fire of burnt offerings, a little girl appeared among them and said she was the spirit of the star in the far north, and that if they would follow her she would guide them. The hunters took her advice and soon reached home, where they held council and called the light that had directed them Star Which Never Moves. When the hunters died they were carried up to heaven and there can be seen trailing after their beloved star every night.

The Eskimos thought this constellation to be four men carrying a sick baby.

Additional designations: Circler of the Midst; Lazy Team; Leopard; The Lesser Bear; Lesser Chariot; Little Dipper; Little Wain; Minor; Small Dipper; Smaller Chariot (Danish); Tail or Train of Light.

Arabic: Abrucab, Abruccaba, or Al Rukkabah, from Al Rakabah (The Riders) or Rukbah (Knee). To further complicate this title, it has been written Dubherukabah and Eruccabah. More popular was Al Dubb al Asghar (The Lesser Bear, which before European influence probably was Bier). This contracted into Dub Alasgar, Dhub Elezguar. Al Fass (The Hold, i.e. in which earth's axle had its bearing). Stars of the bowl were Al

Farkadain (Two Calves or Two Young Ibexes), and the three of the tail were Banat al Naash al Sughra (Daughters of the Lesser Bier). Arabs also likened Ursa Minor to a fish. Here and in Ursa Major early commentators located the Fold, an ancient Arabian stellar form. This conception inspired James Russel Lowell to write:

The Bear that prowled all night about the fold of the North Star.

Chaldee: Rukub (Vehicle).

Euphratean: An-nas-sur-ra (High in Rising); An-ta-sur-ra (Upper Sphere).

Finnish: Vaha Otava or Otawa (Little Bear).

French: Petite Ourse.

Gaelic: Drag-blod (Fire-tail).

German: Kleine Bar.

Greek: Cynosura or Cinsosura (Dog's Tail). Phoenice, Ursa Phoenicia, either from the purple land, realm of lovely northern light, or from the introduction by Phoenicians about 600 B.C. of these stars as nocturnal guides.

Hebrew: R'khubh (Vehicle).

Icelandic: Fiosakonur a Lopti (Milkmaids of the Sky); Litli Vagn (Little Wagon).

Italian: Bogina (Boa); Cornu and Elcorno, said to be errors for carro (Car, also translated Horn). Orsa Minore; Tramontana (Over the Mountain or Star of the Mountain).

Latin: Canes Laconicae
(Spartan Dogs); Catuli (Lapdogs
or Puppies).

Persian: Hafturengh Kihin,
Hapto-iringas Kihin, Heft
Averengh, Heft Rengh, all of
which designate Lesser of the
Seven Bulls, a reference to its
inferior size to Ursa Major.
Ihlilagji (Date-palm Seed or
Fruit).

Phoenician: Doube, or
Dobher, which means the Speaking or Guiding Constellation as
well as Bear.

Spanish: Bocina (Bugle).

The two stars furthest from
Polaris are called the Guards because their presence was believed
to be necessary to protect
Polaris from the bloody and
thievish instincts of the Great
Bear.

Astrologically, because of
their connection with Set, located
in the Great Bear, the stars are
believed to have an evil influence.

The constellation, which
rests within the coils of Draco,
is visible in the night sky
throughout the year, but is said
to reach its point of culmination
about June 27.

Ursa Minor's chief call for
glory is its alpha star Polaris.
Other bright stars are beta,
Kochab; gamma, Pherkad; delta,
Yildun. The Little Dipper
actually is an asterism composed
of the bright stars of the constellation.

VELA (THE SAILS, i.e. of
ARGO). Formerly a part of the
ship Argo, which see. It lies
in the southern sky surrounded
by Carina, Centaurus, Antlia,
Pyxis, Puppis, and comes to
the meridian about March 30.
A named star is kappa,
Markeb.

VIRGO (THE MAIDEN).
Some astronomers have claimed
an age of 15,000 years for this
figure, placing its initial appearance when the sun was in
Virgo at the spring equinox,
harvest time in ancient Egypt.
Others claim that Leo was the
first constellation formed to
mark the harvest month. Although 15,000 years appears to
be an exaggeration, no one knows
when it really came into being;
on one point almost all agree,
the rust of aeons creaks in the
bones of this venerated woman,
and the name originally implied
not merely virgin but virtuous
matron.

In astronomical allegories,
these stars have been an emblem
of the Magna Mater, the triple
deity of birth-growth-death or
birth-death-rebirth, whose
virginity was renewed each
spring or each new moon. Although a producer of life, she
was unable to maintain it. She
taught mankind agriculture,
presided over the harvest, and
then each autumn carried
fertility with her when she entered the world of shadows. Men,
who observed her triumphant
return after a half year in the
world of the dead, hopefully
believed she exemplified resurrection, and that mortals too
returned to live in another form
or in another realm with renewed strength.

Babylonians assigned this constellation to their sixth month,
the Errand or Message of Ishtar, Great Mother beyond com-

parison and prototype of all who follow, who shows herself as the Morning Star. Virtually every heroine of mythology or folklore reveals characteristics to be found in this alluring Mother.

Isis, the thousand-named goddess, said to be the daughter of Hathor or identical with Hathor, was the Egyptian personification of the great power of nature, perpetually bringing forth, rearing, and destroying all things, revered lady of the sky and earth, patroness of marriage, nourisher, who fed her son at her breast, and who yearly made a long arduous journey to gather the pieces of the dismembered body of her beloved brother-husband Osiris that he might be resurrected. She left the harvest to begin her journey and carried a sheaf of wheat in her hand. One day she noticed that Set, her enemy, followed her. When she fled to escape him, wheat heads scattered across the sky and became the Milky Way.

Demeter, stately Greek earth-mother, was one of the great Olympian deities. Zeus, her brother, who ruled the sky, came down upon her, and she became the mother of the summer child Persephone. One day, while gathering flowers on Enna meadows, Persephone was abducted by Aides, who controlled earth's wealth underground. Her mother sought her with such grief earth failed to produce, so Zeus dispatched Hermes to the underworld to obtain Persephone's release. Since she had eaten a pomegranate seed she was magically bound to return to her husband periodically and reign as underworld queen. With the return of Persephone to the upper

earth, Demeter again provided verdure, but each year, during her period of sorrow, the soil became barren. Mythologically, the seed eaten (or sown) transforms into its germ and is endowed with the power to again appear as fruit, but it must return to seed; thus Persephone who had consumed a seed was committed to return to the underworld where the seed would ripen. Persephone is probably a duplicate of Demeter, mother and daughter representing two phases of the vegetative powers of the soil, the mother standing for the entire power, latent or active at all seasons, the daughter for the potency of its youthful or spring and summer aspect.

In earlier myths, Virgo was identified with Rhea, wife of Cronus and mother of Zeus, whose cult was celebrated in the spring with cymbals and drums. This association is of interest to Masons, as Rhea (Earth) is the emblem of the Masonic third degree.

Astraea too, was said to be a form of Virgo. A daughter of Zeus and Themis, she was a virgin goddess of justice, personification of innocence and purity. In the Golden Age she refused to unite with the Titans against Zeus and to avoid a war came to dwell on earth. In the Silver Age, she left her home on a mountain top only after dark; in the Bronze Age, when man's wickedness was apparent, she abandoned earth and returned to live among the deities. Of all immortals, she was the last to linger among men. Her scales were placed next to her in the constellation Libra that she might weigh the good and evil deeds of men.

Other legends place Irene, mistress of peace, or Erigone in these stars. Erigone was a harvest goddess, the virtuous daughter of Icarius, who had been taught the cultivation of the vine by Dionysus. When Icarius had been killed by a band of shepherds who mistrusted him, Erigone in grief hung herself from a tree which towered over her father's grave. They both were transported to the skies, Erigone to become Virgo, Icarius to become Boötes. Their pet dog was made into the Dog Star.

In Roman mythology, Demeter was called Ceres; Persephone, Proserpina; Aides, Pluto; Astraea, Justitia; Irene, Pax. The Romans identified many female figures with these stars, among them Medusa, queen of the night skies. When Medusa offended Minerva, her fair countenance was changed, and she became an object of terror with snakes on her head instead of hair. Minerva, herself, guardian of citadels and of the state was placed here. So was Fortuna, originally an early Italian nature goddess who shaped the harvest and the destines of women in childbirth. Later she was the incorporated will of the gods, and finally the lady of chance.

The story of the harvest or wheat-field maiden appeared in England and Scotland, where she was known as Kernababy (Corn-baby, Kern-baby). A rude image of the female shape was made of the last gleamings of a field and adorned with flowers. This maiden was carried as a charm to a kern supper, which celebrated the harvest. Carts and reapers followed her. Music was played. Songs were chanted. All through the winter she was treasured, and in the spring she was tossed into a stream. Her body fertilized earth; her soul presumably flew skyward.

Rabbis assigned these stars to Asher, the eighth son of Jacob.

In Arabia, where the human form was tabu in worship, these stars were part of a vast design, Zawiat al Awwa (The Kennel of the Barking Dogs). From the safety of their kennel, the dogs yapped at the back of a great celestial Lion, their neighbor. Later, influenced by European lore, they reduced the figure and called it the Innocent Maiden.

Peruvian Indians, who knew these stars as the Magic Mother, celebrated her festival in much the same manner that the Kernababy was celebrated in Britain. The rites were called the Queen's Feast and were dedicated to the maize as well as to women in general.

Configurations. In most representations portrayed as a winged maiden holding in her left hand an ear of wheat or corn. In some illustrations she had a palm branch in her right hand or a caduceus. She also is shown with scales. When with an olive branch, she stands for the Roman Pax, abstract goddess of peace, or the singing Sibyl who carried a branch into the underworld to assure the rebirth of nature in spring. If drawn by lions, the goddess is Cybele, drawn by Leo, the preceding constellation.

Anciently in Egypt shown to

be a sphinx with a woman's head on a lion's body to illustrate the sun passed through these constellations during the Nile's inundation. When a full woman's wingless figure replaced that of the Sphinx, it was out of proportion, and she held a distaff decorated with the stars of Coma Berenices. On certain zodiacs, the portrait was that of Isis, who held the spica or her infant son Horus, the spring sun and last of the divine kings. In the middle ages this figure transformed into the Virgin Mary with the infant Jesus.

Arabs, not permitted to draw the human figure, showed the constellation as stalks of ripened wheat. In the East, the woman's figure once was shown as a sun-burnt maiden with corn in her hand, like a gleaner in the fields. In India, the goddess sits before a fire. The Singalese woman is in a Ship and holds a stalk of wheat. Germans dressed her in a high-necked gown with a train. Occasionally a caduceus, a magic aid to birth and fertility, was carried with wheat or a branch. The sign's pictorial emblem is ♍ .

Virgo is from the Latin meaning Virgin. Additional designations: Ears, i.e. wheat-ears; Goddess; The Maiden; Maiden of the Wheatfield; Mermaid in the Zodiac; Virgin; Virgine; Wheat-bearing Maiden; The Yoke; The Yoke of the Balance, an emblem of Venus, who united persons under the yoke of matrimony. Seamen know the four stars directly below alpha, shaped like a sail, as Spica's Spanker.

Anglo-Norman: Pulcele.

Anglo-Saxon: Maeden.

Arabic: Al Adhra al Nathifah (The Innocent Maiden), from the Greek. This appeared in the middle ages as Adrendesa, Adrenedesa, Eladari, Eleadari. Al Sunbulah (A Sheaf of Wheat). Remnants of this title remain in Sumbela, Sunbala.

Assyrian: Baaltis, Belat, Belit, or Beltis, literally My Lady, a harlot goddess, whose rites were orgiastic. She shared the dignity and power of her consort Bel or Bel-Enlil.

Chinese: She Sang Neu (Frigid Maiden); before Jesuit influence called Shun Wei (Serpent or Quail's Tail).

Christian: Ruth, the gleaner in the fields of Boaz; Saint James the Less; Seven Portuguese Towers; Virgin Mary.

Egyptian: Isis; Sphinx.

England and Scotland: Cornababy, Kernababy, Kernbaby.

Euphratean: Ishtar or Istar. Ki (a Place, i.e. of the moon, and the 20th lunar station was marked by its alpha star). Shiru or Siru (Ear of Corn), a title also applied to its luminary Spica, the star of Spring, which led the constellation. Another title signified Proclaimer of Rain.

French: Vierge.

German: Junckfraw, Jungfrau.

Greek: Astraea (Starry Night); Demeter (Grain-mother or Mother-earth); Erigone (Early Born); Irene (Peace); Pathenos (Virgin, an epithet applied by the Greeks to several of their goddesses); Persephone (Spring Maid).

Hindu: Gul; Kanya (Maiden), in some translations given as Kannae, the mother of Krishna. Parthena, Partina, or Pathona, borrowed from the Greek.

Italian: Virgine.

Judean: Bethulah, the House of Abundant Harvest.

Latin and Low Latin: Ano Atargatis, Cybele, Derceto, Syrorum Dea, various names of the mother goddess applied by classical Roman writers. Arista (Harvest); Aristae Puella or Arista Puellae (Maiden of the Harvest). Ceres spicifera dea (Great Earth Mother with the ear of wheat). Concordia (Harmony); Diana; Fortuna (Fortune); Justa or Justitia (Justice); Medusa, queen of darkness and generation; Minerva, probably meaning to think; Panda; Pantica; Pax (Peace); Proserpina (Spring Maid); Spicifera Virgo Cereris (Virgin Ceres with Ear of Wheat); Thesbia or Thespia, sometimes given as a name of one of the Muses; Urania, Muse of Astronomy; Virgo spicea munera gestans.

Persian: Khosha or Khusak (Ear of Wheat); Secdeidos, or Seclenidos, de Darzama (Virgin in Maiden Neatness).

Singalese: Woman in a Ship, who carries a stalk of wheat.

Syrian: Bethulta, probably identical with Judean Bethulah.

Tamil: Kauni (Maiden).

Turkoman: Dufhiza Pakhiza

(Pure Virgin).

Astrologically, a feminine and therefore an unfortunate sign. Early astrologers said it portended sterility and injustice to the innocent; later astrologers claim it is a sign of eminence, renown, and riches. Its ruling planet is Mercury, and subjects born under its influence are analytical, melancholic, reserved, tactful, and inclined toward science. To the Romans, a comet within its borders portended that deplorable ills would fall on the female half of the population.

It is located along the celestial equator, swinging into both the northern and southern skies. On modern maps the figure is bounded on the north by Boötes and Coma Berenices and on the south by Corvus and Crater. In the cold months, Virgo can be seen in the night sky and reaches culmination about May 26. Its bright stars are: alpha, Spica; beta, Zavijava; gamma, Porrima; delta, Lu Lim; epsilon, Vindemiatrix; eta, Zaniah.

VOLANS or PISCIS VOLANS (THE FLYING FISH). This constellation was introduced about 1603 and biblical scholars asserted it represented Abel the Just. The French call it Poisson Volant, the German name is Fliegende Fisch. Once it was called Passer (Swallow), and as such the Chinese translated the name into Fe Yu. Located close to the southern pole, south of Carina, it is not visible from the United States. Its culmination date is about March 4. None of its stars are named.

VULPECULA or VULPECULA

CUM ANSERE (FOX WITH THE GOOSE). This constellation was formed late in the 17th century by the astronomer, Johannes Hevelius, who on his selection of the title said, "I wish to place a fox with a goose in the space in the sky well fitted for it, because such an animal is cunning, voracious and fierce." The Configuration has been crowded in between Sagitta and Cygnus in the northern sky; perhaps only a cunning creature would devise the space and catch a goose in these close quarters.

The name is from the latin and sometimes is written Vulpecula et Abser (Little Fox with the Goose) or simply Vulpes (Fox). Additional designations are: Little Fox, The Fox. French, Petit Renard avec l' Oie; German, Fuchs, or Fuchschen, mit der Gans; Italian: Volpe colla Oca.

This asterism, which has no bright stars, is interesting solely for its most noteworthy object, the Dumbell, or Double-headed Shot, Nebula, and for the meteor stream Vulpeculids, which appears from June 13 to July 7, and radiates from a point in this group. The constellation reaches the meridian about September 8.

CONSTELLATION SUMMARY. If the first constellations were of importance in the Creation legend, each representing an incident in the emergence of light or life from chaos, they later, along with additional configurations, played an important role in weather, their appearance or disappearance with the sun divulging to those who knew how to read stars whether to prepare for clear or rainy days, warmth

or frost. Dominated by the spirit of commerce, Phoenicians studied the stars relative to navigation, and they probably were the link between Babylonians and Greeks, as Homer wrote, "the stars were sent by Zeus as portents for mariners." Before the 6th century B.C., the 36 Decans, or constellations, had been charted. Each ruled a ten-day period, which necessitated yearly calendar adjustments, usually accomplished with 5 intercalary, or godless, days annually and additional adjustments for the fraction of a day every several years. The Mexicans required 52 years to square their calendar. The 36 Decans were divided into three sets of twelve, one set in the northern sky, one in the southern, one along the plane of the ecliptic or zodiac as follows:

THE DECANS*

Northern	Zodiacal	Southern
Cassiopeia	Aries	Eridanus
Auriga	Taurus	Orion
Cepheus	Gemini	Canis Major
Ursa Minor	Cancer	Argo
Ursa Major	Leo	Hydra-Crater
Boötes	Virgo	Corvus
Ophiuchus	Libra	Centaurus
Hercules	Scorpio	Lupus
Lyra	Sagittarius	Ara
Aquila	Capricorn	?
Pegasus	Aquarius	Piscis Australis
Andromeda	Pisces	Cetus

NOTE: *The modern names of the constellations have been used.

In the versification by Aratus about 270 B.C. of the works of Eudoxus of Cnidus, a 4th century astronomer, 44 constellations were listed, the additions being 7 in the northern sky: Draco, Perseus, Triangulum, Delphinus, Cygnus, Sagitta, Corona; and one in the central or zodiacal group: the Pleiades, later incorporated into Taurus. He included Lepus, which may have been the missing Decan in the southern sky. Hipparchus, an astronomer who wrote about 150 B.C. increased the constellations to 48. Three hundred years later in the 2nd century A.D., Ptolemy, the Alexandrian astronomer, catalogued these in his Almagest. The Ptolemy chart did not add to those stars visible at Rhodes in the time of Hipparchus; he merely allowed corrections for precession, and his chart has served as a basis for all subsequent star-catalogues.

Northern (21)	Zodiacal (12)	Southern (15)
Ophiuchus		Ara
Serpens		Corona Australis
Sagitta		Piscis Austrinus
Aquila		
Delphinus		
Equuleus		
Pegasus		
Andromeda		
Triangulum		

The names wherein Ptolemy in compiling his catalogue differed from modern usage are:

Modern Title	Ptolemy Title
Hercules	Engonasi (Kneeling One)
Cygnus	Potamos (River)
Lupus	Theriou (Beast)
Pegasus	Ippou (Horse)
Equuleus	Ippou protomes (First or Before Horse)
Canis Minor	Prokunos (First or Before Dog*)
Libra	Chelon (Claws)

NOTE: *As the minor dog, this is now referred to as the second dog that accompanies Orion, Canis Major being the first dog. Anciently as the first dog it was the one that warned that Sirius was about to rise.

PTOLEMY'S CHART

Northern (21)	Zodiacal (12)	Southern (15)
Ursa Minor	Aries	Cetus
Ursa Major	Taurus	Orion
Draco	Gemini	Eridanus
Cepheus	Cancer	Lepus
Boötes	Leo	Canis Major
Corona Borealis	Virgo	Canis Minor
Hercules	Libra	Argo
Lyra	Scorpio	Hydra
Cygnus	Sagittarius	Crater
Cassiopeia	Capricorn	Corvus
Perseus	Aquarius	Centaurus
Auriga	Pisces	Lupus

Christian astronomers at various times, such as the Venerable Bede in the 8th century, Julius Schiller in the first quarter of the 17th century, and others, made unsuccessful attemps to liberate the sky from Pagans and populate it with

Christian apostles, saints, popes. and other church dignitaries. E. Weigelius was equally unsuccessful when he sought to displace classical configurations with heraldic forms, the arms or insignia of European dynasties and emblems of commerce.

No notable changes or additions appeared on maps until 1603, when a German astronomer, Johann Bayer, published a Uranometria with 12 new constellations in the southern sky. All had been adapted from observations made by a Dutch navigator, Petrus Theodoric (or Pieter Dirchasz Keyser), who died off Java in 1596. These and inventions since have brought the total to 88. The following generally is agreed to be a complete list of the constellations:

CONSTELLATIONS SEEN ON CURRENT SKY MAPS

Name	Inventor	When Charted or Catalogued
North of the Zodiac -30-		
Andromeda		Before 6th Century B.C.
Aquila (1)		" " "
Auriga		" " "
Boötes		" " "
Camelopardalis	Jacobus Bartsch	1624
Canes Venatici	Johann Hevelius (2)	1690
Canis Minor		Before 150 B.C.
Cassiopeia		Before 6th century B.C.
Cepheus		" " "
Coma Berenices	Ulugh Beg	1437
Corona Borealis		Before 270 B.C.

CONSTELLATIONS SEEN ON CURRENT SKY MAPS - continued

Name	Inventor	When Charted or Catalogued
Cygnus		Before 270 B.C.
Delphinus		" "
Draco		" "
Equuleus		Before 150 B.C.
Hercules		Before 6th Century B.C.
Lacerta	Johann Hevelius (2)	1690
Leo Minor	"	1690
Lynx	"	1690
Lyra		Before 6th Century B.C.
Ophiuchus (1)		" " "
Orion (1)		" " "
Pegasus	"	" " "
Perseus		Before 270 B.C.
Sagitta		" "
Serpens (1)		Before 150 B.C.
Triangulum		Before 270 B.C.
Ursa Major		Before 6th Century B.C.
Ursa Minor		" " "
Vulpecula	Johann Hevelius (2)	1690

Zodiacal -12-

Aquarius		Before 6th Century B.C.
Aries		" " "
Cancer		" " "
Capricorn		" " "
Gemini		" " "
Leo		" " "
Libra		" " "
Pisces		" " "
Sagittarius		" " "
Scorpio		" " "
Taurus		" " "
Virgo		" " "

CONSTELLATIONS SEEN ON CURRENT SKY MAPS - continued

Name	Inventor	When Charted or Catalogued
South of the Zodiac -46-		
Antila	Louis de Lacaille (3)	1763
Apus	Johann Bayer	1603
Ara		Before 6th Century B.C.
Caelum	Louis de Lacaille (3)	1763
Canis Major		Before 6th Century B.C.
Carina (of Argo)		(4)
Centaurus		Before 6th Century B.C.
Cetus		" " "
Chamaeleon	Johann Bayer	1603
Circinus	Louis de Lacaille (3)	1763
Columba	Jacobus Bartsch	1624
Corona Australis		Before 150 B.C.
Corvus		Before 6th Century B.C.
Crater (5)		Before 150 B.C.
Crux	Augustine Royer	1679
Dorado	Johann Bayer	1603
Eridanus		Before 6th Century B.C.
Fornax	Louis de Lacaille (3)	1763
Grus	Johann Bayer	1603
Horologium	Louis de Lacaille (3)	1763
Hydra		Before 6th Century B.C.
Hydrus	Johann Bayer	1603
Indus	Johann Bayer	1603
Lepus		Before 270 B.C.
Lupus		Before 6th Century B.C.
Mensa	Louis de Lacaille (3)	1763

CONSTELLATIONS SEEN ON CURRENT SKY MAPS - continued

Name	Inventor	When Charted or Catalogued
Microscopium	Louis de Lacaille (3)	1763
Monoceros	Jacobus Bartsch	1624
Musca	Johann Bayer	1603
Norma	Louis de Lacaille (3)	1763
Octans	"	1763
Pavo	Johann Bayer	1603
Phoenix	Johann Bayer	1603
Pictor	Louis de Lacaille (3)	1763
Piscis Austrinus		Before 6th Century B.C.
Puppis (of Argo)		(4)
Pyxis (of Argo) (4)	Louis de Lacaille (3)	1763
Reticulum	Isaak Habrecht	18th Century
Sculptor	Louis de Lacaille (3)	1763
Scutum	Johann Hevelius (2)	1690
Sextans	"	1690
Telescopium	Louis de Lacaille (3)	1763
Triangulum Australe	Johann Bayer	1603
Tucana	Johann Bayer	1603
Vela (of Argo)		(4)
Volans (Piscis Volans)	Johann Bayer	1603

NOTES: (1) These constellations cross the celestial equator to appear in both northern and southern skies. (2) The publication of Hevelius's work was posthumous. (3) The publication of Lacaille's work was posthumous. (4) A part of the ship Argo, an immense constellation which had been invented before 6th century B.C. (5) Previously Crater was attached to Hydra.

Also presented here is a table of culminations. Because constellation forms are quite irregular, all dates given are approximate; to give the exact date that a configuration's bulk reaches its meridian seems impossible. Furthermore, a cluster or star may be seen for some time before and after reaching its zenith, depending on whether it is east or west of the meridian, that is approaching or receding from it.

CONSTELLATION CULMINATIONS

Date	Constellation	Date	Constellation
(Night sky of spring -21)			
	Ursa Minor (1)	Apr. 29	Hydra
	Octans (2)	May 12	Corvus
Mar. 21	Pyxis	May 12	Crux
Mar. 30	Vela	May 14	Centaurus
Apr. 8	Sextans	May 14	Musca
Apr. 9	Leo Minor	May 17	Coma Berenices
Apr. 10	Antila	May 22	Canes Venatici
Apr. 15	Chamaeleon (3)	May 26	Virgo
Apr. 15	Leo	June 14	Circinus
Apr. 25	Ursa Major (4)	June 16	Bootes
Apr. 26	Crater		
(Night sky of summer - 24)			
June 23	Libra	July 26	Ophiuchus
June 23	Lupus	July 28	Hercules
July 3	Corona Borealis	Aug. 14	Corona Australis
July 3	Norma		
July 5	Apus (3)	Aug. 15	Scutum
July 7	Triangulum Australe	Aug. 18	Lyra
		Aug. 21	Sagittarius
July 8	Draco (4)	Aug. 24	Telescopium
July 18	Scorpio	Aug. 29	Pavo (3)
July 21	Serpens	Aug. 30	Aquila
July 25	Ara	Aug. 30	Sagitta
Sep. 8	Vulpecula	Sep. 14	Delphinus
Sep. 13	Cygnus	Sep. 18	Microscopium
(Night sky of autumn - 21)			
Sep. 22	Capricorn	Nov. 11	Pisces

CONSTELLATION CULMINATIONS - continued

Date	Constellation	Date	Constellation
Sep. 22	Equuleus	Nov. 13	Cepheus (4)
Oct. 1	Indus	Nov. 18	Phoenix
Oct. 9	Aquarius	Nov. 23	Andromeda
Oct. 9	Piscis Austrinus	Nov. 23	Cassiopeia (4)
		Nov. 29	Cetus
Oct. 12	Grus	Dec. 7	Triangulum
Oct. 12	Lacerta	Dec. 10	Hydrus (3)
Oct. 16	Pegasus	Dec. 14	Aries
Nov. 1	Tucana (3)	Dec. 17	Fornax
Nov. 10	Sculptor	Dec. 22	Perseus

(Night sky of winter - 22)

Date	Constellation	Date	Constellation
Dec. 25	Eridanus	Feb. 4	Auriga
Dec. 25	Horologium	Feb. 6	Camelopardalis
Jan. 3	Reticulum	Feb. 16	Canis Major
Jan. 14	Taurus	Feb. 19	Gemini
Jan. 15	Caelum	Feb. 19	Monoceros
Jan. 27	Orion	Feb. 22	Puppis
Jan. 28	Lepus	Feb. 28	Canis Minor
Jan. 28	Mensa (3)	Mar. 4	Volans
Jan. 30	Pictor	Mar. 5	Lynx
Jan. 31	Dorado	Mar. 16	Cancer
Feb. 1	Columba	Mar. 17	Carina

NOTES: (1) Circumpolar; seen from some point in the northern hemisphere any night of the year. (2) Circumpolar; seen from some point in the southern hemisphere any night of the year. (3) Located far in the south, hence always visible from some point in the southern hemisphere. (4) Located far in the north, hence always visible from some point in the northern hemisphere.

VIII

THE STARS

Companion Star

Have I a brilliant star
to guide my destiny,
or a dull deity,
who rides an ox-drawn car
across a distant bar;
or from a shrouded mist
does Dark Star, satanist,
claw of my soul a scar?

Can my familiar be
high, the rime-frosted light
that never sets, delight
of everyone at sea?
Or does one on a spree,
say a brazen comet,
solo in a death motet,
pretend to care for me?

I reach into each night,
into the everness,
the abyss of darkness.
The beauty of each light
dazzles; I cannot sight
the clue I seek.   My wheel
will spin, but not reveal
my astral acolyte.

Primeval herdsmen and farmers discovered that the stars were heavenly voices or proclaimers, who announced that frost, rain, heat, or arid weather was about to arrive, and they knew where to lead their flocks, what to sow, and what to reap.   According to Berosus, 3rd century B.C. Babylonian priest and historian, among those who broadcast this most desired of information were 10 antediluvian kings, supposedly descendants of divinities, themselves possessed of supernatural virtues, and rulers of 120 saroi for a period of 432,000 solar years.

The basal numbers of Euphratean arithmetic were 6 and 60.   Six is 5 fingers plus 1 hand;   60 is 6 X 10 toes;   60 X 2 feet = 120 saroi (or 360^0), an archaic division of the cosmical circle.   This circle was guarded by 36 Decans (a list of the Decans is given under the Constellation Summary, earlier in this work), each responsible for 10°; each of the 10° contained 60', each of which in turn contained 60"; thus 10 X 60 X 60 = 36,000. The 36,000 seconds for each of the signs along the zodiac gave that circle 432,000 (36,000 X 12) seconds, which in some way corresponded to or represented the same number of solar years. To quote Robert Brown: "We thus come to the preposterous statement that the 10 kings reigned 432,000 years." The lengths of time attributed to their reigns as stellar reduplications obviously had been assigned to correspond to the distances separating certain of the principle stars in or near the ecliptic. Euphratean ideas connected with cosmic periods seem to have influenced other Asiatic nations, and in the Indian system of yugas, or ages of the world, the use of 10 intensified brought the total to 4,320,000 solar years, or a day and night of Brahma. The basal Euphratean numbers of 6 X 60 were used in compiling a year on earth of 360 days (each day corresponded to 1°), and eclipses and other phenomena were predicted with few inaccuracies for a while. When discrepancies began to be noticeable, intercalary days or months were used to adjust the calendar. Eventually, Chaldeans figured the length of the year to be 365 days, 6 hours, and 11 minutes, an excess of only 2 seconds over the true sideral year. Because the distances separating the stars of the rulers were unequal, the dynasties of the ten varied in duration.

TEN ANTEDILUVIAN KINGS

King	Reign in Saroi	Degrees	Probable Ecliptic Star Point	Degrees Controlled by Star
Aloros (Ailuv)	10	30	Hamal	31
Alaparos (Alap-ur)	3	9	Alcyone	10
Amillaros (Amil-ur)	13	39	Aldebaran	43
Ammemon (Umun-an)	12	36	Pollux	36
Amegalaros (Amil-gal-ur)	18	54	Regulus	53
Daonos (Dannu)	10	30	Spica	44
Euedoranchos (Dar-an-khu)	18	54	Antares	53
Amempsinos (Amar-sin)	10	30	Algedi (Giedi)	20
Opartes (Ubara-tutu)	8	24	Deneb Algedi	16
Xisouthros (Xaxisadra)	18	54	Skat (Scheat)	54
	120	360		360

While strategically located stars may have exemplified the will of those highborn, or have been the immortal form conferred on heroes, stars in general were believed to be the souls of dead ancestors, who had become masters of rain and wind, health and disease, wealth and poverty, arbiters of cosmic space and fate, sometimes cordial and obliging, sometimes fiendish and stonyheaded. They frequently had a life of their own, independent of the constellations of which they were a part. Each elucidation of how stars were born, what they might be, what they might do, has been disputed. Usually the sky deity was their king, but curiously enough they sometimes conferred the title on the sun-hero they had slain, as in the case of the Breton Heol. Ladon, Sesa, and others were vigilant dragons who had a thousand eyes (stars) with which to detect trespassers into their realm, the night. Stars have been called the children of Sun and Moon romping about in open courts or meadows, or maidens who never grow old and sing bewitching tunes no mortal can resist. They have been accused of being fierce barbarians, who every morning are slain and every evening come to life again. A star may have been a fire lit by its own flame, a chip broken off a sun or moon, nails that glistened affixed to keep the dome of heaven in place, or sparkling gems attached to the black veil of night. They were the Igigi and the Anunaki, Assyro-Babylonian groups of cruel genii subordinate to the sky-god Anu, a probable source of the conception of angels. In fact, Job identified stars as angels. Those that sank below the horizon became guardians of the riches buried underground or judges of the newly dead. Some star deities found regulations above too exacting and deserted their heavenly relatives for carousing friends below, such as the Tatar, Kara-Khan; and some, like Lucifer, were proud and rebellious, desirous of occupying the supreme throne and were tossed from heaven. Stars that speeded unceasingly by were Never-resting Ones; those that never set, the Imperishables. An ancient legend of unknown origin relates that giants, while throwing stones at the sky, punctured the sky, and at night the light of the solar orb comes through those tiny perforations.

Egyptians recognized in the circumpolar stars the conspirator comrades of Set in his black plot against Osiris, and on this account they were of evil omen. Other stars were parts of the dismembered body of the sun-god Osiris, scattered by these powers of darkness.

The Greek Astraeus, the star-like or starry heavens, was the first husband of Eos, by whom he fathered winds. Sometimes the pair are mentioned as the parents of Astraea, the last of the immortals to dwell on earth, and who, when she ascended into space, became the constellation Virgo.

To offset the hostility of vindictive or irascible supernaturals, Roman emperors, consuls, generals, and priests adorned themselves on high occasions with Toga picta, that is toga's embroidered with stars were worn as talismans. Christians depended on the Bethlehem or Pentagonal Stars.

According to the Hebrews, the sun, moon, and stars performed a dance before Adam in the Garden of Eden.

Bushmen and other African natives had a notion they were gazing upon men, women, children their utensils, domestic fowls, and even wild life, such as lions and tortoises in the hereafter.

The Norse Naglfar or Naglefar, literally nail made, is a ship of death made of the nail pairings of the wicked dead, which glisten at night. The ship is located in the Gulf of Black Grief. Held fast to an island or post, it will not move until Ragnarok. When it does, it will carry the giants for a war with the gods, which will bring about the end of the world. Then again, the star-studded sky is a jeweled chariot drawn by the steed Hrim Faxi (Frosted Mane) from whose bit foam falls every morning that congeals on earth into dew. Nat, the kindly night goddess, a care and worry remover, drives the chariot. In an allied belief, American Indians say dew is the spittle of stars.

German peasants tell children the stars are the eyes of angels, and that each time a child dies, God makes a new star. English rural folk teach the young that it is wicked to point to the stars, but they do not know why. Children in India are taught that the stars are kine, who have the moon as their herdsman.

In Arthurian legend, Leodogrance of Camiliard, father of Guinevere, received from Uther Pendragon, the fertility lord, a gift of the famous Round Table, around which 150 knights (stars that composed a host) were able to assemble. When Arthur became Leodogrance's son-in-law, he was given the table and knights as a wedding present.

Slovenes looked upon the stars as living in constant intercourse with mortals and taking part in their affairs.

Zoroaster, to whom Ahura Mazda had revealed the true path, deposited three germs in Lake Kasu, and then died. He sank into the underworld, where he remained for three days before ascending to heaven. The three germs were guarded by 99,999 fravashis (stars), and once in every millennium they will permit a maiden bathing in the lake to receive one; thus three Saoshyants (prophets) will be born to bring light and goodness into the world. The stars have another function; as the heavenly host that aids Ahura Mazda in his beneficent work and in transmitting his will to mankind, they are the Yazatas or Venerable Ones. From their ranks came Mithra, light and victory bringer; Anahit, water genius, purifier of earth's seed who provided strong companions for men; Atar, fire lord and conqueror of evil.

The Chinese judge Yang Ch'eng, who brought about the cessation of Emperor Wu Ti's yearly levy on servants and comedians at the palace, was an astral deity.

Buto was a Japanese ox-headed king, who passed through three cycles of existence. In one phase he was ruler of the stars and traversed earth to descend to the mansion of the undersea dragon in search of a wife. On his journey, he asked Kotan, king of southern

India, for shelter, and Kotan simply closed his gates in Buto's face. Returning from his marriage, Buto made war on Kotan, cut his body into five pieces and slaughtered his people, before resuming his place in the night sky. The name of the Japanese god of roads, the protector of highways, or the star which guides travelers, is Koshin, which also is the collective designation of the three monkeys who See-no-evil, Hear-no-evil, Speak-no-evil.

The Thein, Burmese rain nats, reside in the stars. Showers occur when they leave their houses and engage in battle; thunder and lightning come when their arms clash. If rain is needed, a village holds a tug-of-war to arouse them.

Dying Pacific Islanders will announce their intention of becoming a star and tell those assembled at the death-bed where to look for them in the skies. In New Zealand, heroes become stars of greater or lesser brightness according to the number of their victims slain in battle. When flowers die on earth, Australian natives believe a breeze lifts them and they float upwards until they find a place in heaven where they bloom perpetually. That is why stars are blue, red, purple, yellow, or white.

Uset, mother of the Sia Indians, gave Ishits (Beetle) a sack of stars to carry from the world below to the world above. Tired by the weight, Ishits stopped to rest. The sack opened and most of the stars flew out. For this offense he was blinded. The few that had remained in the bag, Uset arranged in clusters, placing seven to make the Great Bear, etc. Those that drifted with the wind are scattered about haphazardly. Shiwanni, chief of the Zuni cloud people, did not depend on any messenger. When he wanted stars for the night, he formed bubbles from his spittle and blew them upward.

Peruvians thought that not a human, beast, bird, or plant lived on earth whose image or double did not shine in the night sky. They revered these luminaries as helpful guardians and performed seasonal dances in their honor.

An impression prevails that star names originated in Arabia. This idea derives from the fact that the medieval designations now in use seem to be corruptions of the Arabic, but scholars in that country had in the 8th century A.D., during the reign of Abbasides, while Europe was engulfed in the Dark Ages, simply translated from the Greek of Claudius Ptolemy, a work that was little known in Europe until George of Trebizond (Tarpezuntius), a monk, translated it into Latin from a Vatican manuscript during the 15th century. Several editions of George's work appeared during the 16th century, and from these and the Arabian lists have come the barbarous Graeco-Latin-Arabic terms that appear in modern catalogues. Spellings vary and some are actually abbreviated forms.

Scholars were not the first to name the stars. Men who depended on them, nomads, hunters, mariners, who looked to them for guidance across a desert or at sea, agriculturists who sowed or reaped according to weather prognosticated by the arrival or departure, the brilliance or dimness of the tiny luminaries far out in space, mourners who pleaded for their help; these were the first to describe them and, in the course of thousands of years, established their nomenclature. Among the Arabs, single stars represented single creatures; they did not group several together to form a figure until they were taught to do so by western neighbors. The custom they had followed for centuries, of giving independent importance to individual stars, firmly rooted their distinguishing characteristics as objects or participants in a fable. So we find words which signify horsemen and their trappings, shepherds, herdsmen, maidens, anatomical parts, cattle, oxen, camels, sheep, goats, predatory and wild beasts, birds, reptiles, sea-animals, fruits, grains, nuts, plants, trees, tents, nests, animal stalls or mangers, household articles, ornaments, biers, thrones, boats, wells, and rivers. The Arabs placed still another class in the skies: Al Saidak, The Trusted One; Al Simak, The Lofty One; Al Suha, The Neglected One, which show the influence of celestial beings who assist or hinder living mortals.

According to a note on the National Geographic Magazine's Map of the Heavens, dated December 1957, of the myriad stars in space, only 1,971 can be seen with the unaided eye. Many of these have been discovered in modern times, and the names assigned to them are not associated with fables, some, in fact, are designated simply by letters or numbers. In some cases myths and name meanings once attached to stars known throughout many ages have been lost. This work lists only those stars for which we have been able to locate the significance of the names, the legends, or both. Before we turn to the stars which are to be detailed, we offer here a chart of the 24 most brilliant, placed in order of magnitude in their respective hemispheres.

BRIGHTEST STARS IN SPACE

Northern Hemisphere

Magnitude and Star	Constellation
0.1 Vega	Lyra
0.2 Capella	Auriga
0.2 Arcturus	Bootes
0.5 Procyon	Canis Minor
0.9 Altair	Aquila
1.0 Betelgeuse	Orion
1.1 Aldebaran	Taurus
1.2 Pollux	Gemini
1.3 Deneb	Cygnus
1.3 Regulus	Leo
1.6 Castor	Gemini
1.7 Alioth	Ursa Major
1.7 Bellatrix	Orion

Southern Hemisphere

Magnitude and Star	Constellation
1.6 Sirius (1)	Canis Major
0.9 Canopis	Carina
0.1 Rigil Kentaurus (2)	Centaurus
0.3 Rigel	Orion
0.6 Achernar	Eridanus
0.9 Agena (3)	Centaurus
1.0 Acrux (4)	Crux
1.2 Spica	Virgo

Brightest Stars in Space -cont.

Southern Hemisphere

Magnitude and Star	Constellation
1.2 Antares	Scorpio
1.3 Formalhaut	Piscis Austrinus
1.5 Beta Crucis	Crux

NOTES: (1) The most brilliant star in space. (2) Nearest bright star. (3) Beta Centauri. (4) Alpha Crucis.

In the star list that follows we give, wherever it is known to us, this information: classification in its constellation; color, season in which it culminates, that is, when it is at its zenith and therefore best seen in the night sky; fables; source of name and meaning; additional designations; astrological significance:

ACHERNAR, alpha Eriadni, white, winter. From the Arabic Al Ahir al Nahr, The End of the River, nearly its position in the cluster. Achernar originally had been given to theta star, the farthest in the stream known to Arabians. In the middle ages this was written Acamar, Acarnar, Acharnar pro Acharnahar vel Acharnarim, Acharnar, Acharnarin, Achenar, Achironnahri, Archarnar, Enar. The Chinese called it Shwuy Wei; Dante named it Tre Facelle. It lies as far south one side of the Pole as Crux does on the other; thus it is not seen in latitudes north of Egypt.

ACUBENS, alpha Cancri, double, in the south-eastern claw, spring. From the Arabic Al Zubanath, The Claws. Medieval spellings were Acubene, Azubene. Romans called it Acetabula, Arm Sockets, i.e. of the Crab, and Cirros or Cirrus, the Arm.

ADHARA, epsilon Canis Majoris, double pale green and violet, winter. From the Arabic Al Adhara, The Virgins. Originally applied to a group composed of epsilon, delta, eta, and omicron, all close together, and has persisted as the name of the brightest of the four stars. Other spelling are Adara, Adard, Udara, Udra. Also designated Al Zara, which probably is a mongrel form carrying the same meaning.

ADHIL, xi Andromedae, autumn. From the Arabic Al Dhail, The Train, i.e. of the Garment.

AIN, epsilon Tauri, winter. From the Arabic for Eye.

AL AARAF, a temporary star that appeared in Cassiopeia. Edgar Allan Poe named it after Al Orf, or Urf, the temporary abode of spirits midway between heaven and hell, quite appropriate to it. It disappeared in March of 1574, but had created such a commotion in the 16th century it induced predictions of the second coming of Christ, and was by some believed to be a reappearance of the Star of Bethlehem. Other designations: New Venus, Pilgrim's Star, Star in the Chayre, Stranger, Tycho's Star, either after Tycho (Thyene), one of the Hyades, or Tycho Brahe, Danish astronomer who died in 1601. The Chinese recorded it as Ko Sing, Guest Star.

AL AGHNAM, several dim stars now called The Club of

Hercules; summer. From the
Arabic signifying The Sheep, i.e.
those that were within Al Raudah,
The Pasture, composed of small
unidentified stars in the neighborhood of Hercules.

AL ATHFAR, mu Lyrae, late
in summer. From the Arabic
meaning The Talons, i.e. of the
Falling Eagle.

AL BALI, epsilon Aquarii, a
double in the left forearm, autumn.
From the Arabic Sa'd al Bula,
Good Fortune of the Swallower,
the 23rd manzil. This title may
have come from the fact that it
seemed to absorb or swallow
the light of stars of Capricorn.
Also called Mantellum or Mantile,
Latin for Cloak, and marking
the napkin or towel in the youth's
hand; Pyxis; Ancha, now applied to theta star. Its Coptic
name was Upeuritos, Discoverer.
With mu and upsilon, it was the
Euphratean lunar asterism
Munaxa, Goat-Fish, which the
Chinese called Nü, Girl. In
early drawings shown as a bunch
of grain stalks. The remarkable
Saturn nebula, that in telescopes
looks somewhat like the planet,
is close by.

ALBIREO, beta Cygni, a
binary, the larger topaz yellow,
the smaller sapphire blue, at
the foot of the cross which also
is the swan's beak; best seen
late in summer. The present
title, sometimes spelled Alberio,
Albeiro, or Albirco, appears to
be a typographical error or a
misunderstanding of ab ireo, of
unknown meaning, which appeared
in the 1515 Almagest. Arabs
called this star Al Minhar al
Dajajah (The Hen's Beak), which
appeared in the middle ages as
Menkar Eldigiagich or Hierizim.

ALCAID, eta Ursae Majoris,
white, best seen early in spring.
Also known as Benatnasch,
which like Alcaid derived from
the Arabic Kaid Banat al Naash,
Governor of the Daughters of
the Bier, that is chief of all
the mourners (of Ursa Major).
The names have appeared in
several forms, among them:
Ackair, Alcatel, Alchayr,
Alkaid, Elkeid, Benat Elnanschi,
Benenacx, Benenaim, Benenatz,
Beninax, Bennenatz, Bennenazc.

By Chinese called Yaou Kwang,
Revolving Light. In India it was
Marici, a sage or rishi whose
ghost became one of the bears
of Ursa Major herded by Svati
(Arcturus). In Buddhism,
Marici is a goddess of dawn,
whose name signifies she who
radiates light or she with the
rays of light, quite a fitting description for this star which is
the last in the tail.

AL CHIBA, alpha Corvi, orange
the lowest star, the one in the
crow's beak which pecks at
Hydra; spring. Name from the
Arabic meaning The Tent, and
a desert title for the whole
constellation. Another Arabian
designation was Al Minhar al
Ghurab, The Raven's Beak.
Chinese called it Yew Hea,
Right-hand Linch-pin, and with
other stars it constituted the 13th
Hindu nakshatra called Hasta,
the Hand. Once the leader of
the constellation, it has grown
dim and now is only of fourth
magnitude.

ALCOR, g Ursae Majoris, a
double located in the tail, best
seen in the spring. Although one
of the least conspicuous of the
naked-eye stars, one that is in
fact a test of vision, it is among

the most famous in astronomical folklore. In Greek legend, this star is identified as Electra, who had wandered from her Pleiad sisters and metamorphosed into a fox. To the Norse it was the toe of Orvandel, which Thor, when it became frost bitten, snapped off and tossed into the northern skies. Orvandel himself was the Orion constellation.

Hans Dumken, a wagoner of Galilee, in a Germanic Christian tale, gave a poor man a lift. The man turned out to be Jesus, who offered to reward Hans with the Kingdom of heaven. Hans asked only that he be permitted to drive like the sun from east to west through all eternity. His wish was granted, and he and his wagon were placed among the stars as Alcor, which moves perpetually around the pole from east to west. In a similar English legend, Alcor is Jack on the Middle Horse, the star Mizar being the horse Jack (Alcor) rides. This may be the source of a popular title for the Mizar and Alcor stars, which is Horse and His Rider, Alcor being the rider or cavalier.

Several American Indian tribes speak of Ursa Major as a bear pursued by three hunters (the Bear's tail). The center hunter carries a pot (Alcor) in which to cook the game. To the Blackfeets the star is the youngest of several children who fled from their sister (Ursa Major's main body).

The name, from the Persian, means Friendless One. Additional designations are: Arabic, Al Khawwar, The Faint One; Suha, from Al Sahja, The Forgotten, Lost, or Neglected One, because it can be seen only by a sharp eye. In a proverb the Arabs say, "I show him Suha; he shows me the moon." Other Arabic titles were: Al Sadak, The Test, i.e. of vision; Saidak, True (vision) as well as names signifying Little Letter, Our Riddle, Winter. Chinese: Foo Sing, Supporting Star. German: Alkor; der Hinde, the Hind or Farm Hand; Dumke and Hans Dumken, which means Hans the Thumbkin. Hungarian: Gontzol, a character who resembles the German Hans. Latin: Eques, Horseman or Cavalier; Eques Stellula, Little Starry Horseman. Mongol: Huitung Ot, Cold Star. Norse: Orvandel's Toe.

ALCYONE, eta, Tauri, greenish yellow, winter. The lucida of the Pleiades, Alcyone was one of the daughters of Atlas and Pleione. When Pleione and her daughters were pursued by Orion, they appealed to Zeus, and to save them from the unwelcome advances, the god metamorphosed them into birds and they flew high into the heavens, only to discover the great hunter had followed them. There the chase continues, and they barely keep ahead of him, although occasionally they manage to get out of his sight (set while he is still in the sky). The Pleiades personify rain clouds, Orion the sun. Owing to a confusion that dates back into remote antiquity, this star also is said to represent Alcyone (Halcyone), a daughter of Aeolus, steward of the winds, and the devoted wife of Ceyx. When Ceyx was drowned in a shipwreck, she (a rain cloud) cast herself into the sea to search for him. In pity, the gods made a kingfisher of each, as this bird, noted for its affection, always flies in pairs.

According to a superstition, the kingfisher ever since provides halcyon days, a spell of calm weather in the midst of storms. About 2,000 B.C., at the winter solstice, this Pleiad culminated at nightfall in the mid-heavens, a brooding time of the halycon, whose nest supposedly floated on the sea.

Although now called the Light of the Pleiades, in mythology, Maia was considered the most beautiful of the sisters. Additional designations:

Arabic: Al Jauz or Al Jauzah, The Walnut; Al Wasat, The Central One, also applied to Taygete; Al Nair, The Bright One, all used by desert nomads. In later times the name became Thaur al Thurayya, Bull of the Pleiades, that is the leading one.

Babylonian: Temennu, Foundation Stone, which determined the 4th ecliptic constellation.

Hindu: Amba, the Mother, junction of the nakshatras Krittika and Rohini. In earlier Sanscrit literature, ghost of Arundhati, wife of Vasistha, an air spirit and chief of the Seven Sages, who at death rose to become the stars Ursa Major. Arundhati's sisters, who had married the six other Sages or Rishis, became the other Pleiad stars. Every newly married couple worshipped them on first entering their future home, and then worshipped the Pole-star. This may be symbolic of the prehistoric union of the northern and southern tribes of India.

Italian: Altorich or Altorric, Bright or Brightest One.

As late as the 19th century, astronomers believed this star marked the center of the universe, the point about which starry space revolves, a theory that is fallacious. At 9 P.M. on the last night of the year this star reaches its meridian.

ALDEBARAN, alpha Tauri, pale rose, winter. This star is the lucida of the Hyades, rising about an hour after and southeast of the most lauded cluster in the skies, the Pleiades. Lying along the moon's track, it is occulted time and again. As a lunar star, navigators find it useful in ascertaining their positions.

In an Arabic legend, Aldebaran, a suitor of the Pleaides, was rejected because of his extreme poverty. Later, when he became prosperous, he returned to woo them again, this time driving ahead of him all his Little Camels (the Hyades) to corroborate his boast of newly attained riches. Still, they would not have him, and the persistent lover hopes to break down their resistance by an uniterrupted display of his prosperity.

Exactly which stars compose the Four Royal Guardians of Persian astronomy is not certain. Some say Aldebaran, with the name Taschter or Tishtrya, was sentinel of the east and vernal equinox about 5,000 years ago; some say it marked the west and autumnal equinox with the names Sataves or Satavaesa. Those who disagree make Sirius the Taschter star and Fomalhaut or others the one known as Sataves.

By the Hindus, this luminary was idolized as Rohini, the

beautiful daughter of Prajapati.
The father became mad with
desire for his daughter, who
romped about in the form of an
antelope, and he transformed
into a deer called Mrga to pursue
her. Across the sky she fled
with Mrga behind her until his
thigh was pierced by an arrow
shot by Rudra. Thus with the
rising of Rudra (Sirius), Mrga
(Orion) falls.

Aldebaran is from the Arabic
Al Dabaran, The Hindmost or
Follower, i.e. of the Pleiades.
The name, now appropriated by
the star, originally called atten-
tion to the whole cluster of the
Hyades. Aldebaran marks the
4th manzil, which once was made
up of the cluster, the star then
known as Na'ir al Dabaran,
Bright One of the Follower. Aldebaran has decayed into Addebiris,
Addebara, Aldebaram, Aldeberan,
Debiron. Other Arabic terms
are: Al Fanik, The Stallion
Camel; Al Fatik, The Fat Camel;
Al Muhdiji, The Female Camel;
Hadi al Najm, Tali al Najm,
or Saik al Thurayya, equivalents
of the Latin Stella Dominatrix;
Padan, Furrow. A Later name,
Ain al Thaur, Eye of Taurus,
came from the Latin and was
adulterated by European astronomers into Hain Altor.

Additional designations are:

Accadian: Dil-gan, Messenger of Light, a name also applied
to other stars, possibly as their
positions changed with respect to
the equinox.

Babylonian: Pidnu-sha-Shame,
Furrow of Heaven, which marked
their 5th ecliptic asterism.

Bohemian: Hrusa.

Egyptian; Satet, Water-pourer,
goddess of Nile inundation.

English, Early: Bull's Eye.

Euphratean: I-ku, I-ku-u,
or Ku, Leading Star of Stars, so
honored because it was the
brightest of stars in their first
zodiacal sign.

Greek: An old Greek con-
notation was Torch-bearer.

Hebrew: Fadan, Furrow.
The biblical Kimah is assigned
to this star, probably in connection with the Hyades, given
as Kimah in the Vulgate.
Kimah also is assigned to the
Pleiades. God's Eye or Left Eye
also are Hebrew explanations.

Hervey Island: Aumea, a
native hero.

Hindu: Rohini, Red Deer,
undoubtedly from the star's
ruddiness. Location of the
4th nakshatra.

Khorasmian and Sogdian:
Baharu, Follower.

Latin and Low Latin: Cor
Tauri, Bull's Heart; El Taur,
The Bull; Oculus Australis,
Southern Eye; Oculus Tauri,
Bull's Eye; Stella Dominatrix,
Star that Dominates; Subruffa,
Light Red.

Persian: Paha, Follower;
Taschter or Tishtrya, Creator
Spirit that caused rain and de-
luge, the 4th lunar station.

Syriac: Iyutha, Goat, also
applied to the star Capella.

Aldebaran rises when the sun
sets early in December and

culminates about January 10. Astrologers say it is eminently fortunate, a bringer of riches and honor. Among certain Arabian tribes, if its heliacal rising is unattended by showers, a barren year is the portent.

ALDERAMIN, alpha Cephei, white, autumn. From the Arabic Dhira al Yamin, Right Arm or Forearm, i.e. of Cepheus, Ethiopian king and husband of Cassiopeia. From the title came the following: Adderoiaminon, Al Derab, Al Deraf, Alderaimin, Alderal jemin, Al Deramin, Alredaf, Alredat.

Alderamin will be the Polaris of the year 7,500 A.D.

AL DHIBAIN and DUO LUPI, zeta and eta Draconis, a pair, spring. The names are from the Arabic for the two hyaenas or wolves that lie in wait for the Camel's Foal, the little star Al Ruba, which is protected by the Mother Camel, the larger star in Draco's head. This pair also is called Al'Auhakan, The Two Black Bulls or Ravens, the Arabic word signifying either of these creatures.

AL FIRK (ALPHIRK), beta Cephei, double, white and blue, autumn. From the Arabic, meaning The Flock, may be a mistake, as a single star should not be named a flock. This may have come from Al Kawakib al Firk, The Stars of the Flock, a title for the cluster composed of alpha, beta, and eta. Ficares or Phicares, Fire-kindler, seen occasionally for this pair, was one of the designations for the whole constellation, and had been applied by Arabs to other bright stars.

ALGEIBA (ALGIEBA), gamma Leonis, a binary, bright orange and greenish yellow, spring. The name is from the Arabic Aljebbah, Forehead. No representation of the Lion justifies this position; it may therefore have been part of the ancient gigantic Arabian Lion. After Regulus, this star is the brightest member of the 10th manzil, Al Jabhah, and it may have taken the latter's title, which would make it the Mane, from the Latin word Juba, which appears in several catalogues. Algeiba is not unlikely from the Latin, Arabicized either by error or design in translation.

ALGENIB, gamma Pegasi, autumn. From the Arabic Al Janah, The Wing, or Al Janb, the Side, i.e. of Pegasus, the winged horse. Algenib also is one of the names of alpha Persei, in which case it means Side of Perseus. Sometimes it is written Algemo.

With delta Andromedae, it composed the 27th Arabic manzil Al Fargh al Muhir, also called Al Fargu; and with alpha Andromedae (Alpheratz) composed the 14th Chinese Hsiu Pi or Peih, Wall or Partition.

Algenib with Alpheratz and Caph, beta Cassiopeiae, are called The Three Guides because they are situated in a line almost on the prime meridian.

ALGENUBI, epsilon Leonis, spring. From the Arabic Al Ras al Asad al Janubiyyah, The Southern Star in the Lion's Head. Also called Rasalas. It marked the 14th ecliptic constellation of Babylonia, Rishu A, Head of the Lion; and in China it was Ta Tsze, Crown Prince. With mu, it was called Al Ashfar, The Eyebrows.

ALGOL, beta Persei, a variable, winter. From the Arabic Ras al Ghul, Head of the Demon. Literally, Ghul is mischief-maker and is identical with ghoul. The name decayed into Alove, which is found often. Popularly known as Blinking or Winking Demon or as the Demon Star. Ptolemy catalogued it as "the bright one of those in the Gorgon's head, which some Arabs translated into Nair. Other designations are: Chinese, Tseih She. Hebrew, Rosh ha Satan, Head of Satan. Latin, Caput Larvae, Spectre's Head; Gorgonea prima. Medieval Christian, Rosch hassatan, Head of the Devil; Lilith, the wife of Adam before Eve. Lilith, which is literally night monster or screech owl, was a nocturnal specter, whose wraithlike character was like that of Lilithu, a Babylonian shadowy demoness, beautiful above the waist, a serpent below it, who enticed men in their sleep. In Talmudic lore, rather than submit to Adam, she left Paradise for the regions of the air, became a demoness of the wind. In rabbinical literature of the middle ages, she is described as a hairy spirit who roams about at night seducing men and slaying children, especially the newly born. By Adam, she became the mother of all sheddim (demons). Her children, the Lilim, were asshaunched. The cabala described her as the archfiend of the Gamaliel. In Arabic legend, her husband is the Devil and her children are the jinn. In demonology she was the witch Lilis, one of the characters of Goethe's Walpurgis Nacht.

Its reputation is sinister, and said to be the eye of some hideous demon peering down into space for prey. Ancient astronomers believed it was the most violent and unfortunate star in the skies, and modern astrologers consider it the most dangerous. It reaches the meridian about December 23.

ALGORAB, delta Corvi, double, pale yellow and purple, spring. From the Arabic meaning The Raven. Also Algores.

ALHENA, gamma Geminorum, brilliant white, winter. Also spelled Elhenaat, the name is from the Arabic Al Hanah or Hunah, The Brand or Mark, i.e. on the right side of a horse's or camel's neck. Al Hanah was the 6th manzil and was located in the feet of the Twins. Another of the manzil's names was Al Nuhatai, dual form of Al Nuhat, A Camel's Hump. Some Arabic authorities found in these stars a Bow, with which Orion shoots the Lion. Like the Camel's Hump, the Bow is a curved line. Other names for the star are: Almeisam, Almeisan, Almisam, Almisan, from the Arabic Al Maisan, The Proudly Marching One. It marked the 10th Babylonian ecliptic constellation, Mash-mashu-sha-Risu, Twins of the Shepherd. With eta, it was Mas-tab-ba-tur-tur, The Little Twins, and with eta, mu, nu, and xi, all in the Milky Way, it was the Babylonian lunar mansion Khigalla, the Camel, which was the equivalent of the Khorasmian Gawthaf, the Persian Rakhvad, the Sogdian Ghathaf.

ALIOTH, epsilon Ursae Majoris, a spectroscopic binary, spring. Also written Alabieth,

Alaioth, Alhaiath, Alhiath, Aliath, and Risalioth, all incorrectly derived from Alyat, Fat Tail (of Eastern Sheep), an Arabic name for the star Capella. The Arabs named this star Al Juan, The Black Courser or Horse (of Alcaid). This became Al Huan. After the 16th century, Alcore, Al Haur, Aliare, and Aliore appeared, all from Al Hawar, The White of the Eye or the White Poplar Tree, which suggests it was intensely bright. Still another title attributed to it is Alhut, The Fish.

In China it was Yuh Kang, a gemmeous transverse or cross which was a portion of an early astronomial instrument, while stars nearby were Seang, Minister of State.

To the Hindu it was Angiras, a rishi or sage, whose ghost became one of the bears of Ursa Major herded by Svati (Arcturus).

AL KAB DHI' L INAN, gamma Aurigae, winter. From the Arabic meaning The Heel of the Rein-holder. Identical with El Nath, beta Tauri. With iota Aurigae called Tawabi 'al Ayyuk, The Goat's Attendants.

AL KALBAIN, Tauri, seen in winter. The stars that stretch from the left eye to the left ear of the Bull. Name from the Arabic, signifies The Two Dogs, i.e. of Al Dabaran (Aldebaran), driver or follower of the Pleiades.

ALKALUROPS (ALKATUROPS), mu Bootes, triple, white, spring. The name is from the Greek, meaning Shepherd's Crook, to which the Arabian article al, the,

has been attached. Additional designations are: Alfonsine Tables, Icalurus or Incalurus, Herdsman's Crook or Staff; Latin, Venabulum, Hunting Spear, from its location at the top of the club in Bootes' right hand. With epsilon and psi composed the Arabian Al Aulad al Nadhlat, Low or Mean Little Ones. With omicron and rho composed the Chinese Kang Ho.

ALKES, alpha Crateris, orange, spring. Also spelled Alhes and Alker. All signify The Cup and come from Al Kas, an early name for the whole constellation meaning a shallow basin. The Latin name, Fundus vasis, Bottom of the vase, describes the star's position. Formerly this was the brightest star in the constellation, but it has grown faint.

Al KURUD, theta and kappa Columbae, winter. From the Arabic meaning The Apes.

AL MA'AZ, epsilon Aurigae, winter. Arabian for The He Goat. Also called Al 'Anz. Epsilon with zeta and eta form a small isoscles triangle called The Kids.

ALMACH, gamma Andromedae, ternary, topaz-yellow, emerald-green, blue, autumn. Also spelled Alamac, Alamak, Alamech, Almaac, Almaack, Almak, all from Al 'Anak al 'Ard, a small predatory animal similar to a badger, and popularly known as Al Barid. Usually interpreted to mean The Jackal, the animal that guides the lion to its prey. This name does not seem to be associated with Andromeda and probably comes from a very early Arab astronomy. Also called Al

Rijl al Musalsalah, The Foot of the Woman. In China, this star with others in Andromeda and in Triangulum formed Tien Ta Tseang, Heaven's Great General, which astrologically was honorable and eminent.

AL MINHAR AL ASAD, chi Leonis, double, yellow and blue, spring. From the Arabic meaning The Lion's Nose.

AL NA'IR, alpha of Grus, autumn. From the Arabic meaning The Bright One, i.e. of the Fish's Tail, inasmuch as Arabs included stars of Grus in the Southern Fish. Chinese knew it as Ke.

AL NASL, gamma Sagittarii, yellow, summer. From the Arabic for The Point. Also called Zujj al Nushshabah, of similar meaning, or Al Wazl, The Junction. With beta, delta, and epsilon composed the Chinese Chi or Ki.

AL NATH, autumn. This star is the first in the horns of Aries, therefore the first mansion of the Moon. Name from Arabian means Horn Push or Butting One. Chaucer used this title for alpha star, which usually is called Hamal.

ALNIHAN (ALNILAM), epsilon Orionis, white, winter. From the Arabic Al Nathm, The String of Pearls, or The Ornament of Gold (Buckle), which is the center of the Belt.

AL NIYAT, sigma Scorpii, summer. From the Arabic meaning The Outworks of the Heart, hence a star protecting Antares, the Scorpion's Heart. It has been interpreted to mean the vein which suspends the heart.

ALPHARD, alpha Hydrae, sluggish orange-yellow, spring. The name, meaning The Solitary One, is from the Arabic Al Fard al Shuja, The Solitary One in the Serpent, and also has been written Alfard, Alphard, Alphart, Alpherd, Alphora, Alphrad, Pherd. Arabs also knew it as Al Fakar al Shuja, The Backbone of the Serpent; Al Unk al Shuja, The Neck of the Serpent; Suhel al Fard, Solitary Suhel; Suhel al Sham, Northern Suhail or Suhel. The titles are appropriate as no other bright star appears in this region of the sky. Its Latin name is Cor Hydrae, Hydra's Heart; and medieval titles still in use are Kalb Elhavich, Kalbelaphard, and Collum Hydrae, Hydra's Neck. It is the most prominent star in the Chinese asterism Vermilion or Red Bird.

ALPHECCA, alpha Coronae Borealis, brilliant white, seen in summer. The name, also written Alphaca, is from the Arabian Al Na'ir al Fakkah, The Bright One of the Dish. The name also is said to signify The Broken One, a reference to the incomplete or broken circle of stars that make up the whole constellation.

Latin names are: Gemma, a word related to bud, an allusion to the unopened blossoms and leaves of the floral crown. Gemma Coronae; Gnosia Stella Coronae. Margarita Coronae, the Pearl of the Crown, which among Christians became Saint Marguerite. Munier and Munic used in the middle ages was said to be "of the Babylonians" and intended to convey those gifted in astrology, but it is from the Arabic, synonymous with Na'ir, Bright.

The star marks the loop or knot of the ribbon along which are fastened the buds, flowers, or leaves of the wreath, shown in early drawings with two long streamer ends.

ALPHERATZ, alpha Andromedae, double, white and purplish, autumn. Also called Alpherat and Sirrah, all from the Arabian Al Surrat al Faras, The Horse's Navel, as this star formerly was part of Pegasus, whence it was transferred to the Woman's Hair, and inspired someone to give it the strange title Umbilicus Andromedae. On a sky map the star seems to bind the two constellations. Late Arabian astronomers described the star as Al Ras al Mar'ah al Musalsalah, The Head of the Woman in Chains. With the stars Algenib and Caph composed the Three Guides marking the equinoctial colure, the prime meridian of the heavens. With alpha, beta, and gamma Pegasi, the Great Square, it constituted the double Hindu nakshatra (26th and 27th), Purva and Uttara Bhadrapadas, Former and Latter Auspicious Feet; also called Pratishthana, a stand or support, and Proshthapada, Footstool Feet.

The Chinese name for its 14th hsiu or lunar station, composed of Alpheratz and gamma Pegasi, is Pi or Peih, a wall or fortress. Anciently it was called Lek. These stars composed the 27th lunar station for the following: Arabs, who described it as Al Fargu, Rear Water Spout of the Water-jar, or Al Fargh al Thani, The Second Spout; Coptic people, who called it Artulosia; Khorasmian, whose name was Wabir; Persian with the name Miyan; and Sogdian with the title Bar Farshat,

these last four all meaning Water Spout.

The 17th century English called the star Andromeda's Head.

In astrology it portends honor and riches to all born under its influence.

AL RISCHA (AL RESCHA), alpha Piscium, pale green and bluish, autumn. From the Arabian Al Risha, The Cord, a word which traces back to the Babylonian Riksu, Cord, and refers to the cord or rope drawing up the bucket, which is now called the Great Square in Pegasus. Popularly called Knot Star of The Knot from its position where the two bands tie the fishes together. Additional designations are: Arabic, Al Hait Kittaniyy, The Flaxen Thread or Rope. Latin: Alligamentum linteum (or luteum), Projection of Binding Flax; Linum borum and austrinum, northern and southern Flax; Vincla, Bonds; Commissura Piscium, Desmos, Nodus, Nodus coelestis, Nodus duorum filorum, Nodus Piscium, Sundesmos, all tracing back to Greek words meaning Knot of the Fishes, or the Threads, translated into the Arabic Ukd al Haitain, and coming back into European lists as Kaitain and Okda.

ALSHAIN (ALSCHAIN), beta Aquilae, double, pale orange, summer. The name is from the Persian Shahin Tarazad, meaning Plundering Falcon. This star, which has grown dim in the last three hundred years and is now scarcely of fourth magnitude, flanks Altair on the south. The star to Altair's north is Tarazed, which also comes from the Persian title. The Arabian

name is Al Unuk al Ghurab,
Raven's Neck, from its position
in the neck of the eagle.

AL SHARASIF, beta Cratris,
spring. From the Arabic, meaning The Ribs, i.e. of Hydra.
Located at the southern tip of
Crater.

ALTAIR, alpha Quilae, white
or pale yellow, summer.

During the Han dynasty, over
2,000 years ago, men began to
doubt that the raging torrents of
the Yellow River, China's Sorrow,
could have its source in the gently
flowing stream of the Galaxy. To
settle the matter, Emperor Wu Ti
sent one of his ministers, Chang
K'ien (or Ch'ien) on an expedition to discover the river's
source. Chang K'ien already
had penetrated regions to the
west, fabled abode of giants and
genii, when he set out to trade
with the people of Turkestan. On
another adventure he had been
held a prisoner for ten years in
the north. Fearless, he loved
the mysteries of the wilderness
and the challenge of the unknown.

His course, against the muddy
river's current, was long and
winding. At first he passed busy
villages and farms; gradually
they thinned out, and finally the
last cultivated field lay behind
him. The landscape was wilder
than any he had ever seen, and
steering the boat between jagged
mountain palisades required all
his strength. Growing weary,
he dozed for a short time and,
when he opened his eyes, the
river was placid, a narrow
stream indolently drifting through
a pleasant meadow land with
willows shading both banks. The
air was delightfully clear and
warm, like that of a mild sum-

mer day. After the sun had
set, although he saw no moon,
Chang K'ien was astonished that
the night was without darkness.
A brilliant white light, more
radiant than that of the moon,
outlined the landscape through
the willow trees. Earth, as
well as sky, was a deep sapphire blue; the stream beneath
him was silver and reflected
thousands of stars on its still
surface. The stars themselves
were nearer and brighter than
he had ever seen them. He
knew he must be in the world
above, and he continued on for
days until he reached the
Western Paradise, where the
fragrance of the Peach Tree of
Life intoxicated him. It grew
beside a lake of jewels, its
branches perfumed with cinnamon,
and herbs, its leaves rustling as
birds with iridescent wings
stirred among them. The timid
moon rabbit fled when he approached it, and he saw the
four great creatures who rule
the four quarters, the four
benevolent living things, the Blue
Dragon, who presided over the
east and spring; Vermilion Bird,
who presided over the south and
summer; White Tiger, who
presided over the west and
autumn; Black Tortoise, who
presided over the north and
winter. On he went until he
came to a white city that
stretched along the shore of the
river. There he found a beautiful young woman weaving at the
water's edge, her shuttle flashing the colors of the rainbow as
it went back and forth across
a tapestry as sheer as a spider's
web. Downstream, across the
river, a young herdsman led his
oxen to the water to drink. Chang
K'ien stopped to ask the spinner
if she would give him the
country's name. She smiled,

shook her head, and all she would say was, "Take this shuttle from my loom, and when you return to your own city show it to Kun P'ing, the astronomer. Tell him how you came by it, and he will let you know where you have been today."

The return voyage passed quickly; he traveled with the current, and his boat seemed to glide along without assistance. When he reached home he reported all he had seen to the emperor, and then he hurried to see Kun P'ing. The astronomer was a man of marvelous powers; he was able to harden snow into silver, let sunlight flow in the veins of crude metals until gold was created; he could mount the dragon of the sky, tame him with reins of twisted clouds, and soar above the nine heavens. When he saw the shuttle he questioned the explorer closely concerning the day and hour he had received it, and then referred to his own astronomical calculations. Turning back to Chang K'ien, he said, "On the 7th day of the 7th moon of this year I was just about to observe the annual meeting of Chih Nu and Ch'ien Niu when I saw a stranger star (temporary star or planet) come between them. I wondered about it at the time. You must have been that star; you were without a doubt sailing on the celestial stream."

Ch'ien Niu was a celestial cowherd who had married Chih Nu, a spinning or weaving maid, while on a visit to earth. He brought her back to heaven with him and, they were so happy, they neglected their duties. This greatly displeased the king and queen of heaven, so the queen, with one stroke of her great

silver hair-pin, made a line across the heavens and created a river, the Milky Way, that separated the lovers. The king, sorry for their intense grief, gave them permission to visit each other once a year on the 7th day of the 7th moon. That they might meet, all the magpies in the world gather on that day and place themselves wing to wing to form a bridge on which the lovers may come together. If the night is clear, the lovers burn with five different colors; if rain falls during the day, it indicates that the lovers are weeping for joy upon meeting; showers at night are the tears of parting. By the time the birds break up the bridge and return to their respective homes, there heads are bare, the feathers worn off by the trampling feet of the couple and their retinues. As this event occurs during moulting time, bare heads are understandable. Rain is quite likely, as these are stars of the rainy season. Ch'ien Niu, who typifies the unending longing of love, is the star Altair, whose flocks are the clouds that he leads to the river, Milky Way. His wife is the star Vega, patroness of marriage, who at dawn weaves or harmonizes the forces of night and day, and corresponds to the Fates in occidental myths. Any magpie seen about its usual haunts on this auspicious day is stoned by children for its indifference to its deities. The herdsman, also called Niu Lang, is known as Hikoboshi or Kengiu to the Japanese and Ching Yu to the Koreans. His wife's Japanese name is Ori-hime, and in Japan the festival is called Tanabata. The 7th day of the 7th month was a calculation in the old lunar calendar; the festival falls about mid-August where the western style solar calendar has been adopted.

Altair is from the Arabic name for the Shaft, meaning Flying Eagle, and appears in other forms, such as: Alcair, Alcar, Alchayr, Althair, Athair, Atair, Attair. Additional designations are: Euphratean, Erign, Powerful Bird, or Idxu (Idkhu), Eagle. Khorasmian: Sadmasij, Noble Falcon. Persian: Muru, The Bird. Sogdian: Shad Mashir. Zend: Vanant, the western quarter of the heavens.

Altair and the two bright stars Alshain and Tarazed, that flank it and compose the Shaft of Altair, of Family of Aquila, the Arabs called Al Nasr al Tair, The Flying Eagle, and the Chinese called Ho Koo, a river drum. This asterism formed the 23rd Hindu lunar station Sravana, The Ear, over which Vishnu ruled, and represented the three strides with which the god strode through the heavens, a trident being the symbol. Also known as Asvattha, Sacred Fig Tree, and Srona, Lame. These three stars have been mistaken for the three gems in Orion's belt, although they are not so bright. They are most alike when after dark in mid-October Orion's Belt comes up in the east and The Shaft sets in the west. However, they can be distinguished by the unevenness of the Aquila stars, for those in Orion's Belt are markedly uniform both in brilliance and spacing.

Although important to mariners, who compute longitude at sea by the moon's distance from it, astrologically it is a mischief-maker and a bringer of danger, especially from reptiles.

It is in full beauty when it appears at twilight about June 15th with a bright companion on either side. The meridian is reached about September 1, and it lingers in the sky until mid-October. The Galaxy, supposedly made up of a vast ring of enormously distant stars composed of subsidiary spirals extending around the celestial sphere, is especially brilliant in the vicinity of Altair, where it spans the heavens like a great dimly-luminous arch, that separates into two distinct branches.- Altair marks the junction.

AL TAIS, delta Draconis, deep yellow, spring. From the Arabic meaning The Goat. Its Latin name is Nodus Secundus, Second Knot, possibly because it sinks into the dragon's second coil.

ALTERF (AL TARF), lambda Leonis, red, spring. From the Arabic meaning The Eye, or Glance, i.e. of the Lion. Sometimes said to signify The End. Part of the 9th manzil. The Coptic name is Piautos, Eye; the Persian, Nahn, Nose.

AL THALIMAIN, an asterism composed of iota and lambda in Aquila, summer. From the Arabic meaning The Two Ostriches.

ALUDRA, eta Canis Majoris, pale red, winter. The title comes from Al Adhra, singular form of Al Adhara, and means Virginity or The Virgin. It is in the dog's tail, and with omicrom and other small stars in the constellation composed the Chinese group Ke. See Adhara.

AL ZIRR, xi Geminorum,

winter. From the Arabian meaning The Button. One of the stars
in the 6th manzil.

ANCHA, theta Aquarii,
autumn. From medieval Latin,
meaning The Hip, i.e. of the
water carrier. Despite its name,
it appears on current maps on
the front of the figure in the
belt. The French spell the word
hanche, our haunch. The star's
Chinese name is Lei, a Tear.

ANTARES, alpha Scorpii, a
binary, fiery red and emerald
green, seen in summer.

Along the Euphrates, in
Guatemala, Peru, and other
parts of the world, this had
been a star of the dead. In
Central Asia it was the Grave
Digger of Caravans, because as
long as journeyers saw it rise
in early morning, they believed
that robbers and death would
stalk their trail. To Cherokee,
Pawnee, and other American
Indians, souls at death traveled
southward over the Milky Way, a
road on which diverse dangers,
including treacherous animals
and raging torrents, were encountered. Those who made their
way to the most southerly station
rested for eternity on Antares,
the Spirit Star.

Once this luminary was a
symbol of Selk, Egyptian reptile
goddess or earth mother, who
was proclaimed at sunrise at
the autumnal equinox, the season
of decline for both earth and
the star; or of Isis, who wept
when she discovered all the dismembered parts of her husband's
body except the phallus. In one
phase of Egyptian astronomy,
an immense sky figure, the
Menat, which probably extended
from Antares to Arcturus,

provided those under its influence
with conjugal happiness, and
people wore miniature Menats as
talismans for strength to the
reproductive organs and to assure
rebirth in spring.

Some biblical scholars have
identified the Kesil (K'sil or
Hasil) of the Hebrews with this
star. More often Kesil is said
to be Orion or Arcturus. Nine-
teenth century scholars have connected Antares with the Lance-
star mentioned in the Book of
Job:

Who hath put wisdom into the
Lance-star?
Or given understanding to the
Bow-star?

The identification is sheer
conjecture; Procyon also is said
to be the Lance-star.

Antares is from Greek words
meaning Similar to, a Rival of,
or Equivalent of Ares (Mars),
which is either a reference to
its ruddy hue or the fact that
Scorpion is the House of the war
god. Sophocles called it
Vespertilio, Bat, which in error
has been translated Rebel. The
name also is said to come from
the Arabic Antar's (Antarah's)
Star. Antarah was a mulatto
warrior-hero who lived before
Mohammed.

Additional designations:

Arabic: Kalb al Akrab, Heart
of the Scorpion, an aspect
frequently applied to it. This
name decayed into Aakrab,
Alcantub, Al Kalb (The Heart),
Cabalatrab, Cabolacrabi, Calb-
alarcab, Calbalatrab, Kelbala-
crab.

Babylonian: Hurru, meaning

uncertain, the 24th ecliptic constellation. Also known as Urbat.

Chinese: Hsin, Ta Who, Who
Sing. Antique documents indicate
it was the Fire Star, the Great
Fire, or the Red and Unlucky
Star.

Coptic: Kharthian, the
Heart.

Euphratean: Bilu-sha-ziri,
Lord of Seed; Dar Lugal, the
King who was lord or lightning; .
Kakkab Bir, Vermilian Bird;
Kak-shisa, Creator of Prosperity,
a name more often assigned to
Sirius; Lugal Tudda, Lusty
King; Masu Sar, Hero-King, a
probable reference to the war
lord; Udda-an-khu, Day-Heaven-
Bird, which seems to confirm the
idea that this star, or the con-
stellation, originally was
venerated as an eagle.

Hindu: With stars sigma and
tau Scorpii, it constituted the
nakshatra Jyestha, Oldest.

Khorasmian: Dharind, the
Seizer.

Latin: Cor Scorpii, Heart
of the Scorpion; Insidiata, Lurk-
ing One; Tyrannus.

Persian: Gel, the Red, a
lunar station; Sataves (Satavaesa
or Satevis), one of the four
Royal Stars, which drives away
the stench from waters and
makes them pure. Sometimes
Sataves is identified as Musca
or the Southern Cross.

Sogdian: Maghan sadwis, Great
One saffron-colored.

ARCTURUS, alpha Bootis,
ruddy yellow when near the
horizon red, seen in spring.

The manner in which it follows
Ursa Major around the skies,
always at a safe distance but
nevertheless at the heels of the
great beast, made hunter,
shepherd, or guardian natural
descriptions. All fables connect
Arcturus with the Great Bear.
When the luminaries of the constellation were described as wild
animals, the role of Arcturus
was that of a bold hunter; if
they were seven bulls or oxen
grazing in one of the most northerly of meadows, Arcturus was
their herdsman, if they were
parts of a plough in a field under
cultivation, Arcturus was the
ploughman. He was the sentry
who patrolled the borderline
between equatorial and circumpolar stars, seeing that each
remained in its proper place.

The Greek myths of Arcas and
Icarius are identified with this
star as well as with the constellation Bootes. In some interpretations of the Arthur legend,
his name means ploughman, and
he was the divine instructor of
agriculture in his astral role of
Arcturus; others believe Arctus,
both Bears, was intended, inasmuch as Arthur remained eternally vigilant, awaiting his country's
call for aid. Identification of this
star with the biblical Mezarim
was probably an error in the
Vulgate. Arctus or the Bears
may have been intended.

Among the Arabs, he was the
shepherd who guarded The Fold,
located far in the north, forever
circling the outskirts of his land
to make sure his flocks were
safe. To Persians it was the
Second Calf of Leo, Spica being
the lion's First Calf.

With Spica it marked the tips
of the two horns of the great

Dragon, a giant figure that stretched across the skies from Virgo to Sagittarius in spring and sent rain that aided seeds planted in the sun to grow. These two stars were the first of the Dragon to appear and gave notice of the approach of spring. Its golden hues in the twilight was a reassurance to the Chinese that verdure would soon be seen.

The star's brilliance and position have made it an object of great interest and admiration since prehistoric times, and it appears to have been among the first stars singled out. The present title is from the Greek meaning Bear Guard, or Keeper, or Watcher. Its name may come from two Greek words signifying Bear's Tail, also relating to its proximity to the Bear.

Additional designations are: Javelin Bearer; Runaway Star, a popular name by reason that it has a more rapid motion than any of the other bright stars.

Arabic: Al Haris al Sama, Keeper of Heaven, perhaps from the star's early visibility in the twilight owing to its great northern declination. Al Simak al Ramih, Leg of the Lance Bearer or Lofty Lance Bearer, or Simak Armed with a Lance, inasmuch as the star marked a spear in the hunter's hand. Simak is from the Persian for elevated or high altitude. From this title came Al Ramec, Aramakh, Aramec, Aremech, Ariamech, Ascimec, Azimech, Azimeth, Somech haramach. From the Greek came Kheturus.

Brythonic: Arthur's Wain, Arthur's Wagon; Arthurus; Arture; Wain of Arthur.

Chaldean: Papsukal, Guardian Messenger, divinity of Tibitu, the 10th month.

Chinese: Ta Kio, Great Horn. Another designation carried the meaning Palace of Emperors. Four small stars nearby are Kang Che, Drought Lake.

Eskimoan: Sibwudli, the timepiece of seal netters, who hunted during the season of darkness in December and January. Its circling around the Pole enabled them to judge the passing hours of the night.

Euphratean: Sib-zi-anna, Shepherd of Heavenly Herds or Shepherd of the Life of Heaven. Included in this name was eta star, making one of the several sets of Euphratean Twins. The name also applied to the whole constellation.

German: Arctur.

Greek: Arktos (Arctus), Bear, which applied as well to Ursa Major and Minor. Arktophilaxe or Arktophylax, Bearwarden, which seems more fitting.

Hebrew: Job's Star, an allusion to Mezarim.

Hindu: Aryaman, an Aditya and wooer of maidens, although this may more properly be a name of Capella. Nishtya, Outcast. Although it formed a whole division of the lunar zodiac in India, it is so far north it is quite outside the zodiacal belt along which the sun and moon move. It probably had been selected as the 15th lunar station because it is much brighter than any of the stars in the region to its south; being alone it was

seen as an outcast. Another of
the nakshatra's names is Svati,
Good Goer (perhaps Sword).

Italian and Spanish: Arturo.

Latin and Low Latin:
Arctuzona, Ariture, Arturis.
Audiens (Audens may have been
intended, meaning Audacious or
Bold One). Gladius, Kolanza,
Pugio, indicating the hunter was
at times shown with a sword,
lance, or dagger in his hand.

Persian: Mas-i-miyan-i-as-
man, Great-one-of-the-middle-
of-the sky. Some astronomers
give this as the name of Capella.
Tishtrya (or Tistar), although
this is more often assigned to
Sirius.

Shawnee Indian: White Hawk,
who was the husband of one of
the 12 dancing maidens of Corona
Borealis.

In early ages its influence
was dreaded, star-readers assumed when it was near the
equinoxes that it portended
fierce tempests and bad harvests.
Hippocrates believed that it influenced humans, saying that a dry
season after it rises, "agrees
best with those who usually are
phlegmatic, with those who are
of a humid temperaments, and
with women, but it is almost
inimical to the bilious, and this
disease is apt to prove critical
in these days." Modern astrologers aver that those born under
its influence are destined to have
honor and riches conferred on
them.

Arcturus is a relatively aged
sun surrounded with a veil of
absorbing metallic vapors that
cut off much of his radiance and
gives him a ruddy, fiery hue,

especially when he is seen at the
time of crossing the horizon.
Plautus said that Arcturus was a
stormy sign when he rose and
set.

When moist Arcturus clouds
    the sky.
        (Pope)

Anciently it was famous with
seafarers, and they regulated
their annual festival by its movements in relation to the sun,
but its influence was dreaded.

It is situated near the left
knee of Bootes and, rising when
the sun sets at the end of
March, it is the harbringer of
spring and glorifier of summer.
In Hesiod's time it rose 50 days
after the winter solstice.

ARKAB (URKAB), beta
Sagitarii, double, summer.
From the Arabic Ul Urkub,
Tendon, i.e. united the calf of
the leg and the heel. Popular
titles are Achilles Tendon,
Archer's Tendon. The Euphratean
title was Ur-ner-grub, Sole of
the Left Foot. It lies too deep
in the south to be seen in
northern latitudes.

ARNEB, alpha Leporis, double,
pale yellow and gray, winter.
From the Arabian name for the
whole constellation meaning The
Hare. Also called Arsh.

ASCIAUKAT, alpha of Lynx,
winter. Ptolemy included it
among the stars of Ursa Major.
From the Arabic Al Shaukah,
A Thorn. Also called Mabsu-
that or Mabsutah, Expanded.

ASELLI, delta and gamma
Cancri, late in winter. The
name is from the Latin meaning Asses. The stars are

respectively Ascellus (Asellus) Australis and Ascellus (Asellus) Borealis. Ascellus Australis, delta, is a double of straw color. Its name is literally Southern Little Ass, that is south of Praesepe. Babylonians, who used it to mark their 13th ecliptic constellation, called it Arku-sha-nangaru-sha-shutu, Southeastern Star in the Crab. Ascellus Borealis, The Northern Little Ass, gamma, is a fainter star of straw color. Together they are called Asini, popularly known as the Donkeys. Their Arabian name is Al Himarain, The Two Asses, and with epsilon they mark the 8th manzil called Al Nathrah, The Gap, i.e. in the hair under the Lion (Praesepe). Accadians called them Gu-shir-kes-da, Yoke of the Enclosure. The Chaldaic name for this pair may be translated muddiness, which may have alluded to the discoloring of the Nile, which rose when the sun entered Cancer. Astrologically these two stars give a burning nature, accidents by fire, or a violent death to those under its influence. Weatherwise, their dimness was a conclusive precursor of rain. When fog conceals the Aselli to the northeast, high winds from the south are to be expected; when the southern star is concealed the wind will be from the northeast.

ASTERION, most northerly of the star groups in Canes Venatici, spring. Name from the Greek meaning starry. Sometimes called the northern dog, whereas its companion Chara, is the southern dog.

ATLAS, a double classified as one of the Pleiades, Tauri, intensely white, winter. By Pleione, he became the father of the Hyades and the Pleiades. Revered for his wisdom, he gave mankind a knowledge of astronomy and navigation. In the Titanomachia, the war against Zeus, he sided with the Titans and, when they lost, he was condemned to stand forever supporting the heavens on his back. As an axis god, a pillar, hence a phallus or fertilizer. Calypso, who dwelt on the island of Ogygia, or navel of the sea, was another of his daughters. In later legends he transformed into mountains to hold up the heavens and supposedly stood at the extreme west of the world, probably at northwest Africa, the gate to the Atlantic, the ocean named after him. Also called Pater Atlas. With the star Pleione, Atlas makes the handle of the Pleiad Dipper.

AZELFAFAGE, pi Cygni, summer. Possibly a corrupted form of Adelfalferes from Al Thif al Fara, The Horse's Foot or Track. Or the title may be from 'Azal al Dajajah, The Tail of the Hen, which it marks.

BAHAM, theta Pegasi, autumn. From the Arabic Sa'd al Bahaim, Good Luck of the Two Beasts, or the Lucky Star of the Flock. Also written Biham, which signifies Young of domestic animals. On the Dresden Globe it appears as Al Hawa'im, The Thirty Camels. It is situated at the top of the horse's head.

BATEN KAITOS, zeta Ceti, topaz yellow, winter. From the Arabic Al Batn al Kaitos, The Whale's Belly, although the star is higher up in the body. In the middle ages spelt Batenel Kaitos, Batenkaiton, Boten. In astrology it portends falls and

The Stars 309

blows.

BEEMIM (BEEMUM),
upsilon Eridani, double, winter.
From the Hebrew Bammayim,
In the Water. Also called The-
emim, from the Arabic Al Thalim, The Ostrich, or Al Tauaman, The Twins.

BELLATRIX, gamma Orionis,
pale yellow, slightly variable,
seen in winter. From the Latin
meaning Female Warrior. Also
called Amazon Star. Other
Arabic names were: Al Murzim
al Najid, The Roaring Conqueror
or The Conquering Lion, who
heralded his presence by his
roar, as if this star, in the
giant's left shoulder, the first of
his principal luminaries to appear
above the eastern horizon, announced the coming forth of the
more brilliant Betelgeuze and
Rigel. Al Najid, The Conqueror,
from the foregoing. Al Ruzam,
A Camel, another roarer.

In an Amazon River legend,
the star is a youth, who, in a
canoe with an elder of the tribe,
Tetelgeuze, chases the Peixie
Boi (Pixy Boy), a dark spot
near Orion.

It is the natal star of all who
are destined to receive civil or
military honors. Women under
its influence are lucky and fluent,
as Thomas Hood said, "They shall
have mighty tongues."

BENETNASCH. See Alcaid.

**BETELGEUZE (BETELGEUX,
BETELGUESE),** alpha Orionis,
a binary, irregularly variable,
topaz or orange-red, the color
deepening as the star grows
fainter, which indicates that it
may be entering early stages of
extinction; seen in winter. The
name from the Arabic Ibt al
Jauzah signifies Armpit of the
Center One, or Armpit of the
White Belted Sheep. This
degenerated into Bed Elgueze,
Beit Algueze, Beldengenze,
Beteigeuze, Bet El-geuze. Other
Arabian names: Al Dhira, The
Arm; Al Mankib The Shoulder;
Al Yad al Yamna, The Right
Hand - all of the giant. Ied
Algeuze, Orion's Hand. Mirzam
from Al Murzim, Roarer or An-
nouncer, as herald of compan-
ions to follow. In the middle
ages this degenerated into
Almerzamo nnagied.

A popular title is Martial
Star, and additional designations are: Coptic: Klaria, Arm-
let.

Euphratean: Gula, Lugal, or
Ungal, all meaning King. Other
stars probably were included.
With gamma and lambda, it composed Kakkab Sar, Constellation of the King.

Hindu: Ardra, Moist, alluding
to its stormy character. The
star's rising ushered in the rainy
season. Another Sanscrit name
was Bahu, Arm.

Persian: Besn, Arm.

In Astrology portended civic,
kingly, or military honors.

BOTEIN, delta Arietis,
autumn. From the Arabic Al
Butain, The Bully. With zeta
formed the Chinese Tsin Yin.

BRACHIUM, gamma Scorpii,
summer. Name from the Latin
Brachia, meaning claw or Arm.
Cornu, Horn, was a later addition to the name. Additional
designations: Accadian, Entena-
mas-luv, or Ente-mas-mur,

which was identical with the As-
syrian Etsin, Tail-tip.   Ara-
bic: Al Zuban al Janubiyyah,
The Southern Claw, which con-
tracted into Zuben el Genubi.
Zuban al Akrab, Claw of the
Scorpion, which became Zuban
al Kravi, Zuben Acrabi, Zuben
Hakrabi.   Chinese: Chin Chay,
Camp Carriage.

CANOPUS (CANOBUS,
KANUPUS),   alpha Carina,
bluish white, the second brightest
star in the heavens, seen in
winter from the Gulf States, but
not visible further north.   It
bears the Greek name of an
Egyptian seaport and, by
tradition, the chief pilot of
Menelaus.   The town was twelve
miles east of Alexandria at the
mouth or canpoic branch of the
Nile in the Bay of Aboukir at the
ancient boundary of Asia and
Africa.   Its native name was
Karob, and it was noted for
several temples, among them the
great one of Serapis, Egyptian
underworld and healing or fertility god, who was consulted in
dream oracles, and a temple of
Heracles, who here stood for
Amen.   Serapis typified the
united souls of the two gods
Osiris and Apis (Asar-Hapi) after
death.   Serapis or Osiris was
worshipped in a peculiar form,
a vase with a human head, and is
believed to be identical with the
pilot.   Through an old misunderstanding that the deity was
associated with death rather than
a guardian of riches underground
or a sentinel of the mouth of
the river, the name canopic was
applied to vases with human and
animal heads in which the Egyptians placed internal organs
after embalming.   Aboukir means
Father Cyprus and refers to a
Coptic saint of that name.   Canopus, on the return from the

destruction of Troy, piloted the
fleet of Menelaus into this port.
When he placed his foot on the
ground he was bitten by a poisonous snake and died (the sun
died upon touching earth).   On
the spot of the fatal bite, his
grateful master raised a monu-
ment, and gave the pilot's name
to the city as well as to the
splendid star which rose as he
made his dedicatory speech.   The
connection between Osiris, a
sun deity, and Canopus led Egyptians to call it the Star of
Osiris.   In Ptolemaic times the
city became renowned as a center
of vice and dissipation frequented
by inhabitants of nearby Alexandria, and it was from temple
terraces here that Claudius
Ptolemy made his astronomical
observations and worked on his
theories of the universe that
have survived through the ages.

Additional designations:

Arabic: Al Fahl, Camel Station, a name that indicates that
everywhere, even on the desert,
it was an important star.   A
great favorite among the nomads,
it was the source of many of the
Arabian proverbs, stories, and
superstitions.   It supposedly
imparted the much prized color
to precious stones and provided
immunity from disease.   Hadar,
ground.   Suhail or Al Sahl,
brilliant, which comes from Al
Suhail al Yamaniyyah, Brilliant
one of the South, and which
corrupted into Sihil, Sohayl,
Sohel, Subhel, Suhel, Suhil,
Suhilon.   Suhail became a per-
sonal title in Arabia, the symbol
of that which is brilliant, glorious,
and beautiful, and even to this
day nomads apply it to a handsome person.   Suhail was a
beautiful youth who was situated
in space near the attractive

maiden Al Jauzah, whom he married and murdered, whereupon he was forced to flee and went south, where he remains, to be seen by those only in the southern hemisphere. In another legend, he wooed Al Jauzah, who not only refused him but kicked him into the southern heavens. Among Persians, Suhail is a synonym of wisdom. Another name of the star was Wazn, weight.

Chinese: Laou Jin, The Old Man.

Christians of the 6th century: Star of Saint Catherine, which appeared to Greek and Russian pilgrims as they approached her shrine at Sinai after they had left Gaza, their landing place.

Coptic: Kahi Nub, Golden Earth.

Egyptian: Ptolemaeon or Ptolemaeus, a late title to honor Ptolemy Lagos. Subilon, reason unknown. Several Egyptian temples were oriented to it, probably as early as 6,400 B. C. when it heralded the sunrise at the autumnal equinox and became known as a symbol of Khensu (Khons or Khonus), the first southern star god. Later, perhaps about 2,100 B.C., at least two temples pointed to its setting. In early southern Egypt, it probably was a prominent object in religion and represented the god of waters. Star of Egypt, a protector of the land, became a popular title among the people who adored it.

Euphratean: Sugi, Chariot Yoke. However, this identification is not positive, some astronomers claim it belongs to other stars, especially the lucida of Libra.

German: Schif-stern, Shipstar.

Hindu: Agastya, a rishi who, in an argument with Nahusa, who had permitted a drought to wither earth, hurled Nahusa from heaven and caused him to dwell in snake form for 10,000 years. The sage was a son of Varuna, goddess of waters, and was the helmsman of the Argha, which floated during the deluge. Agastya purified the waters that had been poured out at Indra's command by snakes whose bodies were wrapt in clouds and were poisonous (muddy from rains which preceded his rising). He cleared the waters spontaneously like an act of the heart of one virtuous. Thus he was worshipped as one who drives back impurity and turbidness. In the Avesta the star is mentioned as pushing the waters forward (governing the tides).

Italian: With Achernar and Fomalhaut it made up the Tre Facelle, symbol of Faith, Hope, and Charity.

Latin: Gubernaculum, Rudder; Karbana; Karbarnit. Ponderosus and Terrestris, names which may come from the nearness of the star to the horizon.

Persian: Sataves, the chieftan of the south, protector of the seas and southern quarter, who, when he rises, makes waters pure.

Arabs used its heliacal rising in computing their year; it ripened their fruits, ended the heat of the summer, and set the time for weaning young camels. In a general way it served them as a southern pole star. Hindus fancied it to be in the rudder of

the deluge ship. At the 37th
parallel it is visible just above
the horizon in the evening about
February 6th.

CAPELLA, alpha Aurigae,
brilliant creamy white, winter.
A star of first magnitude that
shines as the heart of Auriga's
imaginary goat. The oldest
record of the star extant is that
on a tablet with a probable date
of 2,000 B.C., which has been
translated, "When on the first
day of Nisan (April), the star
of stars (Dil-gan) and the moon
are parallel, the year is normal.
When on the 3rd day of the month,
Nisan, the star of stars and the
moon are parallel, that year is
full."

In Egypt on the Denderah
zodiac, the star's place is occupied by a mummied cat in the
outstretched hand of a male
figure crowned with feathers, a
badge of most deities. An important star in the temple worship of Ptah, architect of the
universe and cleaver or opener
of the way. It may have borne
that divinity's name, and his
temple at Karnak near Thebes
was oriented to its setting about
1,700 B.C.

Greeks looked upon this star
as the sacred goat Amalthea, who
put aside her own children to
nurse Zeus (Jove), her foster-
child, with her milk. She was
assisted by her sister Melissa,
a bee goddess, who gave the
infant honey. Adrastae and her
sister Ida, or Aige, all daughters
of the Cretan king Melisseus, in
some versions of the legend, were
substituted for one or the other.
Some have said the star was the
horn Zeus had broken off Amalthea when she died, making of it
a wonder and placing it in the

skies, whence it is called
Cornucopia. This title also
has been applied to the horn of
Capricorn, the Sea-goat.

The title is from the Latin
meaning Little She Goat. Additional designations are Horn of
Antimony, Paint Horn.

Accadian: Dil-gan I-Ku,
Messenger of Light, or Dil-gan
Babili, Patron Star of Babylon.

Arabic: Al Hadi, The Singer,
i.e. who rides before a procession and urges on the camels with
the Hadwa. The star's promi-
nence in the evening sky seemed
to give the impression of watching over or driving on the nearby
Pleiades (camels). Al Hadi also
was said to be the overseer of
the Meisir game, the Pleiades
the players. Al Rakib, the
Driver, because it appears in
the evening twilight earlier than
other stars and in this manner
leads or drives them. Mongrel
titles from the above are:
Alathod, Alatudo, Alhajoc,
Alhajoth, Alkatod, Atud, Ayyuk,
which it shared with the constellation. Alcahela may have come
from the Latin Capella. With
zeta and eta, The Kids, this
star formed the group Al Inaz
or Al Anz, The Goat.

Assyrian: I-ku, Leader, i.e.
of the year; Askar, the tempest
god; Ma-a-tu.

Babylonian: Iku or Icu, Goat.
In January-February, Ishtar was
Iku; in May-June, Marduk was
Iku. Each month Marduk was
another star, but his Babylonian
temple was oriented to this one.

Chinese: Woo Chay, Five
Chariots or Chariots of Five
Emperors, with the stars beta,

gamma, theta, kappa.

English poets: Shepherd's Star, an allusion to the season of its culmination, when flocks are tended.

French: Chevre.

Greek: Amalthea.

Hebrew: Ayyuk, Goat. This may have applied to another star. Ash or Ayish is sometimes placed here, but this title more likely belongs to Aldebaran in company with the Hyades.

Hindu: Brahma Ridaya, Brahma's Heart.

Latin and Low Latin: Caper or Capra, She Goat; Capra Olenie, Goatfat. Capella is the diminutive of Capra. Hircus, Goat-smell. Jovis Nutrix, Jove's Nurse, i.e. Amalthea. Olenium Astrum, Fatty Star. Ophiultus, unintelligible.

Lithuanian: Food-bearer, which seems to be related to the Cornucopia.

Peruvian Quichuas: Colca, a star connected with the life of shepherds.

Phoenician: Iyutha, a title also applied to Aldebaran.

Spanish: Cabrilla.

Capella is nearer the north pole than any other 1st magnitude or zero star and is the 5th brightest of all in the firmament. Because it is so high in the sky it can be seen for over 20 hours out of the 24, rising 3 hours and 26 minutes after it sets, every night of the year in some part of its course. It presides over the stars of winter, and in this section of the world, July is the only month in which it is not visible at some time before midnight. Throughout classical times known for its stormy character, and for this reason nicknamed along the Mediterranean the Rainy Goat-starre. Shepherds, who delighted in the wet season that improved their pasture lands rejoiced at seeing Capella. Mariners cursed the star that made navigation dangerous or impossible, and instituted the Natalis Navigationes festival, held when the days of the star's strength were past.

> Tempt not the winds, fore-
> warned of dangers neigh
> When the Kids glitter in the
> western sky.
> (Callimachus)

Astrologically protended civic and military honors and wealth.

CAPH, beta Cassiopeia, double, the larger star is of such a brilliant white the color of the smaller companion is lost in its glare; autumn. The name from the Arabic means The Hand, also is spelled Chaph or Kaff. It is part of the asterism known as the outstretched hand of the Pleiades, which embraces many of the stars between the Pleiades and Cassiopeia. One Arabic name for Cassiopeia signifies The Tinted Hand. Another name of Caph is Al Sanam al Nakah, Camel's Hump, an Arabian title that refers to a contemporaneous Persian figure. With beta Andromedae and gamma Pegasi, it is one of the Three Guides that mark the equinoctial colure, one of the great circles passing through the poles of the heavens. The star is useful in marking sidereal time. When above Polaris and nearest the zenith the astronomical day begins at zero hour, zero minute, and zero second; when due west the sideral time is 6 hours; when south and nearest the horizon, 12 hours; when east, 18 hours. This celestial clockhand thus moves on the heavenly dial contrary to the motion of the hands of terrestrial clocks and at but half the speed. Just north of it is an especially bright patch in the Milky Way.

CASTOR, alpha Geminorum, binary, bright white and pale white, winter. Castor and his twin brother Pollux were among the appealing heroes of Greek mythology. Pollux was immortal being the son of Zeus and Leda, but Castor possessed the ability to die, being the son of Tyndarus, the mortal form of Zeus, and Leda. When finally Castor died, Pollux pleaded with his father to take his life also, and touched by his son's devotion to his brother, the god permitted them to share immortality, one to remain awake while the other slept. Thus they alternated during the hours of day and night, Castor appearing during the period of darkness. He was the first man to ride a horse and remained the greatest charioteer of his time. In later myths, the evening star became an aspect of Apollo. In Europe it has been consistently associated with sun heroes, and medieval astronomers assigned it to Phoebus and Theseus.

Although called the leader of the constellation it now is fainter than its companion, and astronomers generally are agreed that an inversion of their brilliance has taken place in the last three centuries.

Additional designations:

Arabic: Al Awwal al Dhira, First in the Paw or Forearm. This reference is to the supposed figure of an enormous Lion, the nomad's Asad, the outstretched forearm of which alpha and beta (Pollux) marked as the Al Dhira al Mabsutat. Al Ras al Taum al Mukaddim, Head of the Foremost Twin; a term when the Arabs adopted the Greek figure. Rasalgeuze, from which came Algueze and Elgiautzi; terms also applied to beta.

Assyrian: Tur-us-mal-max, Son of the Supreme Temple, an object of great veneration.

Babylonian: Mash-mashu-mahru, The Western One of the Twins. Used to mark their 11th ecliptic constellation.

Greek: Apollo, or Apollon; Castor. Various names from the Doric dialect degenerated during the middle ages into Afelar, Anelar, Anhelar. Aphellan, Aphellar, Aphellon, Apullum, Avelar.

Latin: Eques, Horseman.

Alpha and Beta have often been named as a pair. Among such titles are the following:

Accadian: Supa, Lustrous; a lunar constellation.

Arabic: Al Dhira, The Arm; or Al Zirr, The Button; the 7th manzil. Al Dhira was also the Arabian ell, a measure of cloth about an arm in length. Al Dhira'an became a common desert name for similar pairs of stars.

Assyrian: Mas-mas, or
Tuamu, The Twins. Other
twin stars were known to this
country.

Babylonian: Mas-tab-ba-gal-
gal, The Great Twins, i.e. in
whom the sun and moon are re-
duplicated.

Chinese: Ho Choo. With
stars gamma and delta constituted
the asterism Pih Ho. Alph and
Beta with other stars also constituted the hsiu Tsing, a Well
or Pit.

Coptic; Pimafi, The Fore-
arm, i.e. of the Nile.

English, Old: The Giant's
Eyes or Eyes of the giant Daze.

Hindu: Punarvarsu, Two
Good Again, the 7th nakshatra.

Khorasmian: Jiray. Two
Stars.

Persian: Rakhvad, Canal;
Taraha, Two Stars.

Sogdian: Ghamb, Two Stars.

Together the brothers were
known as the Morning and Evening
Stars, Castor appeared in the
west in the evening, Pollux in the
east in the morning. In astrology,
Castor portends mischief and
violence. Castor is the brightest
and most beautiful double in the
northern skies, and it is the
most northerly of the two leading
stars of the constellation.

CELAENO (CELENO), one
of the Pleiades in Taurus,
silvery white, winter. Although
it can be seen at times by the
naked eye, in mythology,
Celaneno, having been struck
by lightning, sometimes is

identified as the lost sister.

The Sister Stars that once
were seven
Mourn for their missing mate
in Heaven.
(Alfred Austin)

CHARA, beta Canes Venaticus,
an asterism, spring. The name
from the Greek means Joy or
Dear, i.e. to the master's
heart. The group also is known
as the Southern Dog. In its
neck is situated the beautiful
star Cor Caroli. Its companion
is the group Asterion.

CHELEB, beta Ophiuchi, yellow.
spring. From Kalb al Rai,
Heart of the Shepherd or probably Dog of the Shepherd. In
Arabic kalb means both heart
and dog. The title degenerated
into Celabrai, Celbalrai,
Cheleb. This is an example of
how many stars are associated
with the occupations or interests
of the men who first observed
them.

CHORT, theta Leonis, spring.
A corruption of Chortan Two
Small Ribs, i.e. of the Lion.

COR CAROLI, alpha Canum
Venaticorum, double, white and
pale lilac, spring. From the
Latin meaning Heart of Charles
(of England). The honor was
paid to Charles I. In one account, which appears to be incorrect, the name was said to
be meant for Charles II when
Sir Charles Scarborough, court
physician, stated the star had
shown with special brilliancy on
the eve of the king's return to
London on May 29, 1660 after
exile. Charles II doubly
deserved the honor, for he had
founded Greenwich Observatory.
Arabian name: Al Kabd al Asad,

The Liver of the Lion; Chinese called Chang Chen, a Seat. It marks the collar of Chara and is one of the four stars forming the figure known as the Diamond of Virgo.

CUJAM, omega Herculis, summer. The title is from the Latin Caiam, accusative of Caia, a word used for the club of Hercules. Gaiam, Guiam, and Guyam used for this star are incorrect.

CURSA, beta Eridani, topaz yellow, winter. From Al Kursiyy al Jauzah, Chair, or Footstool, of the Central One, i.e. Orion. Earlier nomads placed it among a group they called Al Udha al Na'am, The Ostrich's Nest, several of which were scattered through the constellation. It also appeared as Dhalim, from Al Thalim, The Ostrich, a name also applied to theta. Chinese named it Yuh Tsing, Golden Well.

DABIH, beta Capricorni, double, orange yellow and sky blue, autumn. The name traces to Al Jabbah, The Forehead, or to Al Sa'd al Dhabih, The Lucky One of the Slaughterers, which seems the more likely, a manifestation of the sacrifice celebrated by Arabs at the heliacal rising of Capricorn. The Arabs have given fierce names to several stars in this area. With alpha it composed the 22nd manzil. The name degenerated into Dschabbe and Dshabeh. It is one of the stars of the 9th Chinese Hsiu called Niu (Nieu or Keen Nieu), Ox, which anciently was Ngu or Gu. Dabih marks the head of the Goat.

DENEB, alpha Cygni, brilliant white, culminates in summer. From the Arabic Al Dhanab al Dajajah, The Hen's Tail, it stands for the Tail. More stars bear this title, either alone or in combination with a descriptive word, than any other, and it degenerated into Denebadigege, Denebedigege, Deneb Adige, etc. Another Arabic name was Aridif from Al Ridf, the Hindmost, which became Arided, Arion, Arrioph. Latin scholars of the middle ages called it Gallina, Hen; Os Rosae from the German Rosemund; Uropygium, the Pope's nose of the festive table. Situated at the head of the cross and the root of the swan's tail, in one of the densest parts of the Milky Way, it is, like other stars far to the north, visible at some hour of every clear night throughout the year. Epsilon Aquilae is another Deneb, standing for the Tail of the Eagle.

DENEB, epsilon Delphini, late summer. From the Arabic Al Dhanab al Dulfim, The Dolphin's Tail. Another Arabic name was Al Amud al Salib, The Pillar of the Cross. Stars alpha, beta, gamma, and delta composed Al Ukud, The Pearls or Gems that adored Al Salib. This star, which lights up the dorsal of Delphinus, is known to the Chinese as Pae Chaou, Rotten Mellon. Decayed food has been the embryo for several luminaries, including the moon, in various parts of the world.

DENEB ALGEDI (or ALGIEDI) delta Capricorni, yellowish, autumn. From the Arabic for The Goat's Tail. It was the fortunate one, the bringer of good tidings. Also called Denelbalchedi, which degenerated into Scheddi. With gamma, Nashira, a purple star, called Al Muhibbain, The Two Friends, an allegorical title for any two

closely associated objects, except perhaps two mortals, which
are foreign in the nomad sky.
Probably should be Al Muhanaim,
The Two Bending Stars - in the
flexure of the tail. Deneb Algedi
marked the 28th ecliptic Babylonian constellation Arkat-sha-
hi-na-Shahu, Eastern One in the
tail of the Goat.

DENEB EL OKAB, epsilon
and zeta Aquilae, green, summer. From the Arabic Dhanab al
Okab, The Eagle's Tail.

DENEB KAITOS, beta Ceti,
yellowish white, best seen in
winter. From the Arabian Al
Dhanab al Kaitos al Janubiyy,
The Tail of the Sea Monster
towards the South, i.e. southern
branch of the tail. The title was
Latinized as Denebcaiton. Also
called Diphda, Frog, from Al
Difdi al Thani, The Second Frog,
the star Fomalhaut being the first
frog. This was Latinized as
Rana Secunda. The Chinese gave
this star the strange title of
Superintendent of Earthworks.
Iota Ceti also is a Deneb star,
sometimes spelled Dheneb.

DENEBOLA, beta Leonis,
blue, spring. An abbreviation
from Al Dhanab al Asad, The
Lion's Tail, and formerly the
mark at the tuft. Since the
beauty of the tail has been cut
off to make room for another
constellation, it indicates Leo's
eastern boundary. The title has
been written Denebalecid, Dene-
baleced, Deneb Alased, Deneb
Aleet, Dhanbol-asadi. Also
found are Alazet, Alesit, Dafira,
Nebolellesed, Nebollassid,
Nebulasit, all from a similar
Arabic term for tuft of coarse
hair at the end of the tail. Other
titles were: Al Aktab al Asad,
Viscera of the Lion; Al Kalb,

Heart, i.e. of the Lion; Al
Katab, A Small Saddle, which
seems inappropriate. As Al
Sarfah, The Changer, i.e. of
weather, it marked the 12th
manzil.

Additional designations:

Assyrian: Mikid-isati, Burning of Fire, which may have
been a reference to the hot time
of the year when the sun was
near it; Samu, Blue.

Babylonian: Zibbat A, Tail of
the Lion, which marked the 17th
ecliptic station.

Chinese: Woo Ti Tso, Seat,
or Palace, of the Five Emperors;
included with 4 other inconspicuous stars, each of which was inhabited by a monarch who controlled the site.

Coptic: Asphulia, perhaps
Tail.

Euphratean: Lamash, Colossus; Sa, Blue.

Hindu: Uttara Phalguni, the
12th nakshatra. Also called the
Star of the goddess Bahu, the
Creating Mother.

Khorasmian: Widhayu, Burning One.

Latin: Asumpha, Mutatrix,
Serpha.

Persian: Avdem, the One in
the Tail.

Sogdian: Widhu, Burning One.

Of unlucky influence, portending misfortune and disgrace,
thus opposed to Regulus, the
little king, alpha star, in character as well as in location. It

reaches its meridian May 3, and
Al Biruni wrote of it, "The heat
turns away when it rises and the
cold turns away when it disappears." With Arcturus, Spica
and Cor Caroli constitutes the
noted Diamond of Virgo. In all
probability a brighter star in the
past than it is now.

DIFDA (DIPHDA). See
Deneb Kaitos.

DSCHUBBA, delta Scorpii,
summer. From the Arabic Al
Jabhah, The Front, or Forehead. Additional designations:

Arabic: Iklil al Akrab,
Crown of the Scorpion, which
now appears as Aakrab genubi or
Iclarkrav.

Babylonian: Qablu (or Qabu)
sha rishu aqrabi, Middle of the
Head of the Scorpion and, with
beta, the 23rd ecliptic constellation.

Chinese: Wei, A Tail, and
part of the 6th Hsiu.

Coptic: Stephani, The Crown.

Euphratean: Gis-gan-gu-sur,
Light of the Hero or Tree of the
Garden of Light, which stood in
the midst of the great abyss
and was the prototype of all
Trees of Life.

Hindu: Anuradha, Propitious,
part of the 17th makshatra.

Khorasmian and Sogdian:
Bighanwand, Clawless. With
theta called Khachman, Curved.

Persian: Nur, Bright, part
of the 17th lunar station.

DUBHE, alpha Ursae Majoris,
binary, yellow, spring. An
abbreviation of the Arabic Thahr
al Dubb al Akbar, Back of the
Greater Bear. With beta,
Merak, it is one of the Pointers,
i. e. to the pole star. Being
further north, it is the nearer of
the two, and it is one of the four
stars that form the bowl of the
dipper or hind quarters of the
bear.

Additional designations: The
Keepers, Two Stars, both with
beta.

Chinese: Tien Choo, Heaven's
Pivot.

Egyptian: Ak, Eye, or
prominent one of the constellation. Also Bast Isis, who
watched over childbirth, and Ta-
urt Isis, likewise a maternity
goddess.

Hindu: Kratu, a rishi or sage
whose ghost became one of the
stars of Ursa Major herded by
Svati (Arcturus).

ELDSICH (AL DHIBA), iota
Draconis, orange, summer.
From the Arabic Al Dhih, The
Male Hyena. Also written Ed
Asich.

ELECTRA, in the Pleiades,
winter. For the last several
centuries this star is clearly
visible, but in mythology generally said to be the Lost Pleiad.
A daughter of Atlas and Pleione,
by Zeus she became the mother
of Dardanus, who founded Troy.
When Troy fell to the Greeks,
she took the defeat so much to
heart she left her place among
her sisters in the sky that she
might not see the actual destruction of her beloved city.
In some accounts she disappeared completely, in others
she moved over to the Great

Bear, where she glimmers as a small star (Alcor) beside the central star of the arch. In a third account, she shows herself occasionally to the mortal eye in the form of a comet. In legends attached to the sisters, Celaeno, Merope, and Sterope are variously said to be the Lost Pleiad.

Astronomers of the middle ages spelled the name Electa. Romans called the star Atlantis, after her family name. In Australia, the Pirt-Kapan-noot people have a legend in which this star was the queen of the other six. Beloved by their heavenly Crow (Canopus), who carried her away, she has never been seen since.

EL KOPHRAH, chi Ursae Majoris, red, spring. From the Arabic Al Kafzah al Thaniyah, The Second Spring. Also written al Kaphrah.

EL NATH (AL NATIH), beta Tauri, a binary, brilliant pure white and pale gray, winter. Arabic for The Butting One, a name attributed to its position on the tip of the horn. Belonging to Auriga as well as to Taurus, it is also classified as lambda Aurigae, where it lies on the left ankle, a location which provides it with a second title: Kabd al Inan, Heel of the Reinholder. Additional designations are:

Arabic: Al Karn al Thaur al Shamaliyyah, Northern Horn of the Bull.

Babylonian: Shur-narkabti-sha-iltanu, Star in the Bull towards the North, or Northern Star towards the Chariot, i.e. Aurgia. It marked the 6th

ecliptic station, and the sun was near this star during the early days of spring about 6,000 years ago.

Hindus invoked it as Agni, the first god who had three aspects, those of Grhapati, lord of the domestic hearth; Surya, the sun; Trita, lightning. Together the three were Tryambaka, three-mothered. A god who had three births, he had three bodies; born of two sticks, he was a glutton with a fiery tongue that roamed the earth; born of water, he was a calf (young sun) which grew into a bull that sharpened its horns (rays) and at times appeared among the stars of Taurus; born of the highest heaven, he was an eagle. In his character of guardian of the hearth, he also protected the altar and carried oblations by eating the raw flesh of the sacrifice, for which reason Hutabhuj, Devourer of the Sacrifice, also was applied to the star.

Among astrologers, El Nath portends eminence and good luck.

EL PHEKRAH, theta Ursae Majoris, white, spring. From the Arabic Al Phikra al Thalitha, The Third Spring or Leap, i.e. of the Gazelle. Also called Talita.

ELTANIN, gamma Draconis, double, orange, summer. From the Arabic Al Ras Al Tinnin, The Dragon's Head. Compare Rastaben.

The Boeotian Thebes, city of the Dragon, from the story of its founder Cadmus, shared with its Egyptian namesake the worship of this star in a temple dedicated about 1,130 B.C.

Rameses' great temple at Karnak was oriented to it. All along the Nile it was an important star, and Apet, Bast, Mut, Sekhet, and Ta-urt, all aspects of one mother goddess, were symbolized by its light. The cult drawn from Egypt spread into Greece, Italy, and elsewhere, and a temple to the Magna Mater, adjusted to this luminary was erected at Pompeii. At Thebes in Greece, city authorities finally interfered with the worship of this star, when, in one of its numerous raids on astrologers, they bricked up the opening of the temple whence it was observed.

It never lost its fame, and is the star which led Bradley in 1725, while attempting to verify Hooke's illusory parallax, to discover the laws of the aberration of light. It is the zenith star of Greenwich, and it has been supposed that Flamsteed, Britain's first Astronomer Royal, sank a well at Greenwich Observatory that it might be viewed with the naked eye by daylight as well for the purpose of telescopically measuring its distance from the true zenith at the moment of transit. About 4,000 years ago it was nearer the north pole than any other bright star. Eltanin has become the brightest star of the constellation, surpassing Thuban, alpha Draconis.

Additional designations are: Zenith Star. Mongrel forms combining Arabic and Latin: Etabin, Etanim, Etanin, Etannin, Ettanin, Rasaben, Ras Eltanim, Rastaban, Rastaben.

ENIF, epsilon Pegasi, double, yellow and violet, autumn. From the Arabic Al Anf, The Nose. Also written Aniphol Pharasi, Enf, Enf Alpheras, Enir. Other

Arabic titles were: Al Jahfalah, The Lip; Fum al Faras, The Horse's Mouth. With theta Pegasi and alpha Aquari, it constituted the Chinese hsiu, Wei (Goei, Gui).

ER RAI, gamma Cephi, yellow, autumn. The title indigenous to Arabia means The Shepherd. It also appears as Al Rai and Arrai. The star is far into the north, and, during the latter part of June, a number of small meteors radiate from a point near it. To the Arabs, Cepheus was The Flock.

EVENING STAR. See Morning and Evening Star.

FOMALHAUT, alpha Piscis Austrini, double, red and dull blue, best seen in autumn. Tenth among the bright stars of the southern hemisphere, it is the most brilliant in its sparsely starred region of the sky, and the farthest south of all first magnitude stars seen in the latitude of New York City. To its splendor is added its reddish color, and it so far excels any neighbor it is said to be without an equal or suitable companion. Therefore, it is lonely, but with a gentle melancholy and serenity. About 500 B.C. it was worshipped by the Greeks in sunrise ceremonies in the temple of Demeter at Eleusis. The name is from the Arabic Fum al Hut, Mouth of the Fish. From this came: Fomalhant, Fomalcuti, Fomalhout Algenubi, Fomauth, Fumahand, Fumahuad, Pham al Haut, Phomault, Phomelhaut. Early desert names were: Al Difdi al Awwal, The First Frog; Talim, Ostrich. The Chinese name was Li Lo Sze Mun. A Latin designation was Os Piscis Notii. Styled one of the Persian four

Royal Stars. The identity of the stars is frequently disputed, usually the other three are said to be Aldebaran, Antares, and Regulus. They were the four sentinels that ruled over the other stars and guarded the heaven's four cardinal points.

Much used by navigators in determining longitude. At Cape of Good Hope, and in similar latitudes, it is a zenith star. Astrologers attribute to it eminence, wealth, and power.

FURUD, zeta Canis Majoris, light orange, winter. From Al Furud, The Bright Single Ones. The name may be a transcriber's error, as the meaning usually is given as The Male Apes, and this would make the original Arabic Al Kurud, which once applied to a group composed of several stars in this constellation and in Columba, an asterism also called Al Agribah, The Ravens.

The star occupies a place in the toe of the right hind foot.

GAU, mu Sagittarii, multiple, pale yellow, summer. From the Persian meaning Bull. With zeta, sigma, tau, and phi composed a lunar station known to the Copts as Polis, Foal, and to the Khorasmians as Yaugh, Bull. With nu it comprised the Arabic Ain al Rami, The Archer's Eye, and with xi and omicron it formed the Chinese Kien Sing, Flagstaff.

GIEDI, alpha Capricorni, binary, yellow, autumn. The name, also written Algedi and Algiedi, is from the Arabian Al Jady, The Forehead, although the stars actually are nearer the tip of the sea-goat's horn. The Kid is given as another meaning of Giedi.

With beta it was contained in several lunar stations, such as the:

Accadian: Uz, The Goat.

Arabian: Dabih and the degenerated Dschabbe and Dshabeh, a name often applied to beta alone.

Babylonian: Qarnu Shahu, Horn of the Goat, the 26th ecliptic inn, and a representation of the 18th antediluvian king Amar Sin.

Coptic: Eupeutos or Opeutus, which referred to a sacrifice.

Euphratean: Enzu, Goat; Shak-shadi, probably a sacrifice.

GIENAH, gamma Corvi, spring. From the Arabic Al Janah al Ghurab al Aiman, The Right Wing of the Raven, although on several modern charts it marks the left. Now brightest star in the constellation.

GIENAH, epsilon Cygni, yellow, summer. Like the Corvi Gienah, it stands for The Right Wing of the Raven.

GIRTAB, theta Scorpii, summer. A Euphratean name meaning Seizer or Stinger. Also called Sargas, Director of Sacrifice.

GOMEISA (GOMELZA), beta Canis Minoris, white, winter. From the Arabic Al Ghumaisa, The Weeping One. A name also applied to the constellation as well as to the alpha star. Another title, Al Murzim, is applied for the same reason; it appears first as if to announce the rising of the lucida. The

distance between this star and
Procyon was used by the Arabs
to mark their short cubit or ell;
the line between Castor and Pollux
of Geminini was used to mark
their long cubit. With other
stars, it forms the Chinese
Shwuy Wei.

GRAFFIAS, beta Scorpii,
triple, pale white and lilac, summer. From the Greek for Crab.
Anciently, even into Christian
times, a belief prevailed that the
scorpion was generated from the
crab and words for the two became interchanged. Graffias
also is said to mean barbarian,
as a designation for one of the
Scorpion's claws. Erroneously
it is written Grassias, probably
from an early failure to interpret
f in type. Arabian designations
are: Aakrab schemali, now written Acrab, which may be a
translation from the Greek.
Iklil al Jabhah (Iclilujebbah),
Crown of the Forehead, north of
which part it lies, and one of
the stars of the 17th manzil,
which was regarded as a
fortunate station. Chinese
names were: Fu Kwang, Basket
with Handles; Tien Sze, Heaven's
Four-horse Chariot. It was part
of the 4th hsiu, Fang, Room.

GRUMIUM, xi Draconis,
yellow, summer. A barbarism
from the Arabic for one of the
herds of camels. The word now
is seen in the French groin and
Italian grugno (muzzle).

HADAR, alpha Centauri,
binary, white, spring. From
the Arabic meaning Ground.
Also called Bungula, which appears to be a coined word from
b (beta), a star with which it
often is associated, and ungula,
hoof, and it marks the toe of the
right hoof. Another name is

Rigil Kentaurus. Not seen from
northern areas.

HAEDI. See Kids.

HAMAL, alpha Arietis,
yellow, autumn. From the
Arabic meaning The Full-grown
Lamb. Other spellings are
Hamel, Hammel, Hamul, Hemal.
Among early Greeks this star
held the important position of
herald of the sunrise at the
vernal equinox. At first it
probably was the stellar ram,
which later was assigned to the
constellation. Astrologers in
Ptolemy's time said the star
was dangerous and evil, one
that brought bodily hurts. It
lies slightly north of the moon's
path, and is one of the luminaries
by which terrestrial longitude
is reckoned.

Additional designations:

Arabic: Alnath (El Nath)
Butting One or Horn Push, a
name also associated with a star
in the tip of the Bull's northern
horn. Al Ras al Hamal, The
Head of the Sheep (or full-grown
lamb). Chaucer, the English
poet, used Alnath for this star.

Euphratean: Anuv, Prince;
Arku-sha-rishu-ku, Back of the
Head of Ku; Ask-kar; Dil-gan,
Messenger of Light; Dil-kar,
Proclaimer of Dawn; I-ku, or
Ku, Leading One, i.e. leader
of the heavenly flock, a title
also applied to Capella; Lu-lim,
or Lu-nit, Ram's Eye, or
Male-sheep; Simal, Horn Star.
Also referred to as the Star
of the Flock and associated with
Aloros, first of the ten mythical
kings of Accad anterior to the
Deluge, the duration of whose
reigns proportionately coincided
with the distances that separ-

ated the ten chief ecliptic stars beginning with Hamal. Deduced from this kingly title came the Assyrian Ailuv and the Hebrew Ayil, usually associated with Aldebaran.

Some astronomers have identified this star as the head of the Goose, which appeared among Egyptian constellations.

HOMAM (HOMAN), zeta Pegasi, autumn. From the Arabic Sa'd al Human, The Hero's Lucky Star, or Al Hammam, The Whisper. Other Arabic titles were: Na'ir Sa'd al Bahaim, Bright One of the Two Beasts; Sa'd al Na'amah, Lucky Star of the Ostriches. Chinese called Luy Tien.

HYADES, group in Taurus, winter. This V-shaped cluster outlines the face of the infuriated Bull about to charge down on its hunter Orion. It is composed of gamma, delta, epsilon, and the binary theta Tauri. Aldebaran, the group's lucida, marks the eye of this maddened beast.

The Hyades were daughters of Atlas, axis god who taught astronomy and navigation, and Aethra, atmosphere; sisters of Hyas, a vegetation deity; half-sisters of the Pleiades, with whom they made up the fourteen Atlantides. They were the nymphs who transmitted divine will to priests at Dodona, the most ancient shrine of Zeus. Their messages were contained in the rustling wind in oak and other trees or in the sounds which came from brazen plates suspended from branches and which clapped against one another in a breeze. At Dodona, Zeus entrusted to them the care of his motherless infant son, Dionysus. They likewise were said to be Nysiades, nymphs of Nysa, who were forced into the sea by Lycurgus, king of Thrace, who disapproved of Dionysian revels. When their brother was accidentally killed they wept incessantly and were honored by a place in the heavens for the love they bore him. Ancients believed the soft spring rains that moistened and warmed earth and fertilized crops were their tears, which in the autumn turned cold and caused vegetation to wither and withdraw. They thus symbolized rain clouds. In early times they were said to be seven. In modern times five or six are recognized. The names of the sisters are not applied to individual stars. To the Anglo-Saxons, they were a Boar Throng. Hindus saw a Temple or a Waggon here.

In Chinese belief, chaos contained the five elements in a rudimentary state without body or form. By the efforts of the serpent Nu Kua, an androgynous creature, the world was set in order. Each of the five elements was assigned a domain. Earth was flattened with mountains erected at each of its four corners to support heaven, the space between the hills was molded from yellow soil to make it fertile for humans and animals. No sooner had this paradisic realm been established than the great demon Kung Kung rose at the head of a multitude of dragons from the dark waters of the primordial abyss that encircled earth. He charged as a whirlpool and caused a deluge; he tore down the mountains, and the sky smashed into bits; then he incited the elements to revolt. Water, producer of wood,

conquered fire; fire, producer
of earth, conquered metal; metal,
producer of water, conquered
wood; wood, producer of fire, conquered earth; earth, producer of
metal, conquered water. After
a frenzied siege, Kung Kung was
vanquished. Nu Kua pulled up
reeds and charred them to halt
the flood of water that swirled
over the land, and then collected
stones of the five precious
colors, blue, red, white, yellow,
and black, and repaired the shattered sky. To replace the dam-
aged mountains, the legs of a
tortoise were cut off and made
into pillars which were placed
at the four cardinal points of the
compass to hold up the patched
arch that canopied the earth.
Four great creatures were placed
to act as custodians: Vermilion
Bird sentineled the southern
pillar, Azure Dragon the eastern
pillar, Black Tortoise, his legs
stubbed, the northern pillar,
and White Tiger the western
pillar. The progression of the
elements was permitted to run
on because each action counter-
acted another and established
balance in the universe. All
misfortunes were attributed to
disturbances of this continuity,
and for this reason Taoists oppose
interference with nature. With
his defeat, Kung Kung lost control over sea and rain dragons,
and he abdicated in favor of his
son Yu Shih, whose throne was
on the Hyades.

Unlike his father, Yu Shih had
benevolent as well as destructive
moods. Once, about four thousand years ago, during the reign
of the earthly emperor, Shen
Nung, second legendary ruler
of China, aridity had scorched
the land, many had died, those
who remained alive had little
strength with which to drag

themselves about, when a rain
priest appeared at the capital.
He wore scales of yellow armor
and a wide-brimmed blue straw
hat. Accompanying him was a
one-legged bird. The emperor
entreated the holy man to exercise his magic powers; whereupon he poured some of the
precious water held in reserve
in an earthenware bowl, plucked
a willow branch from a tree
nearby, dipped it into the water,
and sprinkled the earth in all
directions. Almost immediately
dark clouds rolled overhead,
thunder came out of the north,
followed by a torrential rain.
By his costume and his companion the people knew that their
rain priest was none other than
Yu Shih, who had come down to
help them. Occasionally a
one-legged bird appears to men
as a sign of coming storms. In
case of need, this bird can
drink in sea water and spray
it over the land as rain. Yu
Shih had the power to wade
through water without getting
wet, to fly in the air without
wings, to pass through fire without being burned, and after his
visit he returned to heaven,
where he sits on his throne or
stands on a cloud pouring rain
from a water jug.

Records that date back to
1,100 B.C., or possibly earlier,
bring to light sacrifices and
burnt offerings were set out for
these stars.

Cherokee Indians speak of a
man who broke his arm and
grieved because he was of no
value in hunting and war. He
left home and wandered eastward toward the rising sun, and
never returned. Months later
his people saw this star cluster
for the first time and recognized

in it the arm, bent at the elbow, of the man who had wandered into sky-land because he was crippled and useless on earth. In the Amazon country the Indians see the Jawbone of an Ox.

The name is from the Greek and supposedly means to rain, a reference to the wet period by which their morning and evening settings are accompanied late in May and November respectively as well as to the character ascribed to the sisters in mythology, whom Manilius called the, "Sad Companions of the turning Year."

Additional designations are: Moist Daughters; Rainy Hyades; Roman V, from their arrangement; Seven Sisters; Torch; Watery Hyades.

Anglo-Saxon: Raedgasnan, Raedgastran, or Redgaesrum, meaning unknown.

Arabic: Al Dabaran, identical with that of the lucida; Al Kallas, The Boiling Sea, supporting the idea of the asterism's stormy character; Al Kilas, Little She Camels, attributed to the smaller stars in distinction from Aldebaran, The Larger Camel. Al Kilas became Kalais. Al Mijdah, A Triangular Spoon.

Blackfeet: Sta-mixe-tomo, Bull of the Hills.

Chinese: Pi or Peih, anciently Pal, said to have several meanings, namely, Complete, End, Hand-net, Rabbit-net. With stars nu and rho it composed the 19th Hsiu. Among the populace it was known as Announcer of Invasion on the Border and Star of the Hunter, while with astrologers

it generally was Drought Car of Yu Shih, Master of Rain, both probably derived from the Yu Shih legend.

Hebrew: Kimah and Mazzaroth, both without foundation and more correctly applied to the Pleiades and the five planets respectively.

Latin: Palilicium or Parilicium, from the festival of Pales, pastoral goddess and ancient Italian female form of Pan. The feast was celebrated on April 21, which marked the date Aldebaran, lucida of the cluster, vanished in the gloaming, as well as the date of the traditional anniversary of the founding of Rome, originally an abode of shepherds. Rite included bonfires of straw through which flocks were driven for purification. Sidus Hyantis, after Hyas. Thyone (Dione), one of the sisters. Among the masses, the title was Suculae, Little Pigs, that is the young of the sow (Aldebaran). Little Pigs may have been the translation of a Greek title. Among the several explanations given for this name is that continued rains in the Hyades' setting season made roads so muddy the stars seemed to be delighting in slop in the manner of swine. Suculae also may have come from sucus, meaning juice, an idea which suits the moisture tradition attached to the stars. In the middle ages, Sucula and Succidae appeared on star maps. In Roman astrology these were violent and troublesome stars that cause storms and tempests to rage on land and sea.

Southeast of the Pleiades, the Hyades cluster has been famous as one of the most glorious asterisms in space, and it is one of the few stellar objects mentioned by Homer.

HYADUM I, gamma Tauri, winter. From the Latin signifying First of the Hyades. Synonymously it appears as Prima Hyadum and Primus Hyadum. This title may have been inspired by the Arabic Awwal al Dabaran, First of the Dabaran, used long before the Latin designation. With adjacent stars it was the Chinese Choo Wan, Many Princes. Hyadum II is delta Tauri. Nearby these stars is a small nebula, one of the few known to have a variable light.

IZAR, epsilon Bootis, binary, pale orange and bluish green, spring. From the Arabic for Girdle. A long veil-like garment worn by Moslem women is called Izar. Additional designations are: Al Mintakah al'Awwa, Belt of the Shouter; Mizar, The Waist Cloth. All names indicate its place in the figure, and Mizar was turned by early European astronomical writers into: Meirer, Merak, Mezen, Mezer, Micar, Mirac, Mirak, Mirar. In the Alfonsine tables called Perizoma. The contrasting colors of its components are so beautiful in the telescope, moderns have called it Pulcherima, Grace. This star with others composed the Chinese Tso She Ti, an Officer on the left hand of the emperor.

JABBAH, nu Scorpii, triple, summer. Meaning Crown, from the Arabic Iklil al Jabbah, Crown of the Forehead. One of the stars of the 17th manzil.

KAUS AUSTRALIS, epsilon Sagittarii, summer. Lato-Arabic signifying the Southern

(part of) Bow. This may be identical with the Euphratean Nibat Anu.

KAUS BOREALIS, lambda Sagittarii, summer. Lato-Arabic signifying Northern (part of) Bow. Arabs called Rai al Naaim, Keeper of the Ostriches. With mu, Al Thalimain, The Desert Birds or Ostriches. These two stars may have been the Accadian Anu-ni-tum, an aspect of the great mother goddess Ishtar.

KAUS MERIDIONALIS, Lato-Arabic for Middle (of the) Bow. Also called Media. With gamma and epsilon, the Accadian Sin-nun-tu or Si-nu-nu-tum, The Swallow. Delta Sagittarii.

THE KIDS, epsilon, zeta, and eta Aurigae, winter. Three fourth magnitude stars that form a small isosceles triangle, they also are called Haedi; Agni, The Lambs; Al Jadyain, The Two Young He Goats; Capellae, Goats. Individually they are: epsilon, Al Ma'az; zeta, Haedus or Sadatoni; eta, unnamed. Held in bad repute by seamen because they presaged the stormy season on the Mediterranean. So fearful were ancient mariners of the stars, their rising early in October was the signal for the closing of navigation.

KITALPHA, alpha Equulei, autumn. From the Arabian name for the whole figure, Al Kitah al Faras, The Part of a Horse; and a title also applied to the whole constellation. Other designations: Kitalphar, Kitel Phard. The Chinese name was Sze Wei.

KOCHAB, beta Ursae Minoris, reddish, spring and summer. The name from the Arabic means North or North Star and is a title shared with alpha. Variously written Alrucaba, Kochah, Reicchabba. Desert Arabs knew it as Anwar al Farkadain, Lights of the Two Calves; Nair al Farkadain, Bright One of the Two Calves, which became Al Farked and Alferkathan. These were from an early figure here, The Fold, in which these sky animals kept close to their mother. Pre-Islamitic poets designated this star as the Faithful, an allusion to its ever visible position, which made it the constant companion of those who traveled at night. Gamma star, also a constant companion, made a pair called Two Pherkads.

About 1,000 B.C. this may have been the Pole Star of Greek astronomers, as it was the nearest naked-eye star to the pole. In China, it was one of the stars called Ti, The Emperor.

Beta with alpha and others of the configuration constituted a cluster called Circitores, Ludentes, Ludiones, or Saltatores, respectively Circlers, Dancers, or Leapers around the Pole. Beta and gamma alone were known as Guards or Wardens, i.e. of the Pole, and had been used by Spanish navigators. These Guards were used by the common people as a timepiece. In China gamma was Ta Tsze, Crown Prince.

Because it is so far north, Kochab is seen all through the year from some point in the world. It reaches its meridian late in June.

KORNEFOROS (KORNE-

PHORUS), beta Herculis, pale yellow, summer. From the Greek for Claviger or Club Bearer. Also termed Rutilicus, perhaps the diminutive of rutilus, golden red or glittering; or from rutellum, a form of rutrum, a sharp instrument of husbandry or war in Roman times, one that resembled the instrument Hercules carried at times. A rarely used name was Rutilico. The Chinese title was Ho Chung, In the River.

LA SUPERBA, #152 Schjellerup, Canes Venatici, red, spring. Discovered by Father Secchi in the 19th century. So called because the flash of its prismatic rays is superbly beautiful.

LU LIM, delta Virginis, golden yellow, spring. This star was named on the Euphrates and signifies Gazelle, Goat, or Stag; perhaps King or Ruler. With Epsilon it was Mas-tab-ba, possibly Mashu or Mashtu, one of the seven pairs of twin astronomical stars in Babylonia. The Chinese name was Tsze Seang, Second Minister of State, and the Hindus called it Apa or Apas, Carrier of Waters.

MAIA, one of the Pleiades, in Taurus, winter. The first born and the most beautiful of the Seven Sisters. By Zeus she was the mother of Hermes, the wind. Her name means grandmother or increaser, and she parallels the Hindu Maya. Romans identified her with an old Italian fruitful mother of spring, Maia Majesta, and to her the month of May is indebted for its name, which also is written Mea and Maja. Latin writers have written it Majja and have given her the title

Pleias uda, Moist Pleiad, symbolic of the character of the cluster. The Chinese term Mao for the sisters is singularly like that of the Greek. In poetry, husbandmen are cautioned against sowing grain before the time of Maia's setting. Maia and her sisters disappear from the evening sky in April.

MANKIB (MENCHIB, MENKIB), beta Persei, irregularly variable, deep yellow, winter. From the Arabic Mankib al Faras, Horse's Shoulder.

MARKAB, alpha Pegasi, binary, white, autumn. Arabic for saddle, ship, or vehicle, anything ridden upon. Other Arabic terms were Al Arkuwah, The Crossbar, i.e. of the well in which Al Dalw, the Bucket, was used; Matn al Faras, The Horse's Withers or Shoulder; Yad, Forearm, i.e. of the Horse. A medieval corruption was Yed Alpheras, Horse's Hand or Forearm. In China it was Shih, House, and gave its title to the 13th Hsiu. With gamma and zeta, it was the Euphratean asterism Ur-bar-ra, or Lik-bar-ra, the Hyena.

At the junction of the animal's wing and shoulder, it is one of the so-called lunar stars observed in navigation, although it no longer is the bright star of the constellation. Astrologically it portends danger from cuts and fire.

MARKEB, kappa in Vela (Argo Navis), spring. From the Arabic for saddle, ship, or vehicle, anything ridden upon.

MARSIC (MARFIK), lambda Ophiuchui, binary, yellowish white and smalt blue, summer.

From the Arabic meaning Elbow. For others with the same name, see Mirfak.

MASYM, lambda Herculis, deep yellow, summer. From the Arabic Misam, Wrist. Also spelled Maasim, Massym, Masini, Mazim, Mazym. The name was applied to lambda in error; it should have been given to omicron, which remains unnamed, but which indicates the wrist's position. Sir William Herschel settled upon the vicinity of this star as the objective point of our solar system, the Apex of the Sun's Way. The Sun's Quit-point, opposite the Apex, lies midway between the stars Sirius and Canopus. Other investigations indicate the place of Apex may be at xi or upsilon Herculis.

MEBUSTA, epsilon Geminorum, double, brilliant white and cerulean blue, winter. From the Arabic Al Mabsutat, The Outstretched, from the fact that it marked the extended paw of the early Arabic Lion. It now is at the hem of Castor's tunic. In the middle ages the name was written: Meboula, Mebusta, Melucta, Menita, Mesoula, Mibwala. With delta and lambda it comprised the Chinese Tung Tsing.

MEGREZ, delta Ursae Majoris, pale yellow, spring. From the Arabic Al Maghrez, The Tail's Root. In China called Kwan and Tien Kuen, Heavenly Authority. To the Hindus it was the ghost of Atri, a rishi or sage who became one of the bears headed by Svati (Arcturus). Arti, whose name denotes eater and who ruled the other bears, had once rescued the sun and had been saved from burning by the

Asvins.

MEISSA, lambda Orionis, winter. From the Arabic Al Maisan, The Proudly Marching One, a name applicable to any bright star. The original Arabian name was Al Hakah, A White Spot, which accounts for Heka or Hika, occasionally applied to it. Additional designations:

Babylonian: With two smaller stars in the background it constituted the lunar station Mastab-ba-tur-tur, the Little Twins. These were important stars along the Euphrates, inasmuch as they rose with the sun at the summer solstice.

Chinese: Sima Ts'ien, Head of the Tiger; Tsee, Beak; Tsuy He, Pouting Lips; Tzu, To Bristle Up.

Coptic: Klusos, Watery.

Hindu: Andhaka, Blind; Aryika, Honorable or Worthy; Mrigasiras (Mrga), Head of the Stag.

Khorasmian: Ikhma, The Twins.

Persian: Avesr, Coronet; Al Taj, The Crown.

Sogdian: Marezana, Twins.

Ptolemy referred to it as the Nebulous One.

MEKBUDA, zeta Gemini, pale topaz, winter. From the Arabic Al Makbudah, a contracted designation for the Drawn-in-Paw of the great ancient Lion. Some translators say it derived from Al Mutakabbidah, A Culminating Star.

MENKAB (MENKAR), alpha Ceti, orange, winter. From the Arabic Al Minhar, The Nose, or Nostril. Astrologically this star denotes sickness, disgrace and ill fortune, with danger from wild beasts.

MENKALINAN (MENKALINAM, MENKALINEN), beta Aurigae, binary, bluish white, winter. From the Arabic Al Mankib dhi'l 'Inan, The Shoulder of the Rein Holder, a title which seems to come from the Greek.

MERACH (MIRACH), beta Andromeda, yellowish, autumn. From the Arabic Al Marakk, The Loins, or Al Mi'zar, The Girdle or Waist-cloth. Occasionally spelled Mirac, Mirae, Mirar, Mirath, Mirax. This was not an original Arabian title, but one based on Ptolemy's method of locating the star. Earlier in Arabia it was Al Batn al Hut, The Belly of the Fish; Al Kalb al Hut, The Heart of the Fish; Al Risha, The Band (Cord, Ribbon, or Thread), i.e. that united the fishes and a title that now belongs to Pisces. Later in Arabia it was Al Janb al Musalsalah, The Side of the Chained Woman. One of the stars in the Chinese Hsiu called K'uei, Man Astride or Striding Legs, which anciently was Kwet. It is one of the members of the Coptic lunar station Kuton, Thread. It may have been the Egyptian Arit. Romans knew it as Cingulum, Band or Girdle; Ventrale, Belly, from its position in the figure, although now it is in the left hip. Astrologically a fortunate celestial object, portending renown and good luck in matrimony.

MERAK (MIRAK), beta Ursae Majoris, greenish white,

spring. From the Arabic al Marakk, The Loins, i. e. of the Bear. The spelling decayed into Miare, Mizar. Additional designations - Chinese: Tien Seuen, Armillary Sphere. Greek: Helike, a name for the whole. Hindu: Pulaha, a rishi or sage whose ghost became one of the bears of Ursa Major herded by Svati (Arcturus).

MEROPE, in the Pleiades, Tauri, winter. She lost her place as a Pleiad when she married Sisyphus, a mortal. Each time her alliance was compared with that of her sisters, who had married gods, she hid her face in shame, and this caused her light to dim. After a while her equanimity was recovered, and she became radiant again. Now, with a silvery white glow, she shines brighter than the others. In mythology she also typifies the moon or dawn, and her name means mortal.

MESARTIM (MESARTHIM), gamma Arietis, binary, brilliant white and gray, autumn. The name from the Arabic is said to mean The Extremely Fat Ram, or The Two Attendants. The second attendant was Sheratan, beta Arietis, and the luminary they looked after was Hamal. The Persians called these two The Protecting Pair. With beta, it also formed one of the several Arabian celestial Athafiyy (Trivets or Tripods), a rude arrangement of three stones on which the nomad placed his pot or kettle, his open-air kitchen. Others of this name appear in the constellations Draco, Lyra, Musca, and Orion. First Star in Aries was applied to Mesartim because at one time it was nearest to the equinoctial point. The three stars, alpha,

beta, and gamma, were linked by the Jews and called Shalisha (Shalish), a musical instrument of triangular shape, which also is a term applied to Triangulum.

MINTAKA (MINTIKA), delta Orionis, double, white and violet, winter. From the Arabic Al Mintakah, The Belt. Its companion stars in the Belt are: epsilon, Alnilam, String of Pearls, and zeta, Alnitak, The Girdle. Other titles of the three are:

Arabic: Al Alkat, The Golden Grains, Nuts, or Spangles; Al Mizan al Hakk, The Accurate Scale-beam; Al Nasak, The Line; Al Nijad, The Belt.

Chinese: A Weighing Beam, with the stars of the sword as a weight at one end.

Greenland Eskimos: Siktut, the seal hunters who became confused when lost at sea and wandered into the sky.

Hindu: An early term was Isus Trikanda, Three-jointed Arrow; a later title was Mrigasiras, Stag Head.

Khorasmian: Khawiya, Rectitude, probably because the stars formed such a straight line.

Lapland: Kalevan Miekka, Hero's Sword; Niallar, Tavern.

Latin: Balteus, Belt; Jugula (Jugulae), Joined; Vagina, Scabbard, or Sheath; Zona, Belt, or Zone.

Medieval Christian: Baculus Jacobi, Jacob's Rod, or Staff, which German's called Jakob Stab. The Magi; Mary's

Distaff; Our Lady's Wand; Peter's Staff; Three Kings; Three Marys.

Medieval Jews: Mazlatha, Mazzaloth, Mazzalroth. Other biblical scholars understand these ancient Hebrew names for the zodiac or the five planets.

Norse: Fishkikallar, Staff; Frigge Rakken or Frigge Rok, Frigg's or Freya's Distaff.

Poignave Indians: Fuebot, meaning unknown.

Sogidan: Rashnawand, Uprightness, akin to the Khorasmian title.

At Leipsic called Napoleon, and the English in retaliation called the stars Nelson.

To natives of Australia they were young men who danced a corroboree to music played by the Maidens (the Pleiades).

Husbandmen referred to these stars as Rateau, the Rake, or as the Three Mowers, a reference to their autumnal rising; seamen as the Golden Yard-arm; tradesmen as the L, Ell, Ell and Yard, Yard-stick, and Yard-wand or Elwand, inasmuch as the line joining the stars is 3⁰ in length. Astrologically the three portend good fortune and public honors.

MIRA, omicron Ceti, a variable, flushed yellow, reddish when fading, autumn. From the Latin, meaning The Marvelous. Also called Collum Ceti, Mira the Wonderful, Stella Maris, Wonderful Star. Its variations are more or less irregular both in period and brightness, and it bears the distinction of being the first variable star of which any recorded observation had been made; this was in 1596, for which reason it also is called Mira of 1596. This show object is located in the sea-monster's neck.

MIRFAK, alpha Persei, lilac, winter. Also spelled Marfac and Mirzac, it is from the Arabic Marfik al Thurayya, Elbow of the Pleiades or next to the Pleiades. Other titles: Algenib (Algeneb, Chenib, Elgenab, Genib) from Al Janb, The Side, also applied to gamma star. Mughammid or Muhammir al Thurayya, Concealer of the Pleiades. It is at the elbow against the armour of the hero, and lies directly in the Milky Way. As Marfak, used for chi Herculis, a double of yellow and garnet color, seen in summer.

MIZAR, zeta Ursae Majoris, double, white and blue, spring. From the Arabic meaning Girdle or Waistcloth, an inappropriate name; also spelled Mirza, Mizat. Another name was Anak al Banat, Necks of the Maidens, referring to the Mourners at the Bier (the whole constellation). Written incorrectly this became Al Inak and Al Inz, Goat of the Mourners. Another error is Alhiac, Ostrich, which is a bird of the south. In an Arabian myth, when combined with the star Alcor, it is one of the mourners holding her infant child. In North Germany the combined Mizar and Alcor are known as the Horse and the Rider. Each night the rider starts his journey before midnight and returns twenty-four hours later to start over again. His waggon, the constellation, makes a great noise as it goes around the circle. To the Hindus it was Vashishtha, a rishi or sage, whose ghost became one of the bears of Ursa Major herded by Svati (Arcturus).

Because it is so far north, it is seen from some part of the world every night of the year.

MORNING AND EVENING STAR. When one of the bright planets, Jupiter, Mars, Saturn, or Venus, especially Venus, forms a conspicuous object in the eastern sky just before dawn, it is called the Morning Star, when it is visible just after sunset in the west, it is distinguished as the Evening Star. Figuratively the Morning Star announces the birth of a messiah, is a bringer of light, and warmth, forerunner, one who announces or guides. Among North American Indians it was symbolized by an equi-armed red cross. A Pawnee Indian source of life, fruitfulness and strength. In rites to the Morning Star a man was painted red (life color) all over, clad in leggings, and wrapped in a robe. A downy feather, painted red, was put on his head. The feather represented soft light clouds, the red a touch of the ray of the coming sun. A hymn was sung, and a captive virgin was sacrificed, the body used to fertilize the fields of maize. In Lithuanian folk songs the twin stars are servitors of Sun, the Morning Star kindling the light, the Evening Star preparing the bed. Mythologically the double aspect usually typifies twins of light and darkness, or the dual nature of a single deity, the Evening Star ushering in darkness, chill, the unknown, opener of the way to the afterworld. Frequently the pair are secondary supernaturals in the service of a supreme god, or they may be androgynous, performing as primitive man saw the universe as a conjunction of man and woman, symbolizing the generative and productive powers of nature, harmony, as well as inner or self-conflict. Various names by which the pair is known are:

CULTURE	MORNING STAR	EVENING STAR
Abyssinian	Ashdar or Athtar, male aspect (1)	Ashdar or Athtar, female aspect (1)
Algonquin	Wabung Annung (Wabun), male	
Arabian	Athtar (1) Azizos, male	Almakah (Almaqah) Monimos, male
Aramaic (Palmyrene)	Azizu (Azizos), male	Arsu, female
Assyro-Babylonian	Ishtar (Astarte), male aspect (2)	Ishtar (Astarte), female aspect (3)
Blackfeet Indian	Apisirahts (Episors), male	
Canaan	Shahru	Shalmu
Christian	Christ, male Star of Bethlehem(4)	

CULTURE	MORNING STAR	EVENING STAR
Egyptian	Horus, male Nuter Dua (5) Green Falcon (6)	Set, male
Greek	Aphrodite, Bearded, male (7) Heosphorus (Eosphoros) or Phosphorus, male Pollux or Hercules male	Aphrodite, female (8) Hesperus (Hesper), male Castor or Apollo, male
Hebrew	Jachin (9)	Boaz (9)
Hebrew, Early	Anat-Bethel (Anat-Yaw), male (10)	Anat-Bethel, female (11)
Hindu	Asvins, male Buddha, male	Asvins, male Rauhinya
Japanese	Myojo-Tenshi, male (12)	
Mexican	Citlalatonac (Quetzalcoatl), male	Tlauizcalpante Cutli, male Xipe Toltec, male(13)
Nabataean	Allat (Sa'd), male (14)	Allat, female(15)
Navaho	Hastsheyalti, male	Hastshehogan, male
New Zealand	Eye of Maui, the Sun	Eye of Maui, the Sun
Norse	Orvandel's Toe(16) Brisingamen (17)	Brisingamen (17)
Pawnee	Great Star or Warrior, male (18)	Bright Star (19)
Phoenician	Sydyk (Hettu, Sudus, Zedek), male	Misharu (Misor), male
Roman	Lucifer, male (20)	Vesper (Vesperugo), male (21) Noctifer(Nocturnus), male (22)
	Venus, male as- pect (2)	Venus, female aspect (3)
Semitic	Anat (Hanata) (23)	Anat (Hanata) (23)
Siberian	Solbon (Tsholbon), male (24)	Solbon (Tsholbon), male (24)
Sumero-Accadian	Sulpa-uddu (25)	Nuzku (26)
Syrian	Azizos, male	Monimos, male Arsa, female (27)

NOTES: (1) Same as Ishtar; see notes 2 and 3. (2) An androgynous

deity, in the morning a war god in male aspect. (3) An Andryogy-
nous deity, which in the evening appears as a goddess of love and
harlotry. Sacred prostitution was a temple ritual in early religions
of Western Asia and Eastern Europe. It was not looked upon as an
orgy of lust, but was performed by daughters or sons of noble families in the service of the great earth mother. The rite was one of
sympathetic magic to provide plentiful crops and herds as well as
children, and the money so earned was donated to the goddess.
Children born of these unions were regarded as sacred, virgin born,
and brought up by the temple. Usually the act was held silently in
the dark, so that no one knew who lay with whom, nor who was the
father. (4) Typifies Christ ascending to heaven. (5) The rising god,
nocturnal representation of the hidden sun deity, the soul of Osiris,
or the one who ferries Osiris. (6) Guardian of the Tree of Immortality. (7) An androgynous deity, in the morning a war god in male
aspect. See note 3. (8) Goddess of love and harlotry. See note 3.
(9) Pillar of Solomon's Temple. Also associated with the Zodiacal
Light. (10) A war god. See notes 2 and 3. (11) Goddess of love and
harlotry. See note 3. (12) A boy who appears in person to wise and
virtuous men. (13) Literally, our lord the flayed, a vegetation
deity who opened the way to the afterlife. (14) A fate and war god.
Male form of an androgynous deity. (15) Goddess of love and harlotry. See note 3. (16) A designation also applied to the star Alcor.
(17) Necklace of Freyja, fertility goddess. (18) Grandfather of all
humans, appointed by Tirawa, supreme ruler of Tirawahut, great
circle of heaven, to drive all sky spirits westward. (19) Grandmother of all humans, appointed by Tirawa to guard clouds, lightning,
thunder, winds. (20) A Roman light hero. (21) A word allied to west.
(22) A word allied to night. (23) Identical with the Nabataean Allat.
(24) Horse lover who rides the sky with a lasso in hand and watches
over his great herd (stars). (25) A phase of Nabu as awakener,
messenger of the morning Sun. (26) A phase of Nabu, messenger of
the ghost world, who lulls with his magic wand. (27) A fate goddess.

MUPHRIDE (MUFRIDE), eta
Bootis, binary, pale yellow and lilac, spring. From the Arabic meaning Solitary Star of the Lancer.

MURZIM (MIRZAM), beta
Canis Majoris, winter. From the
Arabic meaning Roarer, The Proclaimer or Announcer, i.e. of the
rising of Sirius. In remote times
in the desert, it was Al Kalb, The
Dog, i.e. which runs in front of
Sirius. With beta Canis Minoris
called Al Mirzama (or al Mirzama-
ni) al Shi'rayain, Two Siren An-
nouncers. Its Chinese name is Kuen
She.

MUSCIDA, Omicron Ursae
Majoris, spring. A corrupted form
of Latin coined in the middle ages
for muzzle or mouth of an animal.
Later unjustly attributed to "the
Barbarians" (Arabs). Located in
the Bear's nose.

NAOS, eta Argus Navis in Puppis, reddish, spring. From the
Greek meaning Dwell, and referring to the principal chamber of a
temple, the one in which dwells the
deity's statue. At Eridu associated
with Ea-Oannes, the human fish,
greatest god of the Kingdom and
lord of waves. Chinese called
Tseen She, Heaven's Altar. Invisible north of the 30th parallel;
notable into prehistoric times as
a star which varied from occasional faintness in light.

NASAK AL SHAMIYYAH, an asterism composed of stars in Ophiuchus and Hercules, seen in summer. From the Arabic meaning The Northern Boundary, i. e. of Al Raudah, The Pasture.

NASAK AL YAMANIYY, an asterism composed of stars in Ophiuchus and Serpens, seen in summer. From the Arabic The Southern Boundary, i. e. of Al Raudah, The Pasture.

NASHIRA, gamma Capricorni, autumn. From the Arabic Al Sa'd al Nashirah, The Fortunate One or Bringer of Good Tidings. Additional designations: Arabic: Sa' dubnashira, Saib' Nasch-ru-ah. Babylonian: Mahar sha hi-na Shahu, The Western One in the Tail of the Goat, a star that marked the 27th ecliptic asterism. Chinese: with stars in Aquarius and Pisces, Luy Pei Chen, Intrenched Camp.

NEKKAR (NAKKAR), beta Bootis, golden yellow, spring. From the Arabic meaning Drover; also applied to the whole constellation. Chinese name: Chaou Yaou or Teaou, To beckon, excite, or move. With stars gamma, delta, and mu constituted the Arabic asterism Al Dhi'bah, The Female Wolves, or Hyaenas. This cluster was an early one, before the Arabs adopted the Greek forms. With other celestial animals in the neighborhood they supposedly lay in wait for occupants of The Fold (Ursa Minor).

NIHAL (NIBAL), beta Leporis, a triple, deep yellow and blue, winter. From the Arabic meaning The Camels Quenching Their Thirst. Originally the name was applied to four brighter stars in the constellation.

NUNKI, sigma Sagittarii, summer. A Euphratean term signifying Star of the Proclamation of the Sea, the Sea being the section of sky occupied by Aquarius, Capricorn, etc. This sky area often is simply designated Water. Another meaning given for the name is Star of the Holy City, i. e. Eridu, on the Persian Gulf. With zeta and pi may have composed the Accadian Gu-shi-rab-ba, Yoke of the Sea.

OCULUS BOREUS, epsilon Tauri, winter. Latin name meaning Northern Eye, applied during the middle ages.

PHACD (PHACT, PHAD, PHECDA, PHEGDA, PHEKDA), gamma Ursae Majoris, topaz yellow, spring. From the Arabic Al Fahdh, The Thigh, a reference to its location. Chinese called Tien Ke, an Armillary Sphere; also Ke Seuen Ke. Hindu name was Pulastya, and it was one of the Ursa Major bears herded by Svati (Arcturus).

PHAET (PHACT, PHAD), alpha Columbae, winter. The name seems as to come from the same source as Phacd. Chinese called Chang Jin, Old Folks.

THE PLEIADES, a cluster in Taurus, winter.

...........not a mighty space
Holds all, and they themselves
are dim to see.
(Aratos)

These words well describe this Tauri cluster, tightly rosetted in a small region of the sky. Nevertheless, the misty light of these stars has always been a bewitching one. History, poetry, mythology, astronomy, all literature contains recurrent allusions to them. Rites connected with them are of unknown origin, their worship predating history. On the Euphrates they once led the lunar mansions. When first recognized in Egypt they probably rose heliacally at the beginning of April and were the sign of spring's return for a title, Great Year of the Pleiades in the Hermetic Books, the Egyptian sacred canon, may have referred to the time they began the astronomical year for the cycle of precession, which requires about 25,900 years. In Chinese annals of 2,357 B.C. they are mentioned and seem to have been among the first observed in that country. At that date, its lucida, Alcyone, was near the vernal equinox; now it is 24⁰ north of the celestial equator.

Far and wide, with their lunar rising in autumn, they were bringers of death, while their tears in the spring caused the Deluge. Midnight on about November 1, when the cluster reached its zenith, prayers for the dead were recited; that was the hour souls traveled to their last resting places. These observations passed from generation to generation; they were widely observed in the southern hemisphere, in the Orient, in ancient Britain, and elsewhere.

Australian aborigines say the stars are Young Girls, musicians, playing to Young Men, the stars of Orion's Belt, who dance. The Finns have likened them to a Sieve with holes in it. A conception of them as dancers is world-wide. Pagan Arabs, Berbers, other African tribes, the Dyaks of Borneo, and many far separated peoples have believed this asterism to be the center of the universe

and have placed on it the seat of immortality. As late as the 19th century, a German astronomer fallaciously said that the universe revolved around Alcyone, the cluster's most famous star.

Many primitive nations began the year with the Pleiad-month, November, when its stars rose after the sun went down. At Busiris, Egyptians commenced the feast of Isis, or Hathor, on November 17. Elsewhere the origin of fire and the know-how of rice culture were credited to these stars. All over the southern hemisphere their last visible rising after sunset is a time to jubilate the waking-up to georgic pursuits. South Africans term them hoeing stars. In their spring rising in the Greek month which was the equivalent of our May-June, Athena's clothes-washing festivities were held. Their midnight culmination in Moses' time, ten days after the autumnal equinox, may have determined Yom Kippur, the day of atonement.

Calendars were influenced by the Pleiades, in fact a Pleiad calendar may have preceded the lunar and solar calendars. The position of the stars with respect to seedtime and harvest made them easy seasonal markers. A Greek philosopher divided the year into four by relating the position of the Pleiades to the sun; winter began with their autumnal setting, ending with the spring equinox, when they became companions of the solar orb; summer began when they appeared with Arcturus; autumn when they were visible in the night sky. In Rome, Caesar established the beginning of summer with their heliacal rising and the commencement of winter with their cosmical setting. Mexicans adjusted their calendars every fifty-two years. These people believed when the end of the world would finally arrive it would come at the end of this fifty-two year cycle in the month of November, when the Pleiades were the guiding spirits. While humans were sacrificed, the entire population spent the night on its knees awaiting the terrifying doom. In the morning they knew that the gods had been propitiated by their offerings, and that life might go on for another span of fifty-two years.

In Egyptian lore, Ra, the sun, gave birth through his eye to Hathor. Thus she represented wisdom or tears. When the father decided to stop the slaughter she was causing with floods, he made her drunk with the waters of the Nile. A personification of the great vigor of nature that perpetually brought forth, reared, and destroyed all things, she multiplied into seven fates that foretold the future, especially of children at birth. This seven-powered goddess has been said to appear either as the bright stars of Ursa Major or as the Pleiades. Egyptians observed three solemn days that ended when these stars culminated at midnight. These days were associated with the tradition of a deluge or other race-destroying disaster. The rites began on the 17th day of Ethyr (our November), which agrees with the Mosaic Deluge account, namely the 17th day of the 2nd month of the Jewish year. A rather bizarre statement appears in the Talmud. 'When the Holy One, blessed be He, wished to bring the Deluge upon the world, He took two

stars out of the Pleiades and let the rains fall. When he wished to arrest the flood, He took two stars out of Arctus and plugged the holes." A conception of holes in the sky is quite universal. In another Biblical account, during the siege of Jerusalem by Antiochus Epiphanes, the people behind the city wall wanted for water until the Pleiades set and then a shower of rain fell upon them.

The lingering influence of ancient faiths is manifested in their number, seven. Anciently it was used as a round or whole number as moderns use ten or twelve; loosely a considerable amount as a hundred now is used. It was sacred to Mesopotamian astronomers, who saw the seven colors of the rainbow, the seven stars in the Bear constellations, the seven powers, etc. Even into this day, seven is credited with special virtues and as a number especially endowed with good luck.

To the aborigines of Africa and Borneo, these stars were conceived to be pullets.

In the Odyssey, Homer describes the Pleiades as seven Doves that start out from the west with ambrosia for the infant Zeus. One of the Doves was lost when passing the Wandering Islands, the Symplegades, twin rocks at the gateway to the Black Sea that opened and closed continually and crushed whatever tried to pass between them. This story may be derived from the same source as that of the bird sent out by the ship Argo, which also appears in astronomical lore. This columbine description may have originated in the ancient custom of setting pigeons loose in the festivities at the opening of navigation.

The tales told about these stars in ancient Greece were many. They were the pious daughters of Atlas, who grieved so at the hardship of their father, who bore the firmament on his shoulders, that they were rewarded with a place in heaven and set whenever they were permitted to relieve him of his burden. They were the seven daughters of Pleione. While hunting in the woods of Boeotia, they were seen by Orion, who was so enthralled by the beauty of the mother and daughters, he pursued them for five years. When at last they appealed to Zeus, the god, to save them, transformed all into pigeons and they flew into the sky. However, the Mighty Hunter and his Dogs followed them, and there the passionate chase continues, the birds always just out of the Hunter's reach. Like their sisters, the Hyades, they killed themselves for grief when their brother Hyas was accidentally slain, is another explanation for their being in heaven.

Atreus, light hero and legendary king of Mycenae, father of the warriors Agamemnon and Menelaus, promised to sacrifice the most beautiful animal in his flock to Artemis. When he discovered a golden lamb (sunlit cloud), he strangled it but greedily hid the fleece in a chest. Aerope, daughter of Atreus, was seduced by her uncle Thyestes, and gave the fleece to her lover, who then usurped the throne (he, who controlled the sunlit cloud was sun-king). Atreus made a pact with his brother that he was to regain the throne when the sun reversed itself. One morning the sun was in total eclipse. Interpreted to be the sun setting in the east, Atreus regained his kingdom. The Pleiades were chosen to accompany the sun when Zeus manifested his power in favor of Atreus.

The Romans called the cluster by the name of a garment that hung outside a broker's shop. This garment led to the name Petticoat Lane for a well-known London street.

At their midnight culmination, the Celtics, like those in many other parts of the world, held weird observances that filled the air with a witchlike mystery. Every fire in the land was extinguished that the ghosts of those who had died during the year might travel to their last resting place in the west. Once the stars had passed the meridian, the Druids lighted new fires which were carried by fast runners the length and breadth of the land, and in this way each village started its fire with a sacred flame. This ceremony echoes in All Hallow's Eve, All Saint's Day, and All Soul's Day. In France people preserve an old custom by carrying baskets of food to the cemeteries, where they eat lunch at the graves of ancestors. More important than this November 1st ritual was the one held in the Spring, when the Pleiades rose on the first day of May, which was the time of Beltane, fire of the god Bel. Exactly midway through the year after the observance of death or approach of winter was this festival dedicated to rebirth or the approach of warm weather, when the Pleiades rose at dawn.

Humans were sacrificed to Bel in the Beltane fire. Into the 19th century these holy fires were kindled. Oatcakes, toasted in the flames, were broken up into small bits, one piece being blackened with charcoal. Each man drew one of the broken parts; the man who drew the burnt piece was the chosen sacrifice. He was forced to leap three times through the heart of the flame. Even into the present these bonfires are lighted. Although the participants dance mirthfully around them, they are offshoots of the terrifying conflagrations which consumed humans and had been lighted to celebrate the end of frost and the return of warmth to the earth. A Roman writer described how the British Apollo appeared to his flock every 19 years during the Beltane festival. He could be seen dancing until the Pleiades rose, and the people, in frenzied revelry, danced too.

A Christian legend among the Teutonic people related that Jesus, when he passed a bakery, was attracted by the odor of newly baked bread. He asked for a loaf and the baker refused him. However, the man's wife and daughters, who overheard the request, secretly supplied the bread. In reward they were placed in the sky as the Seven Stars. The baker was changed into a cuckoo. While he sings his plaintive call in the spring, from Saint Tiburtus Day on April 14 until Saint John's Day on June 24, his wife and daughters hold an exalted place. The Gaels had a similar story, and called the stars Crannarain, Baker's Shovel. The English term, Cuckoo Bread, for the wood sorrel that flowers in northern woods in June, came from this tale.

To the Hottentots they were Khunusiti, Old Wives, who locked out their husband, the star Aldebaran, because he failed to find game while hunting.

The Mongols, like the Greeks and others, tell of a missing star. Seven robbers, Ursa Major, carried off one of the sisters. The one kidnaped was called Huitung Ot, Cold Star (Alcor), because it was taken from warm equatorial skies, where the sisters still live, and abducted to icy regions of the north. They also knew the stars as Mechit, a Monkey, who held its head in its hands. As mariners used these stars as guides when at sea, the Mongols employed them, along with other luminaries, to time the pace of their caravans.

Persians formerly called November, Mordad, Angel of Death. The festival of the dead was celebrated at the midnight culmination of these stars on the 17th of Mordad, and no petition presented to Persia's ancient kings on that date was denied.

In Hindu mythology, a son of Siva was born without a mother. His father gave him to the care of six nurses, the Krittika (Pleiades), and he took their name, Karttikeya, or son of the Krittika. The nurses also formed the 3rd nakshatra or resting place of the Moon, over which Agni was the regent. To honor Agni, master of fire, these stars were pictured as a flame. This illustration also may have alluded to the great star-festival, or Feast of Lamps, held in the Pleiad month,

Kartik, our October-November. This rite became the famous Feast of Lanterns celebrated in Japan. Incorrectly, the Hindus have represented the stars as a razor, or knife, with a short handle, the radical word kart in their title meaning to cut. In another legend, the stars are seven sisters married to seven sages, who are the luminaries of Ursa Major.

The Chinese and others of the East still ritualize a Feast of the Dead in November by kindling bonfires along the rivers and sailing paper boats which carry a lighted candle. At this time of the year the souls of the dead supposedly cross the sea to the eternal home.

Hervey Tonga Islanders divided the year in two, the first Matariki, or Matarii nia (Pleiades Above), began when the stars appeared on the horizon in the evening and continued while they remained above after dusk; the second Matariki, or Matarii i raro (Pleiades Below), began when they ceased to be visible after the sun set and continued until they again appeared above the horizon in the evening. Before man inhabited earth, the islanders believed, this group formed a single star, the most brilliant in the sky. His light was as great as that of the quarter moon, and when he appeared he danced on the sea and lifted darkness from the earth. However, he had one great weakness; he was as vain as he was handsome and brilliant, and constantly boasted that his splendor was greater than that of any star. One day, the great god Tane, guardian of heaven's four pillars, heard him say, "I am more beautiful than any

of you, more beautiful than the gods, even more beautiful than the jeweled heavens themselves." Tane's anger was not to be restrained, and he called on Mere (Sirius) and Aumea (Aldebaran) to help him drive this ill-bred and unneighborly creature out of the skies. Mere, the second brightest star, readily agreed to help eliminate his rival, as did Aumea, who was located so close, the great star's white glow dimmed his own. One dreary night, when all stars were obscured, the three allies crept up behind their enemy. As stealthily as they approached, they were seen, and the great beauty, alarmed, fled and found refuge under the waters of a stream (Milky Way), but Mere ran to the river's source and diverted the waters. The unprotected fugitive then hid under the arch of heaven, far beyond the silver palaces of the gods. Swift of foot, he had left his pursuers behind, but the determined Tane not to be outwitted, lifted Aumea and, with all his might, hurled his startled comrade at the runaway. The force with which Aumea struck shattered the great star into six pieces, which then were given the title Tauono. The satisfied god retrieved Aumea and, with Mere, called a truce. The six fragments limped back to their original place, but since that time fail to compete with either Mere, which became the most radiant of all stars, or with Aumea. Their pride has not permitted them to bow completely to the facts of their existence, and sometimes their whisper, that they are more lovely as six than as one, can be heard in the wind, and on dark nights they huddle together to see their reflection in the mirrors of lakes and oceans.

The stars of Tauono become the favorite Polynesian Avelas, Seaguides, when night voyages are made from island to island. Until the middle of the 19th century, when Christianity finally prevailed in this section of the world, they were objects of worship.

Dyaks and Malays of Borneo see the stars as six chickens followed by the mother hen, who always remains invisible. At the time of the year that the stars are invisible, the Dyaks say, "The Hen broods her Chicks." When the stars are seen, they say, "The cuckoo calls."

Native Australians hold a midnight New Year's corroboree in November to honor this group, which they aver is "very good to the black fellows." These furious, noisy nocturnal dances and songs around a fire celebrate tribal victories as well as pay homage to the dead. In a legend, the cluster represents a queen and her six attendants. Long ago the Crow (Canopus) fell in love with her but she refused to become his wife. The Crow spied upon her and discovered that she hunted for white edible grubs in tree barks, whereupon he changed himself into such a grub. The six maidens vainly tried to pick him out of the bark with wooden hooks, and when the queen tried with a pretty bone instrument, he transformed himself into a giant and ran after her. Ever since that time the cluster is composed only of the six attendants. Australian aborigines also relate that some pretty maidens on earth were followed by a group of young men called Beriberi (Singalese term for a disease). To escape,

the girls climbed to the tops of trees, whence they sprang into the skies. One maiden, less agile than the rest, was called the shy one, and is represented by the least bright star of the group. The Beriberi followed the girls and found a place in Orion's Belt, where they continue the chase.

Eskimos of Smith Sound call the cluster Nanuq, Bear. A number of dogs were chasing a bear across the ice. Gradually the bear and dogs rose up into the air. In the sky, they turned to stars, the bear becoming the large star in the center of the group.

Among American Indians, stories and beliefs linked to the Pleiades are numerous. A legend that the stars are lost children who are driven by hunger to take refuge in the sky prevails in the north. South American tribes see in them a swarm of bees, glowworms, or a heap of grain. Along the Amazon River they believe when the cluster is low in the sky birds sleep in the lower branches of trees and go higher to roost as the stars rise. These luminaries also supposedly influence reptiles, and in that valley Indians say only when these stars are visible is the bite of a snake poisonous. Contrariwise, reeds intended for arrows must be cut while these stars are visible or they will be worm eaten.

The Blackfeet, Iroquois, and others regulated their most important feasts by these stars. Among the Blackfeet all tribes turned out for the mysteries which included two sacred vigils.

Particulars relating to both feasts are lost in antiquity, but it is known that in the Innis-siman, the Grave or Burying of the Seed Feast, at the disappearance of the asterism from the night sky, men performed the dances. This solemn blessing and planting of the seed that opened the agricultural season had much in common with the Hebrew Passover and some Pagan mysteries held to honor Ceres. In the Mon-toke, Meeting of the Absent One, women were the active participants. On the last day of occulation, Vestals of the Sun, virgins, who figured in most of the nation's sacred feasts, performed the Manistam, Flag-pole Dance. In the autumn festival, at the Ocan, which means building a harvest or strong crop, these virgins presided over the gifts to be distributed to warriors and danced the Sta-pas-can, Dance of the Dead, which began at sunset and ended at dawn. The Blackfeet had seven classes of warriors, and the two stages of initiation to the mysteries were divided into three. All medicine men also were initiated into these three degrees. Mostly their ordeals were connected with the numbers three, seven, or ten. Seven Ma-tie warriors for the meeting of all the clans performed a dance which personified the Pleiades. Each star originally was a bird, a Crow, Partridge, Owl, Eagle, Crane, the Yellow or Golden Bird, called the Pokina, who was Chief Bird or Leader. These were the supernatural forms of brothers who nightly had guarded the sacred seed. To keep sleep away during the long dark hours they danced around the field. This so pleased Episors, the Morning Star, he lifted them into the

heavens that all the stars might rejoice in their perpetual dance. In Heaven they became Ekit-sikuno, the Seven-One. The word root for perfect or perfection is contained in this name, thus they were the seven perfect ones, although one of the birds, lost in the sky, could not be seen, and no one knew exactly which bird it represented.

In another Blackfeet legend, the stars were boys who ascended to heaven when they ran away from home because their father gave to their sisters, rather than to them, the yellow skins of buffalo calves the men had slain.

The Kiowa imagined them to be beautiful dancing girls. This likewise was an Algonquin belief, to whom the stellar maidens were the daughters of a sky chief. They descended in a basket to dance in a circle on the prairie, and tossed a brilliant ball from one to the other until they noticed they were observed by Algon, a young warrior. They fled, but he succeeded in capturing the loveliest of all. In great sadness the others returned to their lofty home without her. This is related to the swanmaiden theme, in which the girl is a mist- or rain-bringer, kidnaped by a youth (agricultural lord). Also this accounts for the divine heritage of man, and exemplifies the nobility of a celestial being as well as the greed of mankind or the desire of man to rise to loftier realms.

Like the Blackfeet, the Iroquois and other American nations, on all holy days presented the calumet toward this cluster with invocations for life-giving goods, long life and happiness. Women swore by the Pleiades, men by the Morning Star. In Iroquois myth, seven little Indian boys lived in a log cabin in the woods. Every starlit night they joined hands and danced about while they sang the Song of the Stars. The stars, who looked down, loved these children and beckoned to them. One night, when the children were disgruntled with their supper, they responded and allowed themselves to be placed in starland. The youngest boy became homesick and longed to return to earth. He often cried and when he did, he covered his face with his hand, thus dimming his light.

According to the Onondagas, a long time ago a clan of Indians went through the woods in search of a good hunting ground. When they found a place that abounded with wild life they began to set up lodgings for the winter. While the adults were occupied the children danced and sang. An old man in a white feather dress, with hair that dazzled like polished silver, appeared among them and directed them to stop dancing lest evil fall upon them. The children laughted at the old man, and gradually they rose from the ground. Someone said, "Do not look back," but one child disobeyed this warning also and became a falling star. The others reached heaven safely and remain huddled together.

To the Cherokees they were Unadatsugi, The Group, or Antisutsa, The Boys. Seven boys practiced shooting by firing at a bundle of corn cobs. Their mothers, annoyed, told them to do their shooting elsewhere. They went over a hill and disap-

peared. When they failed to return in a reasonable time their parents became worried and organized a search party. Before long they perceived the boys in a circle engaged in the feather-dance, accompanied by the sound of the ahuli, an ancient drum. The terrified parents noticed that as they danced they rose higher and higher. In alarm they tried to pull them down with poles, but they were out of reach and continued to dance until they became specks in the sky. They were seven stars for seven days-and then one, creating a fiery trail, fell to earth. Where it landed a palm tree grew, and the fallen star itself transformed into an old man, who warned of coming floods. He remained on earth for seven years. Before he disappeared he left his footprint on a rock. The stars, although they had become six, were still called seven, and if not propitiated by the feather-dance caused frost which injured the crops. The bundle of corn cobs suggests the granary, which was one of the constellation's symbols in China and Peru. The fall of one star may be connected with a Deluge story; possibly the fall of a Taurid meteor is echoed here. In any event, the Deluge in all legends of the world has been ascribed to the Pleiades, whose autumn culmination coincides with a rainy season.

In another Indian legend, seven brothers went on the warpath, and coming upon a beautiful maiden who was all alone, they adopted her to be their sister. One day the men left their youngest brother to watch over their sister while they went hunting. No sooner had the hunters left than the young boy saw some game, and he set off in pursuit of it. Whereupon a buffalo appeared outside the sister's tent and lured her onto his back. The elder brothers were dismayed upon their return to learn that she had disappeared. A search was organized, and they saw her in the center of a fierce herd of buffaloes. The younger brother cleverly tunneled beneath the animals and rescued the girl. Once she was safely back with them the brothers placed a high fence around their quarters. The enraged buffaloes battered it until it was torn down, only to discover that the maiden and her brothers had been carried skyward out of their reach.

Among the Shasta Indians of Oregon, Coyote went to a dance with Coon. On Coyote's return home he sent his children after some game he had killed and, when they brought it in, he prepared a grand feast. The youngest child was not invited, and his hurt was so deep he went to Coon's children and told them Coyote had killed their father. While Coyote was away from home they avenged the supposed slaying by slaughtering all the other Coyote children. Coyote, unable to find any of his sons, hunted everywhere. At last he perceived a cloud of dust and in the middle of it he noticed Coon's children and his youngest child. Vainly he ran after them, but his pursuit was useless because they kept rising higher and higher until they became the Pleiades. Coyote's child is the faintest star in the cluster. In winter, when the Coons are in their holes, the Pleiades are most brilliant and continually visible. In summer, when the

Pleiades are not to be seen, the Coons run about.

In a Gutamalan epic, Hunahpu and Xbalanque were twins born of the spittle of Hunhun Ahpu, the great overlord, by the earth maiden Xquiq. At dawn the underworld giants led by Zipacna slew the 400 warriors (stars) of Hunhun, who every evening was forced to restore them to life. The twins decided to aid their father by outwitting Zipacna. They pretended to be building a house and began by digging a vast hole. As they anticipated, when the curious Zipacna came along he asked what they were doing. They bewailed the difficulty they were having in making the hole for the foundation deep enough and persuaded him to go down into the cavity to see what the trouble might be. As soon as he dropped into the pit the brothers buried him under tree trunks and stones, and then continued to erect their house over the supposed grave. Zipacna, however, was unharmed. When he recovered from the jolt to his pride, he planned his revenge. No sooner had the architects and guests they had invited met to hold a house warming than Zipacna, without warning, rose. Earth quaked, cracked, and split open. This he followed up with a throwing out of his arms and a puffing up of his chest. The house and all in it were flung sky high, where the brothers and their friends huddled together to form the Pleiades.

The phenomenon of a lost star may be based purely on phantasy. Seven stars may have been seen in Babylonia, where in the clear tropic air more stars are visible than in more northerly latitudes.

Or the astronomers of that
nation, disregarding exactness,
assigned seven, their number of
perfection or completeness, to
the cluster. This number descended into the myths of other
nations. Inasmuch as the origin
of the discrepancy has been lost,
to explain seven or more in a
group where only six were
visible, the story of a missing
star was invented. Even into
modern time, six are said to
be visible to the naked eye;
some observers with exceptional-
ly keen sight claim to see seven;
nine bright stars generally are
catalogued. The nine in Greek
mythology are the parents,
Atlas, the father, and Pleione,
the mother, and their seven
daughters. Atlas was condemned
to stand on the northwest corner
of Africa, then the extreme west
of the world, supporting the
heavens on his shoulders, for
the part he played in the war
against Zeus. Pleione was the
atmosphere. Their seven
daughters were Alcyone, Maia,
Electra, Merope, Taygete,
Celaeno, Asterope or Sterope.
The lost or dim Pleiad has been
said to be variously Electra,
Merope, or Sterope.

In the southern hemisphere,
where the seasons are reversed
from those in the northern
hemisphere, various aborigines
contend the Pleiades are the
source of summer heat. The
sun, they insist cannot be, for
it shines in cold as well as
warm weather, whereas these
stars appear in the spring and
disappear when summer ends.

Many modern customs had
their origin in November Pleiad
functions, as elections in the
United States, which derive from
the ancient convocation of tribes
at this season. Masonic
organizations hold memorial services in November, when the
Pleiades, since times long
passed, supposedly cause all
life in nature to be at low ebb
in preparation for winter's long
sleep. In Masonic symbolism,
these Seven Stars are emblematic
of the vernal equinox, associated
with their heliacal rising. Thus,
they are a token of immortality,
death in the autumn, rebirth in
spring.

Pleiades, also written Pliades
or Pleiads, is the plural of
Plias, which comes from a
Greek word meaning to sail,
and, at the heliacal May rising
of this asterism, navigation was
considered safe in Greece; its
autumnal setting coincided with
the cold weather that ended
navigation. Another derivation
of the word expresses full or
many, which concurs with the
meaning of the Arabic Al
Thurayya and the Hebrew Kimah.
Pliada was used in the middle
ages for showers, and they
shared the rainy character
ascribed to their sisters, the
Hyades. Pleione, mother of the
seven, also is said to be the
source of the name, and probably is the most likely.

Additional designations: Atlas
Born; Band, from a Greek word
which indicated the members of
the group were united into a
fillet; Brood-Hen star Vergiliae;
Coop; Dancers, a conception of
American Indians; Flock of clusterers; Girdle, a conception
from Arabic literature which
had them appear like the folds
of a silken sash bedecked with
gems. Many poets wrote they
were bound together, formed a
necklace, or a rose. Still
other titles were: Girl, from a

Serbian story of a girl, prob-
ably the star Alcyone, in charge
of this brood. Golden Cluck Hen
and her Five Chicks; Hencoop;
Hen with Her Chickens. Hes-
perides, sister of the Pleiades;
Narrow Cloudy Train of Female
Stars; Nocturnal Timekeeper;
Old Atlas's Children; Seamen's
Starres; Seven Atlantic Sisters;
Seven Virgins; Starry Seven;
Virgin Stars. As a coat of arms
for merchants the cluster was
called The Multiplication Table.

Anglo-Saxon: Sifunsterri,
Seven Stars.

Arabic: Al Najm, The Con-
stellation, par excellence, or
The Star, i.e. of piercing
brightness. Al Thurayya, The
Many Little Ones, the 3rd
manzil, and a diminutive form
of Tharwan, Abundance, either
from their appearance or from
the plentiful crops produced by
their abundant rains. Al
Thurayya became distorted during
the middle ages in Europe into
Altorich, Altorieh, Atarge,
Atauria, Athorace, Athoraiae
Benat, Atorage, Elnasch;
Syryan Voykodzyun, Night Star;
Turanya, Herd of Camels.

Assyro-Babylonian: Kimmatu
or Kimtu, Family Group.

Babylonian: Atorage, a lunar
station.

Chinese: Gang, of unknown
significance; Mao, Maou, Mau,
anciently Mol, probably meaning
The Constellation, and composing
the 18th hsiu. Another name
signified Seven Sisters of Industry.

Danish: Aften Hoehne, Eve
Hen.

Egyptian: Athur-ai, Stars of
Athyr or Hathor, great cosmic
mother; Chu or Chow, a former
spelling for the hieroglyph for
Khu, god of light; Neith or
Nit, snake goddess, a self-
begotten virgin, whose son was
Ra. One significance of
Neith is Shuttle, inasmuch as
she was mistress of the loom,
i.e. wove the universe. Her
face was green to typify earth
over which she was queen.

English of middle ages:
Atlantes daughtres sevene.

Euphratean: Combined with
the Hyades, these stars were
the Mastab-ba-gal-gal-la, The
Great Twins, i.e. of the
ecliptic.

Europe of middle ages:
Peleiades, Pliade.

French: among the peasantry,
Cousiniere, Mosquito Net.

Gaelic: Crannarain, Baker's
Peel or Shovel; Grigirean,
Griglean, Grioglachan, a
Ladle; Meanmnach.

German: Gluck Henne;
Plejaden; Schiffahrts Gestirn,
Sailor's Stars; Siebengestirn, a
numerical title also applied to
the seven bright stars and to the
planets.

Hebrew: Kimah, Cluster or
Heap. Rabbis have called them
Filiae Tabernaculi, Tabernacle
of the Daughters; Succoth or
Sukkoth Benoth, Booths of the
Maidens or Tents of the
Daughters. Succoth Benoth in
the Bible also is said to be in-
tended for association with
Zarbanit, an epithet of Beltis,
Babylonian mother goddess
worshipped in Samaria by

Asiatic immigrants as wife of
Marduk, and without astral im-
plication, or to be the booth or
tent in which women prostituted
themselves for the sake of
Mylitta, Chaldean cosmic mother.

Hervey Island: Matariki,
Little Eyes; Tauono, The Six,
sometimes written Tau, a title
resembling Taurus, the constellation of which they are a
part.

Hindu: Karteek, Kartiguey,
Krittikeya, or Krittika, General
of Celestial Armies or Nurses
of the General.

Hungarian: Fiastik; Heteveny;
Hete-wane.

Italian: Plejadi; Pulsiniere,
Poussiniere, or Gallinelle, the
Pullets; and the peasant simile,
la Racchetta, the Battledore.

Languedoc: Cousigneiros,
Mosquito Net.

Latin and Low Latin:
Butrum, incorrectly written
Drutum, Bunch of Grapes. Also
likened to the dove with a purple
breast that resembles discolora-
tion by wine, or the dove, a
migrator in the vintage season.
On ancient coins, doves had
breasts made of bunches of grapes;
in early Christian symbolism the
bird and fruit were associated.
Eoae Atlantides, Dawn Atlantides; Globus Pleiadum, Ball
Pleiades; Glomerabile Sidus,
Rounded Star or Asterism;
Massa Gallinae, Massive Birds
or Hens; Signatricia Lumina;
Vergiliae or Sidus Vergiliarum,
for the group's rising after Ver,
the Spring. Incorrectly written
Virgiliae.

Mongol: Mechit, Monkey.

Norwegian: Killukturset, Dogs
Baiting a Bear; Niedgierreg,
meaning unknown.

Persian: Parur, Parvig,
Parviz, Parwin, Perv, Perven,
Pervis, popularly Peren, all
meaning Begetter, i.e. of all
things, probably because they
once began the year.

Polish: Baby, meaning Old
Wife.

Russian: Baba, Old Wife;
Nasedha, Sitting Hen.

Santal: Sar en, meaning unknown.

Serbian Yakut: Urgel, Air
Hole, i.e. of the sky through
which streams of cold draught
come from the upper heaven.

Sicilian: Sette Palommielle,
Seven Pigeons or Dovelets.

Sogdian: Parvi, derived from
the Persian.

Solomon Islands:Togo ni samu,
Company of Maidens.

South American Indians:
Cajupal, Six Stars. Along the
Paraguay River the Abipones
name is: Groaperikie, Grandfather. In May, on the reappearance of the asterism, this
ancestor, Grandfather of all,
was welcomed back with dances
and shouts of joy, as if he had
recovered from an illness.

Spanish: las Siete Cabrillas,
The Seven Little Nanny Goats.

Swedish: Suttjenes Rauko, Fur
in Frost, these stars believed
to be the cloak of a servant
turned out into the cold by his
master.

Syrian: Kima, Cluster or Group, which in the middle ages corrupted into Gemat.

Teutonic: Seulainer.

Tonga Islands: Matarii, Little Eyes.

Turkish: Ulgher.

Welsh: Y tur tewdws, Close Pack.

Despite the high regard in which these stars were held, astrologers attributed to them blindness and accidents to sight, a reputation shared with all clusters. Arabs are particularly afraid of them, fearful that the forty days in which they disappear into the rays of the sun is a time when great harm befalls mankind. One saying is that, 'When the star rises, all harm rises from the earth." On the other hand the ancient Greeks believed that in autumn, under the Pleiades, people died in great numbers.

Located beyond the Bull's head, near the ecliptic, their dual nature, which, on the one hand makes them bringers of joy and rebirth and on the other makes them bringers of doom and death, is due entirely to this position, which evenly divides the year. On or about May 1, they rise with the sun at dawn; on or about November 1, they rise with the moon at dusk. Through the winter months, when the sun is low and feeble and earth is without fruit, they are visible in the night sky, and this marks them as essentially stars of cold weather.

PLEIONE, one of the Pleiades

in Taurus, winter. Mother of the sisters and included as one of the stars in the cluster. The spectrum of this luminary shows bright hydrogen lines, which may at times give it a temporary brilliancy, and for this reason some astronomers aver this star, rather than one of the daughters, is the true Lost Pleiad. The name, from the Greek, literally is more or much and signifies the vast expanse of space or atmosphere. It also is written Mater Pleione or Plione. Arabs called it Al Thuraja, from Al Thurayya, the title applied to the whole constellation Taurus as well as to the Pleiad cluster.

POLARIS, alpha Ursae Minoris, double, topaz yellow and pale white.

Shakespeare in Julius Caesar wrote incorrectly:

　　　　　　　　constant as the
　　Northern Star,
　　Of whose true fixed and resting quality
　　There is no fellow in the firmament.

The North Star is not fixed. A slight oscillation due to the attraction of the sun and moon on earth's bulge causes precession of the equinoxes which affects the Pole Star as well as all others. About 4,000 years ago Thuban of Draco ruled the luminaries, then came Kochab of Ursa Minor. The present star will recede in favor successively of stars in Cepheus, in Cygnus, and, about 11,500 years hence, Vega of Lyra, whose reign will last for about 3,000 years. After that the shift repeats itself, Thuban,

Kochab, Polaris, and back to the others. The entire cycle takes between 25,695 to 25,868 years with long periodic gaps when no star holds the honor. The motion created by the planets makes precise calculation impossible. Neither is Polaris at the exact north; it is simply the nearest naked-eye star to the Pole. That it appears to be steadfast has made it not only useful as a nocturnal guide, but the most celebrated of all stars. Its dependable beckoning light, that has lured men into adventure and exploration, also has inspired considerable poetry. William Cullen Bryant, in his Hymn to the North Star, wrote:

> ...on thy unaltering blaze,
> The half-wrecked mariner,
>   his compass lost,
> Fixes his steady gaze,
> And steers, undoubting, to
>   the friendly coast;
> And they who stray in peril-
>   ous wastes by night,
> Are glad when thou dost shine
>   to guide their footsteps right.

Widely the star has been revered as a paradise or as the throne of a supreme, upright (male), unbiased, unwavering divine judge, the great father, the eye of heaven, the accurate pivot of the universe.

Eridu, Sumerian paradise where the first man was created and where the souls of the dead passed on the way to the Great Deep, was stationed in the center or navel of the earth. In it grew a dark pine, symbolic of the male creative energy, which had a white crown that extended into the heavens. This crown, the Pole Star, was the couch of the mighty mother of the world, Zikum. The imagery is an expression of the dual principles of nature, male and female, which are necessary to perpetuate the everlasting cycle of death and rebirth. About the same time the story of Anshar, Babylonian father of all the gods and grandfather of Marduk was first recited. Anshar with his spouse Kishar emerged from chaos. Together they represented the entire cosmos, he the male that is above, she the female in whom fertility was germinated. When he officiated as Polaris, lord of the night sky, he and his six assistants, the other Small Dipper stars, assumed goat or satyr shape, and along with the rest of the firmament danced around the Pole, his phallus the fecundator of all things.

When Set, Egyptian demon of darkness, decided to imprison his brother Osiris, the sun, in darkness, he instructed his most masterly craftsmen to fashion a box of fragrant woods. Without difficulty he persuaded Osiris to step inside the box, and then sealed the cover. This magnificent coffin became the luminous Pole Star.

Phoenician navigators were probably the first to use Polaris as a station from which to maintain their course. About 600 B.C. they introduced its superiority to the Greeks, who until that time had depended on the Big Dipper.

The Greeks, like the Euphrateans, venerated the star as their supreme deity's throne, and here Zeus whiled away the hours of the night. Kerkuon, too, was an impeller or axis god. The inventor of wrestling, he contended with Theseus at the Pole or Axis and bent down the tops of trees as well as the overreaching branches of the Cosmic Tree, which Theseus kept straightening. A spirit of darkness, his name suggests turning to the left, whereas Theseus, a light hero, fought for the right order of the universe.

When the Norse gods vanquished their enemies, the giants, they dismembered the body of Ymir, who had been born from icy chaos, and placed the parts in their enormous vat, the World Mill, which ground out clouds from his brains, earth from his flesh, mountains from his bones, plants from his hair, rocks from his teeth, sea from his blood, and a wall for their own defense from his eyebrows. They wanted the world they had created to hold together; they also wished to see the sky they had molded from his skull revolve, so they drove the Veralder Nagli (World Spike) into the center of the universe. It is like a long barbecue spit that runs from Pole to Pole, on which earth turns as if it were smoking meat. One end of the rod is secured to the north rim of the universe by a nailhead ornamented with brilliant gems, and this nailhead is the Pole Star. Saxons worshipped Irminsul as their sacred pillar or World Tree. Originally it was the seat of ancestral souls, later the seat of gods and finally it corrupted into Hangman's Stone, and its earthly counterpart was a gallows on which sacrificial fertility victims were hung.

The Finno-Ugrian nail of the sky is Boahje-Naste. Here a young and beautiful maiden highly skilled in spinning weaves the universe. When Arcturus, the archer, shoots down Boahje-Naste, the heavens will fall and bring

about the end of the world. Another Finnish name for the spike is Taehti, also the name of the god around whom the firmament revolves.

Santa Claus has his home on North Star, and here every Christmas the fat jolly man harnesses reindeers to the sleigh in which he journeys on a world-wide trip of toy-giving to children who have behaved well during the year. For naughty children he leaves birch rods.

In another Christian concept, Saint Jerome applied the title Stella Maris to the Virgin Mary without nautical or astral connection. A star, however, has always been a symbol of virtue, particularly of chaste women, so that this title, which embraces Miriam, the Jewish form of the name, was used to glorify the most faithful star in the heavens.

Arab Pagans despised the star as the worst villain in the sky, the slayer of Al Na'ash, the warrior mourned by all circumpolar stars that moved in a slow funereal procession throughout the night. Ostracized, he remains alone, imprisoned in the cold barren north by the circular march of the mourners of the man he killed. Arabs also believed the star to be the hole in which the axle of earth was borne.

Moslems used Al Kiblah (Polaris) to aid them when in a strange location in establishing the direction of the Kabah in Mecca, toward which every good Moslem must turn his head in prayer. The Kabah, a square house, was probably an early

Sabaean temple. In Moslemic
tradition, it was built in heaven
and let down by angels directly
under its celestial site that Adam
might have a tabernacle on earth
of radiant clouds. When he
died it vanished and Seth, the
patriarch, built one of stone and
clay that was swept away by the
Deluge. Finally Abraham and
Ishmael erected the present
building to house Al Hajar al
Aswad, a ruby or jacinth,
brought from heaven by Gabriel.
The holy trophy is now called
the Black Stone because it has
been blackened by pilgrim's tears
or the kisses of sinners.

In Hindu legend, Dhruva was
the son of a king. Because of
the jealous intrigues of the king's
second wife, he and his mother
Suniti were banished from court
and sent to live in a little
cottage just outside a wild forest
that no man had ever penetrated.
When he was nine years of age,
Dhruva asked his mother for
permission to visit his father.
Although her misgivings were
great, Suniti gave her consent to
such a visit. For three days the
boy walked before he reached the
city, and there he found the
marble palace with floors inlaid
with colored gems. Fountains
sprayed in the courtyard, and the
rooms inside were richly furnished, tapestries hung on the
walls and the lights were dazzling.
The king took his son on his knee,
told him how proud he was that
the boy had grown handsome and
strong, and asked about his life.
Dhruva described how he and
his mother lived in the shadows
of the tall black trees, how little
sun entered their cottage, and
that his only companions were
deer and other animals, and
that he was so lonely he often
grew sad. The king heard his

second wife plan with her servants to kill the boy, and fearing
for his son's life, told him he
must leave for his home by the
forest, but he added, "Even though
you are far away remember
always that I love you."

All the way home the boy
kept thinking, my father is
king, he loves me, yet he cannot keep me beside him. If he
is weak and powerless, where
shall I find strength. When he
reached home he told Suniti
what had happened, and asked,
"Is anyone stronger than my
father?"

"Yes, little one, Lotus-eyes
is stronger."

"Where does he live?"

Suniti shook her head. She
did not want to tell him that
Lotus-eyes was a god and therefore not to be found. When
Dhruva pressed for an answer
she merely said, "You cannot
reach him. In the heart of
the forest he lives with the
bear and the tiger."

After his mother fell asleep,
Dhruva prepared a knapsack
with provisions and pushed his
way in the underbrush among the
trees, and soon he was lost
under the thick heavy branches.
For days he walked and heard
nothing but the wind and the wild
animals and birds. Eventually
he came to the tiger's lair.
The beast was just about to
spring at him when Dhruva
cried, "Are you Lotus-eyes?"
and the tiger hung his head and
furtively turned away. At the
den of the great brown bear,
Dhruva again asked, "Are you
he, Lotus-eyes?" and the bear
likewise crept away.

At last he came to a clearing which seemed to him must be the heart of the forest, and there he sat down to wait. Before long the forest sage Narada appeared and asked, "You seek the Lotus-eyed?"

"Yes, yes, are you he?"

"No, my son, I am not, but I can tell you how to find him. Remain here in the forest and pray to him; think of Lotus-eyes until you no longer see the trees or the sky above you or the wild beasts, and you have no thoughts other than of him." Then Narada disappeared and Dhruva knew he had been speaking to a rishi, one of the seven wise men of India who live in the seven stars of Ursa Major, in disguise.

Days passed into months, months passed into years, years turned into centuries, and still Dhruva remained at his prayers. White ants came and built a world of stars around him without his noticing them. Even after he had discovered that Lotus-eyes really existed in his own heart, he still sat motionless in prayer. So steady and so immobile he had become the heavens revolved around him, and the Pole Star, the luminary that never shifts, never leaves its place, but always shines as a helpful guide in the north is none other than Dhruva Lok, the Place of Dhruva, the young prince who is lost in meditation and oblivious to the universe that circles around him. Dhruva is often used as a metaphor for that which is steadfast, faithful, and constant.

According to the Mandaeans, across the sky, which is a great sea of clear, pure water, but of more than adamantine solidity, stars, planets, and other bodies sail. Its transparency permits us to see even to the pole-star, the central sun around which the universe moves, and at the gate that leads to the realm of Abathur, who sits on the farthest verge of light and weighs the deeds of departed spirits. Appeal is made to the star for intercession with Abathur.

A frog, in Mongolian and Siberian lore had been turned upside down that its feet might be used as posts to hold up the universe, each leg located at one of the four corners or cardinal points. Out of its navel rose Sumbur, the sacred mountain that marked the center of the world. On Sumbur grew a seven-storied birch tree of life, which had Polaris perched on its summit. This lofty realm was sacred, it was the seat of judges of the dead, and the profane were not permitted to place their feet on it. Tartars called the spirit of this highest heaven Khaira-Khan. Pillars were erected of iron and gold which were worshipped as representations of the deity, and animal sacrifices were made to it. Siberians had a black-smith (probably lightning) god, Torem, who dwelled in a tent next to the heaven post (North Star). He taught men how to use the anvil and prepare iron, and he and his sons tied their reindeer to the post.

Shang Ti, Chinese ruler of heaven and earth, had his throne here. Two ministers of state helped him administer all the complicated organization of the sky above and earth below. These two, who helped him regulate the seasons and in

general govern the universe were
the Spirit of the Great Bear, who
ruled the heavenly realms, and
the Spirit of T'ai Shan, the sacred
mountain, who ruled China. They
were called Stars that assist.
A number of shrines and temples
to the Great Bear star are to be
found along the pilgrim path leading to T'ai Shan's summit. At
the very top stands a square
dedicated to the seven Bear
stars. In the imperial cult,
Shang Ti was worshipped only by
the emperor, the son of heaven,
and therefore no temples were
erected in his honor. When
T'ien Pao, eternal sovereign of
Jade Heaven, was reincarnated
he appeared as Pei-chi Chen
Chun, a North Pole god.

In a Taoist fable, Tou Mu
was a maiden so virtuous, she
attained a knowledge of celestial
mysteries and was able to
cross the sea at will without
wetting her feet as she skimmed
over the waves, and in this way
she was able to save many
sailors from drowning. The king
of North China heard of her
many virtues and ever-increas-
ing wisdom, and made her his
wife. They both lived a great
span of years, and when the
time came for her to pass into
the other world, the Lord of
Heaven himself invited her, her
husband and nine sons to live
in the palace of the Pole. In
time Tou Mu became its goddess,
and was seated on a throne of
lotus. In her eighteen hands
she held the registry of life and
death of mortals and the list of
gods. In her forehead she had
a third eye so that she was
able to see everything. For those
who prayed to her with sufficient
faith she had the power to pro-
long life.

All circumpolar stars circled
around the North Star in homage,
the whole area formed by the
procession being the Purple
Subtle Enclosure. A name by
which Polaris is addressed is
Star of Red Myrtle, and in
Chinese literature the Forbidden
City in Peking was at times
called Red City. This reference
was intended to identify the
palace of the emperor with that
of the emperor of stars.

Ama-no-minaka-nushi,
Japanese primeval deity, stood
motionless in the center of
cosmos, and sprouted like a
weed out of chaos. He shared
his abode, Ame-no-iha-ya, with
Taka Minusubi, the male principle and Kamu Minusubi, the
female principle, therefore
was one of a trinity. Ame-no-
iha-ya, literally Heaven's Rock
Dwelling, was the celestial
center in which the axis was
fixed, or the Pole Star. The
throne of the god was Ame-no-
iha-kura.

During the American Civil
War, slaves and prisoners of
war who escaped from the south
lay hidden during the day and
moved onward at night, depending on the trustworthy beams of
Polaris for guidance.

The name Polaris is from the
Latin meaning pole or stake.
Additional designations are:
Angel Stern; Chariot Star;
Golden Peg; High One of the
Enclosure of Light; Judge of
Heaven; Loadstar or Lodestar,
Way or Guide Star; Merchant's
Guide; Northern Axle; Pivot
Star; Pole Star; Ship Star;
Spindle; Star of Arcady, earthly
home of Callisto and Arcas,
spirits of Arctos, collective
name of the two Bears; Star

of the Sea; Steering Star; Stella Maris, Stella Polaris, Tyrian Cynosure, i.e. Phoenician Guide.

Anglo-Saxon: Irminsul, Soul of Irmin; Scip-steorra, Shipstar.

Arabic: Al Jadi, The Young He Goat, which subsequently deteriorated into Giedi and Juddah. Al Jadi was the slayer of Al Na'ash (Ursa Major). Al Kaukab al Shamaliyy, Star of the North, which may have been used by early nomads for beta, once closer to the pole. Al Kiblah, which signified the star least distant from the pole. As marking the pole it was Al Kutb al Shamaliyy, The Northern Axle or Spindle, from Al Kutb, an under-pin of a mill around which the upper stone turns. Al Ruccabah, from the constellation. Mismar, needle or pin.

Chinese: Pih Keih; To Shin; Ti Tso, Emperor's Seat; Tien Hwang Ta Ti, Great Imperial Ruler of Heaven; Tow Kei, Northern Square.

Euphratean: Bil or Pul, Pole Star. A different star may have been intended, for, during the milleniums that have passed, the polar point slowly approaching our pole star once was far removed from it. (Kochab, beta Ursae Minoris, or Thuban, alpha Draconis, may have held the office when Bil or Pul was first applied).

Finnish: Taehti, Star of the Top of the Heavenly Mountain.

Greek: Cynosura or Phoenice, both names borrowed from the constellation.

Hindu: Dhruva, a light deity and attendant of Indra. Grahad-

hara, Pivot of the Planets, may have been an earlier pole star. Kasyapa, father of Garuda, lord of birds.

Italian: la Tramontana, Over the Mountain or Star of the Mountain, a title shared with the constellation. A popular saying about a man along the Mediterranean is "He has lost his Tramontane," when he has lost his bearings.

Japanese: Ama-no-minaka-nushi, Pole-star God; Ame-no-iha-ya, Pole-star God's Dwelling.

Latin: Navigatoria; Pollaris.

Mayan: Xaman Ek.

Spanish: Nortes, North.

Turkish: Yilduz, The Star, i.e. par excellence. Its light was said to have been concealed for a time after the capture of Constantinople.

In Arabia and Egypt, astrologers warned their followers to beware of the star, it was evil, a portent of death. In spite of this the Arabian masses believed that a fixed contemplation of this star would cure itching of the eyelids.

POLLUX, beta Geminorum, orange tinted, winter. The immortal twin of the mortal Castor, he shared his immortality with his brother, spending half his life, or alternate days, in the underworld that his brother might wander in the world above, thus they typified dawn and dusk, sun and moon, day and night, light and darkness. They were particularly the morning and evening stars, Pollux appearing in the east in the morning to usher in light and Castor in the west in the evening to usher in darkness. Their devotion to each other has made them the world's most renowned examples of brotherly love. Pollux was the greatest pugilist of his time, and his outstanding virtue was valor. In later myths, the morning star became an aspect of Heracles as a companion and twin of Apollo, who appeared in the evening star. Although about 300 years ago Castor was the lucida of Gemini, Pollux is now the brighter star.

The name is from the Greek Polydeukes. Additional designations are:

Arabic: Al Ras al Jauza, The Head of the Twin, which degenerated into Rasalgauze, Rasalgense, Rasalgeuze. Al Ras al Taum al Mu'ah-h-ar, The Head of the Hindmost Twin. Al Thani al Dhira, The Second in the Forearm, an early name.

Assyrian: Tuamu. With alpha star called Mas-mas, Twins.

Babylonian: Mu-sir-kes-da, Yoke of the Inclosure. Mashmashu-arku, Eastern One of the Twins, as the determinant of the 12th Babylonian asterism.

Latin and Low Latin: Polluces; Pugil, Pugilist. The name Hercules (Heracles) degenerated in early catalogues into Abrachaleus, which had been derived from the Arabic Ab (Father) and the Greek name; this again contracted into Aracaleus, Iracleus, Heraclus, Garacles. Other degenerate names used for both alpha and beta as a pair are Elhakaac and Ketpholtsuman,

but no clue to their origin has been found.

In astrology, Pollux, in contrast to Castor, is considered a fortunate star, portending eminence and renown, perhaps because light in mythology is regarded as virtuous and darkness as evil. This is one of the stars much used by navigators in taking lunar observations.

PORRIMA, gamma Virginis, binary, slightly variable, pale yellow, spring. Carmenta, Roman goddess of springs, was the leader of the Carmenae, who sang a child's destiny at birth. At first she was worshipped as two goddesses, the Carmentes, individually called Porrima (Antevorta, Prorsa, Prosa) and Postvorta (Postverta), invoked according to whether the child was born facing forwards or backwards, or for her knowledge of the future or past. Later the two were considered to be one, Carmenta, with her first two aspects as sisters or companions. In modern Italy the cult survives, and she is appealed to for aid in childbirth. The star has been given the various names of the sisters: Antevorta, Postvorta, Prorsa, Prosa, with Porrima the most popular.

This star has been used to designate the actual Arabic angle or corner of the Kennel of the Barking Dogs, described under the constellation. As one star in Babylonia, gamma was called Kakkab Dan-nu, Star of the Hero, and as a binary it marked the 19th ecliptic mansion, Shur-mahru-shiru, The Front, or West, Shur. Chinese knew it as Shang Seang, High Minister of State.

PRAESEPE, a cluster in Cancer, late winter. The historical and other interest in this cluster of small stars has been great. Aratos' poem celebrated it as a weather-guide, indicating that weather patterns would follow certain appearances of the group. Pliny wrote, "Praesepe, not visible in a clear sky, presages a violent storm; if murky, a sign of rain." It provided Galileo with one of the earliest telescopic proofs of a mass of stars, individually invisible to the naked eye, which appear to the unassisted eye as one star. Galileo thought he had discovered forty-odd stars; the modern telescope reveals 363 separate suns. This magnificent aggregation on a clear night presents a misty apparition, and has been mistaken for a comet.

In Christian lore it has been referred to as the Manger in which Christ was born, or the Crib, and has been compared to the Breastplate of Righteousness. With the Aselli it represented Saint John the Evangelist. In the 17th century, the Manger was the fancied coat of arms for farmers in a set of heraldic signs. In Arabic tradition, it is the Stall into which the two asses, Ascellus Australis and Ascellus Borealis, supposedly fled. In English folklore it is known as the Beehive.

Other spellings are Praesaepe, Praesaepis, Praesaepia, Praesapium, Presebre, Presepe, and additional titles are: The Little Cloud, The Little Mist, Whirling Cloud, all relating to its nebulous quality. Arabic: Al Ma'laf, The Stall, which decayed into Meeleph and Melleff. Chinese: Tseih She Ke, Exhalation of Piled-up Corpses. Coptic: Ermelia, Nurturing. Astrologically, as all clusters, it threatened mischief and blindness.

PROCYON, alpha Canis Minoris, binary, white lightly tinged with yellow, winter. With Sirius, one of the Dogs of the great hunter Orion, Sirius being the Great Dog, Procyon being the Little Dog. In another Greek legend, the star is said to be the heavenly form of the faithful dog Maera, which belonged to Icarius, who had been taught vine cultivation by Dionysus. When Icarius offered some wine to a band of shepherds they drank too freely and became drunk. Their companions, believing the shepherds had been poisoned, killed Icarius and buried his body under a tree. His daughter Erigone, in a search for her father, was led to the spot by Maera, who sat howling on the grave from which he had scratched some earth away. Erigone, in grief, hanged herself on the tree, and the deeply touched deities placed Icarius in the sky as the constellation Bootes, or the star Arcturus in Bootes; Erigone as the constellation Virgo; Maera as Icarium Astrum (star of Icarius) or Procyon. Icarius typifies fertility; Maera the shining rays which revealed to Erigone, the harvest maid, that fertility had come to an end. Scratching by a dog is symbolic of rebirth.

To the Arabs, the star was known as Al Ghumaisa, Dim, Watery-Eyed, or Weeping, either from the fact that this star is dimmer than her twin, Al-abur (Sirius), or because of the following fable. Al-abur and Al-ghumaisa were the sisters

of Suhail (Canopus), who abducted Al Jauzah (Rigel).
Shortly after his marriage,
Suhail slew his wife and fled
toward the South Pole. His
sisters became ashamed and
angry, and Al-abur pursued him
across the Milky Way, where
she paused to rest and became
the lucida of Canis Major. Al
Ghumaisa wept for both Suhail
and her wandering twin until her
eyes became weak. Jointly the
twin Dog Stars were Al Ahawat
al Suhail, The Sisters of Canopus.
Quite possibly the name Al
Ghumaisa may have been derived
from the Euphratean term,
which meant Water-Dog.

As the rising of Sirius
warned the Egyptians that the
Nile's inudation was about to take
place, so the appearance of
Procyon warned that Sirius, with
its dog-days of scorching heat
was about to rise. Many of its
names apply to its character and
have been given to the constellation as well as to the star.
Procyon, which literally is Before
the Dog is a Roman transliteration of a Greek term meaning
Rising Before His Companion Dog.
Other designations are:

Arabic: Al Ghumaisa, or Al-
Gumaisa, whose legend is related above, and from which were
derived these hybrids: Algomeiza,
Algomeysa, Algomisa, Algomyso.
Al Shi'ra al Shamiyyah, Star of
the North, or Left, shortened to
Al Shamiyyah, Aschemie,
Aschere. Siair Siami, which
agrees with a title occasionally
used in English, i. e. Northern
Sirius. Shamiyyah, from the
Arabic adjective meaning north,
or on the left side, is sometimes
added to the name to indicate
its geographical position, that is
it may be seen toward Sham

(Syria) in the north.

Babylonian: Known as the
Scepter of Bel.

Chinese: Combined with beta
and smaller stars to form the
group Nan Ho.

Euphratean: Titles applied
to the star have not been
definitely verified, but Kakkab
Paldara, Pallika, or Palura, all
related to the meaning Star of
the Crossing of the Water-Dog,
and indicating its position close
to the Milky Way, The River of
Heaven, seem to be appropriate.

Greek: Pur Cahen, a title that
supposedly came from Egypt,
and related to its dog-like
character.

Hervey Island: Vena, a goddess.

Hindu: Singe Hanuant.

Latin and Low Latin: Antecanis, Antecanem, Antecedens
Canis, alluding to its rising
before the other Dog Star.

Persian: Vanand; a doubtful
title more often applied to
Regulus.

In astrology it portends good
fortune, especially wealth and
fame.

PROPUS, eta Geminorum,
binary and variable, winter.
From the Greek meaning The
Projecting Foot, a name which
indicates its position before
Castor's left foot. Another
Greek term applied to the star
is Tropus, Turn, which refers
to the apparent turning point of
the sun's course at the summer
solstice, which once was marked

by this star, and now is marked
by gamma, just eastward. Additional designations are: Arabic:
Tejat Prior, from Al Tahayi, an
anatomical term. With gamma,
it composed their asterism Al
Nuhatai, A Camel's Hump.
Babylonian: Maru-sha-pu-u-
mash-mashu, Front of the Mouth
of the Twins, marking the 8th
ecliptic configuration, and placing
the figure in a position reversed
to that in which it is now portrayed. Chinese: Yue, Battle Ax.
Persian: Pish Pai. Astrologically it portended lives of eminence
to all born under its influence.

RAS ALGETHI (RAS ALGETTA),
alpha Herculis, double, orange
red and bluish green, summer.
From the Arabic Ras al Jathiyy,
Head of the Kneeler, which is a
translation from the Greek, The
Title corrupted further into
Rasaben, also used for the con-
stellation; Rasacheti, Ras Algathi,
Ras Algeti, Ras Algetta, Ras
Algiatha, Ras Algothi, Ras
Alhathi, Ras Alheti, Ras Elh-
hati. The nomad title was Al
Kalb al Rai, The Shepherd's
Dog. Chinese called it Ti Tso,
Emperor's Seat; also Tsin.

RASALHAGUE (RAS AL-
HAGUE), alpha Ophiuchi,
double, sapphire-blue and pale
grey, summer. From the
Arabic Ras al Hawwa, Head of
the Serpent Charmer, or Col-
lector. The original has been
altered into Alangue, Alhague,
Azalange, Hawwa, Ras Alaghue,
Rasalange, Rasalangue, Rasala-
gue, Ras Alhagas, Ras Alhagus,
Ras al Hangue, Ras al Hayro.
The Moors wrote it as El Hauwe.
Desert Arabs called it Al Rai,
The Shepherd. Also used for
gamma Cephei.

RASTABAN (RASTABEN),
beta Draconis, probably binary,
yellow, spring. From the
Arabic Al Ras al Thuban, The
Dragon's Head. On the desert
it was combined with gamma,
mu, upsilon, and xi to form Al
'Awaid, The Mother Camels.
Alwaid, used for the group,
may come from this or from Al
'Awwad, The Lute Player.
Other of the nomad titles were
Al Rakis, The Dancer, or The
Trotting Camel, and Al Shuja,
The Snake, which contracted
into Asuia. In the middle ages
it was given the Latin title
Quinque Dromedarii, Five
Dromedaries. The Chinese
name was Tien Kae for beta
and gamma.

REGULUS, alpha Leonis,
double, brilliant white and deep
blue, spring. Although the
faintest of the twenty stars
described as the brightest of
first magnitude, its dominant
position of about only a half a
degree north of the ecliptic has
given it a place of importance
in astronomy and astrology.
About 3,000 B.C., when it
probably was located at the
summer solstice, it was believed
to be the absolute monarch of
space, the star that ruled the
affairs of heaven and kept all
other stars in order, a notion
that persisted into the 17th
century. Because its position
is so close to the path of the
sun, late in August it is almost
obscured by the solar ball, and
on New Year's day appears on
the horizon a little north of east.
As one of the so-called lunar
stars it is much observed by
navigators.

The name, from the Latin, is
a diminutive of Rex and signifies
Little King, or Prince. Addi-

tional designations are: Great Star, Heart of the Royal Lion, King Star, Kingly Star, Lion's Heart, Regulus Denebola, Royal Star, Star of the King.

Accadian: Amil-gal-ur, 5th antediluvian king-of-the-celestial-sphere.

Arabian: Al Kalb al Asad, Heart of the Lion, which degenerated into Calb-alezet, Calb-elesit, Calb-elez-id, Kalbelasit, Kalbeleced, Kalbeleceid, Kalbol asadi, Kale Alased. Malikiyy, Kingly.

Babylonian: Sharru, The King which marked the 15th ecliptic station.

Chinese: Niau, The Bird.

Euphratean: Gus-ba-ra, The Flame or Red Fire.

Hindu: Magha, The Mighty, a component of the 10th nakshatra.

Khorasmian: Achir, Possessing Luminous Rays. Throughout classical days it supposedly caused the Summer's heat, a reputation shared with the Dog Star.

Latin and Low Latin: Basilica Stella, Basiliscus, Cor Leonis (Lion's Heart), Regia, Rex; and Tuberoni Regia and Tyberone, which rose from a misconception of a line by Pliny, rendered, "The star called by Tubero the Royal One in the Lion's Breast." Lucius Tubero was a literary friend of Cicero.

Persian: Miyan, Center; Vanant (Vanand), meaning Seizer, Smiter, or Stinger. It was the leader of the four Royal Stars, which were assigned to the cardinal points, and known as the Guardian of Heaven.

Sogdian: Magh, The Great.

Turanian: Masu, The Hero.

On a Minevite tablet, this

statement is written, "If the star of the Great Lion is gloomy the heart of the people will not rejoice," but generally early astrologers saw it as a giver of glory, riches, and power. Those under its influence have especially royal nativity.

RIGEL, beta Orionis, double, white tinged with blue and sapphire blue, winter. In Norse mythology, it marked one of the great toes of Orvandel (Orion), the other, when it became frost bitten, having been broken off by Thor and tossed into the northern sky, where it became the star Alcor.

The name, which means Foot, came from the Arabic Rijl Jauzah al Yusra, Left leg of the Jauzah (Giant), and contracted into Regel, Rigel Algeuze, Riglon. Also called Al Jabbah, The Mighty One, which degenerated into Algebar, Algibbar, Elgebar. Early popular names were Rai al Jauzah, Herdsman of the Jauzah, and Al Najid, The Conqueror. Some apply the Hebrew Kesil to this star rather than to the whole constellation.

It is said to have a marine or watery character, possible because it is the star closest to Eridanus, or because seamen fear the role that the stormy Orion plays in navigation. Astrologically, splendor and honors are the lot of those born under it. Although the beta star, it is the brightest in the constellation.

ROTANEV, beta Delphini, double, greenish and dusky, late summer. Reversed spelling of Venator, Latinized name of an assistant to the astronomer Giuseppi Piazzi. Incorrectly written Rotanen, Rotanin.

ROYAL STARS OF PERSIA.
So much speculation exists regarding the four monarchs, who
sat on thrones at the cardinal
points and supposedly governed
the universe, held each star in
its proper course, and maintained
the regular order of the seasons,
they deserve a few words devoted exclusively to them. Their
Persian names are Vanant,
Sataves, Haptok Ring, and
Tishtrya, and the modern names
most often assigned to them are
Regulus, Antares, Fomalhaut,
and Aldebaran, which follow each
other at a distance of about six
hours and thus mark, not only
the four quarters of the heaven,
but the equinoctal and solstitial
colures, the imaginary circles
used to divide the skies. If
the order of these stars coincide
with that of the Persian names,
Regulus is the ruler par excellence,
or leader, and the others follow in
order as shown here:

Throne Location About 3000 B.C.	When Star Was Brightest	Modern Throne Location	When Star is Brightest	Persian Name	Modern Name
South	Summer-Solstice	East	Spring	Vanant	Regulus
West	Autumn-Equinox	South	Summer	Sataves	Antares
North	Winter-Solstice	West	Autumn	Haptok Ring	Fomal-haut
East	Spring Equinox	North	Winter	Tishtrya	Alde-baran

Writers have been in wide
disagreement as to the corres-
dence of Persian and modern
names. Here are some of
their allocations:

Persian Name	Conjectured Assignment	Culmination (Present Time)
Vanant (Vanand, Venant)	Regulus* Vega	Spring Summer
Sataves (Satavaesa, Satevis, Çatavaeça)	Antares Crux Musca	Summer Late Spring Late Spring
Haptok Ring (Haptoiringa, Hapto-iringas, Hafturengh, Hastorang, Heft Averengh, Heft Rengh)	Fomalhaut Ursa Major+	Autumn Spring

Persian Name	Conjectured Assignment	Culmination (Present Time)
Tishtrya (Taschter, Tistrya)	Aldebaran Sirius	Winter Winter

NOTES: * Once marked the summer solstice; due to
the precession, now culminates in spring. + Because
it is near the North Pole, most of its stars never set.
Ursa Major, along with Vega, Crux, and Musca, are so
far from the ecliptic, they are very doubtful assignments.

RUCHBAH, delta Cassiopeiae,
autumn. From the Arabic Al
Rukbah, The Knee. Also spelled
Rucba, Rucbar, Ruchbar.

RUKBAT, alpha Sagittarii,
summer. The name meaning
Knee is from The Arabic Rukbat
al Rami, Knee of the Archer.
Also written Rucba, Rucbah,
Rucbar, Ruchbar ur Ramich,
Rukbah. In early works it
appears as Al Rami, The Archer.
With beta known as Al Suradain,
The Two Surad, desert birds, described as larger than sparrows
and doves, either yellow or a
variegated black and white like
magpies. This or epsilon may
have been the Euphratean star
Nibat Anu, the One of the Sky.

SADACHBIA, gamma Aquarii,
greenish, autumn. Name meaning Lucky Star, from the Arabic
Al Sa'd al Ahbiyah, usually said
to mean The Lucky Star of Hidden Things, or Hiding Places,
because when it emerges from
the sun's rays to appear in the
evening sky, all hidden worms
and reptiles, buried during the
preceding cold weather, creep
out of their holes. The word
Ahbiyah is the plural of H'iba,
Tent, and the full title has
been translated The Lucky Star
Surrounded (Hidden) by the
Tents, which seems reasonable
since it rises in the spring
twilight when, after the winter's

suffering, the tents of nomads
are raised on fresh pastures
in agreeable weather. Felicity
of Tents also has been given
as the meaning, and the tents
are said to be the stars zeta,
eta, and pi. Chinese knew the
group as Fun Mo, The Tomb.

SADALMELIK (SADAL MELIK),
alpha Aquarii, pale yellow,
autumn. From the Arabic Al
Sa'd al Malik, The Lucky One
of the King, or Al Sa'd al Mulk,
Lucky One of the Kingdom.
The King may be identical with
the Sumerian sun-god Moloch.
In the middle ages it was called
El Melik; Phard, which is unintelligible; and among astrologers.
Sidus Faustum Regis, Star of the
Happy or Fortunate Regent. A
component of the 12th Chinese
Hsiu, Wei, Steep or Dangerous,
anciently Goei or Gui, Foundation.

SADALSUUD (SADAL SUUD),
beta Aquarii, pale yellow,
autumn. From the Arabic Al
Sa'd al Su'ud, The Luckiest of
the Lucky Stars, from its rising
with the sun when the winter has
passed and the season has become one of gentle continuous
rain. Sadalsuud, which is an
echo of ancient astrological
associations also is the title of
the 24th manzil. Incorrectly
written Saud or Sund. A title
of medieval astrologers was

Fortuna Fortunarum.

With xi Aquarii and some-
times other stars, beta has
formed a lunar resting place,
variously called: Chinese: Heu,
or Hsu, The Void. Coptic: Upu-
ineuti, Foundation. Euphratean:
Kakkab Nammax, Star of Mighty
Destiny. Hindu: Kalpeny, meaning not known. Persian: Bunda,
Foundation.

Some of the smaller stars
below Sadalsuud, the Arabs
called Al Au'a, plural of Nau,
which simply signifies star.

SADATONI, zeta Aurigae,
winter. Derived from the Arabic
Al Said al Thani, The Second
Arm. Also called Saclateni,
which probably is from the same
source. One of the three Kids
that form a small isosceles triangle below and to the west of
Capella.

SADR, gamma Cygni,
Summer. Meaning The Breast,
from the Arabic Al Sadr al
Dajajah, The Breast of the
Hen. Incorrectly written Sudr.
Chinese called Tien Tsin, the
name of a city, which sometimes is given to a cluster of
which this is a component.

SAIB NASCHRUAH, gamma
Capricorni, summer. From Al
Sa'd al Nashirah, The Fortunate
One or Bringer of Good Things.

SAIPH, kappa Orionis,
winter. Meaning Sword, from
the Arabic Saif al Jabbar,
Sword of the Giant. This name,
which has been given to other
stars in the sky, here applies
to the sword which hangs from
the Belt.

SARGAS, theta Scorpii,

summer. A Eurphratean name,
signifying Director of the Sacrifice. Located in the Milky Way.
Also called Girtab, Seizer or
Stinger.

SARIR BANAT AL NA'ASH,
theta and others of Ursa Major.
An Arabic title meaning Throne
of the Mourners. The space
around these stars is known as
Al Haud, The Pond, i.e. into
which Gazelles spring for safety
when the Lion (Leo Minor)
lashes his tail. Nearby stars
are called Thufr al Ghizlan,
Tracks of the Gazelle.

SCHEAT, beta Pegasi, ir-
regularly variable, reddish-
yellow, autumn. Although
believed to be from either the
Arabic Al Said, The Upper Part
of the Arm, or from Sa'd,
Good Luck, it usually is said to
mean Leg, and is located in the
left upper foreleg of the flying
horse. Corruptions of the
above were Saidolpharazi, Scheat
Alpheraz, Seat Alfara, Seat
Alpheras. Arabs also knew it
as Mankib al Faras, Horse's
Shoulder, which degenerated into
Almenkeb or Menkib.

Beta formed one corner of
the Great Square and with alpha
constituted the Arabic manzil
Al Fargh al Mukdim, or Al
Fargh al Awwal, First or Upper
Spout; the 13th Chinese Hsiu,
Shih, or Ying She; the 26th
Hindu nakshatra, Purva Bhadra-
pada, sometimes called Proshthapada, Carp, Ox, Footstool,
or Feet; as well as the Coptic
Artulos, the Khorasmian
Farshat Bath, and the Persian
Vaht, these latter titles all
pertaining to water. Astrologically it portends danger to mankind from water.

SCHEDAR, alpha Cassiopiae, double variable, reddish and a bluish tint, autumn. From the Arabic Al Sadr, The Breast, it is the same word as Sadr, a title given above, and has also been written Schedir, Seder, Shadar, Shedar, Sheder, Shedir, Shedis, Zcdaron. Also called Dath Elkarti, from one of the constellation's names.

SCHEMALI, iota Ceti, winter. From the Arabic Al Shamaliyy, the Northern Branch of the Tail.

SEGINUS, gamma Bootis, spring. From Kheturus, Arabic orthography from the Greek Arcturus, alpha Bootis. Also written Ceginus, Chegninus, Cheguius.

SHAULA, lambda Scorpii, summer. This star and others in Scorpius have appealed to Pacific Islands as heroes or as the implements of deities. One tale, in which Maui is a fisherman, is told under the constellation. In another, Tangaroa, Polynesian cosmic- or world-soul, is an angler who uses a fish-hook, composed of lambda, mu, and nu, and tugs to the surface the island of Tongareva. When Vatea, lord of the bright sky, whose abode is the Thin Land, is the fisherman, the island group Tonga is drawn-up. For bait Vatea had used a piece of flesh cut from his own thigh. One legend tells of the parents of two children, a little girl Piri-ere-ua, and a still smaller son. The parents treated their offspring like contemptible slaves. When the abuse of these hateful elders became unbearable, Piri-ere-ua and her brother fled into the heavens. Unwilling to lose these menial workers, the parents pursued them. All four run a constant race in the sky, where they appear as stars, the parents as lambda and nu, the children as the binary mu, which has the title The Inseparables. Fortunately for the children, they are able to remain just out of the reach of the larger pair in the chase across the night.

The name is from the Arabic Al Shaulah, The Sting, because of where it lies, or from Mushalah, Raised, which refers to the bearing of the Sting when ready to strike the heel of Ophiuchus, or from Tali al Shaulah, That which follows the Sting. Another translation is Turned-up Part of the Scorpion's Tail. In the middle ages the name appeared as Alascha, Mosclek, Shauka, Shomlek or Schomlek. It was a component of the 19th manzil, and with nu composed one of the seven pairs of Euphratean twins. As such it was called Ma-a-su. In the Valley, this pair also was called Sharur, Cyclone, which was the weapon of Zamama (Aquila), a harvest and war deity, who with it subdued the Eagle which became his emblem. The Coptic title for the pair was Minamref, Sting. With other stars of Scorpio, lambda formed the Hindu 19th nakshatra Visritau, Two Releasers, perhaps from the belief that these luminaries brought relief from lingering diseases. Among astrologers, quite naturally, the stinger is an unlucky star.

SHELIAK, beta Lyrae, a short period variable, binary, very white, summer. From the Persian for Tortoise, which had been derived from Chelus, a Greek name for the whole constellation. Chelus was the little tortoise from whose shell Hermes had constructed the first stringed instrument. Also written Shelyak, Shiliak, Shilyak.

SHERATAN, beta Arietis, white, autumn. From the Arabic Al Sharat meaning A Sign, perhaps the sign of the year's beginning, when, about the time of Hipparchus, Aries marked the vernal equinox. However, this is mere conjecture. The name also has appeared as Al Ashrat, Al Natih, Al Sharatain, Sharatan. Some have applied all these names to the moon stations composed of beta with alpha or other stars. Additional designations for the lunar rests are- Babylonian: Mahru-sha-rishu-ku, Front of the Head of Ku (Khu, a light god); Chinese: Teen Ho; Coptic: Pikutorion, Protector; Persian; Padevar, Protecting Pair. Sogdian, Bashish, Protector.

SHUR-NARKABTI-SHA-SHUTU, zeta Tauri, yellow, winter. From the Babylonian meaning Star in the Bull towards the South, or Southern Star towards the Chariot. Determinant of the Babylonian 7th ecliptic constellation. In astrology, a star of mischievous influence. The Chinese name is Tien Kwan, Heavenly Gate. The Crab Nebula is a mere one degree to the northwest.

SIDUS LUDOVICIANUM, variable of Ursa Major, spring. It lies at an obtuse angle formed with the stars Alcor and Mizar and was first discovered in 1691. When it was seen again in 1723, the astronomer believed he had discovered a planet and named it after his sovereign, Ludwig V, a landgrave of Hesse-Darmstadt.

SIRIUS, alpha Canis Major, binary, brilliant white with a tinge or green or blue and yellow, culminates in winter.

The Dog has driven
the Cock from his high perch;
days are humid and hot.

Not only because of its surpassing brilliancy, but because it can be seen from any spot on earth, Sirius has been a nocturnal guide in all parts of the world from the most remote times. This brightest star in the heavens has been worshipped, adored, and feared in all ages.

The clear day and night skies over Egypt favored the development of astronomy, and astronomy played an important part in religion. Egyptians believed in the existence of divine wills, not different, simply superior in range and power to their own. Inasmuch as the stars were shapes in which deities displayed themselves, each temple was oriented to its star, or genius, for guidance in fixing festival dates, ascertaining nighttime hours, etc. Exactly which stars were worshipped has not been conclusively determined. Sirius is the only star that can be identified without doubt, its hieroglyphs appearing on monuments and temple walls throughout the Nile country. Its worship can be traced back to about 3,285 B. C. with its heliacal rising at the summer solstice or Egyptian New Year. This noble star served the nation well in a variety of ways and each had been commemorated.

To indicate that Sirius opened the year he was given two heads, that of an old man for the pass-

ing year and that of a young man
for the year that was coming in;
or he was portrayed as a porter
bearing the keys of the portal to
be unlocked. Sirius, pathfinder,
opener of the ways, guardian of
the horizon and solstice, who
conducted the dead into the hall
Amenti, the hidden land in the
west, and weighed their hearts
against the feather of truth
was none other than Anubis,
jackal- or dog-headed guardian of
tombs and patron of embalmers.
Priests, who were his intimates,
kindled his worshipers into a
feverish pitch of anticipation.
When their excitement had been inflamed to the point of frenzy,
the Herald, or faithful Hound-
headed divinity, appeared to
warn farmers of the Nile Valley
that waters would sweep over
the land, which would renew its
fertility and devour its locusts.
To show them what they must
do, he had wings on his feet;
he carried a stew-pot, his
feather under his arm, and two
reptiles and a duck followed him.
So cautioned, land-dwellers
carried provisions to places of
safety and, in appreciation for
this great service, conferred on
him the titles Nile Star and King
of Suns.

In female form the star was
Hathor, great cosmic mother,
bringer forth and destroyer
whose name literally is House of
Hor (Wisdom), and who had the
head of a cow with a disk (sun)
between her horns (crescent
moon), and who appeared high
above the hills in the west.
Like Anubis, she had a mansion
in Amenti, realm of the dead,
where she was queen. Ra, lord
of the midday sun, castrated himself and with the blood drops
created man. He descended to
earth to live among those he

had formed, but found man so
wicked, he quickly rose again
to his throne in the heavens,
and commanded Hathor (Sirius)
to send a deluge. When he saw
the slaughter she was causing,
he relented, flooded the Nile
and made her drunk with the
waters so she would forget mankind. She then multiplied into
seven Hathors (the seven bright
stars of Ursa Major), in which
form she foretold the future,
especially of children at birth.

At Thebes the star was the
adored Isis, sister-wife of
Osiris, a name to which Sirius
is related, and when he was
cut into pieces by his brother
Set, she lamented and wept
until her tears caused the Nile
to overflow. With the title Her
Majesty, or Her Mighty of
Denderah, her statue, a cow
recumbent in a boat, her head
surmounted by a star, was
placed in a small temple built
about 700 B.C. Anukt, who
accompanies her, carries two
pitchers from which water
flows, to suggest that inundation
follows the star's rising. In
prayers of Upper Egypt, she was
addressed as Isis Sati, Isis
Sothis, Satet, literally Pour Out,
or Strew. For a long period,
in Egyptian mythology, the star
was the resting-place of the
goddess's soul, and for this
reason an auspicious star. The
cosmic mother, under the name
Satet, was the wife of Khnemu,
master of the waters coming
from the underworld (southern
skies), and Khnemu thus also
counted it one of his forms or
mansions. When revered as the
husband of Isis, the star was
Osiris. Later it belonged to
Thoth, celestial architect, inventor of letters and numbers,
time regulator, and the ibis,

which stands in water, became its symbol.

Perhaps the value of this star to husbandmen along the Nile, has given the name Egyptian X to the figure formed by the stars Procyon, Phaet, Betelgeuze, and Naos, with Sirius marking the center where the two triangles meet.

In Greece, as in the Euphratean Valley, it marked the beginning of the hot sultry season, which parched. People on the island of Ceos in the Aegean Sea predicted from its appearance at its heliacal rising whether or not the year would be a healthy one. The star's culmination was celebrated at midnight in the great temple of Demeter at Eleusis, probably at the initiation of the Eleusinian mysteries. In Homer it is the great star of Autumn, the shield of Diomedes. Although next to Achilles (spring sun), Diomedes was the bravest of the Greeks in the Trojan War, the star was an evil omen, a bringer of fevers, for the hero had stolen the Palladium on which the fate of Troy had depended and, in so doing, exposed himself to the wrath of those divinities who favored the city. The season actually intended was not autumn; late summer would be more accurate.

Romans, who were not astute star-gazers, accepted Greek observations without studying conditions in their own age or country, and thus firmly established the belief in dog-days and the alliance of the Dog and the Lion with unhealthy midsummer heat that persists into the present time. When the sun came close to Sirius, Roman farmers sacrificed dogs of a reddish or fawn color to it that their fields might be rid of rust and mildew and their grains and vines reach a healthy maturity. Angry stars or deities were conceived to be red, and a dog of the same color was sacrificed to them. Because of this rite, some believe the star was anciently red; others hold it always has been a brilliant white and yellow. Dante, on the other hand, called the star Veltro, the Messiah in greyhound form.

The Teutonic giant Thjasse betrayed his sister Idun and helped the evil Loki carry her and her golden apples of youth (vegetation) to the underworld. No sooner had he done this then the gods in Asgard became old and feeble and, with their lack of virility, earth became frostbound. Loki, god of fire, was prevailed upon to rescue Idun. He disguised himself as a falcon and transformed Idun into a nut, which he carried in his claws. Thjasse, in the form of an eagle, pursued Loki and was about to overtake him just outside the walls of the heavenly city. The anxious gods on the ramparts set great logs ablaze, and Thjasse, taken by surprise, was overcome by snoke. For his mischief he was slain and placed in the heavens as the Dog-star.

Zulamith the Bold, in a Finnish saga, was separated from his beloved, Salami the Fair. For a thousand years they toiled until they built the bridge, the Milky Way. Upon its completion they rushed into each other's arms and fused into one to become the lucida of Canis Major.

In Hebrew lore, Caleb of the tribe of Judah, was sent with one man from each tribe to investigate the land of Canaan. Of the twelve sent only Caleb and Joshua reported favorably and therefore were the only two males of their generation permitted into the Promised Land, the others all perishing in the crossing of the Red Sea. Caleb probably personified the Heavenly Dog, Joshua the spring Sun. He implies the necessity of intelligence to the successful quest of salvation. The twelve are by some identified as the zodiacal signs, but the signs as we know them seem not to have been organized in that remote period.

In an Arabian fable, Al-abur (Sirius) resided with his sister Al Ghumaisa (Procyon) in Canis Minor until they were disgraced by their brother Suhail (Canopus), who murdered his bride. Al-abur pursued her brother. She paused to rest among the stars of Canis Major and remained there to become its lucida. Although Mohammed forbade his followers to engage in star worship, he gave much honor to one star, believed to be this, and several Arabian tribes are known to have venerated it.

Early Persian star-gazers, who lacked instruments to aid them, believed Sirius made an appearance in a different shape every ten days, once as a cow, once as a handsome youth, now becoming a horse, etc., and in all these guises watched over mortals and brought fertility to the earth. In the Zend Avesta, under the name Tishtrya it appeared in three different manifestations during the 30 days of rain which precipitated the Great Flood. It also marked one of the Four Quarters of the Heavens. (See Royal Stars of Persia). The Zoroastrian Ormuzd designated this star to be overseer of the east (north in modern times because of the precession of the equinoxes), to be bright and happy and provide joyful dwelling. Previously, in primeval days Ormuzd punished mankind with a deluge. Since then, in the form of a white bull with golden horns, or a white bull with golden ears, he descends into Vourukasha (Heavenly Sea) in the center of which grows Gaokerna, the Tree of Life, to battle the monster Apaosha (drought). When he is victorious, vapors fertilize the land.

In earliest Sanscrit mythology the star was Sukra, the rain-god before he was replaced by Indra, at which time he rode away on a cat and located on the planet Venus. In later myths, the star appears as Sivanam (Dog), who awakened the sleeping Ribhus, artisan gods who dwelled in mid-air, to produce rain.

Tane, Polynesian primeval forest deity, separated his parents, Rangi, the sky and Papa, the earth, who were in constant copulation. In three heaves he raised the sky, first to tree tops, then to mountain tops, finally to where it is, and he clothed his father, giving him stars. The dazzling brilliance of one star, Matariki (The Pleiades), seemed immodest to Tane, so with Aldebaran and Sirius, he entered into a plot to smash it into bits. Thus, Sirius was rid of his only rival, and became the sky's most radiant star.

Hervey Islanders set their courses at sea by its light; Australian natives conceived it to be an eagle.

Cherokee Indians revered two Dog stars who stood watch at opposite sides of the Southern Sky, where the Milky Way touches the horizon. They never are seen at the same time, but one or the other is always a visible guard. Traditionally, a soul after the body's death, crosses a raging torrent on a narrow pole, from which the cowardly fall off and are swept into oblivion in the waters below. Those who succeed in crossing, first go eastward, then westward, to the land of Twilight. At a point where the road turns off, Gili, a dog, is encountered, who must be propitiated with food. After the feeding a soul continues on until it comes upon another dog that must be fed. The unfortunates, insufficiently provided with provisions, will be stopped. The first will not permit him to return whence he originally came; thus he will remain a prisoner forever between the two animals. The trail undoubtedly is the Milky Way, which practically all North American Indians call Path of Souls, and which at the horizon appears to bend. The two stars at the alternate ends of the turn are unquestionably Sirius and Antares.

Symbolically, the dog or hound stands for courage, fidelity, guardianship, intelligence, watching, the chase, in particular the divine hunt for souls, all characteristics that pertain to Sirius.

No doubt exists that this star appeared in the stellar system of Euphrateans, but a difficulty has been experienced in identifying its name. Some account it one aspect of Marduk. Among the appellations assigned are: Dushisha, Accadian for Director, because it came at the New Year to direct the passing of time, a name which had the identical meaning of the Assyrian Mes-ri-e and was related to the Babylonian Kak-shisha or Kaksisa (Dog that Leads), star of the south. Other titles appropriate to its shimmering, changing light are: Kak-ban, Chaldean for Dog; Kakkab kasti, Bow Star; Kak-shidi, probably meaning, Creator of Prosperity, a character granted to the star; Kal-bu Sa-mas, Assyrian for Dog of the Sun; Mul-lik-ud, Accadian Dog Star of the Sun; Su-ku-du, Assyrian for Restless Wanderer, Impetuous, or Blazing. Quite possibly the two great stars known to Babylonians as Bow Star and Lance Star which followed Marduk (Orion), that is served as the weapons of Marduk, were Sirius and Procyon. If so, this may be the source of the deer-slayer story related under Canis Major.

Sirius, often written Sirion or Syrius, is most commonly recognized as the Latin form of a Greek word meaning scorching or glittering, which originally was an adjective applied to any tremulous motion of light in the skies, but in time led to the name The Scorching One, quite a fitting name for this, the brightest of all stars. Poets and scholars have given various sources for the name. It is said to be derived from the Arabic Siraj, Glimmery One, or it may be a corruption of Shira from Al Shira or Al Sira, The Doorkeeper, the star which opens and shuts the door of the hot rainy season, or Al Shira al jamanija, or Al Shira Al

Yamaniyyah, Bright Star of
Yemen. This was extended into
Al Shira al Abur Al Yamaniyyah.
Al Abur refers to the Canopus
legend, related under Procyon,
and resembled Egyptian, Greek,
Persian, Phoenician, and
Roman names meaning Shining
One. All may have a common
source in the name of the Hindu
sun deity Surya. Yamaniyyah
originated as an Arabic adjective
meaning southern or more correctly on the right side, which indicated it might be seen setting
over the province of Yemen, and
the complete translation might be
rendered The Bright Shining Star
of Passage of Yemen. Leader,
referring to its character, is a
designation that also appears in
Euphratean, Greek, Persian,
Phoenician, and Vedic writings.
Other derivations of Sirius are a
Phoenician word meaning Chief
One; the Egyptian Cahen Sihor,
or their Hesiri, which Greeks
called Osiris; or the Teutonic
Syr, a name of Freya, mistress
of the sun-god Od.

Additional designations:

Arabic: Barakish, Of a
Thousand Colors, referring to
its scintillating nature. Suhail,
which is a general designation for
bright stars, and particularly
applied to Canopus.

Blackfeet Indian: Emita-stok-
sis, Dog-face.

Chinese: Lang Hoo; Tseen
Lang, Heavenly Wolf; Ti'en Kou,
although they did not seem to
give as much importance to this
star as other nations.

Egyptian: Sihor, Nile Star;
Solechin, Starry Dog; Sothi or
Sothis, Brightly Radiating One,
or Fair Star of the Waters, which

was created in the beginning of
time along with the sun. Actually,
this last is a Graeco-Egyptian
term, which in the vernacular
became Sed, Sepet, Sept, Septit,
Sopdit, Sopet, or Sot. Sothis
gave its name to the Sothic
period, the cycle of 1460 years
by which means Egyptians adjusted their calendars to the
length of the year, which began
on the day that this star rose
with the sun at the summer
solstice. Inasmuch as they used
a year of 365 days with no day
equivalent to the day of a modern
leap year, after 1460 years a
complete year was gained, and
the star again appeared in its
proper season at the summer
solstice, and a new cycle
started. Another way the
Egyptians calculated time was
by the 36 stars or groups of
stars that followed each other at
intervals of about 10 days and
were thus called Decans. In this
calculation, the time between the
rising of Sirius at one dawn until
its next rising was 360 days.
Five non-calendar or intercalary
days were added to account for
365.

European, of the middle ages:
Arabic and Latin mongrels -
Alsere, Ascher, Aschere,
Aschere Aliemini, Ecber, El-
scheere, Gabbar, Habor, Halabor,
Scera, Shaari lobur, Sirius
Jemenicus. These names also
were applied to the constellations.

Hebrew: H'asil, but they more
often called it by the Egyptian
Sihor. Reference to the He
Goats (Devils) may be a reference to this star and to Procyon,
the two Sirii or Shi'rayan, that
gave light in their Land of Bondage and were worshipped by their
taskmasters. Some say it is
the Mazzaroth mentioned in the

Book of Job, and which in the King James version is given as one of 12 zodiacal, or all of the 12, signs, and which is identified as the Lucifer of the Vulgate. Others say it is Mazzaloth, the Vulgate Duodecim Signa. Still others say it is Kimah, which appears variously in the Vulgate as Arcturus, Hyades, or Pleiades.

Hervey Island: Mere, a native hero.

Persian: Sira, Chieftain's Star. Tishiga, Tishtyra, Tistar, or Tistrya, which likewise means Chieftain's Star, is a title also assigned to Aldebaran. A later name is Tir, Arrow, which connects this star with the Sanscrit Lubdhaka story told under Canis Major.

Phoenician: Hannabeah, Barker or Monitor.

Roman: In Rome, as elsewhere, it shared the constellation's titles, probably was the source of them, especially the endearment Canicula.

Its early astrological influence in Europe was feared; it supposedly caused drought, fevers, and plagues. The dog, which in many quarters has an evil reputation, probably contributed to this belief. In late astrology, wealth and renown is the reward of those born under the influence of Sirius.

SITULA, chi Aquarii, autumn. A Latin term for Water-jar or Bucket. Also said to be derived from Sitis, Thirst, the Waterman's urn having been drawn by some as an oven. Another name is Urna, and it marks the southern edge of the urn, near the overflow. Also alluded to

as The Outpouring Wine. Arabic names were Al Dalw and Satl, the last somewhat similar to the Latin and probably derived from it.

SKAT, delta Aquarii, autumn. As frequently has been the case, much disagreement exists as to the source and meaning of the name. Among those given are: the Arabic Al Said or Sa'd, The Lower Part of the Leg; Al Sak, The Shin Bone; Al Shi'at, A Wish. Other spellings are Scheat, Scheat Edeleu. Additional designations: Chinese: Yu lin Keun, Imperial Guard; adjacent stars included in this asterism. Euphratean: Hasisadra (Xasisadra, or Xisouthros), 10th antediluvian king, the hero of the Deluge. Here, as in the following, the star was probably a component part of a lunar station formed with other stars: Khorasmian: Mashtawand; Persian: Khatsar; Sogdian; Shawshat.

SPICA, alpha Virginis, brilliant flushed white, spring. Generally understood to indicate the wheat ear held by the Virgin who provided fertility. In Babylonia, it marked the 20th ecliptic asterism as well as a lunar station and personified Beltis, wife of Bel, who later was given the whole constellation.

Egyptians at one time knew it as the Lute-Bearer. What the song of the Lute-Bearer was is not known. A temple at Thebes was oriented to this star's setting as early as 3,200 B.C., a temple that may have been dedicated to Min, personification of the male principle. Min, symbolized by the phallus and portrayed as ram-headed, was

merged with Khnumu, a corn-
god honored at harvest festivals.
Another temple of the Sun at Tell
al Amarna was oriented to Spica
about 2,000 B.C. This star,
with Arcturus of Bootes and
Antares of Scorpio, is said to
have been part of the immense
figure of Menes, an early king who
was known as the great unifier
and lustful drunkard. When immortalized, his name became a
generic term for the golden or
white sun bull.

About 150 B.C. it furnished
Hipparchus with the data which enabled him to discover the precession of the equinoxes, although
earlier records of Babylonia,
Egypt, and Greece may indicate
a vague practical application of
the precession without a precise
knowledge of its character.

Its isolated position in a
fairly empty region of the sky,
which left it unprotected, inspired
the Arabian name which signifies,
Solitary, or Defenceless, One.
Nomads compared it with its
bright northern neighbor Arcturus
by saying these were two warriors,
one stood Unarmed, weapon-
less, while the other was armed
with a lance of nearby stars. Leo
was a greatly extended figure on
the desert and included this as
well as other stars of Virgo.

In China, Spica and Arcturus
formed a pair to make the
Horns of the Dragon, and spring
was calculated from the time
the full moon first appeared
between these horns. With
warmth of feeling, a great display
of joy, the people, who used
the skies as a calendar, watched
the winter draw to a close when
the Moon "rode the Dragon's
Horns." This association with
spring may have been the reason

Show Sing, god of long life,
may have chosen Spica for his
home. This venerable and wise
old man rode about on a stag
accompanied by a bat, symbol
of happiness and longevity.
Show Sing, smiling and kindly,
always carried peaches, the
fruit of immortality. Occasionally he left his home on the star
and visited earth, and on one of
his trips he had a rare adventure. A youth, 18 years of age,
named Chao Yen, lived in a
small village in South China.
One day Chao Yen's father
consulted a fortune teller and to
his horror learned that his son
was destined to die before his
19th birthday.

Outwardly Chao Yen accepted
the dismal news calmly. He
pursued his usual habits, and
while hunting in the forests
of South Mountain one day he
roamed into foothills where game
was plentiful. After he had
shot two deer, he sought a bit
of shade in the forest that had
become almost shadowless under
the noon sun, and threw himself
under an oak to rest. All
about him was hushed, even the
hawk that circled above him
drifted without seeming to move
its wings. Chao Yen dosed off.
He thought he had barely closed
his eyes when he opened them
again, but the shadows were
long, and darkness had engulfed
his surroundings. Near by Chao
Yen two men were seated at a
chess board. One was a man
of regal bearing and a bold
manner, whose robe was of a
blue-black material on which
stars were embroidered in groups
of seven; his face, bent low over
the chess board was framed by
thick black hair that was made
radiant by some inner light.
His companion, older, was a

cheerful man with an enormously high forehead. His clothes were green, and beside him lay a long staff and gourd.

"Thirty-eight," the younger man said. "A reasonable life, if not overly long." Before he went on with the game he wrote on a tablet. A few minutes later he said, "Twenty-three, much too short."

The ivory pieces were moved in silence for a while, then the older man cried, "Eighty-nine, how grateful that man will be to me."

Chao Yen realized the men were playing with human lives. Overcome with curiosity, the awe he had felt at first passed from him and he stepped from his hiding place under the oak. "What strange game is this you play in which the stakes are obviously the lives of men," he asked.

"I am the spirit of Pih Tow (Pei Tou), the Northern Measure," the younger man answered calmly, "and my opponent is Show Sing (Shou Hsing) from the Southern Sky, the god of longevity. He fixes the dates of men's births and my duty is to fix the time of death. We are gambling for the length of life that each child born today is to have."

Chao Yen thought sadly of his own fortune and struck with a sudden inspiration cried, "You can help me, you can help me. The sages have said I am fated to die in a few weeks before I reach a full 19 years. Play for my life again, and perhaps you can win time for me."

Pih Tow shook his head,

"Once a life has been decided and its span is written in the great record book, not even the gods can change the register.

"Surely the gods are more powerful than fate," Chao Yen pleaded. "If you would make my life a long one, I would burn incense for you and wax candles, every day. I would sing to you."

The faces of the chess players remained fixed as though nothing had been said.

"I would bring you fine offerings, see I am an excellent hunter. I would place meat and wine and silks at your altars. Here is the fresh venison I killed this morning; each day I will go into the forests and hunt for you."

Pih Tow smiled. "I cannot possibly erase the characters that are written in the Book of Death, nor can we gamble twice for the same life, but I can reverse the characters which say 19 (十九) and make them read 91 (九十) a life long enough for any man."

Overcome with gratitude, Chao Yen threw himself to the ground. When he looked up he was alone. Afraid that he had been dreaming, he rose to leave for home. Before he departed he went to pick up his game, but it had completely disappeared, and Chao Yen realized the gods had taken it.

In the dark skies above the forest, the star of Show Sing twinkled merrily. While in the north, the seven stars of Pih Tow seemed brighter than usual. Chao Yen lived his full

ninety years and faithfully performed the services he had promised the gods.

Spica, from the Latin,
signifies The Ear of Corn
(Wheat), which the Virgin
usually holds in her left hand.
Additional designations are:
Little Lance-bearer, from a
Greek title; Propitious One of
Seed and Star of Prosperity,
from Euphratean lists.

Arabic: Al Adhara, from a
name of the constellation; Al
Hulbah, The Bristle; Al Simak
al Azal, The Defenceless or
Unarmed Lancer, the One who
Rises High. This last title ap-
peared among Latin writers as
Inermis Asimec, and eventually
as Acimon, Alaazel, Alacel,
Alaraph, Almucedie, Aschimech
inermis, Azimech, Azimon,
Eltsamecti, Hazimeth Alhacel.
Also used were Sembalet
Eleandri, Sombalet, and Sunbala,
from the constellation. Sak al
Asad, Shin-bone of the Lion, and
a name signifying Calf of the
Lion was another Arabic title.

Babylonian: Dan-nu, Hero of
the Sky Furrow; Emuku Tin-tir-
ki, Mighty Abode of Life; Sa-
sha-Shiru, Virgin's Girdle.

Chinese: Anciently Keok or
Guik, a special star of springtime. After the Jesuits, it was
called Kio, the Horn or Spike.

Coptic: Khoritos, Solitary.

Egyptian: Repa, The Lord.

English: Newton, a modern
attempt to honor the great natural
philosopher; Virgin's Spike.

European alchemists: Al-
haiseth, from the Arabic Al

Simak al Azal.

French: l'Epi.

Hebrew: Shibboleth, Ear of
Wheat.

Hindu: Sitra (Çitra), Bright,
the 14th nakshatra, Sparegha
(Çparegha), Point, i.e. Spica.

Italian: Spigha.

Khorasmian: Akhshafarn,
Point.

Latin: Arista, Aristae Puella,
Erigone, all shared with the
constellation. Spicum. Stachys,
from the Greek for Ear of Corn.

Persian: Chushe, Ear of
Wheat (or Corn); Spur (Çpur),
Point.

Sogdian: Shaghar, Point.

Syrian: Shebbelta, Ear of
Wheat (or Corn).

Turkish: Salkim, Ear of
Wheat (or Corn).

In early astrology, like the
constellation, a sign of unfruit-
fulness and a portent of injustice to the innocent; in later
astrology a sign of eminence,
renown, and riches. This is
one of the lunar stars made
much of in navigation. With
Arcturus, Cor Coroli, and
Denebola, this star forms the
noted Diamond of Virgo.

STEROPE, one of the Pleiades,
Taurus, widely double, winter.
At the upper edge of the Pleiad
cluster, her name signifies
lightning, and like her sister
Merope she is said to have
married a mortal, Oenomaus,
king of Pisa, in Ellis. Ashamed

that she had disgraced her family by this act, she wasted away, and has on occasions been identified as the Lost Pleiad. The marriage had other tragic consequences. Sterope bore a daughter Hippodamia, a name meaning horse-tamer. Oenomaus, warned by an oracle that he would perish by his son-in-law's hand, demanded that each of Hippodamia's suitors should overcome him in a chariot race. Since he had magic steeds, all suitors lost or were put to death until Pelops raced him. In that contest Hippodamia bribed Oenomaus's charioteer to remove a spoke from the wheel, and her father met his death. A Latin name for the star was Steropes sidus.

SUALOCIN, alpha Delphini, a wide double, pale yellow, late summer. The title is the reversed spelling of the given name of Nicolaus Venator, assistant and successor of the astronomer Giuseppi Piazzi, Director of the Palermo Observatory. The last name, Venator, in reverse, Rotanev, appears as the name of beta Delphini. One astronomical writer states these names are from the Arabic Scalooin, Swift, as the flow of water, and from the Arabic and Chaldee Rotaneb or Rotaneu, Swiftly Running, as water in a trough, but these statements appear to be without foundation. On one sky map the star appears as Scalovin.

SULAFAT, gamma Lyrae, bright yellow, summer. From the Arabic for Tortoise. This title also applied to the whole constellation. Jugum, Latin for Yoke or Join, formerly seen for it, came from a misunderstanding of a text, where the word probably was used merely to designate

the star's position on the frame of the Lyre.

TALITHA (TALITA), iota Ursae Majoris, binary, yellow and purple, spring. From the Arabic Al Kafzah al-thalithah, The Third Leap, or Spring, of the Gazelle. It relates to a legend in which Gazelle jumps for safety when the Lion (Leo Minor) lashes his tail. Another form of the name is Al Phikra al Thalitha. It is located in one of the front paws.

TARAZED, alpha Aquilae, golden yellow, summer. Meaning Plundering or Soaring, from the Persian Shahin Tarazed, The Plundering, or Soaring, Falcon. Also spelled Tarazad.

TEGMINE (TEGMEN); zeta Cancri; quadruple; yellow, orange, yellowish, changeable; spring. From the Latin meaning The Covering (of a marine object, such as a crab).

TEJAT (TEJAT POSTERIOR), mu Geminorum, double, crocus yellow and blue, winter. From Al Tahayi, an early Arabic anatomical term, also applied to the head of Orion, although here it appears in the foot of Castor. Also called Nuhatai, Camel's Hump. Additional designations: Babylonian: Arku-sha-pu-u-mash-mashu, Back of the Mouth of the Twins, a component of the 9th ecliptic asterism. Chinese: Tsing, a hsiu. Latin: Calx, Heel. Persian, Pish Pai, a name also applied to nu.

TAYGETE (TAYGETA), one of the Pleiades of Taurus, binary, lucid white and violet, winter. Lacedaemon, son of Taygete by Zeus, founded

Sparta, and she was idolized as patroness of the state. Romans called her Soror Pleiadum, and Virgil used her to fix the two seasons of the honey harvest, which he dated, "As soon as the Pleiad Taygete has displayed her comely face to the earth, and spurns with her foot the despised waters of the ocean, or when the same star, fleeing the constellation of the watery Fish, descends in sadness from the sky into wintery waves."

Arabs called this star Al Wasat, The Central One; by some, and more aptly, applied to Alcyone.

TEREBELLUM, a Sagittarii cluster composed of alpha, beta, and omega on the hind quarters of the horse, summer. The name is a diminutive of the Latin Terebra, Borer. In Roman antiquity the Terebra was a military siege-engine used to punch or bore a hole in a wall. It consisted of a long sharp-pointed beam working in a groove on rollers. The Chinese call these stars Kow Kow, Dog's Country. The asterism is too far south to be seen in the latitude of New York City.

THE THREE STARS. The Band or Belt of Orion. See under Orion.

THUBAN (THUBIN), alpha Draconis, pale yellow, summer. Although no longer the constellation's brightest star, having faded from second magnitude to below third, it is known as its leader by virtue of its position as one of the Wardens of the Pole. From about 3,700 B.C. to 1,500 B.C. it was the North Star, ruler of all luminaries, whose mansion was the closest

to the Pole, but in the course of the precession of the equinoxes, it was deprived of its kingdom, which, after periods of darkness, fell, first to Kochab, and then to Polaris. However, in about 23,000 A.D. it shall again prevail for a while at the zenith, again appear as the only fixed point in space, around which all the heavens seem to revolve, a cycle explained under Polaris. During the periods of darkness at the Pole, nothing seems to be at rest, all stars, as well as everything else in the universe, appear to be in motion, as if searching for one to reestablish the serenity of the spheres.

The world's first great conqueror, Sargon I of Akkad, who was accounted of miraculous birth inasmuch as his mother was a virgin priestess of the sun-god, appeared during the reign of Thuban in about 2,500 B.C. In a wicker basket he was set adrift on the Euphrates, where he was found by Akki, a water-drawer, who taught him gardening. Beloved by Ishtar, he was made king of Mesopotamia, and became the earliest great warrior in recorded history. Sargon probably was an historic king into whose biography sun-deity attributes had been woven.

The star's name, from the A-rabic, means Dragon, symbolically quite a fitting character for one who controls the seasons, for in mythology, the dragon is both a withholder and provider of rain, a conqueror and releaser of light. Many early sun kings, such as Sargon, were provided with dragon aspects or dragon tails for their agricultural or underworld aspects.

Evidence of Thuban's importance may be perceived in the many titles bestowed by ancients. Among them: Dragon's Tail, High Horned One, High One of the Enclosure of Life, Life of Heaven, Proclaimer of Light. Additional designations:

Accadian: Dayan Esiru, Prospering Judge, or Crown of Heaven. Dayan Same, Judge of Heaven; Dayan Shisha, Judge Directing, as having the highest seat among the heavenly host; Dayan Sidi, Favorable Judge; Tir-an-na, Life, or Judge, of Heaven. All allude to the god Caga Gilgati, whose name it also bore.

Arabian: Al Dhih, The Male Hyena; Dhi-bah, Hyenas; titles also applied to other stars. These corrupted into Addib, Adib, Adid, Adive, Eddib, El Dsib. Thuban and Al Tinnin, translated from the Greek for dragon, are likewise used for the constellation Draco.

Chinese: Yu Choo, Right Hand Pivot.

Persian: Azhdeha, Serpent or Dragon.

This star is so located that, when it is the Pole Star, the figure swings around it as if on a pivot, like the hands of a clock moving in reverse direction. Inasmuch as it is so far north, it may be seen in the night sky throughout the year from some areas of the northern hemisphere.

ULA, nu and xi Ursae Majoris, spring. From the Arabic meaning The First Leap.

UNUK AL HAY (or HAI), alpha Serpentis, double, pale yellow and blue, summer. From the Arabic, Unk al Hayyah, Neck of the Snake. Also called Alioth, Alyah, Alyat, probably terms for the fat tail of sheep in the East, that at one time may have figured in this place on an Oriental sky map. The words are not Arabic; they may be derived from the Persian, and in the middle ages corrupted into Alangue, Ras Alaugue. Medieval astrologers called it Cor Serpentis, Heart of the Serpent. With lambda it was the Chinese Shuh, a territorial title.

VEGA (WEGA), alpha Lyrae, steel blue, summer. The second brightest star in this latutude, and by far the brightest of the whole circle of successive Pole stars, it was worshipped by the Egyptians as Maat, goddess of justice and truth. Personification of original and celestial reason, she determined divine harmony, law, and order. She was the great mother who led departed souls to Osiris for judgment, and she stood by while the weighing of hearts took place and shared in the decisions. Her emblems were five rays and the feather, which in judgment scenes, appears on the scales balanced against a heart. She was the female counterpart of Thoth, the principle which governed the good kings of ancient Egypt, and her name is the root of magistrate, major, mare, and mayor.

The Roman people also greatly revered this star. The beginning of autumn, season of the great harvests, was indicated by its morning setting, and an allusion to its expected rising early in May caused Cicero to remark caustically, "Yes, it

will rise, if the edict allows
it." This contemptuous comment
referred to Caesar's arbitrary,
if sensible, interference with
the course of time, when he took
a hand in calendar adjustments,
a meddling that created as much
dissatisfaction in his day as did
Pope Gregory's reforms in the
16th century. Superstitions,
deeply rooted, make many fear
calendar changes.

Throughout the east, this
star has exerted a strong influence. It was of especially good
omen because, under its sway,
the gods vanquished evil (darkness). The Hindus figured it
as a three-cornered nut of an
aquatic plant, or as a triangle.

In China, a youth, Tung Yung,
of a family that once had been
wealthy but had fallen on hard
times, suffered other misfortunes.
His older brothers all died of
sickness, his crops failed, and
finally his father died, at a time
he was so poor, he had not the
means with which to buy even a
plain wooden coffin. Nothing
was left to sell except himself.
With a price on his head, he
stood in the market square where
wealthy land owners might see
him. Handsome and strong, he
commanded a price large enough
to provide his father with a
funeral that included magnificent
offerings of incense, gold and
silver paper money, paper dogs,
horses, and chariots, and other
things that might be useful to his
father in the realm beyond life.
Tung Yung was even able to
erect a small tomb ringed with
trees, where the spirit of his
father might come and enjoy the
cool evening breezes.

As a slave, Tung Yung
labored from sunrise to sunset.

He lived alone in a little hut,
with no one to prepare his rice
or care for him, and often, too
weary to cook even the simplest
meal, he fell onto the hard
wooden planks of his bed without eating. In spite of his
great strength, his health began
to fail, he became hot with
fever, and his fellow workers
despaired of his life. But, the
all-seeing, all-knowing Lord of
Heaven, who, from his throne
of stars had observed Tung
Yung, determined that such
filial devotion should not go un-
rewarded. He summoned his
daughter, Chih Nu, goddess of
spinning, and sent her along
the silver pathway from heaven
straight down to the bedside
of the stricken youth. When
Tung Yung opened his eyes and
saw a lovely maiden standing
beside his bed, hope revived in
his heart, and the fever soon
passed from his body. Her
beauty was so great, he dared
not ask whence she came. Finally
she smiled and said simply that
she had traveled from afar to
become his wife. Tung Yung
accepted the statement without
questioning her further.

No matter how back-breaking
his labors, Tung Yung went
about his work singing. His
suppers were served at a table,
his bed soon had a thick mattress,
his house was warm and clean,
and Chih Nu always greeted him
with a smile. Every evening,
after her household chores were
done, his wife sat down at a
loom and wove tapestries, such
as he had never dreamed of.
Her sheer silks contained strange
forms of phantom-like horsemen
and chariots drawn by dragons.
The colors were foamy white,
azure blue, emerald green, a
delicate crimson, violet, and

yellow. The banners carried by the riders trailed off like clouds. In each dragon's beard was the glimmer of the mystic pearl, and in each horseman's helmet was a jewel of rank, for she was weaving the seasons. Tung Yung began to suspect his wife was not an earthly creature, but afraid to break the spell, he said nothing. Her handiwork became famous. People came from all corners of the globe and crowded around the little hut to outbid each other for her silks. Before long, her magic loom had provided, not only enough money to ransom Tung Yung from slavery, but to purchase wide fields for him with a comfortable house and servants of his own. When this was done, and their little son was more than a year old and no longer needed her milk, she knew her errand was done, and she yearned to see once more her home in heaven. Without the heart to say farewell, she gazed sadly at her sleeping husband and son, and then mounted the silver road that would lead her back to her heavenly kin. By the immortals she was given a great welcome and presented with a castle of her own, the star Vega, the most brilliant in the northern sky. There she presides over weaving and spinning; each of her embroideries of the seasons seems more beautiful than the one that preceded it, and each one to come is eagerly awaited in turn. Young girls, upon first learning to use the shuttle and loom, pray to her for skill. This tale is one of the many forms of the Chih Nu legend related under Altair.

Vega, or Wega, is from the Arabic Waki, which in turn derived from the Greek, which came back into Europe during the middle ages as Veka, Waghi. It means Falling Eagle, or Vulture, in contrast to Altair (Chi'en Niu, the celestial lover of Chih Nu), which is Flying, or Soaring, Eagle. As the brightest star in this latitude, it is called Glory of the Summer Heaven; because of its flashing radiance, it is termed Arclight of the Sky, for its song, which can be heard in the wind, it is Harp Star. Additional designations are:

Arabic: Alahore, Allore, Alohore; Athafiyy, Trivets or Tripods. This was the people's Athafiyy; astronomers called fainter stars, some they observed through telescopes mounted on tripods, by this name.

Babylonian: Dilgan, Messenger of Light, a name also applied to other luminaries.

Chinese: Chih Nu, Spinning, or Weaving, Maid.

Egyptian, Maat.

Hindu: Abhijit, Victorius, a component of the 19th makshatra.

Japanese: Ori-hime, Spinning Maid; Princess Shokujo.

Latin: Fides, Lute; Fidicula, Fidis, Lyre-shaped instrument; Lyra, a name for the constellation; Veka, Vuega vel Vagieh; Wahgi.

Persian: Vanant, or Vanand, the name of a yazad (angel) who rode in a chariot and smote all noxious creatures, including the king of demons who personified darkness. The yazad also guarded the gates of Albors, navel of the earth around which the sun and moon revolve and site of Mithras' mansion, to keep fiends and witches from entering and breaking up the road and thereby hindering the passage of the solar and lunar balls and the stars. Vanant is also a name given to Regulus. See Royal Stars of Persia.

Owing to the precession of the equinoxes, Vega will be the Pole Star in about 11,500 years. Because it is so far toward the north, it is visible at some hour of every clear night throughout the year from various places in the northern hemisphere.

VINDEMIATRIX, epsilon Virginis, bright yellow, spring. Originally Vindemiator, or Vindemitor, from the Latin meaning Grape Gatherer. When this star rose with the sun, it heralded the time of vintage or harvest. Other names with the same significance were Provindemia major and Provindemiator. Another epithet was Protrigetrix. A Greek title might be rendered Fruit-plucking Herald. It appears to be the one known on the Euphrates as Kakkab-Mulu-izi, Star Man of Fire, perhaps a title of Laterak, Divine King of the Desert. Its classical Arabian name was Mukdim al Kitaf; its popular name was Almuredin, from Al Muridin, Those who Send Forth. Traces of these words remain in Alacast, Alaraph, Alcalst, Almucedie. In China it was Tsze Tseang, Second General.

The numerous titles from early times suggests an unusual interest in a star now inconspicuous. When the zodiac was formed about 2,100 B.C., this star, probably brighter

then, may have been seen before sunrise at Babylon about August 20. This would have been too late for the vintage, which might indicate its tradition is older than that of the zodiac.

WASAT (WESAT), delta Geminorum, double, yellowish white and purple, winter. From the Arabic Al Wasat, The Middle, i.e. of the constellation, and located in the lower half of Pollux's right arm. Some say the star has its name from its position near the ecliptic, the central circle, but many are closer. Chinese name is Ta Tsun, Great Wine Jug.

THE WATER, lambda Aquarii, red, autumn. Most prominent star in the Aquarii cluster called The Stream, or The Outpouring. Lambda marked the 25th Hindu nakshatra called Satabhisha, whose regent was Varuna, goddess of waters and chief of the Adityas.

WAZAN, beta Centauri, white, spring. From the Arabic for weight. Also called Agena.

WEZEN (AL WAZN), delta Canis Majoris, variable, light yellow, winter. From the Arabic meaning The Weight, i.e. probably to balance Sirius, the star which seems to rise with difficulty or heavy weight from the horizon. It lies at the hound's hind quarter.

WEZN (WAZN) beta Columbae, Winter. From the Arabic Al Wazn, The Weight.

YED POSTERIOR, epsilon Ophiuchi, red, summer. The name meaning The Hand Following, or Behind, is from a

combination of the Arabic Yed
and the Latin Posterior. Addi-
tional designations: Accadian; A
Component of the lunar station
Mulubat, Man of Death. Chinese:
Tsoo, the name of a feudal state.
Euphratean: Nitax-bat, Man of
Death. Persian: with others com-
posed Garapa, Serpent Tamer.
In astrology, a star of evil
influence.

YED PRIOR, delta Ophiuchi,
yellow, summer. The name
meaning The Hand Before, or
the Former Hand, is from a
combination of the Arabic Yed
and the Latin Prior. Of the
two stars in the hand it is
the one nearer the ecliptic.
Chinese name: Leang, A Mast.

ZANIAH, eta Virginis,
spring. From the Arabic Al
Zawiah, The Corner or Kennel.
Chinese name: Tso Chih Fa,
Left Hand Maintainer of Law.

ZAURAK (ZAMACK), gamma
Eridani, double, yellowish
and pale grey, winter. From
the Arabic Al Na'ir al Zaurak,
meaning The Bright Star of the
Boat, implying a craft traversed
the stream Eridanus; perhaps an
allusion to the Ark.

ZAVIJAVA (ZARIJAN), beta
Virginis, pale yellow, spring.
From the Arabic Al Zawiah,
The Angle, Corner, or Retreat,
i.e. Kennel of the Howling Dogs
that followed on the heels of
Leo. Once this was the bright
star of a greatly extended figure
that incorporated other stars of
Virgo and linked with Canes
Venatici. Other descriptive
epithets are Al Bard; The Cold,
which it supposedly brings, and
Warak al Asad, the Lion's
Haunches. With others, beta
marked the manzil Al Awwa,

which was of good omen, and with
beta Leonis formed the Al Nah-
ran, The Two Rivers, inasmuch
as these stars rose in the season
of heavy rains.

Additional designations:
Babylonian: Shepu-arku Sha-A,
Hind Leg of the Lion, to which
the old Arabian lion roughly
corresponded. It marked the
18th ecliptic station. With
Faniah, eta star, formed the
pair Ninsar and Urra-gal. Ninsar, Lady of Heaven, perhaps an
epithet of Ishtar, and Urra-gal,
god of the city of Ur, a site of
moon worship, were one of the
seven famous pairs found in
Babylonian astronomy. Ninsar
also was the title of a lunar
station. Chinese: Yew Chih
Fa, Right-hand Maintainer of
Law. Coptic: Abukia; Khorasmian: Afsasat; Persian;
Mashaha; Sogdian: Fastashat;
these last four probably all of
the Arabic significance.

ZOSMA (ZOZMA), delta
Leonis, triple, pale yellow,
spring. From the Greek for
Girdle, or Loin Cloth, although
it is located at the lion's rump,
near the tail. Arabs called it
Al Thahr Al Asad, The Back of
the Lion, a correct title, which
contracted into Dhur and Duhr.
Chinese called it Shang Seang,
Higher Minister of State.

With theta star, Chort, it
constituted the following lunar
mansions: Arabic: Al Zubrah,
The Mane, i.e. of the lion. Al
Haratan (Chortan, or Khurt),
The Two Little Ribs (or Holes).
Al Kahil al Asad, The Space
between the Lion's Shoulders.
All are inappropriate titles.
Coptic: Pikhorion, Shoulder.
Egyptian: Messu, Heart of Su
(Shu), light god and quickening

principle. Euphratean: Kakkab Kua, stars of the god Kua, the oracle. Khorasmian: Armagh, The Great. Sogdian: Wadha, The Wise.

ZUBENELGENUBI (ZUBEN ELGENUBI), alpha Librae, a wide double, pale yellow and light grey, summer. Located in the southern scale of the Balance, at a joint where two lines of the configuration branch or angle off into different directions. This star ushered in the Peruvian wet season, which was celebrated with a purification by bathing at the junction where two streams branched off, an example of similarities in widely separated peoples. The name from the Arabic Al Zuban al Janubiyyah, which was a translation from the Greek, means The Southern Claw, i.e. of Scorpius, which is close by, and which ancients linked to Libra. In corrupted form the name appeared as Janib, Zubenelgubi.

Additional designations:

Arabic: Al Kiffah al Janubiyyah, The Southern Tray of the Scale. Al Wazn al Janubiyyah, The Southern Weight, which decayed into Vazneganubi. Mizan Aliemin, from the title name, Al Mizan, The Scale Beam.

Arabo-Latin: Kiffa australis, Southern Tray.

Latin: Lanx Meridonalis, Midday (or Middle) Tray, Platter, or Weight.

Zubenelgenubi was the determinant of several lunar inns, which usually included beta star, such as:

Arabian: Afr, a very ancient title; Al Zubanah, or Zaban, To Push.

Babylonian: Nuru-sha-Shutu, Southern Light; Zibanitu, To Push.

Coptic: Pritithi, Two Claws.

Euphratean: Entena-mas-luv, Star of the Tailtip, suggesting it indicated the end of the immense, but undetermined Hydra. Sugi, ruled by Beltis, or Bilat, The Lady, a harlot goddess whose rites were orgiastic.

Hindu: Visakha, Branched. Figured as a decorated gateway.

Khorasmian: Ighnuna, Claw-possessing.

Persian: Çrob (Srob), Horned.

Sogdian: Ghanwand.

ZUBENESCHAMALI (ZUBEN ESCHAMALI), beta Librae, variable, pale green, summer. From the Arabic Al Juban al Shamaliyyah, a translation from the Greek, meaning The Northern Claw, i.e. of Scorpio. Also written Zuben el Chamali, Zubenelgemabi, Zubenhakrabi. Additional designations: Arabic; Al Kiffah al Shamaliyyah, The Northern Tray of the Scale. Arabo-Latin: Kiffa borealis, Northern Tray; Vazneschemali, Northern Weight. Babylonian: Nuru-sha-Iltanu, Northern Light, the 22nd ecliptic station. Latin: Lanx septentrionalis, Tray, Platter or Weight of the North. This star with alpha composed several lunar inns. See under Zubenelgenubi.

STAR SUMMARY. Sir James Jeans once said the universe has as many stars as all the beaches of all the oceans of the world have grains of sand. Of these countless twinkling specks in space, not more than 4,000 are visible without a telescope since the naked eye cannot see a star less than 6th magnitude, and these can be seen only on the clearest and most perfect of nights. If awed by their mysterious beauty, from his first awareness of them, man used stars for practical purposes. Before recorded time he adjusted his life according to the color, size, position, and time seen (or not seen) of these tiny sparkling objects, and they have never lost their power to influence mortals. Phoenicians, who, for purposes of navigation, developed the art of reading the skies into an exact science, gave to the world a system that has persisted through the centuries. Into this day and age, 57 stars are selected by the United States Naval Observatory for navigational purposes. Each is brighter than third magnitude, hence easily seen, and, each is so located, one may be found in space from some point on Earth's surface at some hour during any night of the year.

THE NAVIGATIONAL STARS

Star	Constellation
Northern Sky (26)	
Aldebaran	Taurus
Alioth	Ursa Major
Alkaid	Ursa Major
Alphecca	Corona Borealis
Alpheratz	Andromeda
Altair	Aquila
Arcturus	Bootes
Bellatrix	Orion
Betelgeuse	Orion

Star	Constellation
Deneb	Cygnus
Denebola	Leo
Dubhe	Ursa Major
El Nath	Taurus
Eltanin	Draco
Enif	Pegasus
Hamal	Aries
Kochab	Ursa Minor
Markab	Pegasus
Menkar	Cetus
Mirfak	Perseus
Pollux	Gemini
Procyon	Canis Minor
Rasalhague	Ophiuchus
Regulus	Leo
Schedar	Cassiopeiae
Vega	Lyra

Southern Sky (31)	
Acamar	Eridanus
Achernar	Eridanus
Acrux	Crux
Adhara	Canis Major
Al Na'ir	Grus
Alnilam	Orion
Alphard	Hydra
Al Suhail	Vela
Ankaa	Phoenix
Antares	Scorpio
Atria	Triangulum Australe
Avior	Carina
Canopus	Carina
Capella	Auriga

The Navigational Stars, continued

Star	Constellation	Star	Constellation
Difda	Cetus	Rigil Kentaurus	Centaurus
Fomalhaut	Piscis Austrinus	Sabik	Ophiuchus
Gacrux	Crux	Shaula	Scorpio
Gienah	Corvus	Sirius	Canis Major
Hadar	Centaurus	Spica	Virgo
Kaus Australis	Sagittarius	Zuben-elgenubi	Libra
Menkent	Centaurus		
Miaplacidus	Carina		
Nunki	Sagittarius		
Peacock	Pavo		
Rigel	Orion		

Polaris is not counted among these navigational stars. Its importance, since the Phoenicians pointed out its usefulness in locating the north, has set it apart as a unique guide to navigators and nomads.

IX

HOST OF HEAVEN

Kobabim

Lustrous Host of Heaven,
where are you to be found:
behind a sulky cloud
that casts sullen silence
on hills where winds are hushed;
or is your council held
in the wide-open sky
when nights are clear and your
reflections tantalize
the breeze that pursues them
over meadow and stream?
Have you, aged, settled
into lesser lights, or
have you retained all your
viripotent powers?
Unrecognized, removed
from early where aways,
wasted without offspring;
these may be your fate.　Yet,
concealed in the vacuum
of time, your sapience,
like that of a valient
warrior who has grown
too old for battle but
not to chart wars, resolves
when the tempest or cold
must strike, when days and nights
shall be warm and moist, where
the winnowing-fans scatter
grain, which fields are to be
hard and arid, which soft
and fertile, when river
beds are to be dry, when
streams are to overflow
and flood the land.　Only
the fool can disbelieve
that you no longer are
a fixer of fate, that,
though hidden, you do not
come forth in your season.

Sinai in early times was a　　plateau site of moon worship,

the name itself inherited from Sin, Assyrian lunar deity. Furthermore in Yahweh rites the sacred seasons were those of the new moon, the Sabbath was obviously lunar and in pre-exilian days coincided with the full moon. Angels and archangels, personfications of heavenly bodies composed a Host of Heaven, battalions that served Yahweh, the Lord of Hosts. These attendants constituted a retinue which fought on high while the earthy armies of Yahweh's people contended below to impose His will. In the frenzy of battle, clouds darkened the sky, torrential rains flooded the earth, cataclysms erupted, cyclones swirled across the deserts, tempests uprooted trees and cities. When the Host of Heaven accomplished a mission, skies cleared and stars twinkled gaily along with the light of the moon.

In time the Host became a council of ministers composed of beneficent and malignant ruhoth, spirits, who executed the works of God. Each appears to have had assigned, as a home or place of government, or as one of the aspects of his being a star or group of stars, which stood to the right and to the left of the Lord. Stars were called Kobabim, and the position taken by them, the manner in which clouds drifted over them, atmospheric conditions, eclipses, comets, and meteors in their vicinity, became messages only decipherable by Kobabim-readers. Thus the belief that celestial forms and activity expressed divine will prevailed among early Jews as well as it did among the peoples of neighboring nations. The horse was consecrated to the Sun, ruler of the day, the lamb was sacrificed at the Passover

season, the goat was a sin offering on the Day of Atonement. Tophet, a favorite spot at the extremity of the Valley of Hinnon (Gehenna), was set aside for the adoration of idols to whom children were sacrificed. Drums were played to drown out the cries, and Tophet means both drum playing and place to be spat on.

When Ahab, king of Israel from about 875 to 853 B.C., and Jehoshaphat, King of Judah, desired to war against the Syrians at Ramoth-Gilead, they joined forces, but before they engaged in action they consulted a forecaster who undoubtedly started his prophecy in the established manner, "I have seen the Lord on His throne and all the Host of Heaven stood by Him on the right and on the left."

Isaiah, great prophet of exile, denounced the "dividers of heaven," the Babylonian astrologers who sought to read the stars and in effect acknowledged a pantheon of gods. Still, rites tied to divination persisted, and a particular class of kobabim was venerated. A century later Josiah, king of Judah, tried to abolish this worship as one that aroused the wrath of God. Jeremiah, a major prophet of Josiah's reign, commanded the Jews, "Fear not the signs of heaven at which the heathen are dismayed."

The superstitious beliefs were not completely wiped out, but because the Host of Heaven had something of the aspect of subordinate or lesser divinities, few star names were written in the Bible, and a positive identification of these few, most of which appear in the Book of

Job, with contemporary names has never been accomplished; therefore any classification anywhere in this work that treats a star in the Bible as a star with which we moderns are familiar is conjecture. Giovanni Virginio Schiaparelli, late 19th century astronomer and biblical scholar, compiled the following table of star names:

NAMES OF STARS IN THE ANCIENT VERSIONS OF THE BIBLE

Biblical Reference	Hebrew	Targum(1)	Peshitta(2)	Old Latin	Vulgate
Amos, V, 8	kimah	kima	kimah	-	Arcturus
Amos, V, 8	kesil	kesila	'iyutha(3)	-	Orion
Isaiah, XIII, 10 Genesis, VI, 4	kesil-ehem	nefilehon (4)	hailawa-thelon(5)	omnia luminaria eius	splendor earum (Arcturum)
Job, IX, 9	'ash	'ash	'iyutha	Arcturus (Septentrio)	Arcturus
Job, IX, 9	kesil	nifla(6)	gabbara(7)	Vespertinus (Vesperus)	Orion
Job, IX, 9	kimah	kima	kimah	Pleiades (Vergilias)	Hyades
Job, IX, 9	hadre theman	idderone shitre mazzalayya bisetar daroma(8)	hedar al taimna	Interiora Austri (Austri ministerium)	Interiora Austri
Job, XXXVII, 9	heder	idderon 'ila (9)	tauwane	Promptuaria	Interiora
Job, XXXVII, 9	mezarim	kawwat-mezarim (10)	zarifta(11)	Promptuaria	Arcturus
Job, XXX, VIII, 31	kimah	kimetha	kima	Pleias	Pleiades
Job, XXX, VIII, 31	kesil	nifla	gabbara	Orion	Arcturus
Job, XXX, VIII, 32	mazzaroth	shitre-mazzalayya(12)	'agalta (galta) (13)	Mazuroth	Lucifer

Name of Stars in the Ancient Versions of the Bible -continued

Biblical Reference	Hebrew	Targum(1)	Peshitta(2)	Old Latin	Vulgate
Job, XXX-VIII, 32	'ayish	zabetha (14)	'iyutha	Vesper	Vesper
Kings, XXIII, 5	mazza-loth	mazzelatha	mauzelatha	-	Duodecim Signa

NOTES: (1) Literally, translation into any language; in Talmudic period Targum probably meant Armaic translation of the Bible; (2) Earliest Syriac version of the Bible. The literal meaning of the word is simple or direct, indicating that it conforms closely to the Hebrew. (3) This term may be related to Ayish and may refer to Auriga or the Star Capella; or 'iyutha may refer to the head of the Celestial Bull, stars that compose the Hyades. (4) Giants. (5) Hosts. (6) Giant. (7) Strong Man. (8) Planet Chambers of the South. (9) Upper Chamber. (10) Window of mezarim. (11) Pouring rain. Sa'adya in the Arabic version has the same meaning. (12) Path of the planets. (13) Carriage. (14) Pleiades.

Excerpts from the summary by Schiaparelli on the table are given here:

ASH and AYISH are probably two different ways of writing the same word. Both resemble the Arabic Na'sh or Na'ash, a bier or portable litter, used by ancient nomads to designate alpha, beta, gamma, and delta of the Great Bear, the well-known quadrilateral or four wheels of Wain. Benatna'sh, the daughters of Na'sh, was applied to the three stars epsilon, zeta, and eta, which form the tail of the Bear or pole of the Wain. In Job reference is made to the "children of Ayish," which in the Vulgate is identified as Vesper, which seems incredible, and as Arcturus, which may be a mistake for Arctus. Ash also is a term for moth, a destructive insect, and the Hyades have the appearance of a moth at rest, when the moth holds its wings detached from its body, but spread over in such a way as to form a cloak, more or less similar to an isosceles triangle. The Hyades form such a triangle. Although the simile relating to children may apply to the Pleiades, which laic imagination compared to a Hen surrounded by her Chickens, the Hyades seem more likely, as the Hebrew for Pleiades appears to be Kimah. A third possibility for the children of Ayish is The Kids, children of Capella, the she-goat. Thus Ash or Ayish may be Arctus, the Great Bear; Aldebaran, parent of the Hyades; Capella, mother of The Kids, with Aldebaran the most likely identification. The mistake of Arcturus for Arctus may have come about by an error in translating Ash or Ayish bear instead of bier.

HADRE THEMAN. Hadre or Heder is derived from the root hadar, which denotes the innermost or most strongly defended apartment of a dwelling, where articles of greatest value are kept, the penetralia. Metaphorically it is used to indicate the most internal and secluded part of anything. Theman signifies right side when bearings are taken while facing the east; furthermore it means south wind. A statement in the Book of Job, "Out of heder (hadre) cometh the tempest," i.e. storms such as a sirocco, which bring oppressive winds and heat. Five first magnitude stars in the southern sky, which began with Canopus as the one furthest south and ended with Sirius as the one furthest north, visible when the Book of Job was written, have been among those said to compose the famous Chambers of the South. Consequently Hadre theman and Heder may be considered part of the Chambers, a brilliant constellation seen on the southern horizon.

KESIL (K'SIL). This Hebrew name generally is understood to mean foolish and frequently in the Bible implies a sense of impiety. Jews saw in Kesil the form of a man chained for his folly or his impiety.

The question, "Can thou loose the bands?" verifies this. Inasmuch as the plural form Kisilim (Kesilehem) also appears, more than one star is involved, and the only constellation which agrees with the picture of tight bands is the splendid Orion, who is bound at the waist. This striking figure is found in the cosmography of all peoples of the torrid and temperate zones, and was well known to the Jews.

KIMAH. Probably connected with the Arabic root kum or the Assyrian root kanu, which mean cluster or heap, which leads to the conclusion this is a cluster of stars. Chains of Kimah may be metaphorical; if so the logical reference is to the Pleiades, the most obvious cluster or stars chained to one another, and which in consequence of its conspicuous light awakened universal attention. As in the case of Kesil, the Vulgate has given more than one rendering to Kimah.

MAZZAROTH (MAZZALOTH). Probably no star in the Bible has been given as varied an identification. It has been said to signify signs of the lunar zodiac, the twelve signs of the solar zodiac, the Galaxy, Canis Major, the Greater or Lesser Bear, Sirius, the Morning and Evening Stars, the planets. This last seems the most probable. The word itself may derive from the root that was the source of the Babylonian matsartu, with the meaning to watch or guard. While the twelve zodiacal belt stars played an important part in ancient astronomy and astrology and were often looked upon as stars that forewarned, the premonitory stars par excellence were the planets, which form the principal basis for all astrology. The zodiac of twelve constellations was not formed as early as the time of Josiah (7th century B.C.), and therefore could hardly have been referred to in the statement in the Second Book of Kings, "King Josiah put down the priests who worshipped and burnt incense to Baal, the Sun, the Moon, Mazzaloth, and all the Host of Heaven."

The question, "Dost thou make mazzaroth come forth in his season?" clearly marks it a star or collection of stars subject to periodic appearances and not always visible. To "come forth" is to rise above the horizon. The Bears were both absolutely circumpolar for the latitude of Palestine at the time the Book of Job was written, and therefore could not "come forth" at any season. Mazzaroth might more easily stand for the lunar than the solar zodiac, but again the weight falls in favor of the five planets, which at Babylon and Nineveh were placed among the great divinities. Hebrews were well aware of these beliefs, and the Bible expression compares with some on Babylonian monuments. Thus Mazzaroth, the determiner of fate, is most likely the planets. The only other plausibility might be two bright stars, the morning and evening sentinels, who watched over the fortunes of their idolizers. Mazzaloth is a later Hebrew form taken from the Targum.

MEZARIM (MIZRIM). With Ash or Ayish presumed to stand for Aldebaran, Mezarim probably refers to the Great Bear, Arctus, or perhaps the Two Bears. If Jews and Arabs had not noted these stars in a perpetual dance around the Pole on their own account, which seems improbable, for poets from time immemorial in widely separated parts of the earth have sung of their glory and grace, these people certainly would have been made acquainted with them by the Phoenicians, who, when at sea, used the Lesser Bear to find the north and who intermingled in Palestine and surrounding countries for centuries. That these stars had the characteristics of the far north is obvious from lines in the Book of Job:

> Out of the heder cometh the tempest;
> Out of the mezarim cometh the cold.

Arcturus seems to have been written in error for Arctus in the Vulgate. Both words are literally Bear. Mezarim (Mizrim), or its plural Mizrayim is the dual of Mizreh, which means winnowing-fan, instrument with which grain is scattered in the air for sifting when the chill sets in. Both Mezarim and Mizreh have their roots in zarah, which bears the sense disperse, expand, ventilate. The Bears can be conceived to be winnowing-fans or bowls with handles. Coincidentally, the Chinese conceived these stars to be ladles.

NAHASH BARIAH. The meaning of these words is fugitive serpent. Some interpreters think this is Draco, the Dragon, which winds between the two Bears. Draco is an artificial constellation, invented by ancients who felt the necessity of occupying all the heavens

with groups of figures as a
simple method of naming the
stars.   Much doubt exists that
this phrase in Job XXVI, 13,
refers to a constellation or any
astronomical myth.

    To offer a synopsis, Ash
or Ayish designates Aldebaran
with the Hyades; Hadre theman,
the Chambers of the South, including Canopus and Sirius;
Kesil is for Orion; Kimah for
the Pleiades; Mazzaroth for the
five planets; and Mezarim for
the two Bears, whereas Nahash
bariah is without astronomical
significance.

X

STARS OF CHINA

Dreams under the stars;
Who, but the most astute sage,
can say which are true.

Most religions recognize four divine creatures, who guard the quarters of the universe and admit each season in turn. Those of the occident, which had their prototype in the Euphratean Valley, are the Eagle, Ox (or Bull), Lion, and Man; whereas the four benevolent animals of China, the Ssu Lang, who presided over the four directions, or Ssu Fang, were: Ch'ing Lung (Tsing Lung), Azure Dragon, ruler of the east and spring season; Feng-huang (Chu Ch'ieh, or Choo Neaou), Vermilion, or Red, Bird, ruler of the south and summer season; Pai Hui (Pih Hoo), White Tiger, or Ch'i lin, Unicorn, ruler of the west and autumn season; Kuei Shen (Heung Woo), Black Tortoise, or Dark Warrior, ruler of the north and winter season. The universe controlled by these four contained all the stars in space, which were placed within three large yuen (enclosures), the Tsze Wei, which held the northern circumpolar stars; the Tien She, which contained those in the middle; the Tai Wei, which contained those in the south that were visible to the astronomers.

The Chinese were astute observers of celestial phenomena, and some cosmic titles appear in literary works which may date back to 2,500 B.C, or perhaps when the historical records of China are said to have begun with the legendary Yellow Emperor, who supposedly mounted his throne in 2,698 B.C. and reigned for 100 years. China's Golden Age, which began with this emperor, lasted for almost 500 years; the rulers and the ruled alike were incorrupt, and peace and prosperity reigned. About the 8th century B.C. history began to separate from fable and learning was encouraged. Historians and poets were encountered at court. In 221 B.C. a military genius overthrew the feudal lords and proclaimed himself, "First Emperor." He desired everything to begin with his reign, including literature. All books, except those which dealt with medicine, divination, and husbandry, were burned. Over 450 scholars were put to death for disobeying his imperial commands; others were banished for life. When in 206 B.C., the House of Han overthrew the tyrant, the only books available were those that had been bricked up in walls or otherwise cleverly concealed.

Temptation was great, forgeries offered as works of considerable antiquity appeared. The Chinese from early ages undoubtedly possessed a code of ceremonial observances,

but the Li Chi, or Book of
Rites, which some attribute to
Confucius, probably had not been
compiled earlier than the 1st
century B.C. Scholars generally
are of the opinion that no stellar
work of consequence had been
done in China before 1,200 B.C.
About 600 B.C. a chart was
drawn there correctly showing
1,460 stars. This chart is
now in France at the Royal Library of Paris. Although configurations of their asterisms differ from those of other nations, in
most instances they are composed
of stars whose recognition goes
back to Euphratean cultures. In
the Li Chi, similarities between
the Chinese and Pythagorean music systems are remarkable, and
the conclusion that one had
been derived from the other is
unavoidable. At least one Greek
state of the 3rd century B.C.
had intercourse with China, and,
from records that appear to be
genuine, the Greek scale appeared two centuries before the
Chinese scale.

About the year 104 B.C., the
Chinese adopted a cycle of 19
years, which period brings the
solar and lunar year together.
This very cycle Meton introduced in the 5th century B.C.
and Athenians adopted it about
330 B.C., over two centuries
before the Chinese. If some
Chinese usage was not the result
of direct contact between Greece
and China, it may have been via
Persia or India, countries with
which Greece and China had considerable exchange.

About the time of Mahomet,
that is during the 6th and 7th
centuries A.D., while Europe
was lost in the shadows of the
Dark Ages, the Chinese apparently were influenced by the Arabs,

who had knowledge of both
Pagan Greek and Chaldean findings in the field. Additional
changes were due largely to
Jesuits, who settled among them
in the 16th century, and fam-
iliarized them with European
configurations.

The Chinese had three great
periods of star naming. In the
first, prior to 1,200 B.C.,
titles were those of articles
and animals indigenous to
peoples of rural areas. Although
throughout its history in China,
astronomy seems to have been
under the supervision of the
state, which regulated private
and public life, titles suggest
early astronomers, as in other
parts of the world, were also
tillers of the soil, herdsmen,
or men who had come out of
similar surroundings. During
the second period, after 1,200
B.C., and throughout the Chou
Dynasty, titles reveal an imperial
origin. Early works appear to
have been almost completely in
the interests of astrology.
Almanacs of magic and fortune-
telling that related to the stars
were composed. A court as-
tronomer-astrologer's life depended on his ability to read
celestial objects. A head might
come off if one failed to accurately predict an eclipse and
correctly determine how such a
phenomenon might effect the
emperor, his family, or the
nation. The third period of
star naming, influenced by the
Jesuits, was called Sze Kwo
Ming, that is, Western Nation
Names.

Until Jesuits convinced them
otherwise, the Chinese believed
that life on earth mirrored that
in outer space. The world
above contained useful articles,

anatomical parts, animals, as well as places, titles, or occupations. North Star remained stationary while others revolved around it, as if in homage, in the same way the emperor's court was the center of the world below. Circling stars were courtiers around the celestial throne. If the realm in the sky was a happier one, without famine or disease, it was subject to the same laws as that inhabited by mankind. Supernaturals had imperfections as well as mortals; they were inflamed by like emotions and like desires, and people believed that as long as their lives duplicated in every detail the pattern of those who lived among the stars, peace and happiness would be theirs. When an astronomer had proper insight and knowledge, the land was prosperous. If famine, invasion, or civil war destroyed the harmony of the nation, it was because an astronomer lacked the ability to decipher the signs above, and he was slain. A sage's most important functions were to forewarn when locusts might descend on the farms, when the time was most auspicious for seeding or reaping, and when someone intended to organize a rebellion against the emperor. Necessity compelled astronomer-astrologers to develop a sixth sense, which made them aware of the temper of the masses as well as the most subtle changes in atmosphere, and they predicted weather with extra-ordinary accuracy.

Chinese astronomers named many more stars than their western counterparts, who, while they probably identified as many or more, called them by Greek or Roman letters, or by numerals. The list that follows gives only a small percentage of the vast number of Chinese cluster and star names. The western parallels shown generally are approximations. Disagreements in various works, not only of the exact luminaries involved, but of the transliterations, make a complete and exact Chinese catalogue difficult. We hope, however, that the list as offered will serve as a key to Chinese stellar lore and in that respect be of some interest and value.

CHANG CHEN, A Seat, alpha Canum Venaticorum (Cor Caroli).

CHANG JIN, Old Folks, alpha Columbae (Phaet).

CHANG SHA, Long Sandbank, zeta Corvi.

CHAOU, the name of a feudal state, lambda Herculis.

CHAOU YAOU (or TEAOU), To Beckon, Excite, or Move; alpha (Arcturus) and beta (Nekkar) Bootis. Also called Ta Kio, Great Horn.

CHA SZE, Carriage-shop, upsilon Serpentis.

CHI (KI, KIT), Winnower, or Sieve; beta, gamma, delta, epsilon Sagittarii. Seventh hsiu. In ritual called Feng Shi, General of the Wind.

CHIAC, The Horn; alpha (Spica), zeta, theta, iota Virginis. Unlucky period for buying land or building houses; good time to marry daughters.

CH'IEN NIU (KIEN NIU, NIU LANG), Herdsman, or

Cowherd; alpha Aquilae. Lover of Chih Nu and typifies unending longing of love.

CHIH NU (CHIH NEU), Spinning, or Weaving Maid; alpha (Vega), eta (Zaniah), epsilon (Vindemeatrix) Lyrae. Sweetheart of Ch'ien Niu. Harmonizer, i.e. of the seasons.

CHIN CHAY, Camp Carriage, gamma Scorpii (Brachium).

CHOO, Club, or Staff; alpha Arae.

CHOO, Pillar; nu, tau, upsilon, phi, chi Aurigae.

CHOO WAN (CHOO WANG), Many Princes; gamma (Hyadum I, and stars between the horns of Taurus). Some or all of these stars may have been a part of the 19th hsiu.

CHO-T'I, Leaders, i.e. those who lead or take the hand; a triangle of faint stars in Bootes. They were special attendants of Chaou Yaou, the spring star, and were leaders because of the belief that they provided a fixed direction for the swinging of the Great Bear's tail. Ancient Chinese recognized a "rule of the Cho-t'i, one that presumably governed the relationship that existed between Arcturus (Chaou Yaou) and the Great Bear (Tseih Sing) and their common use for calendar purposes on which the whole of Chinese astronomy was at one time based. Thus its motion was used as a measure of time. Also called She Ti.

CHOW (CHOU), name of a feudal state; eta Capricorni.

CHOW (CHOU), title of an imperial dynasty, beta Serpentis, a star that does not appear to have been named by other nations.

CHOW TING (CHOU TING), Imperial Caldron, i.e. of the Chow dynasty; mu and omega of Coma Berenices.

CHUEN SHWO, a mythical figure; gamma Telescopii.

CHUNG SHAN, Middle Mountain, xi and upsilon Herculis. Recent investigations place the apex of the Sun's Way here instead of at lambda Herculis (Masym), which rarely is shown on sky maps.

E CHO, Curious Sparrow, the constellation Apus. Also called Little Wonder Bird.

FANG, Room, Apartment, or House; beta (Graffias), delta (Dschubba), pi. rho, and upsilon Scorpionis. Anciently spelled Fong. The 4th hsiu. An unlucky season. With alpha (Antares), it shared the title Ta Who.

FOO CHIH, Ax and Skewer, gamma and iota Ceti.

FOO LOO, By-path, zeta and lambda Cassiopeiae.

FOO PIH, significance, unknown, gamma Hydrae.

FOO SING, Supporting Star, g or 80 Ursae Majoris (Alcor).

FOO YUE, Headsman's Ax, four or five small stars in Aquarius.

FUN MO, Tomb; gamma, zeta, eta, pi, tau Aquarii.

HAE SHIH, Sea Stone,

kappa Velae.

HAN, name of an old feudal state, zeta Ophiuchi.

HEANG LOW (KIANG LEU), The Dog; the constellation Aries. Also termed Five Reservoirs of Heaven, House of the Five Emperors, Lake of Fulness. After Jesuits called Pih Yang, White Sheep. With Taurus and Gemini constituted White Tiger, western quadrant.

HEA TSAE, Lowest Steward, theta Draconis.

HEEN YUEN, a name which referred to that of the imperial family; ten stars of Leo, including alpha (Regulus), and also small stars reaching into Leo Minor. Regulus, the great star of the cluster, was known to the Chinese as Niau, Bird.

HEUEN KO, Heavenly Spear, gamma Bootis (Seginus).

HEU LEANG, The Empty Bridge, kappa Aquari.

HING CHIN, the constellation Coma Berenices.

HIUEN HIAU (HIUEN HEAOU, KWEI SHEN), composed of Capricorn and stars in Aquarius and Sagittarius.

HO, one of the measures of China; composed of small stars in Hercules and iota and kappa Ophiuchi.

HO CHOO, alpha Geminorum (Castor).

HO CHUNG, In the River, beta Herculis (Korneforos).

HO KEEN, Between the River, gamma Herculis.

HO KOO, River Drum, Alpha (Altair), beta (Alshain), and gamma (Tarazed) Aquilae.

HO NEAOU, Fire Bird, the constellation Phoenix.

HOO SHE, Bow and Arrow, delta (Wezen), eta (Aludra), and kappa Canis Majoris with stars in Puppis.

HOW, the Duke, alpha Ophiuchi (Ras Alhague).

HOW KUNG, the Empress, b Ursae Minoris, an inconspicuous star, wife of beta, Ti.

HSIN, the Heart; alpha (Antares), sigma and tau in the heart of Scorpio, ruled by the Fox. In China, the fox is the crafty companion of fairies. At the age of 100, it supposedly transforms itself into a wizard with magic powers; at 1, 000 it enters heaven. Incense is burned at shrines to appease him. As the heart, this probably refers to the organ of Ching Lung, Azure Dragon, one of the four great divisions of their zodiac. This asterism was a component of Ta Who, which see. Under the name Who Sing, Fire Star, it was invoked in worship for protection against conflagration and had great influence in the raising of silkworms. A propitious time for weddings and building, or construction, of any kind.

HSING, The Star; seven stars in Hydra, including alpha (Alphard), ruled by the horse. An unlucky period in general.

HSU, Emptiness, alpha Equulei (Kitalpha) and beta

(Sadalsuud) Aquarii, ruled by the rat. A lucky period. Also called Heu, Hiu, Hu. Anciently called Ko, the central one of seven hsiu, that, taken together, were known as Kuei Shen (Heung Wu, or Woo), the Black Warrior in the northern sky.

HWA KAE, State Umbrella, sundry small stars of Cepheus, also some probably within the boundaries of Camelopardalis.

KAE UH, The Roof, omicron Aquarii, a little southwest of Sadal-melik, alpha Aquarii.

KANG CHE, Drought Lake, four small stars near alpha Bootis (Arcturus).

KANG HO, a River in China; mu, rho, sigma Bootis.

KAOU PIH, zeta Dorado

KE, Wild Cock; eta, omicron, and other stars in Canis Major. Also the name of alpha of Grus (Al Na'ir).

KEEN PI, Two Parts of a Lock, lambda (Shaula) and upsilon, Scorpii.

KEOK (GUIK), Springtime, alpha Virginis (Spica). A special star of the spring season. After the Jesuits called Chio (Kio), Horn, Angle, or Spike, and with others formed the 1st hsiu.

KEUN NAN MUN, Camp's South Gate; phi and chi Andromedae.

KEW HO, The Nine Rivers, alpha (Ras Algethi) and mu Herculis.

KIN YU, Goldfish, the constellation Dorado. Doubtlessly introduced by Jesuits.

KOO SHE. Same as Hoo She.

KO SING, Guest Star. Identical with Al Aaraf, temporary star that appeared among those of Cassiopeia and disappeared in March of 1574.

KO TAOU, Porch-way, xi, omicron, pi, and upsilon Cassiopeiae.

KOW, the Dog, stars in Sagittarius.

KOW KIN, Hook and Latch, omega Scorpii.

KOW KWO, Dog's Country, omega and other stars of Sagittarius.

KUEN SHE, Soldier's Market, beta Canis Majoris (Murzim).

KUEN TSING, an Army Well, several stars in Lepus.

KUH, Weeping, mu Capricorni, at the extreme end of the tail.

KWA CHAOU, Gourd, alpha (Sualocin), beta, gamma, delta, zeta Dephini.

KWAN SOO, Cord, the constellation Corona Borealis.

KWAN WEI, Bright Fire, lambda Cancri.

KWEI (KUEI, KUT), Ghost, or Cloudlike; gamma and delta (the Aselli), eta, and theta Cancri. With Tsing, stars in Gemini, made up Shun Show, a kung or solar mansion.

LANG TSEANG, General, p

of Coma Berenices.

LANG WEI, official Rank, a, b, c, d, e, and f of Coma Berenices.

LAOU JIN, Old Man, alpha Carinae (Canopus). An object of worship down to at least 100 B.C.

LEANG, a MAST, delta Ophiuchi (Yed Prior).

LEEN TAOU, Paths Within the Palace Grounds, eta Lyrae.

LEE SZE, a Series of Shops, lambda Ophiuchi with neighboring stars.

LEI, A Tear, theta Aquarii (Ancha).

LEW (LOU, LU), Mound, or Train of a Garment; alpha (Hamal), beta (Sheratan), gamma (Mesartim) Arietis. Ruled by a dog. Lucky period for building.

LIEU, Willow Branch, or LIU, Circular Willow Garland. The constellation Hydra, and the 24th hisiu.

LING TAE, Wonderful Tower, chi, c, and d Leonis.

LI SHIH, Coarse Sandstone; pi, chi, omega Tauri.

LOU. Same as Lew.

LOW, Trailing; alpha, beta, gamma, iota Arae.

LUH KEA, some sort of an anatomical term. An asterism within the boundaries of Camelopardalis.

LUY PEIH CHIN, Camp with Intrenched Walls; iota, lambda, sigma, and phi Aquarii, with other stars in Capricorn and Pisces.

LUY TIEN, Thunder, zeta Pegasi.

MAH FUH, Horse's Belly, beta Centauri.

MAO (MAOU, MAU), meaning uncertain, perhaps The Constellation, as it composed the 18th hisu, formed by the Pleiades. Anciently called Mol, or Gang.

MEEN TOO, Cloth Measure, the stars of Hercules in the section once designated as Cerberus.

MEIH FUNG, Bee, probably a translation of Apis, one of the titles of Musca Australis, which these stars form.

MO-KI, Goat-Fish, for the constellation Capricorn. Originally a Bull or Ox; after the Jesuits a Goat-Fish.

NAN HAE, Southern Sea, xi Serpentis.

NAN HO, The Southern River, alpha (Procyon), beta and eta Canis Minoris.

NAN MEN, South Gate, i.e. of the sky; alpha (Rigil Kentaurus) and beta (Agena) Centauri. Alpha, as the determinant of the two, is called Nan Mun.

NEAOU CHUY, Beak Bird, the constellation Tucana.

NIAU, The Bird, alpha Leonis (Regulus). The great star in Heen Yuen.

NIU (NIEU, KEEN NIEU),
Ox, or Bull; stars in Capricorn
and Sagittarius. The 9th hsiu,
or lunar station, which was in
some way intimately connected
in religious worship associated
with the rearing of silkworms.
Anciently called Ngu, or Gu.

NIU LANG, Cow, or Ox,
Herd. Same as Ch'ien Niu,
which see.

NIU SHE, Palace Governess,
or Literary Woman; psi 1 and
psi 2 Draconis.

NU (MO, MU, NIU, WOO
NEU), Woman or Girl; eta, mu,
upsilon, and 9 Aquarii. Perhaps
it included another unidentified
star. The 10th hsiu. Anciently
written Nok.

NUY PING, an Inner Screen,
composed of some stars of Leo
Minor.

PAE CHAOU, Rotten Mellon,
epsilon Delphini (Deneb).

PA KUH, The Eight Cereals;
delta, eta, iota, kappa, xi,
Aurigae.

PAOU PING, Precious Vase,
the constellation Aquarius, a
modern name.

PEE, The Tortoise, the
constellation Corona Australis.

PEH-KIH-KIUN, Ruler of the
North Pole. Also Pei-chi-chen-
chun.

PEIH LEIH, Lightning, alpha
and others of Pisces.

PI (PEIH),Wall or Fortress,
alpha Andromedae (Alpheratz)
and gamma Pegasi. Anciently
called Lek. The 14th hsiu.

PI (PEIH), said to have
several meanings, namely Complete, End, Hand-Net, Rabbit-
Net. Composed of the Hyades
and nu and rho Tauri. Anciently
called Pal. A component of the
19th hsiu. About 1,000 B.C.
a title of the Hyades was Yu
Shih, General or Ruler or Rain.
This character must have come
from western Asia, where early
rains coincided with the heliacal
rising of this asterism. In
China they merely foretold rain
which followed the rising by almost two months. Small adjacent
stars were Tien Lin, Celestial
Public Granary; the two groups
together becoming Announcer of
Invasion on the Border.

PIH TOW (PEI TOU), the
Northern Measure, stars of
the Big Dipper. Death deity.

PIK, Partition, or Wall,
i.e. between the Old and New
Year. Stars of Pegasus.

PING SING, The Star
Screen; several in Lepus.

PING SING, Tranquil Star,
iota of Hydrus.

SAN KUNG, Three Honorary
Guardians, i.e. of the Heir
Apparent; 3 stars in the head of
Canes Venatici (Asterion).

SEAOU TOW, Small Measure,
or Dipper; some of the larger
stars of Chamaeleon, unnamed
in the occident.

SEAOU WEI, Small Tail, i.e.
of the Lion; stars of Leo Minor.
The stars of Leo Minor with
those of the greater Lion composed their giant Dragon,
which mounted the highest
heavens, and also another figure
called the State Chariot.

SE HAN, the name of a Chinese district; epsilon, zeta, theta, iota, xi Librae.

SE IH MUH, Cleft Tree, or branches cut for firewood; stars of Sagittarius. Also called Chi (Ki, Kit), Sieve; Tew (Dew, Tow, Nan Tow), Ladle or Measure; Jin Ma, the Man-Horse, probably a Jesuit title. Other epithets were Milk Dipper, Temple, Tiger.

SHANG CHIN, Higher Minister. An asterism within the boundaries of Camelopardalis.

SHANG PIH, The Higher Minister, zeta Draconis.

SHANG SEANG, Higher Minister of State, delta Leonis (Zosma). Also the name of gamma Virginis.

SHANG TSAE, the Minor Steward, eta Draconis.

SHANG TSEANG, The Higher General, upsilon Coma Berenices. Also the name of sigma Leonis.

SHANG WEI, The Higher Guard, or Double Guard; keppa Cephei. Also the name of an asterism within the boundaries of Camelopardalis.

SHAOU PIH, The Minor Minister, phi Draconis.

SHAOU WEI, The Minor Guard; an asterism within the boundaries of Camelopardalis.

SHAY FUH, Serpent's Belly; from stars of Hydrus toward Tucana.

SHAY SHOW, Serpent's Head, epsilon and zeta Hydrae.

SHAY WE, Serpent's Tail. From stars within the boundaries of Hydrus, which stars are uncertain.

SHE, The Secretions, a small group of stars of Columba.

SHE LOW, A Market Tower, nu Ophiuchi.

SHEN, The Mixer, seven stars in the shoulders; belt and legs of Orion; ruled by the ape. A period of discord and calamity.

SHE TI, The Leaders; two groups of three small stars, eta, tau, upsilon, and zeta, sigma, pi Bootis, the first group on the right of Arcturus, the second group on the left. Called leaders because they assign a fixed direction to the tail of the Great Bear, which, as it revolves, points out the 12 hours of the horizon. Also called Cho-t'i.

SHIH, House, alpha Pegasi (Markab). Component of the 13th hsiu.

SHIH CHIN, Ape, the twins Castor and Pollux, alpha and beta Geminorum. Also called Yang-Yin, Male-Female.

SHIH TSZE KEA, title of Crux, the Southern Cross, an equivalent of our title.

SHING KUNG, Divine Temple, the stars of Scorpio's tail.

SHOU HSING (SHOU SHEN, SHOW SING), star of Longevity, a name for Libra. Some identify with Canopus or Spica. When seen, national peace is assured; when invisible, dire calamities may occur. The god is por-

trayed as bald and wrinkled with
an elongated forehead which ends
in a point. His mien is happy.
He carries a crook, a peach,
and rides a fawn whose head is
turned to look at the god. Sometimes accompanied by a bat.
When with a fawn, or stag, and
a bat, signifies, "May three
stars, good luck, riches, and
longevity, shine upon you." Also
called Nan-chi-lao-jen, Old Man
of the South Pole. After the
Jesuits, when it definitely stood
for Libra, it was called Tien
Ching, Celestial Balance, and
our figure was copied. China
had a law for the annual regulation of weights, which supposedly
had been enacted under the
influence of this sign. In early
solar zodiacs Libra was represented by the crocodile or dragon,
the national emblem.

SHUH, title of a Chinese
territory; alpha (Unuk al Hay)
and lambda Serpentis.

SHUN HO, the Quail's Fire,
made up of stars in Leo. In
the 16th century, when the
Chinese formally adopted our
constellation, they used the name
Sze Tsze, Lion.

SHUN SHOW, Quail's Head,
or Ram; the constellation Cancer
and a cluster of Gemini stars.
One of the 12 kung or solar mansions. Modern title: Keu Hea,
the Crab. The Quail is one aspect of the great Vermilion Bird,
and with stars in Leo and Virgo,
this marked the residence of the
noted bird, emperor of the south.

SHUN WEI, Quail's Tail, or
Serpent, stars of Virgo. Original-
ly part of the noted stellar
figure, Vermilion or Red Bird.
After the Jesuits, known as
She Sang Neu, Frigid Maiden.

SHWANG YU, Two Fishes;
Pisces, a modern name.
Anciently called Koei (K'uei,
Kwei), Striding Legs, or Tseu
Tsze, Pigs. Part of the 15th
hsiu.

SHWUY WEI, alpha Eridani
(Achernar).

SIMA TS'IEN, Head of the
Tiger, lambda Orionis (Meissa).
Other designations: Tsee,
Beak; Tsuy He, Pouting Lips;
Tzu, To Bristle Up.

SING KI, Starry Record;
the constellation Capricorn and
stars of Sagittarius. Also Mo
Ki, Goat-Fish.

SUN, The Child, theta and
kappa Columbae.

SZE FOO, Four Official
Supporters of the Throne, an
asterism within the boundaries
of Camelopardalis.

SZE FUH, Four Great
Canals; stars within the boundaries of Monoceros.

SZE WEI, alpha of Equuleus.

TAE, a feudal state name,
iota Capricorni.

TAE WEI (SHAOU WEI),
Minor Guard, stars between
Leo and Virgo.

T'AI SUI, The Great Year,
the planet Jupiter.

TAI YI, xi, omicron, sigma
Draconis. This group is about
ten degrees from the tail of the
Bear and may have marked the
Pole in the epoch of the com-
mencement of Chinese astronomy.

TA KIO, Great Horn, alpha

Bootis (Arcturus). Also called Chaou Yaou, To Beckon or Excite, and a third designation carried the meaning Palace of the Emperor.

TA LEANG, The Great Bridge. The name was from an early designation of the Hyades and Pleiades, later applied to the constellation Taurus. In very early astronomy, Taurus was an aspect or part of the White Tiger, god of wealth. When the Jesuits introduced western nomenclature, it became Kin Neu, Golden Ox, guardian of fertility. As one of the kung, or solar mansions, it was represented by a cock or hen, recalling the hen and her brood of chickens ascribed to the Pleiades.

TANG SHAY, The Dragon, pi Cygni with about 20 other stars in Cygnus, Andromeda, and Lacerta.

TA TSUN, Great Wine Jar, delta Geminorum (Wasat).

TA TSZE, Crown Prince, epsilon Leonis (Algenubi). Also the name of gamma Ursae Minoris.

TA WHO, The Great Fire, also an emperor's name. An asterism composed of Hsien (Antares), the Heart, as well as the 4th lunar inn, Fang, A Room, and other stars of Scorpio. In early zodiacs, it was represented by the Hare, an animal also associated with the Moon. This cluster was the central one of the seven lunar mansions that constituted the Ch'ing Lung (Tsing Lung), Azure Dragon. When the emperor was surrounded by his sons and courtiers (other stars), who announced the principles of his government, the name of this cluster, which composed the emperor's council-hall, was Ming t'ang. In the 16th century, the name Tien He, Celestial Scorpion, was substituted by Jesuits.

TEEN HO, b, e, o, and z Arietis.

TI, Bottom, alpha, beta, gamma, epsilon Virginis. Later extended to include delta, mu and nu. Third hsiu. Anciently Dsi, and still earlier I Shi.

TI, The Emperor, beta Ursae Minoris (Kochab).

TIEN CHOO, Heaven's Kitchen; delta, epsilon, pi, rho, sigma Draconis.

TIEN CHOO, Heaven's Pivot, alpha Ursae Majoris (Dubhe). Also known as Kow Ching.

TIEN CHUEN, Heaven's Ship, eta Persei.

TIEN HO, Celestial River, the Galaxy. Also known as the Silver River, whose fish were frightened by the new moon, which they imagined to be a hook.

TIEN HWAN, Heaven's Sewer; phi Ceti, a quadruple star, the parts being of 5th and 6th magnitude.

TIEN HWANG TA TI, Great Imperial Ruler of Heaven, alpha Ursae Minoris (Polaris), around which the circumpolar stars turn in homage, the whole forming the Purple Subtle Enclosure. Also called Pih Keih, Ta Shin.

TIEN KE, Heavenly Stable; theta, rho, and sigma Andromedae.

TIEN KE, Heaven's Record, theta Herculis with small adjacent stars.

TIEN KE, an Armillary Sphere, gamma Ursae Majoris (Phacd). Also called Ke Seuen Ke.

TIEN KEAE, Heavenly River, xi and upsilon Tauri.

TIEN KIANG, Heavenly River, theta Ophiuchi and adjacent stars.

TIEN KOU, Heavenly Dog. Sometimes identified as Sirius, sometimes as stars nearby. The Chinese believe an eclipse is caused when the Heavenly Dog swallows the Moon or Sun. Firecrackers are set off, drums or metal pans are beaten, shouts are sent skyward, all sorts of hideous noises are made to scare the beast away and implore heaven to force the monster to disgorge his victim. If a family falls under its rule no son shall be born or, if born, will be short-lived.

The Japanese equivalent is Tengu, a class of goblins who inhabit wild mountain areas or fly in the air. They are reincarnations of arrogant and vengeful priests or warriors. They have large aquiline noses, symbols of pride, and the inferiors, who serve their chief Sojobo, have the beaks of birds. They are boastful and send volcanoes and tempests.

TIEN KUEN, Heavenly Authority, delta Ursae Majoris (Megrez). Also called Kwan.

TIEN KWAN, Heavenly Gate,

zeta Tauri (Shur-Narkabti-Sha-Shutu). In astrology considered of mischievous influence.

TIEN LI, Heavenly Reason, for the square of Ursa Major. The center of the square was called Kwei, an object of worship.

TIEN LUY CHING, Heavenly Walled Castle, lambda and xi Capricornus. Marks the extreme end of the tail.

TIEN MEAOU, asterism probably formed from stars in Argo.

TIEN PIEU, Heavenly Casque, stars of Scutum and some of Aquila.

TIEN SEANG, Heavenly Minister of State; a sixth magnitude star of the constellation Sextans, which had been given the number 2306.

TIEN SEUEN, An Armillary Sphere, beta Ursae Majoris.

TIEN SHI YUEN, Enclosure or Heavenly Market. A comparatively void space that appears between stars nu and epsilon of Serpens.

TIEN SZE, Heaven's Four-horse Chariot, beta Scorpii. Also called Fu Kwang, Basket with Handles. It presided over silkworms and its rising ushered in the commencement of work in that great industry.

TIEN TA TSEANG, Heaven's Great General, gamma Andromedae (Almach) and stars in Triangulum. Astrologically honorable and eminent.

TIEN TSIN, the name of a

city; alpha, beta, gamma, and delta Cygni.

TIEN TSZE, Heaven's Festival, small stars in Taurus of the Pleiad group, near the Hyades.

TIEN YUEN, Heavenly Enclosure; alpha, gamma, delta Persei with other stars.

TIEN YUEN, Heaven's Temporary Granary, iota Ceti.

TIEN YUEN, Heavenly Park; gamma, delta, epsilon, eta Eridani, and others near it.

TI TSO, Emperor's Seat, alpha Herculis (Ras Algethi). Also called Ti, Emperor.

TI TSO, Emperor's Seat, alpha Ursae Minoris (Polaris). Other designations: Peh-kih, or Pih Keih; Tien Hwang Ta Ti, Great Imperial Ruler of Heaven; To Shin; Tow Kwei, Northern Square.

TOO SZE, Butcher's Shop, stars of Hercules in the section once designated as Cerberus.

TOO SZE KUNG, Superintendent of Fireworks, beta Ceti.

TOU-MU (TOW-MOO), The Bushel Mother, alpha Ursae Minoris (Polaris). Tou Mu, a beautiful maiden, attained such a profound knowledge of celestial mysteries, she shone with a heavenly light, was able to cross the seas and pass from sun to moon. The king of Chou Yu, in the north, hearing of her many marvelous virtues, married her, and they had nine sons, who became the Jen Huang, or the first human sovereigns of fabulous antiquity to succeed the celestial sovereigns. Eventually, she

and her family were invited to heaven and placed in palaces there. Tou Mu was made the pivot of the Pole and given the title Queen of the Doctrine of Primitive Heaven. A fate-goddess, this North Star mother kept the registry of the life and death of mortals and the list of gods. She had a third eye in her forehead that she might be able to see everything. Her nine sons resided on neighboring stars and paid her homage. Two of them were the Northern and Southern Bushels (Small and Large Dippers), the first dressed in white and ruled death, the second dressed in red and ruled birth. This star had several other titles; see Ti Tso.

TOW KWEI, Northern Square; alpha, beta, gamma, zeta, eta Ursae Minoris.

TSAE CHING, the Favorite Vassal; a star in Coma Berenices known as 2629.

TSAN (SHEN, or SHI CH'EN), Confused, or Mixed, the three prominent stars in the Belt of Orion with others. Also a name for the whole constellation, which very anciently was part of the White Tiger. An early title for the prominent Belt stars was Sal, Three Kings, or Three Stars. Probably the original 21st hsiu.

TSAOU FOO (TSAO-FU, TSAU-FU), a charioteer of Mu Wang, 5th emporer of the Chou Dynasty, about 536 B.C. Stars delta, epsilon, zeta, nu Cephi. Located in the head of the king.

TSEEN FOO, Heavenly Raft, theta Aquilae.

TSEEN HWANG, Heavenly Pool; mu, rho, sigma Aurigae.

TSEEN KE, Heaven's Record, psi Velae.

TSEEN KOW, Heavenly Dog, a star in Vela.

TSEEN KWAN, Heaven's Round Granary; alpha, gamma, delta, lambda, mu, nu, omicron, xi Ceti.

TSEEN LANG, Heavenly Wolf, alpha Canis Majoris (Sirius). Also called Lang Hoo and Tien Kou, Heavenly Dog. Astrologers said that when unusually bright it portended attacks from thieves.

TSEEN O, Heaven's Ridge, iota Arae.

TSEEN PEEN, Heavenly Casque, gamma, h and g Aquilae; also stars in Scutum.

TSEEN SHE, Heaven's Altar, eta Argus Navis in Puppis (Naos).

TSEEN TSANG, Heavenly Lance, theta, iota (triple stars) and chi (a double star).

TSEEN YIN, Dark Sky, delta and zeta Arae.

TSEIH KUNG, The Seven Princes; delta, mu, nu, pi, psi, and chi (a binary) Bootis. This is one of the groups unnamed in the west.

TSEIH SHE, Piled-up Corpses, beta Persei.

TSEIH SHE KE, Exhalation of Piled-up Corpses; Praesepe, a cluster in Cancer.

TSEIH SING, Seven Stars; the constellation Ursa Major. Also known as the Government and Pih Tow (Pei Tou),

Northern Measure, or Bushel. After the Jesuits called Ti Tche, Emperor's Chariot.

TSEIH TSING.   Piled-up Fuel; chi Gemini.

TSEW KE, Wine-falcon; xi, chi, omega Leonis with kappa and xi Cancri.

TSIH, a Shed; the constellation Lepus.

TSIH, a Whip; gamma Cassiopae.   Appears in Cassiopeia's girdle.

TSIH TSIN, Heap of Fuel; mu Cancri and chi Geminorum.

TSI KUNG, Palace of the Heavenly Emperor; probably the whole of the constellation Draco.

TSIN, name of a feudal state; theta Capricorni.

TSING (CHING), Well, or Pit; eight stars in the knees and feet of Gemini.   The 22nd hsiu. Also called Ho Choo and Pih Ho. See Kwei and Shun Show.

TSING KEW, Green Hill, beta and xi Hydri.

TSIN YIN, delta and zeta Arietis.

T'SI TSIANG, The Seven Goers, constellation Ursa Major. Other titles: Kwei, an object of worship for the center of the Square; Pih Tow, Northern Measure or Bushel; Ti Tche, Emperor's Chariot; To Wei, Jade Palace of Shang Ti, heaven's supreme ruler, a Taoist title; Tseih Sing, Seven Stars, or the Government.   All other gods (stars) circulate in homage around Shang-ti.

TSO CHIH FA, Left-hand Maintainer of Law; eta Virginis (Zaniah). Westward of this star is the point of the autumnal equinox, known as Tien Mun, Twan Mun, or Yih Mun, Heaven's Gate.

TSO CHOO, the Left Pivot, iota Draconis.

TSO HEA, Left-hand Linchpin, beta Corvi, a star unnamed except in China.

TSO KANG, Left Watch, epsilon Arae.

TSO KE, The Left Flag, rho Aquilae.

TSOO, name of a feudal state, epsilon Ophiuchi (Yed Posterior).

TSO SHE TI, Officer who Stands at the Left Hand of the Emperor; epsilon, zeta, xi, omicron, and pi Bootis.

TSOW KAOW, Hay and Straw, epsilon, rho, Sigma Ceti.

TSU KE, the name of a flag; zeta Cancri and kappa, xi Leonis.

TSUNG TING (TSUNG JIN), a Relative, stars of Ophiuchus that once composed the head of the now extinct constellation Taurus Regalis.

TSUNG TSING, an ancestral star, chi Herculis and two others nearby.

TSZE, a Son, lambda Columbae.

TSZE SEANG, Second Minister of State, delta Virginis. The name also is applied to theta Leonis.

TSZE TSEANG, Second General, epsilon Virginis (Vindemeatrix).

TUNG HAE, Heavenly Eastern Sea; zeta, eta Serpentis.

WAE CHOO, The Outer kitchen, composed of stars within the boundaries of Monoceros.

WAE PING, a Rolled Screen, delta and other stars of Pisces.

WAN CHANG, Literary Illumination; theta, nu, and phi Ursae Majoris.

WANG LEANG, the name of a celebrated charioteer of the Tsin Dynasty, about 470 B.C.; prominent stars of Cassiopeia. Also Yuh Lang.

WE, Danger: alpha Telescopii.

WEI (GOEI, GUI), Danger or Steep; alpha Aquarii (Sadalmelik) and epsilon and theta Pegasi. The 12th hsiu.

WEI, The Belly, composed of the constellation Musca Borealis. The 17th hsiu.

WEI, The Tail, probably of the Azure Dragon. Delta, epsilon, and other stars of Scorpion. The 6th hsiu. Anciently called Mi or Vi.

WEN-CH'ANG, the patron of classical studies and learned ministers and officers, whose rule maintains the Tao (Road or Way) among mortals. One or more stars of the Great Bear. Known in ancient literature as Sze-ming, Director of Fate.

WHO SING (HUO SHING),
Fire Star; alpha (Antares) and
tau Scorpii. See Hsin.

WOO, a Pestle, pi Pegasi.

WOO CHAY, Five Chariots,
or Chariots of the Five Emperors;
alpha (Capella) Aurigae, and
beta (el Nath) Tauri.

WOO CHOO HOW, The
Seven Feudal Princes, i.e. of
China. A small group of Coma
Berenice's stars toward Virgo.

WOO CHOO SHIH, The Seven
Feudal Princes; a group of
small stars of Gemini. Also
written Woo Choo How.

WOO TI TSO, Seat of the
Five Emperors, who are surrounded by twelve other groups
variously named after officers
and nobles of the empire. B
Leonis (Denebola) and four inconspicuous stars.

WOO and YUE, names of
old Feudal States; epsilon and
zeta Aquilae.

YANG MUN (YANG MEN),
The South Gate, alpha Lupi.

YANG-YIN, Male-Female,
the Two Principles; corresponds
to Gemini or perhaps only to the
two twin stars, alpha and beta.
In early Chinese solar zodiacs
appeared as Shih Chin, The Ape.
Also called Shih Ch'en, a title
transferred from Orion, and
Jidim, an important object of
worship.

YAOU KWANG, Revolving
Light, eta Ursae Majoris.

YEN, name of a feudal state,
zeta Capricorni.

YEW CHIH FA, Right-hand
Maintainer of Law, beta Virginis
(Zavijava).

YEW HEA, Right-hand Linch-
pin, alpha Corvi (Al Chiba).

YEW KANG, Right-hand
Watch, probably at the temple
door; eta Piscium.

YEW KE, the Right Flag;
delta, eta, iota, kappa Aquilae.

YEW SHE TI, Officer Who
Stands at the Right Hand of the
Emperor; eta, nu, tau in the
feet of Boötes.

YI (I, YH, YIH, YEN),
Wings or Flanks, composed of
22 stars in Crater and in
Hydra's 3rd coil. The 27th
hsiu. Long life, happiness,
and riches to the builder in
this period. The whole constellation Crater may have been
the Heavenly Dog shot by Chang,
divinity of the 26th hsiu, which
bore his name.

YIN TIH, Unostentatious
Virtue; an asterism within the
boundaries of Camelopardalis.

YIN-YANG. See Yang-Yin.

YU CHOO, Right Hand Pivot,
alpha Draconis. The space
toward iota being Chung Ho Mun.

YUE, Battle Ax, eta Geminorum (Propus).

YUEN WEI, unidentified
stars in Draco, while the dragon
itself was the national emblem,
the Chinese Dragon was among
stars known as our Libra.

YUH KANG, A Cross or
Gemmeous Transverse, a portion

of an early astronomical instrument; epsilon Ursae Majoris (Alioth). Stars nearby composed Seang, Minister of State.

YUH TSING, the Golden Well, beta Eridani (Cursa). Sometimes the name is applied to tau Orionis, a star in the same vicinity.

YU LIN KEUN, Imperial Guard; delta, tau, chi, and the triple psi Aquarii, as well as some stars in Pisces.

YU NEU, The Honorable Lady, pi Leonis.

YUN YU, Cloud and Rain; kappa and lambda Piscium.

YU SHIH, Rain Bringer, the Hyades of Taurus.

XI

A FEW WORDS IN CONCLUSION

Shepherd-poet-priest, a natural progression for those who comprehended divine shapes in celestial mosaics and divine will in atmospheric activities. As shown previously in this work, so-called primitives imagined that mortals in after-life ascend in star-form, or as dwellers in mansions on stars, to become companions of those who live, love, hate, labor, determine destiny, and sport in space with the deities who had been progenitors of the human race. Among some peoples, such as the Hindu, physical death is merely a channel for reincarnation. In all parts of the globe, the religious and esoteric have not questioned these or such-like beliefs; the open-minded have tolerated, toyed with, and conceded these ideas are fascinating; the cynic has scoffed at them. And, now, along comes science!

In an article entitled Biography of an Atom - and the Universe, which appeared in the New York Times Magazine of October 13, 1963, J. Bronowski, the author, opens with the words, "This is the profile of a single atom..." The atom he profiles is one of carbon, whose birth began in a young star, or mass of nuclei hydrogen, over 4 billion years ago. It remained in its womb until the star aged, used up its helium, and exploded. With others, the carbon atom scattered in space, and eventually was caught up in the hydrogen of

a new star, or Sun. When the planets were drawn from the Sun, the carbon bit was contained in the part that became Earth, and since Earth first came into being, the carbon atom has remained unchanged. It has existed as part of many different objects: grass, the cow that fed on the grass, the mother who quenched her thirst with the cow's milk or had eaten the animal's flesh, the child born to the woman, and in turn her descendants, until finally, with the death of one, the ashes of a funeral pyre. Perhaps it became part of a diamond that had hardened in soil where the ashes had been scattered, or it may have drifted with the wind and been breathed in by the leaves of a tree and turned into syrup when bathed by sunlight. It may simply have become carbon dioxide. The carbon atom possesses the secret of infinity. It does not die. The X-chromosomes of each individual contains a carbon atom, whose career is varied and everlasting. Thus, that which once was part of a dinosaur, civet cat, or slow-moving worm, may now be part of one who governs some great state. Someday, after a life of billions of years, when Earth is burned up by Sun, the carbon speck may go back into space to float around until it reaches another star, where, like the things of which it once was a part, its identity may disappear, for it may be broken

408

up by some violent atomic collision, and its pieces used in the
formation of new atoms. Through
which sense did our long-gone
ancestors become aware that stars
were indeed our forefathers, and
that the life gifted to us never
really dies?

DESTINY

I descend from my star.
In the darkness of space
I swirl for untold time,
borne by a solar wind
in and out cold vapors,
across breadths of dry dust.
I plunge into heavy seas,
and I struggle to rise
to the surface.   Perhaps
a moment of light, and,
on the currents that lead
to my star, I ascend.

THE GREEK ALPHABET

Early astronomer-astrologers, who identified objects in space with deities, dead ancestors, or other supernaturals, provided them with names that described their roles, and thus converted the skies into a setting for dramatic lore. Johann Bayer, about 1603 A.D., who did not believe the Pagan concept of creation and was disinterested in poetry, introduced the use of Greek letters to distinguish the stars of each constellation in order of their brightness. When a constellation contained more than 24 bodies, Latin characters were used, and, when they in turn were exhausted, identification was made by numerals. For convenience, the Greek alphabet is presented here:

APPENDIX B

GREEK ALPHABET

Α α a	Alpha		Ν ν	Nu
Β β ϐ	Beta		Ξ ξ	Xi
Γ γ	Gamma		Ο o	Omicron
Δ δ	Delta		Π π ϖ	Pi
Ε ε	Epsilon		Ρ ρ	Rho
Ζ ζ	Zeta		Σ σ s	Sigma
Η η	Eta		Τ τ	Tau
Θ θ ϑ	Theta		Τ υ	Upsilon
Ι ι	Iota		Φ φ φ	Phi
Κ κ	Kappa		Χ χ	Chi
Λ λ	Lambda		Ψ ψ	Psi
Μ μ	Mu		Ω ω	Omega

908

BIBLIOGRAPHY

BOOKS:

Abetti, Giorgio, History of Astronomy, New York, 1952.

Alexander, Hartley Burr, Latin American Mythology, Boston, 1920.

--North American Mythology, Boston, 1916.

Allen, Richard Hinckley, Star Names and Their Meanings, New York, 1899.

Ananikian, Mardiros, H., Armenian Mythology, Boston, 1925.

Anesaki, Masaharu, Japanese Mythology, Boston, 1928.

Baker, Robert H., Introducing the Constellations, New York, 1957.

Barton, Samuel Goodwin, and William Henry Barton, A Guide to the Constellations, New York, 1928.

Bentley, John, A Historical View of Hindu Astronomy, London, 1825.

Biruni, Abu'l, Book of Instruction of the Art of Astrology (Translated and edited by R. Ramsey Wright), London, 1934.

Blake, John Frederick, Astronomical Myths, London, 1877.

Bok, Bart Jan, Astronomer's Universe, London, 1958.

Bok, Bart Jan, and Priscilla F. Bok, The Milky Way, Cambridge, Mass., 1957.

Bowditch, Charles P., Numeration, Calendar and Astronomy of the Mayas, Cambridge, Mass., 1910.

Bowditch, Nathaniel, American Practical Navigator, Washington, 1958.

Boyile, V., Fundamental Principles of Yi-king, London, 1934.

Brinton, Daniel G., Myths of the New World, New York, 1876.

--Native Calendar of Central America and Mexico, Philadelphia, 1893.

--Notes on the Codex Troano and Maya Chronology, Salem, 1881.

Brown, Lloyd A., The Story of Maps, Boston, 1950.

Brown, Robert Jr., Researches into the Origin of the Primitive Constellations of the Greeks, Phoenicians and Babylonians, London, 1899.

Brown, Robert Hewitt, Stella Theology and Masonic Astronomy, New York, 1882.

Brugsch, H., Die Agyptologie, Leipzig, 1891.

Bryan, Carl Robinson, The Zodiacal Bible, Los Angeles, 1935.

Bundehesh (Bundeshesh), Bombay, 1908.

Burritt, Elijah H., The Comet of 1832 and the Principle Constellations and Fixed Stars That Lie Along Its Path, Hartford, 1932(?).

--Geography of the Heavens, Hartford, 1833.

--Geography of the Heavens and Celestial Atlas, Hartford, 1856.

Carnoy, Albert J., Iranian Mythology, Boston, 1917.

Chambers, George F., Handbook of Descriptive As-

tronomy, Oxford, 1867.
--Story of the Stars, New York,
1910.
Chwolson, Daniel A., The
Semitic Nations (Translated
by E.M. Epstein), Cin-
cinnati, 1874.
--Die Ssabier und der Ssabismus,
St. Petersburg, 1856.
Clerke, Agnes M., Astronomy,
New York, 1898.
--System of the Stars, London,
1905.
Cole, John, A Treatise on the
Circular Zodiac of Tentyra
in Egypt, London, 1824.
Cook, Arthur Bernard, Zeus,
Cambridge, 1914.
Cornford, F.M., From Religion
to Philosophy, London, 1913.
--Plato's Cosmology, London,
1937.
Crane, Louise, China in Sign
and Symbol, London, 1927.
Cumont, Franz V.M., Astrology
and Religion Among Greeks
and Romans, New York, 1912.
--L'Egypte des astrologues,
Brussels, 1937.
--The Mysteries of Mithra
(Translated by Thomas J.
McCormack), Chicago,
1903.
Dalrymple, Alexander; Edmund
Halley, a Collection of
Voyages, London, 1775.
Degani, Meir H., Astronomy
Made Simple, Garden City,
1955.
Dixon, Roland B., Oceanic
Mythology, Boston, 1916.
Dowson, John, A Classical
Dictionary of Hindu Myth-
ology, London, 1953.
D'Oyly, Rev. G., Remarks on
Sir William Drumond's
Oedipus Judaicus, London,
1866.
Drumond, Sir William, Oedipus
Judaicus, London, 1811.
Ellis, William, Polynesian Re-
searches, London, 1832.
Faroughy, Abbas, A Concise

Persian Grammar, New York,
1944.
Farrer, J.A., Star Lore.
Ferguson, John C., Chinese
Mythology, Boston, 1928.
Flammarion, Camille, Astronomy
for Amateurs (Translated by
A. Welby), New York, 1904.
--Dreams of an Astronomer
(Translated by E.E.F.
D'Albe), New York, 1923.
--Popular Astronomy (Translated
by J.E. Gore).
--Wonders of the Heavens
(Translated by Mrs. N.
Lockyer), New York, 1871.
Flamsteed, John, Catalogue of
Stars, London, 1798.
--Celestial History, London,
1712.
Frazer, J.G., Golden Bough,
New York, 1935.
Gall, James, An Easy Guide to
the Constellations, New
York, 1903.
Gill, David, Catalogue of 1680
Stars, Edinburgh, 1907.
--Catalogue of 1293 Stars,
Edinburgh, 1915.
Gill, William Wyatt, Myths
and Songs of the South
Pacific, London, 1995.
--The South Pacific and New
Guinea, Sydney, 1892.
Goldziher, Ignacz, Mythology
Among the Hebrews (Trans-
lated by R. Martineau),
London, 1877.
Grimaldi, A.B., The Mithraic
Tablets, Cambridge, 191-(?).
--Catalogue of Zodiacs and
Planispheres, London, 1905.
Groot, Jan Jakob Maria de,
Religion in China, New York,
1912.
Guthrie, W.K.C., The Greeks
and Their Gods, Boston,
1951.
--Orpheus and Greek Religion,
London, 1935.
Hagar, Stansbury, Celestial Plan
of Teotihuacan, Mexico,
1912.

--Elements of Maya and Mexican
Zodiacs at Santa Rita, Wein,
1909.

--Maya Day Sign Manik, Lan-
caster, Pa., 1915 (?).

--What Was The Star of
Bethlehem, Northfield, Minn.,
1918.

Halley, Edmund, Catalogue of
Ptolemy, Ulugh Beigh, Tycho
Brahé, Halley, Hevelius;
London, 1843.

Harley, Timothy, Moonlore,
London, 1885.

Harte, Ethel Bret, Zodiacal
Influence from Seed to
Flower, London, 1927.

Hartland, E.S., Primitive
Paternity, London, 1909.

Hearn, Lafcadio, Romance of the
Milky Way, Boston, 1905.

Hinke, William John, A New
Boundary Stone of Nebuck-
adrezzar, Philadelphia,
1907.

Holman, Addie A. (Mrs. Jesse
B.), The Zodiac, Austin,
Texas, 1924.

Holmberg, Uno, Finno-Ugric
and Siberian Mythology,
Boston, 1927.

Hooke, S.H., Myth and Ritual,
Oxford, 1933.

Jastrow, Morris, Religion of
Babylonia and Assyria, Boston, 1898.

Jobes, Gertrude, Dictionary of
Mythology, Folklore, and
Symbols, New York, 1961.

--Index to the Dictionary, New
York, 1963.

Jones, Sir William, Works, in
6 volumes (Particularly
articles on Antiquity of Indian
Zodiacs, Asiatic Miscellany,
Coptic Zodiacs), London,
1799.

Jurdak, Mansur Hanna, Astronomical Dictionary,
Beirut, 1950.

Keith, A. Berriedale, Indian
Mythology, Boston, 1917.

Khareghat, Muncherji, P.,

Identity of Some Heavenly
Bodies in Iranian Writings,
Bombay, 1914.

Kippax, John R., The Call of
the Stars, New York, 1914.

Knobel, Edward Ball, Ptolemy's
Catalogue of Stars, Washington, 1915.

--Ulugh Beg's Catalogue of
Stars, Washington, 1917.

La Caille, Nicolas Louis de,
A Catalogue of 9766 stars
in the Southern Hemisphere,
London, 1847.

Langdon, Stephen II., Babylonian
Menologies, Oxford, 1935.

--Semitic Mythology, Boston,
1931.

Lewis, Sir George C., An
Historical Survey of the
Astronomy of the Ancients,
London, 1862.

Lippman, F., The Seven
Planets, London, 1895.

Lokyer, Joseph N., Astronomy,
London, 1875.

--Dawn of Astronomy, London,
1894.

--The Heavens, London, 1872.

Lum, Peter, The Stars in Our
Heavens, New York, 1938.

Mackenzie, Donald A., Egyptian
Myth and Legend, London.

--Indian Myth and Legend,
London.

--Myths of Babylonia and
Assyria, London.

--Myths of Crete and Pre-
Hellenic Europe, London.

--Pre-Columbian America,
London.

--Teutonic Myths and Legends,
London.

McCaffery, Ellen (Conroy),
Astrology, Its History and
Influence, New York, 1942.

--The Symbolism of Colour,
London, 1921.

Mackey, Sampson Arnold,
Ancient Zodiacal Constellations, Norwich, 1834.

--Man's Best Friend or Evils
of Pious Frauds, Norwich,

1826.
--More Pious Frauds, Norwich,
   1831.
--Mythological Astronomy of
   Ancients, Norwich, 1821.
--Original Design of the Ancient
   Zodiacal and Extra-Zodiacal
   Constellations, Norwich,
   1934.
MacCulloch, John Arnott, Celtic
   Mythology, Boston, 1918.
--Eddic Mythology, Boston,
   1930.
Machal, Jan, Slavic Mythology,
   Boston, 1918.
Mathew, Robert Henry, Chinese
   Dictionary, Cambridge, Mass.
   1943.
Maunder, Edward Walter,
   Astronomy of the Bible,
   London, 1908.
--The Stars as Guides, London,
   1916.
Mitchell, Ormsby MacKnight,
   Astronomy of the Bible, New
   York, 1868.
Moore, Patrick, A Guide to the
   Stars, New York, 1960.
Morgan, Harry T., Chinese
   Symbols and Superstitions,
   South Pasadena, 1942.
Mott, Francis John, Meaning of
   the Zodiac, Boston, 1941.
Muller, W. Max, Egyptian
   Mythology, Boston, 1918.
Munitz, Milton K.,Space, Time and
   Creation, Glencoe, 1957.
--Theories of the Universe from
   Babylonian Myth to Modern
   Science, Glencoe, 1957.
Neely, Henry M., Stars by
   Clock and Fist, New York,
   1956.
Newcomb, Simon, An Observa-
   tion of the Zodiacal Light to
   the North of the Sun,
   Chicago, 1905.
Olcott, William T., Field Book
   of the Skies, New York, 1929.
--Star Lore of All Ages, New
   York, 1911.
Origen, Contra Celsum (Trans-
   lated by Henry Chadwick),

Cambridge, Eng., 1953.
Palingenius, Marcellus, Zodiake
   of Life (Translated by
   Barnabie Googe), London,
   1588.
Peters, John P., Nippur, New
   York, 1896.
Pickering, James Sayre,
   Captives of the Sun, New
   York, 1961.
--1001 Questions Answered About
   Astronomy, New York, 1958.
--The Stars are Yours, New
   York, 1948.
Plunket, Emmeline, M., Ancient
   Calendars and Constellations,
   London, 1903.
Porter, Jermain Gildersleeve,
   Stars in Song and Legend,
   Boston, 1901.
Proctor, Mary, Evenings with
   the Stars, New York, 1925.
--Our Stars Month by Month,
   New York, 1937.
--Romance of the Sun, New
   York, 1927.
--Star and Constellation Chart,
   New York, 1900.
--Stories of Starland, New York,
   1898.
--Wonders of the Sky, New
   York, 1932.
Proctor, Richard Anthony,
   Essays on Astronomy,
   London, 1872.
--The Expanse of Heaven, New
   York, 1883.
--Flowers of the Sky, London,
   1883.
--The Great Pyramid, New York,
   1883.
--Half Hour with the Stars,
   London, 1871.
--Handbook of the Stars, London,
   1866.
--The Moon, New York, 1873.
--Mysteries of Time and Space,
   New York, 1883.
--Myths and Marvels of As-
   tronomy, New York, 1877.
--Old And New Astronomy, New
   York, 1892.
--The Seasons Pictured in 48

Sun Views of Earth and 24
Zodiacal Maps, London,
1885.

Rassam, H., Asshur and the
Land of Nimrod, London, 1897.

Renick, Dorothy W., Star Myths
from Many Lands, New
York, 1931.

Rolleston, Frances, Mazzaroth,
London, 1862-65.

Saulnier, S. L., Observations
on the Circular Zodiac of
Denderah, London, 1823.

Schiaparelli, Giovanni Virginio,
Astronomy of the Old Testament, Oxford, 1905.

Scott, Sir James Goerge, Indo-
Chinese Mythology, Boston,
1918.

Smyth, William Henry, Cycle
of Celestial Objects (Beford
Catalogue), London, 1844.

Sykes, Egerton, Everyman's
Dictionary of Non-classical
Myths, New York, 1952.

Thompson, R. C., Reports of the
Magicians and Astrologers of
Nineveh and Babylon, London,
1900.

Townsend, George, The Oedipus
Romanus, London, 1819.

Velikovsky, I., Earth in Up-
heaval, Garden City, 1955.

--Worlds in Collision, New York,
1950.

Vince, Samuel, A Complete
System of Astronomy,
London, 1823.

Von Hagen, Victor Wolfgang,
Ancient Sun Kingdoms of the
Americas, Cleveland, 1961.

--The Jicaque Indians of
Honduras, New York, 1943.

Wainwright, G. A., The Sky
Religion in Egypt, Cam-
bridge, 1938.

Webster, Doris, Origin of Signs
of the Zodiac, New York,
1940 (?).

Webster, James Carson, Labors
of the Months in Antique and
Medieval Art, Evanston,
1938.

Werner, Alice, African Mythology, Boston, 1925.

White, W. B., Seeing Stars,
Chicago, 1942.

Williams, C. A. S., Outlines of
Chinese Symbolism and Art
Motives, Peiping, 1931.

Wright, Merlin H., Chart of the
Heavens.

Zadde, Arthur J., Making
Friends with the Stars,
New York, 1948.

ARTICLES:

Aiyar, B. V. Kamesvara, Lunar
Zodiac of the Brahmanas,
Indian Antiquary Journal,
Vol. 48, 1919.

Arab Stellar Calendar, Sudan
Notes and Records, Vol.
16, 1933.

Barton, G. A., Babylonian
Calendar, American Oriental
Society Journal, Vol. 31,
1911.

Bober, Harry, The Zodiacal
Miniature, Warburg Institute
Journal, 1948.

Bollaert, William, Astronomy
of Red Man of the New
World, Anthropological
Society Memoirs, Vol. 1,
1865.

--Maya Hieroglyphic Alphabet of
Yucatan, Anthrological Society
Memoirs, Vol. 2, 1865,

Bolton, Carrington H., A Relic
of Astrology, Journal of
American Folklore, 1898.

Bronowski, J., Biography of an
Atom - and the Universe,
New York Times Magazine,
October 13, 1963.

Buckstaff, Ralph N., Stars and
Constellations of a Pawnee
Sky Map, American
Anthropologist, 1927.

Carus, Paul, Chinese Thought,
Open Court, 1907.

--Zodiacs of Different Nations,
Open Court, 1906.

Colebrook, H. T., On the Indian

and Arabian Division of the
Zodiack Table, Asiatic
Society Researches, 1807.

Cope, Leona, Calendar of
Indians North of Mexico,
University of California
Publications in American
Archaeology and Ethnology,
1919.

Encyclopaedia Britannica, 11th
Edition, Cambridge, 1911,
Articles:

--Angel, Vol. 2, page 5B.

--Astrology, Vol. 2, page 795B.

--Astronomy, History of, Vol. 2,
page 808D.

--Aurora, Vol. 2, page 927A.

--Babylonian and Assyrian Astronomy, Vol. 3, page 107D.

--Babylonian and Assyrian
Mythology, Vol. 3, page 114A.

--Constellation, Vol. 7, page 11C.

--Earth (Precession), Vol. 8,
page 800D.

--Egypt (Cosmic Deities), Vol.
9, page 51B.

--Egypt (Soul), Vol. 9, 56B.

--Gilgamesh, Vol. 12, page 18C.

--Hindu Astronomical Solar
Month, Vol. 13, page 492D.

--Mandaeans Mythology, Vol. 17,
page 556B.

--Mythology, Vol. 19, page 128A.

--Star, Vol. 25, page 784D.

--Temple Zodiacs, Vol. 26,
page 606D.

--Zodiac, Vol. 28, Page 993B.

Fewkes, Jesse Walter, Pueblo
Culture, Pan-American
Scientific Congress Report,
1917.

--Sun Worship of Hopi Indians,
Smithsonian Institute Report,
1920.

Fowler, James, On Medieval
Representations of the Months
and Seasons, Archaeologia,
1873.

Gallatin, Albert, Synopsis of
Indian Tribes in North
America, Archaelogia Ameri-
cana, 1836.

Gandz, Solomon, Zodiacal

Light in Semitic Mythology,
Proceedings of American
Academy for Jewish Re-
search, 1943.

Goldziher, Ignacz, Religion of
Iranian Peoples, Die Oriental-
ischen Religionen, 1906.

Grimaldi, Rev. A. B., Zodiacal
Arrangement of the Stars,
Journal of Transactions of
the Victoria Institute, Vol.
38, 1906.

Hagar, Stansbury, The American
Zodiac, American Anthrologist,
1917.

--The Celestial Bear, Journal
of American Folklore, June,
1900.

--Cherokee Star Lore, Boas
Anniversary Volume, 1906.

--Cuzco, The Celestial City,
International Congress of
Americanists Proceedings,
1902.

--Four Seasons of Mexican
Ritual, American Anthropologist, April-June, 1911.

--Houses of Rain and Drought,
International Congress of
Americanists Proceedings,
1913.

--Maya Zodiac at Acanceh,
American Anthropologist,
January-March, 1914.

--November Meteors in Maya
and Mexican Tradition,
Popular Astronomy, August-
September, 1931.

--Peruvian Asterisms and Their
Relation to Ritual, International Congress of Americanists, 1904.

-- Peruvian Star Chart of Salcamayhua, International
Congress of Americanists,
1900.

--Zodiacal Temple of Uxmal,
Popular Astronomy,
February, 1921.

Hutchings, Allis M., Signs of
the Oriental Zodiac, Hobbies,
1937.

Ilamateuctli, Computation of

of Time Among Toltects and
Aztecs, American Antiquarian,
Volumes 30-31, 1908-1909.

Kingsmill, Thomas W., Two
Zodiacs, Journal of North
China Branch of the Royal
Asiatic Society, 1907.

Korean Review, A Leaf from
Korean Astrology, Vol. 2,
1902.

L'Heureux, Jean, Ethnological
Notes, Blackfeet; Journal
of the Anthropological
Society of Great Britain,
1886.

Maunder, E. Walter, Jeremias
and Astral Mythology in the
Old Testament, London
Quarterly Review, 1918.

Maya Society, A Planetary
Calendar in Facsimile, Maya
Society's Publication 17, 1935.

Mishkin, Bernard, Cosmological
Ideas Among Indians of
Southern Andes, Journal of
American Folklore, 1941.

National Geographic Society,
Map of the Heavens, December, 1957.

Nuttall, Zelia, Astronomical
Methods of Mexicans, Boaz
Anniversary Volume, 1906.

--Fundamental Principles of Old
and New World Civilizations,
Peabody Museum of American
Archaeology and Ethnology,
1901.

Pavri, Kursedji, E., Astronomy
of the Avesta, Iranian Association Journal, 1924-5.

Pinches, Theophilus, G., The
Morning Star in the Gospels,
Journal of the Transactions of
the Victoria Institute, Vol.
38, 1906.

Playfair, John, Remarks on the
Astronomy of the Brahmins,
Transactions of the Royal
Society of Edinburgh, March
2, 1789.

Rawlinson, H.C., Memoir on
Babylonian and Assyrian Inscriptions, Royal Asiatic

Society Journal, Vol. 14,
1851.

--On the Birs, Nimrod, or the
Great Temple of Borsippa,
Royal Asiatic Society Journal,
Vol. 18, 1861.

--Persian Cuneiform Inscrip-
tions at Bhistun, Royal
Asiatic Society Journal,
Vol. 10, 1847-49.

Spinden, Herbert J., Question
of the Zodiac in America,
American Anthropologist,
1916.

Thibaut, G., On Hypotheses of
Babylonian Origin of So-
called Lunar Zodiac,
Asiatic Society of Bengal,
Vol. 63.

Thorpe, W.A., Creatures of
the Chinese Zodiac, Apollo,
Vol. 11, 1930.

Upham Edward, The Chakkraea
and the Four Zodiacs, History and Doctrine of Budhism
of Ceylon, 1829.

Whish, C.M., Origin and
Antiquity of Hindu Zodiack,
Literary Society Transactions
Journal, 1827.

Whitney, William D., On the
Avesta, American Oriental
Society Journal, 1856.

Willson, R.W., Astronomical
Notes on the Maya Codices,
Peabody Museum of Ameri-
can Archaeology and Ethnology,
Vol. VI, No. 3, 1924.

INDEX

Where the Arabic "al" in a name is understood to be a simple article, as the English "the," it has been so treated in this index. Thus Al Karb al Ibl is listed as Karb al Ibl, Al. Inasmuch as writers of the middle ages charted al (the) as part of the name, the stars are so listed in Chapter VIII, The Stars.

A

A (aleph). 255
Aakrab (Aakrab genubi). 243, 304, 318
Aaraf, Al. (Al Orf, Urf). 145, 291, 396
Aaron. 184, 215, 229, 246
Abantiades. 228
Abathur. 352
Abeille. 210
Abel. 168, 212, 276
Aben (Aben Ezra). 173
Abhijit. 35, 378
Abigail. 112
Abrachaleus (Aracaleus, etc.). 355
Abraham (Abraham's Ram, Abraham with Isaac). 123, 147, 240, 241, 257, 268, 351
Abrucab (Abruccaba). 271
Absalom (Absalom's Hair). 152
Absyrthe. 127
Abukia. 380
Abur, Al. 356, 367
Acamar (Acarnar, Achenar). 291
Acatli. 52
Acerra. 119
Acetabula. 291
Acetes. 168
Achernar. 177, 291, 311
Achilles (Achilles and Patroclus). 165, 180, 366
Achilles Tendon. 307
Achir. 359
Acimon. 373
Ackair (Ackiar). 292
Acliluschemali (Aclushemali). 157

Acrab (Aakrab schemali). 322
Acrisioniades. 228
Acrisius. 227
Acris Venator. 146
Acrobo. 243
Acrux. 163
Actaeon. 26, 135, 137
Acubens (Acubene). 134, 291
Adam (Adam and Eve). 113, 126, 138, 181, 187, 188, 218, 241, 245, 252, 288, 297, 351
Adara (Adard, Adhara). 291
Addebiris. 295
Adderoiaminon. 296
Adelfalferes. 308
Adhara (Al Adhra). 291, 303, 373
Adhil. 291
Adhra al Nathifah, Al. 275
Adhupakarik. 183
Adib (Addib, Adid, Adive). 376
Adige (Adigege). 165
Aditi. 34, 167, 181, 215
Adler (Adler mit dem Antinous). 118
Adonis. 186, 230
Adrendesa (Adrenedesa). 275
Aeetes. 123, 190
Aegeus. 251
Aegoceros. 141
Aegyptus. 120, 257
Aeolos. 120, 293
Aequinoctialis. 125
Aequoreus Juvenis. 115

419

Fargu). 31, 296, 300
Fargh al Mukdim. 31, 362
Fargh al Thani, Al. 300
Fargu, Al. Same as Fargh al
Muhir.
Farkad, Al (Al Farkadain). 271,
327
Farked, Al. 327
Farshat Bath. 362
Fasariva. 203
Fasch. 177
Fascia. 45, 104
Fass, Al. 271
Fastashat. 380
Father of Light. 139
Fatik, Al. 295
Fatima's Hand. 144
Faulx, The. 178
Fawaris, Al. 165
Fearr. 254
Feast of Isis (or Hathor). 336
Feast of Lamps (Feast of Lan-
terns). 339, 340
Feast of Tabernacles. 29
Feast of the Dead. 340
Feather of Truth. 201
Felis (Canis Minor). 137
Felis or Faelis (Formed by
La Lande). 177
Feluco. 235
Feng Shi. 393
Fenice. 229
Fera. 205
Fera Major. 267
Fersaus. 228
Festival of the Moon. 36
Fe Yu. 276
Fiastik (Heteveny). 347
Ficares (Phicares), 148, 296
Fides (Fidicen, Fidicula
Fidis). 208, 378
Fiery Trigon. 125
Fifaus (Fikaus). 148
Figliuola di Monoi, La. 157
Fig Tree, The. 303
Fikaus (Ficares). 148
Filiae Tabernaculi. 346
Filia Ursae. 267
Findbennach. See White Horned
Bull.
Fionn MacCoul. 28
Fiosakonur a lopti. 271
Fire. 203

Fire Drake. 173
Fire Star. 305, 395
Firk, Al. 149, 296
Firmament. 11, 92, 93
First Calf. 305
Fische. 231
Fish Dorado. 168
Fishes, The. 229, 232
Fishes of Hea (or Ea). 231
Fish-hook or Maui (Fish of
Maui). 241-242
Fish that Swallowed Jonah.
150, 167
Fiskikallar. 331
Five Planets. 82, 87, 88
Five Reservoirs of Heaven.
395
Fixas. 231
Flagellum Christi. 153
Flamingo, The. See Grus.
Flamminger. 149
Fleche. 235
Fleur de lis. 210
Fliege. 210
Fliegende Fisch. 276
Flock, The. 295, 320
Flock of Clusterers. 345
Flood, The (Also see Deluge).
191
Flumen (Fluss Eridanus). 177
Fluvius. 177
Fluvius Aquarii. 115
Fly, The. 210
Flying Dutchman. 121
Flying Eagle. 116, 117, 206,
303, 378
Flying Fish, The. 276
Flying Grype, The. 118
Flying Horse, The. 226
Flying Serpent. 193
Flying Star, The. 229, 268
Foal, The. 175
Focus, 119
Fold, The. 149, 271, 305,
327, 335
Fomalhaut (Fomalcuti,
Fomalhout Algenubi, Fumahand,
Pham al Haut, etc.). 15, 233,
294, 311, 320, 360
Fong. 394
Fontis Musarum Inventor. 226
Foo-Chih. 394
Food-bearer, The. 313

G

Final Note: In our researches we have found conjecture offered as fact, disagreements as to spellings, the identities of stars,
the number of stars in an asterism, the borders of constellations,
etc. Additionally, we may have misunderstood certain statements.
And so, we borrow from L'Envoi of Richard Hinckley Allen and
quote Alfonso de Cartagena, who said, "Unto those Three Things
which the Ancients held impossible, there should be added this
Fourth, to find a Book Printed without erratas."